W9-BWQ-361

PEARSON

ALWAYS LEARNING

PSC 1515
Energy and the
Natural Environmental

Fourth Custom Edition for Miami Dade College—North

Taken from:
Conceptual Integrated Science, Second Edition,
by Paul G. Hewitt, Suzanne Lyons, John Suchocki, and Jennifer Yeh

Environment: The Science Behind the Stories, Fifth Edition,
by Jay Withgott and Matthew Laposata

Earth Science, Fourteenth Edition,
by Edward J. Tarbuck and Frederick K. Lutgens

Cover Art: Courtesy of Eyewire/Getty Images.

Taken from:

Conceptual Integrated Science, Second Edition,
by Paul G. Hewitt, Suzanne Lyons, John Suchocki, and Jennifer Yeh
Copyright © 2013, 2007 by Pearson Education, Inc.
Upper Saddle River, New Jersey 07458

Environment: The Science Behind the Stories, Fifth Edition,
by Jay Withgott and Matthew Laposata
Copyright © 2014, 2011, 2008 by Pearson Education, Inc.
Upper Saddle River, New Jersey 07458

Earth Science, Fourteenth Edition,
by Edward J. Tarbuck and Frederick K. Lutgens
Copyright © 2015, 2012, 2009, 2006, 2003 by Pearson Education, Inc.
Upper Saddle River, New Jersey 07458

All rights reserved. No part of this book may be reproduced, in any form or by any means, without permission in writing from the publisher.

This special edition published in cooperation with Pearson Learning Solutions.

All trademarks, service marks, registered trademarks, and registered service marks are the property of their respective owners and are used herein for identification purposes only.

Pearson Learning Solutions, 501 Boylston Street, Suite 900, Boston, MA 02116
A Pearson Education Company
www.pearsoned.com

Printed in the United States of America

1 2 3 4 5 6 7 8 9 10 V O Z N 18 17 16 15 14

0002000010271943666

SR

ISBN 10: 1-323-05175-9
ISBN 13: 978-1-323-05175-7

Table of Contents

Chapters 1, 3 –11, and 13 are taken from: *Conceptual Integrated Science*, Second Edition,
by Paul G. Hewitt, Suzanne Lyons, John Suchocki, and Jennifer Yeh.

Chapters 2, and 14 –16 are taken from: *Environment: The Science Behind the Stories*, Fifth Edition,
by Jay Withgott and Matthew Laposata.

Chapter 12 is taken from: *Earth Science*, Fourteenth Edition,
by Edward J. Tarbuck and Frederick K. Lutgens.

CHAPTER 1
About Science

MODERN CIVILIZATION is built on science. Nearly all forms of technology—from medicine to space travel—are applications of science. One such application is *Curiosity*, the latest vehicle to explore the surface of Mars. Tenny Lim, lead designer of its descent stage, stands in front of a model of Curiosity in the photo above to show its size. Tenny's science and engineering career was ignited when she was in Paul Hewitt's conceptual physics class.

Science is a way of seeing the world and making sense of it. Science is also a human endeavor, as Tenny well knows when she teams with other investigators at Jet Propulsion Laboratory in California. Science is the culmination of centuries of human effort from all parts of the world, making it the legacy of countless thinkers and experimenters of the past.

1.1 A Brief History of Advances in Science

EXPLAIN THIS How did the advent of the printing press affect the growth of science?

When a light goes out in your room, you ask, "How did that happen?" You might check to see if the lamp is plugged in or if the bulb is burned out, or you might look at homes in your neighborhood to see if there has been a power outage. When you think and act like this, you are searching for *cause-and-effect* relationships—trying to find out what events cause what results. This type of thinking is *rational thinking*, applied to the physical world. It is basic to science.

Today, we use rational thinking so much that it's hard to imagine other ways of interpreting our experiences. But it wasn't always this way. In other times and places, people relied heavily on superstition and magic to interpret the world around them. They were unable to analyze the *physical* world in terms of *physical* causes and effects.

The ancient Greeks used logic and rational thought in a systematic way to investigate the world around them and make many scientific discoveries. They learned that Earth is round and determined its circumference. They discovered why things float and suggested that the apparent motion of the stars throughout the night is due to the rotation of Earth. The ancient Greeks founded the science of botany—the systematic study and classification of plants—and even proposed an early version of the principle of natural selection. Such scientific breakthroughs, when applied as technology, greatly enhanced the quality of life in ancient Greece. For example, engineers applied principles articulated by Archimedes and others to construct an elaborate public waterworks, which brought fresh water into the towns and carried sewage away in a sanitary manner.

When the Romans conquered ancient Greece, they adopted much of Greek culture, including the scientific mode of inquiry, and spread it throughout the Roman Empire. When the Roman Empire fell in the 5th century AD, advancements in science came to a halt in Europe. Nomadic tribes destroyed much in their paths as they conquered Europe and brought in the Dark Ages. While religion held sway in Europe, science continued to advance in other parts of the world.

The Chinese and Polynesians were charting the stars and the planets. Arab nations developed mathematics and learned to make glass, paper, metals, and certain chemicals. Finally, during the 10th through 12th centuries, Islamic people brought the spirit of scientific inquiry back into Europe when they entered Spain. Then universities sprang up. When the printing press was invented by Johannes Gutenberg in the 15th century, science made a great leap forward. People were able to communicate easily with one another across great distances. The printing press did much to advance scientific thought, just as computers and the Internet are doing today.

Up until the 16th century, most people thought Earth was the center of the universe. They thought that the Sun circled the stationary Earth. This thinking was challenged when the Polish astronomer Nicolaus Copernicus quietly published a book proposing that the Sun is stationary and Earth revolves around it. These ideas conflicted with the powerful institution of the Church and were banned for 200 years.

FIGURE 1.1
A view of the Acropolis, or "high city," in ancient Greece. The buildings that make up the Acropolis were built as monuments to the achievements of the residents of the area.

Modern science began in the 17th century, when the Italian physicist Galileo Galilei revived the Copernican view. Galileo used experiments, rather than speculation, to study nature's behavior (we'll say more about Galileo in chapters that follow). Galileo was arrested for popularizing the Copernican theory and for his other contributions to scientific thought. But, a century later, his ideas and those of Copernicus were accepted by most educated people.

Scientific discoveries are often opposed, especially if they conflict with what people want to believe. In the early 1800s, geologists were condemned because their findings differed from religious accounts of creation. Later in the same century, geology was accepted, but theories of evolution were condemned. Every age has had its intellectual rebels who have been persecuted, vilified, condemned, or suppressed but then later regarded as harmless and even essential to the advancement of civilization and the elevation of the human condition. "At every crossway on the road that leads to the future, each progressive spirit is opposed by a thousand men appointed to guard the past."*

1.2 Mathematics and Conceptual Integrated Science

LEARNING OBJECTIVE
Recount how mathematics is a key in formulating good science.

EXPLAIN THIS What is meant by "Equations are guides to thinking"?

Pure mathematics is different from science. Math studies relationships among numbers. When math is used as a tool of science, the results can be astounding. Measurements and calculations are essential parts of the powerful science we practice today. For example, it would not be possible to send missions to Mars if we were unable to measure the positions of spacecraft or to calculate their trajectories.

You will make some calculations in this course, especially when you make measurements in lab. In this book, we don't make a big deal about math. Our focus is on understanding concepts in everyday language. We use equations as guides to thinking rather than as recipes for "plug-and-chug" computational work. We believe that focusing on computations too early, especially on math-based problem solving, is a poor substitute for learning the concepts. That's why the emphasis in this book is on building concepts. Only when concepts are understood does computational problem solving make sense.

1.3 The Scientific Method—A Classic Tool

LEARNING OBJECTIVE
List the steps in the classic scientific method, and cite other processes that advance science.

EXPLAIN THIS What other processes besides the classic scientific method advance science?

The practice of **science** usually encompasses keen observations, rational analysis, and experimentation. In the 17th century, Galileo and the English philosopher Francis Bacon were the first to formalize a particular method

*From Count Maurice Maeterlinck's "Our Social Duty."

MATH CONNECTION

Equations as Guides to Thinking

In this book we recognize the value of equations as guides to thinking. What we mean by this is that simple equations tell you immediately how one quantity is related to another. When you study gravity, you will learn about the inverse-square relationship—a mathematical form that comes up over and over again in science. In Appendix D, you can study exponential relations in general. But, to start off, let's consider two basic mathematical relationships:

The direct proportion The more you study for this course, the better you'll do. That's a direct proportion. Similarly, the more coffee you drink, the more nervous you'll feel. The longer time you drive at a constant speed, the farther you travel. If you're paid by the hour, the longer you work, the more money you make. All these examples show relationships between two quantities, and in each case, the relationship is a direct proportion. A direct proportion has the mathematical form $x \sim y$. Direct proportions have graphs of the form shown here.

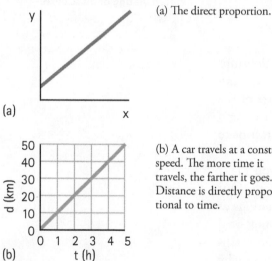

(a) The direct proportion.

(a)

(b) A car travels at a constant speed. The more time it travels, the farther it goes. Distance is directly proportional to time.

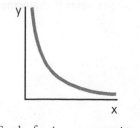

(b)

The inverse proportion Some quantities are related to each other so that as one increases, the other decreases. The *more* you compress an air-filled balloon, the *smaller* it becomes. The *more* massive a grocery cart, the *less* it accelerates when you push it. These quantities are related through the inverse proportion, which has the mathematical form $y \sim \frac{1}{x}$. Inverse proportions have graphs of the form shown here.

Graph of an inverse proportion.

Note that these mathematical relations have been stated as proportional relations, rather than as *equations*. For a proportional relation to be stated as an equation, the numbers and units on both sides must be the same. We can state a direct or indirect proportion as an exact equation by inserting a *proportionality constant*, k, into the relation. Proportionality constants make the numbers and units on both sides of an equation match up.

For example, consider Hooke's law. Hooke's law tells us about springs and other stretchy, elastic objects. Imagine a spring, such as a Slinky. According to Hooke's law, the more a Slinky is stretched, the harder it is to stretch it further. Written as a direct proportion, Hooke's law is

$$F \sim x$$

where F is your pulling force and x is the distance the spring is stretched beyond its resting length. But F, a force, has units of newtons (N) and x, a distance, has units such as centimeters (cm). We convert Hooke's law into an equation by inserting k into the relation. The value of k in this case depends on the shape and material of the spring. For a common Slinky-type metal coil, the proportionality constant k is about 2.5 N/cm. Now we can state Hooke's law as an exact equation:

$$F = kx$$

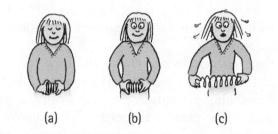

(a)   (b)   (c)

(a) An unstretched spring. (b) The spring is stretched past its resting length. (c) Stretching the spring further takes more force. This is Hooke's law, $F = kx$.

Problems

1. A freely falling object picks up a speed of 10 m/s during each second of fall. This is expressed as $v = gt$, where v is the speed picked up, g is the acceleration of free fall, and t is the time of fall. What type of mathematical relation is this?
2. A spring stretches and compresses according to Hooke's law, which states $F = kx$, where F is the force, k is the spring constant, and x is the stretched or compressed distance. For a certain spring with a spring constant of 3 N/cm, how much force is needed to stretch this spring 4 cm past its resting length?

Solutions

1. This relationship is of the form $x \sim y$, a direct proportion.
2. $F = kx = \left(3\frac{\text{N}}{\text{cm}}\right) \times (4 \text{ cm}) = 12\text{N}.$

for doing science. What they outlined has come to be known as the classic **scientific method**. It essentially includes the following steps:

1. **Observe** Closely observe the physical world around you.
2. **Question** Recognize a question or a problem.
3. **Hypothesize** Make an educated guess—a *hypothesis*—to answer the question.
4. **Predict** Predict consequences that can be observed if the hypothesis is correct. The consequences should be *absent* if the hypothesis is not correct.
5. **Test predictions** Do experiments to see if the consequences you predicted are present.
6. **Draw a conclusion** Formulate the simplest general rule that organizes the hypothesis, predicted effects, and experimental findings.

Although the scientific method is powerful, good science is often done differently, in a less systematic way. In the Integrated Science feature at the end of the chapter, "An Investigation of Sea Butterflies," you will see a recent application of the classic scientific method. However, many scientific advances involve trial and error, experimenting without guessing, or just plain accidental discovery. More important than a particular method, the success of science has to do with an attitude common to scientists. This attitude is one of inquiry, experimentation, and humility before the facts.

UNIFYING CONCEPT
● *The Scientific Method*

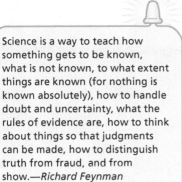

Science is a way to teach how something gets to be known, what is not known, to what extent things are known (for nothing is known absolutely), how to handle doubt and uncertainty, what the rules of evidence are, how to think about things so that judgments can be made, how to distinguish truth from fraud, and from show.—*Richard Feynman*

1.4   The Scientific Hypothesis

LEARNING OBJECTIVE
Describe the value of testing for furthering scientific knowledge.

EXPLAIN THIS Why do scientists work only with hypotheses that are testable?

A scientific **hypothesis** is an educated guess that tentatively answers a question or solves a problem in regard to the physical world. Typically, experiments are done to test hypotheses.

The cardinal rule in science is that all hypotheses must be testable—in other words, they must, at least in principle, be capable of being shown wrong. In science, it is more important that there be a means of proving an idea wrong than that there be a means of proving it right. This is a major feature that distinguishes science from nonscience. The idea that scientific hypotheses must be capable of being proven wrong is a pillar of the philosophy of science, and it is stated formally as the **principle of falsifiability**:

> **For a hypothesis to be considered scientific it must be testable—it must, in principle, be capable of being proven wrong.**

At first this principle may seem strange, for when we wonder about most things, we concern ourselves with ways of finding out whether they are true. Scientific hypotheses are different. In fact, if you want to determine whether a hypothesis is scientific or not, look to see whether there is a test for proving it wrong. If there is no test for possible wrongness, then the hypothesis is not scientific. Albert Einstein put it well: "No number of experiments can prove me right; a single experiment can prove me wrong."

For example, Einstein hypothesized that light is bent by gravity. This idea might be proven wrong if starlight that grazed the Sun and could be seen during an eclipse were not deflected from a normal path. But starlight *is* found to bend as it passes close to the Sun, just as Einstein's hypothesis would have predicted. If and when a hypothesis or scientific claim is confirmed, it is regarded as useful and as a steppingstone to additional knowledge.

Consider another hypothesis: "The alignment of planets in the sky determines the best time for making decisions." Many people believe it, but this hypothesis is not scientific. It cannot be proven wrong, nor can it be proven right. It is speculation. Likewise, the hypothesis "Intelligent life exists on planets somewhere in the universe besides Earth" is not scientific.* Although it can be proven correct by the verification of a single instance of life existing elsewhere in the universe, there is no way to prove it wrong if no life is ever found. If we searched the far reaches of the universe for eons and found no life, we would not prove that it doesn't exist "around the next corner." A hypothesis that is capable of being proven right but not capable of being proven wrong is not a scientific hypothesis. Many such statements are quite reasonable and useful, but they lie outside the domain of science.

CHECK YOURSELF

Which statements are *scientific* hypotheses?

(a) Better stock market decisions are made when the planets Venus, Earth, and Mars are aligned.

(b) Atoms are the smallest particles of matter that exist.

(c) The Moon is made of Swiss cheese.

(d) Outer space contains a kind of matter whose existence can't be detected or tested.

(e) Albert Einstein was the greatest physicist of the 20th century.

CHECK YOUR ANSWER

All these statements are hypotheses, but only statements a, b, and c are scientific hypotheses because they are testable. Statement a can be tested (and proven wrong) by researching the performance of the stock market during times when these planets were aligned. Not only can statement b be tested; it has been tested. Although the statement has been found to be untrue (many particles smaller than atoms have been discovered), the statement is nevertheless a scientific one. Likewise for statement c, where visits to the Moon have proven that the statement is wrong. Statement d, on the other hand, is easily seen to be unscientific because it can't be tested. Last, statement e is an assertion that has no test. What possible test, beyond collective opinion, could prove that Einstein was the greatest physicist? How could we know? Greatness is a quality that cannot be measured in an objective way.

LEARNING OBJECTIVE
Discuss how experimentation helps prevent the acceptance of false ideas.

1.5   The Scientific Experiment

EXPLAIN THIS Why do experiments trump philosophical discussion in science?

A well-known scientific hypothesis that turned out to be incorrect was that of the greatly respected Greek philosopher Aristotle (384–322 BC), who claimed that heavy objects naturally fall faster than light objects. This hypothesis was considered to be true for nearly 2000 years—mainly because

---

*The search for intelligent life in the universe is, however, ongoing. This search is based on the *question*: Might there be intelligent life somewhere besides on Earth? This question is the starting point for scientific observations of the physical world, but strictly speaking it is not a scientific hypothesis. A hypothesis is a sharper scientific tool than a question—a better, more finely honed instrument for separating scientific fact from fiction.

nearly everyone who knew of Aristotle's conclusions had such great respect for him as a thinker that they simply assumed he couldn't be wrong. Also, in Aristotle's time, air resistance was not recognized as an influence on how quickly an object falls. We've all seen that stones fall faster than leaves fluttering in the air. Without investigating further, we can easily accept false ideas.

Galileo very carefully examined Aristotle's hypothesis. Then he did something that caught on and changed science forever. He *experimented*. Galileo showed the falseness of Aristotle's claim with a single experiment—dropping heavy and light objects from the Leaning Tower of Pisa. Legend tells us that the objects fell at equal speeds. In the scientific spirit, one experiment that can be reproduced outweighs any authority, regardless of reputation or the number of advocates.

Scientists must accept their experimental findings even when they would like them to be different. They must strive to distinguish between the results they see and those they wish to see. This is not easy. Scientists, like most people, are capable of fooling themselves. People have always tended to adopt general rules, beliefs, creeds, ideas, and hypotheses without thoroughly questioning their validity. And sometimes we retain these ideas long after they have been shown to be meaningless, false, or at least questionable. The most widespread assumptions are often the least questioned. Too often, when an idea is adopted, great attention is given to the instances that support it. Contrary evidence is often distorted, belittled, or ignored.

The fact that scientific statements will be thoroughly tested before they are believed helps to keep science honest. Sooner or later, mistakes (or deceptions) are found out. A scientist exposed for cheating doesn't get a second chance in the community of scientists. Honesty, so important to the progress of science, thus becomes a matter of self-interest to scientists. There is relatively little bluffing in a game where all bets are called.

Experiment, not philosophical discussion, decides what is correct in science.

1.6 Facts, Theories, and Laws

EXPLAIN THIS How does a theory relate to a collection of facts?

LEARNING OBJECTIVE
Distinguish among facts, theories, and laws.

When a scientific hypothesis has been tested over and over again and has not been contradicted, it may become known as a **law** or *principle*. A scientific **fact**, on the other hand, is generally something that competent observers can observe and agree to be true. For example, it is a fact that an amputated limb of a salamander can grow back. Anyone can watch it happen. It is not a fact—yet—that a severed limb of a human can grow back.

Scientists use the word *theory* in a way that differs from its use in everyday speech. In everyday speech, a theory is the same as a hypothesis—a statement that hasn't been tested. But scientifically speaking, a **theory** is a synthesis of facts and well-tested hypotheses. Physicists use quantum theory to explain the behavior of light. Chemists have theories about how atoms bond to form molecules. The theory of evolution is key to the life sciences. Earth scientists use the theory of plate tectonics to explain why the continents move, and astronomers speak of the theory of the Big Bang to account for the observation that galaxies are moving away from one another.

Theories are a foundation of science, but they are not fixed. Rather, they evolve. They pass through stages of refinement. For example, since the theory of

Facts are revisable data about the world.

Theories interpret facts.

SCIENCE AND SOCIETY

Pseudoscience

For a claim to qualify as "scientific" it must meet certain standards. For example, the claim must be reproducible by others who have no stake in whether the claim is true or false. The data and subsequent interpretations are open to scrutiny in a social environment where it's okay to have made an honest mistake but not okay to have been dishonest or deceiving. Claims that are presented as scientific but do not meet these standards are what we call **pseudoscience**, which literally means "fake science." In the realm of pseudoscience, skepticism and tests for possible wrongness are downplayed or flatly ignored.

Examples of pseudoscience abound. Astrology is an ancient belief system that supposes a person's future is determined by the positions and movements of planets and other celestial bodies. Astrology mimics science in that astrological predictions are based on careful astronomical observations. Yet astrology is not a science because there is no validity to the claim that the positions of celestial objects influence the events of a person's life. After all, the gravitational force exerted by celestial bodies on a person is smaller than the gravitational force exerted by objects making up the earthly environment: trees, chairs, other people, bars of soap, and so on. Further, the predictions of astrology do not hold true; there just is no evidence that astrology works.

For more examples of pseudoscience, turn on the television. You can find advertisements for a plethora of pseudoscientific products. Watch out for remedies for ailments from baldness to obesity to cancer, for air-purifying mechanisms, and for "germ-fighting" cleaning products in particular. While many such products do operate on solid science, others are pure pseudoscience. Buyer beware!

Humans are very good at denial, which may explain why pseudoscience is such a thriving enterprise. Many pseudoscientists themselves do not recognize their efforts as pseudoscience. A practitioner of "absent healing," for example, may truly believe in her ability to cure people she will never meet except through e-mail and credit card exchanges. She may even find anecdotal evidence to support her contentions. The placebo effect, can mask the ineffectiveness of various healing modalities. In terms of the human body, what people believe *will* happen often *can* happen because of the physical connection between the mind and the body.

That said, consider the enormous downside of pseudoscientific practices. Today there are more than 20,000 practicing astrologers in the United States. Do people listen to these astrologers just for the fun of it? Or do they base important decisions on astrology? You might lose money by listening to pseudoscientific entrepreneurs or, worse, you could become ill. Delusional thinking, in general, carries risk.

Meanwhile, the results of science literacy tests given to the general public show that most Americans lack an understanding of the basic concepts of science. Some 63% of American adults are unaware that the mass extinction of the dinosaurs occurred long before the first human evolved; 75% do not know that antibiotics kill bacteria but not viruses; 57% do not know that electrons are smaller than atoms. What we find is a rift—a growing divide—between those who have a realistic sense of the capabilities of science and those who do not understand the nature of science and its core concepts or, worse, think that scientific knowledge is too complex for them to understand. Science is a powerful method for understanding the physical world—and a whole lot more reliable than pseudoscience as a means for bettering the human condition.

> Those who can make you believe absurdities can make you commit atrocities.—*Voltaire*

the atom was proposed 200 years ago, it has been refined many times in light of new evidence. Those who know only a little about science may argue that scientific theories can't be taken seriously because they are always changing. Those who understand science, however, see it differently: Theories grow stronger and more precise as they evolve to include new information.

LEARNING OBJECTIVE
Distinguish between the natural and the supernatural.

1.7 Science Has Limitations

EXPLAIN THIS What is the fundamental difference between the natural and the supernatural?

Science deals with only hypotheses that are testable. Its domain is therefore restricted to the observable natural world. Although scientific methods can be used to debunk various paranormal claims, they have no way of accounting for testimonies involving the supernatural. The term *supernatural* literally means "above nature." Science works within nature, not above it. Likewise, science is unable to answer philosophical questions, such as What is the purpose of life?, or religious questions, such as What is the nature of the human spirit? Although these questions are valid and may have great importance to us, they rely on subjective personal experience and do not lead to testable hypotheses. They lie outside the realm of science.

> We each need a *knowledge filter* to tell the difference between what is true and what only pretends to be true. The best knowledge filter ever invented for explaining the physical world is science.

1.8 Science, Art, and Religion

LEARNING OBJECTIVE
Discuss some similarities and differences among science, art, and religion.

EXPLAIN THIS When are science and religion compatible, and when are they incompatible?

The search for a deeper understanding of the world around us has taken different forms, including science, art, and religion. Science is a system by which we discover and record physical phenomena and think about possible explanations for such phenomena. The arts are concerned with personal interpretation and creative expression. Religion addresses the source, purpose, and meaning of it all. Simply put, science asks *how*, art asks *who*, and religion asks *why*.

Science and the arts have certain things in common. In the art of literature, we find out about what is possible in human experience. We can learn about emotions from rage to love, even if we haven't yet experienced them. The arts describe these experiences and suggest what may be possible for us. Similarly, knowledge of science tells us what is possible in nature. Scientific knowledge helps us to predict possibilities in nature even before they have been experienced. It provides us with a way of connecting things, of seeing relationships between and among them, and of making sense of the great variety of natural events around us. While art broadens our understanding of ourselves, science broadens our understanding of our environment.

Science and religion have similarities also. For example, both are motivated by curiosity about the natural world. Both have great impact on society. Science, for example, leads to useful technological innovations, while religion provides a foothold for many social services. Science and religion, however, are basically different. Science is concerned with understanding the physical universe, whereas many religions are concerned with spiritual matters, such as belief and faith. Scientific truth is a matter of public scrutiny; religion is a deeply personal matter. In these respects, science and religion are as different as apples and oranges and yet do not contradict each other.

> Art is about cosmic beauty. Science is about cosmic order. Religion is about cosmic purpose.

Ultimately, in learning more about science, art, and religion, we find that they are not mutually exclusive. Rather, they run parallel to each other like strings on a guitar, each resonating at its own frequency. When played together, they can produce a chord that is profoundly rich. Science, art, and religion can work very well together, which is why we should never feel forced into choosing one over another.

That science and religion can work very well together deserves special emphasis. When we study the nature of light later in this book, we will treat light as both a wave and a particle. At first, waves and particles may appear to be contradictory. You might believe that light can be only one or the other, and that you must choose between them. What scientists have discovered, however, is that light waves and light particles *complement* each other and that, when these two

No wars have ever been fought over science.

ideas are taken together, they provide a deeper understanding of light. In a similar way, it is mainly people who are either uninformed or misinformed about the deeper natures of both science and religion who feel that they must choose between believing in religion and believing in science. Unless one has a shallow understanding of either or both, there is no contradiction in being religious in one's belief system and being scientific in one's understanding of the natural world.* What your religious beliefs are and whether you have any religion at all are, of course, private matters for you to decide. The tangling up of science and religion has led to many unfortunate arguments over the course of human history.

CHECK YOURSELF

Which of the following activities involves the utmost human expression of passion, talent, and intelligence?

(a) painting and sculpture

(b) literature

(c) music

(d) religion

(e) science

CHECK YOUR ANSWER

All of them. In this book, we focus on science, which is an enchanting human activity shared by a wide variety of people. With present-day tools and know-how, scientists are reaching further and finding out more about themselves and their environment than people in the past were ever able to do. The more you know about science, the more passionate you feel toward your surroundings. There is science in everything you see, hear, smell, taste, and touch!

LEARNING OBJECTIVE
Relate technology to the furthering of science, and science to the furthering of technology.

1.9 Technology—The Practical Use of Science

EXPLAIN THIS What does it mean to say that technology is a double-edged sword?

Science and technology are also different from each other. Science is concerned with gathering knowledge and organizing it. **Technology** enables humans to use that knowledge for practical purposes, and it provides the instruments scientists need to conduct their investigations.

Technology is a double-edged sword. It can be both helpful and harmful. We have the technology, for example, to extract fossil fuels from the ground and then burn the fossil fuels to produce useful energy. Energy production from fossil fuels has benefited society in countless ways. On the flip side, the burning of fossil fuels damages the environment. It is tempting to blame technology itself for such problems as pollution, resource depletion, and even overpopulation. These problems, however, are not the fault of technology any more than a stabbing is the fault of the knife. It is humans who use the technology, and humans who are responsible for how it is used.

---

*Of course, this does not apply to certain religious extremists, who steadfastly assert that one cannot embrace both their brand of religion and science, and aspects of some religions, including the world's largest ones, that are distinctly anti-science.

Remarkably, we already possess the technology to solve many environmental problems. This 21st century will likely see a switch from fossil fuels to more sustainable energy sources. We recycle waste products in new and better ways. In some parts of the world, progress is being made toward limiting human population growth, a serious threat that worsens almost every problem faced by humans today. Difficulty solving today's problems results more from social inertia than from failing technology. Technology is our tool. What we do with this tool is up to us. The promise of technology is a cleaner and healthier world. Wise applications of technology *can* improve conditions on planet Earth.

> There are many paths scientists can follow in doing science. Scientists who explore the ocean floor or who chart new galaxies, for example, are focused on making and recording new observations.

1.10 The Natural Sciences: Physics, Chemistry, Biology, Earth Science, and Astronomy

EXPLAIN THIS Why is physics considered to be the basic science?

LEARNING OBJECTIVE
Compare the fields of physics, chemistry, biology, Earth science, and astronomy.

Science is the present-day equivalent of what used to be called *natural philosophy*. Natural philosophy was the study of unanswered questions about nature. As the answers were found, they became part of what is now called *science*. The study of science today branches into the study of living things and nonliving things: the life sciences and the physical sciences. The *life sciences* branch into such areas as molecular biology, microbiology, and ecology. The *physical sciences* branch into such areas as physics, chemistry, the Earth sciences, and astronomy. In this book, we address the life sciences and physical sciences and the ways in which they overlap—or *integrate*. This gives you a foundation for more specialized study in the future and a framework for understanding science in everyday life and in the news, from the greenhouse effect to tsunamis to genetic engineering.

A few words of explanation about each of the major divisions of science: Physics is the study of such concepts as motion, force, energy, matter, heat, sound, light, and the components of atoms. Chemistry builds on physics by telling us how matter is put together, how atoms combine to form molecules, and how the molecules combine to make the materials around us. Physics and chemistry, applied to Earth and its processes, make up Earth science—geology, meteorology, and oceanography. When we apply physics, chemistry, and geology to other planets and to the stars, we are speaking about astronomy. Biology is more complex than the physical sciences because it involves matter that is alive. Underlying biology is chemistry, and underlying chemistry is physics. So physics is basic to both the physical sciences and the life sciences. That is why we begin this book with physics, then follow with chemistry and biology, and finally investigate Earth science and conclude with astronomy. All are treated conceptually, with the twin goals of enjoyment and understanding.

1.11 Integrated Science

EXPLAIN THIS Who gets the most out of something—one who has an understanding of it or one without understanding?

LEARNING OBJECTIVE
Relate learning integrated science to an increased appreciation of nature.

Just as you can't enjoy a ball game, computer game, or party game until you know its rules, so it is with nature. Because science helps us learn the rules of nature, it also helps us appreciate nature. You may see beauty in a tree, but you'll see more beauty in that tree when you understand how trees and other plants trap solar energy and convert it into the chemical energy that sustains nearly all life on Earth. Similarly, when you look at the stars, your sense of their beauty is enhanced if you know how stars are born from mere clouds of gas and dust—with a little help from the laws of physics, of course. And how much richer it is, when you look at the myriad objects in your environment, to know that they are all composed of atoms—amazing, ancient, invisible systems of particles regulated by an eminently knowable set of laws.

Understanding the physical world—to appreciate it more deeply or to have the power to alter it—requires concepts from different branches of science. For example, the process by which a tree transforms solar energy to chemical energy—photosynthesis—involves the ideas of radiant energy (physics), bonds in molecules (chemistry), gases in the atmosphere (Earth science), the Sun (astronomy), and the nature of life (biology). Thus, for a complete understanding of photosynthesis and its importance, concepts beyond biology are required. And so it is for most of the real-world phenomena we are interested in. Put another way, the physical world integrates science, so to understand the world we need to look at science in an integrated way.

If the complexity of science intimidates you, bear this in mind: All the branches of science rest upon a relatively small number of basic ideas. Some of the most important unifying concepts are identified at the back of this book and in the page margins where they come up. Learn these underlying ideas, and you will have a tool kit to bring to any phenomenon you wish to understand.

Go to it—we live in a time of rapid and fascinating scientific discovery!

LEARNING OBJECTIVE
Apply the scientific method to a biological investigation.

Integrated Science 1A
CHEMISTRY AND BIOLOGY

An Investigation of Sea Butterflies

EXPLAIN THIS How does reproducibility relate to the validity of research?

UNIFYING CONCEPT

● *The Scientific Method*
Section 1.3

Let's consider an example of a recent scientific research project that shows how the scientific method can be put to work. Along the way, we'll get a taste of how biology and chemistry are integrated in the physical world.

The Antarctic research team headed by James McClintock, Professor of Biology at the University of Alabama at Birmingham, and Bill Baker, Professor of Chemistry at the University of South Florida, was studying the toxic chemicals Antarctic marine organisms secrete to defend themselves against predators (Figure 1.2). McClintock and Baker observed an unusual relationship between two animal species, a sea butterfly and an amphipod—a relationship that led to a question, a scientific hypothesis, a prediction, tests concerning the chemicals involved in the relationship, and finally a conclusion. The research generally proceeded according to the steps of the classic scientific method.

1. **Observe** The sea butterfly *Clione Antarctica* is a brightly colored, shell-less snail with winglike extensions used in swimming (Figure 1.3a), and the amphipod *Hyperiella dilatata* resembles a small shrimp. McClintock and Baker observed a large percentage of amphipods carrying sea butterflies on their backs, with the sea butterflies held tightly by the legs of the amphipods (Figure 1.3b). Any amphipod that lost its sea butterfly would quickly seek another—the amphipods were actively abducting the sea butterflies!

FIGURE 1.2
The Chemical Ecology of Antarctic Marine Organisms Research Project was initiated in 1988 by James McClintock, shown here (fifth from left) with his team of colleagues and research assistants. In 1992, he was joined by Bill Baker (second from right). Baker is shown in the inset dressing for a dive into the icy Antarctic water. Like many other science projects, this one was inter-disciplinary, involving the efforts of scientists from a wide variety of backgrounds.

2. **Question** McClintock and Baker noted that amphipods carrying butterflies were slowed considerably, making the amphipods more vulnerable to preda-tors and less adept at catching prey. Why then did the amphipods abduct the sea butterflies?
3. **Hypothesize** Given their experience with the chemical defense systems of various sea organisms, the research team hypothesized that amphipods carry sea butterflies to produce a chemical that deters a predator of the amphipod.
4. **Predict** Based on their hypothesis, they predicted (a) that they would be able to isolate this chemical and (b) that an amphipod predator would be deterred by it.
5. **Test predictions** To test their hypothesis and predictions, the research-ers captured several predator fish species and conducted the test shown in Figure 1.4. The fish were presented with solitary sea butterflies, which they took into their mouths but promptly spat back out. The fish readily ate uncoupled amphipods but spit out any amphipod coupled with a sea but-terfly. These are the results expected if the sea butterfly was secreting some sort of chemical deterrent. The same results would be obtained, however, if a predator fish simply didn't like the feel of a sea butterfly in its mouth. The results of this simple test were therefore ambiguous. A conclusion could not yet be drawn.

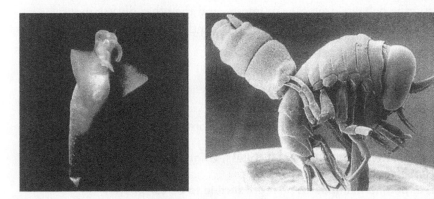

(a)   (b)

FIGURE 1.3
(a) The graceful Antarctic sea but-terfly is a species of snail that does not have a shell. (b) The shrimplike amphipod attaches a sea butterfly to its back even though doing so limits the amphipod's mobility.

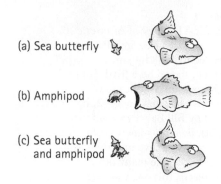

FIGURE 1.4
In McClintock and Baker's initial experiment, a predatory fish (a) rejected the sea butterfly, (b) ate the free-swimming amphipod, and (c) rejected the amphipod coupled with a sea butterfly.

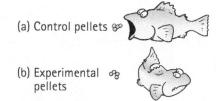

FIGURE 1.5
The predator fish (a) ate the control pellets but (b) rejected the experimental pellets, which contained sea butterfly extract.

Pteroenone

FIGURE 1.6
Pteroenone is a molecule produced by sea butterflies as a chemical deterrent against predators. Its name is derived from *ptero-*, which means "winged" (for the sea butterfly), and *-enone*, which describes information about the chemical structure. The black spheres represent carbon atoms, the white spheres hydrogen atoms, and the red spheres oxygen atoms.

All scientific tests need to minimize the number of possible conclusions. Often this is done by running an experimental test along with a **control**. Ideally, the experimental test and the control should differ by only one variable. Any differences in results can then be attributed to how the experimental test differed from the control.

To confirm that the deterrent was chemical and not physical, the researchers made one set of food pellets containing both fish meal and sea butterfly extract (the experimental pellets). For their control test, they made a physically identical set containing only fish meal (the control pellets). As shown in Figure 1.5, the predator fish readily ate the control pellets but not the experimental ones. These results strongly supported the chemical hypothesis.

Further processing of the sea butterfly extract yielded five major chemical compounds, only one of which deterred the predator fish from eating the pellets. Chemical analysis of this compound revealed it to be the previously unknown molecule shown in Figure 1.6, which they named pteroenone.

6. **Draw a conclusion** In addition to running control tests, scientists confirm experimental results by repeated testing. In this case, the Antarctic researchers made many food pellets, both experimental and control, so that each test could be repeated many times. Only after obtaining consistent results in repeated tests can a scientist draw a conclusion. McClintock and Baker were thus able to conclude that amphipods abduct sea butterflies in order to use the sea butterflies' secretion of pteroenone as a defense against predator fish.

Yet, this conclusion would still be regarded with skepticism in the scientific community. Why? There is a great potential for unseen error in any experiment. A laboratory may have faulty equipment that leads to consistently wrong results, for example. Because of the potential for unseen error from any particular research group, experimental results must be *reproducible* to be considered valid. This means that other scientists must be able to reproduce the same experimental findings in separate experiments. Thus you can see that it is a long road from bright idea to accepted scientific finding! The plodding, painstaking nature of this process is beneficial, though—it is the reason that scientific knowledge is highly trustworthy.

As frequently happens in science, McClintock and Baker's results led to new questions. What are the properties of pteroenone? Does this substance have applications—for example, can it be used as a pest repellent? Could it be useful for treating human disease? In fact, a majority of the chemicals we use were originally discovered in natural sources. This illustrates that there is an important reason for preserving marine habitats, tropical rainforests, and the other diverse natural environments on Earth—they are storehouses of countless yet-to-be-discovered substances.

CHECK YOURSELF
1. What variable did the experimental fish pellets contain that was not found in the control pellets?
2. If the fish had eaten the experimental pellets, what conclusion could the scientists have drawn?
3. Why must experimental findings be reproducible to be considered valid?

CHECK YOUR ANSWERS

1. Sea butterfly extract.
2. The scientists would have had to conclude that the predator fish were not deterred by the sea butterfly secretions and thus that the amphipods did not capture the sea butterflies for this reason.
3. Reproducibility of results is essential because every research project may contain unseen errors.

For instructor-assigned homework, go to www.masteringphysics.com (MP)

SUMMARY OF TERMS (KNOWLEDGE)

Control A test that excludes the variable being investigated in a scientific experiment.

Fact A phenomenon about which competent observers can agree.

Hypothesis An educated guess or a reasonable explanation. When the hypothesis can be tested by experiment, it qualifies as a *scientific hypothesis*.

Law A general hypothesis or statement about the relationship of natural quantities that has been tested over and over again and has not been contradicted; also known as a *principle*.

Principle of falsifiability For a hypothesis to be considered scientific, it must be testable—it must, in principle, be capable of being proven wrong.

Pseudoscience A theory or practice that is considered to be without scientific foundation but purports to use the methods of science.

Science The collective findings of humans about nature, and the process of gathering and organizing knowledge about nature.

Scientific method An orderly method for gaining, organizing, and applying new knowledge.

Technology The means of solving practical problems by applying the findings of science.

Theory A synthesis of a large body of information that encompasses well-tested hypotheses about certain aspects of the natural world.

READING CHECK QUESTIONS (COMPREHENSION)

1.1 A Brief History of Advances in Science

1. What launched the era of modern science in the 17th century?

1.2 Mathematics and Conceptual Integrated Science

2. Why do we believe that focusing on math too early is a mistake in an introductory science course?

1.3 The Scientific Method—A Classic Tool

3. Specifically, what do we mean when we say that a scientific hypothesis must be testable?

1.4 The Scientific Hypothesis

4. Is any hypothesis that is not scientific necessarily unreasonable? Explain.

1.5 The Scientific Experiment

5. How did Galileo disprove Aristotle's idea that heavy objects fall faster than light objects?

1.6 Facts, Theories, and Laws

6. Distinguish among a scientific fact, a hypothesis, a law, and a theory.

7. How does the definition of the word *theory* differ in science versus in everyday life?

1.7 Science Has Limitations

8. Your friend says that scientific theories cannot be believed because they are always changing. What can you say to counter this argument?

1.8 Science, Art, and Religion

9. What is meant by the term *supernatural*, and why doesn't science deal with the supernatural?

10. Why do religious questions—such as What is the nature of the human spirit?—lie outside of the domain of science?

1.9 Technology—The Practical Use of Science

11. Clearly distinguish between science and technology.

1.10 The Natural Sciences: Physics, Chemistry, Biology, Earth Science, and Astronomy

12. In what sense does physics underlie chemistry?

13. In what sense is biology more complex than the physical sciences?

1.11 Integrated Science

14. Why should we study integrated science?

THINK INTEGRATED SCIENCE

1A—An Investigation of Sea Butterflies

15. What two scientific disciplines were needed to understand the curious behavior of the Antarctic amphipods?

16. When was a control used in the investigation of the amphipods and sea butterflies? Why was a control necessary?

17. What was McClintock and Baker's hypothesis? Was it a scientific hypothesis? Why?

THINK AND DO (HANDS-ON APPLICATION)

18. Use the scientific method: (1) Based on your observations of your environment, (2) develop a question, (3) hypothesize the answer, (4) predict the consequences if your hypothesis is correct, (5) test your predictions, and (6) draw a conclusion. On a sheet of paper, describe in detail how you performed each step of the method from (1) through (6).

THINK AND SOLVE (MATHEMATICAL APPLICATION)

19. The more candy bars you add to your diet per day, the more weight you gain (all other factors, such as the amount of exercise you get, being equal). Is this an example of a direct proportion or an inverse proportion?

20. State the relation in Exercise 19 in mathematical form. (Hint: Don't forget to include a proportionality constant with appropriate units.)

21. Give an example of two quantities that are related in an inverse proportion that you have observed in your daily life? Express this relation in mathematical form.

THINK AND EXPLAIN (SYNTHESIS)

22. Are the various branches of science separate, or do they overlap? Give several examples to support your answer.

23. In what way is the printing press like the Internet in the history of science?

24. Which of the following are scientific hypotheses? (a) Chlorophyll makes grass green. (b) Earth rotates about its axis because living things need an alternation of light and darkness. (c) Tides are caused by the Moon.

THINK AND DISCUSS (EVALUATION)

25. Discuss the value Galileo placed on experimentation over philosophical discussions.

26. What do science, art, and religion have in common? How are they different?

27. Can a person's religious beliefs be proven wrong? Can a person's understanding of a particular scientific concept be proven wrong?

28. In what sense is science grand and breathtaking? In what sense is it dull and painstaking?

An oysterman unloads his catch on the shores of the Chesapeake Bay

2

Environmental Systems and Ecosystem Ecology

Upon completing this chapter, you will be able to:

- Describe the nature of environmental systems

- Define ecosystems and evaluate how living and nonliving entities interact in ecosystem-level ecology

- Outline the fundamentals of landscape ecology, GIS, and ecological modeling

- Assess ecosystem services and how they benefit our lives

- Compare and contrast how water, carbon, nitrogen, and phosphorus cycle through the environment

- Explain how human impact is affecting biogeochemical cycles

The Vanishing Oysters of the Chesapeake Bay

Baltimore
Washington, D.C.

UNITED STATES

Chesapeake Bay

Atlantic Ocean

"I'm 60. Danny's 58. We're the young ones."

—Grant Corbin, Oysterman in Deal Island, Maryland

"The Bay continues to be in serious trouble. And it's really no question why this is occurring. We simply haven't managed the Chesapeake Bay as a system the way science tells us we must."

—Will Baker, President, Chesapeake Bay Foundation

A visit to Deal Island, Maryland, on the Chesapeake Bay reveals a situation that is, unfortunately, all too common in modern America. The island, which was once bustling with productive industries and growing populations, is suffering. Economic opportunities in the community are few, and its populace is increasingly "graying" as more and more young people leave to find work elsewhere. In 1930, Deal Island had a population of 1237 residents. In 2010 it was a mere 471 people—and only 75 of them were under age 18.

Unlike other parts of the country with similar stories of economic decline, the demise of Deal Island and other bayside towns was not caused by the closing of a local factory, steel mill, or corporate headquarters. It was caused by the collapse of the Chesapeake Bay oyster fishery.

The Chesapeake Bay was once a thriving system of interacting plants, animals, and microbes. Blue crabs, scallops, and fish such as giant sturgeon, striped bass, and shad thrived in the bay. Nutrients carried to the bay by streams in its roughly 168,000 km^2 (64,000 mi^2) **watershed**—the land area that funnels water to the bay through rivers—nourished fields of underwater grasses that provided food and refuge to juvenile fish, shellfish, and crabs. Hundreds of millions of oysters kept the bay's water clear by filtering nutrients and phytoplankton (microscopic photosynthetic algae, protists, and cyanobacteria that drift near the surface) from the water column.

Although oysters had been eaten locally for some time, the intensive harvest of bay oysters for export began in the 1830s, and by the 1880s the bay boasted the world's largest oyster fishery. People flocked to the Chesapeake to work on oystering ships or in canneries, dockyards, and shipyards. Bayside towns prospered along with the oyster industry and developed a unique maritime culture that defined the region.

But by 2010 the bay's oyster populations had been reduced to a mere 1% of their historical abundance, and the oyster industry was all but ruined. Perpetual overharvesting, habitat destruction, virulent oyster diseases, and water pollution had nearly eradicated this economically and ecologically important species from bay waters. The monetary losses associated with the fishery collapse have been staggering, costing the economies of Maryland and Virginia an estimated $4 billion in lost economic activity from 1980 to 2010 alone.

One of the biggest impacts in recent decades on oysters is the pollution of the bay with high levels of the nutrients nitrogen and phosphorus from agricultural fertilizers, animal manure, stormwater runoff, and atmospheric compounds produced by fossil fuel combustion. Oysters naturally filter nutrients from water, but with so few oysters today, elevated nutrient levels have caused phytoplankton populations in the bay to increase. When phytoplankton die, settle to the bay bottom, and are decomposed by bacteria, oxygen in the water is depleted (a condition called **hypoxia**), which creates "dead zones" in the bay. Grasses, oysters, and other immobile organisms perish in dead zones when deprived of oxygen. Crabs, fish, and other mobile organisms are forced to flee to habitats where oxygen levels are higher, but they face smaller food supplies and increased predation pressure. Hypoxia, along with other human impacts on the Chesapeake Bay, cause it to be included on the Environmental Protection Agency's list of highly polluted waters.

Recent events in the Chesapeake have, at long last, given reason for hope for the recovery of the Chesapeake Bay system. The EPA agreed in 2010, for the first time in the region, to hold bay states to strict pollutant "budgets" that aim to substantially reduce inputs of nitrogen and phosphorus into the bay by 2025. Further, oyster restoration efforts are finally showing promise (see THE SCIENCE BEHIND THE STORY, pp. 32–33) in the Chesapeake. If these initiatives can begin to restore the bay to health, Deal Island and other communities may again enjoy the prosperity they once did on the scenic shores of the Chesapeake.

Earth's Environmental Systems

Understanding the rise and fall of the oyster industry in the Chesapeake Bay, as with many other human impacts on the environment, involves comprehending the complex networks of interlinked systems that comprise Earth's environment. These include physical systems ranging from matter and molecules up to magma and mountains. They include biological systems ranging from organisms and populations to communities of interacting species. In ecosystems they involve the interaction of living creatures with the nonliving entities around them. Earth's systems encompass cycles involving rock, air, and water that shape our landscapes and guide the flow of chemical elements and compounds that support life and regulate climate. We depend on these systems for our very survival.

Assessing questions holistically by taking a "systems approach" is helpful in environmental science, in which so many issues are multifaceted and complex. Such a broad and integrative approach poses challenges, because systems often show behavior that is difficult to predict. The scientific method is easiest when researchers can isolate and manipulate small parts of complex systems, focusing on manageable components one at a time. However, environmental scientists are rising to the challenge of studying systems holistically, helping us to develop comprehensive solutions to complicated problems such as those faced in the Chesapeake Bay.

Systems involve feedback loops

A **system** is a network of relationships among parts, elements, or components that interact with and influence one another through the exchange of energy, matter, or information. Earth's environmental systems receive inputs of energy, matter, or information, process these inputs, and produce outputs. As a system, the Chesapeake Bay receives inputs of freshwater, sediments, nutrients, and pollutants from the rivers that empty into it. Oystermen, crabbers, and fishermen harvest some of the bay system's output: matter and energy in the form of seafood. This output subsequently becomes input to the nation's economic system and to the digestive systems of people who consume the seafood.

Sometimes a system's output can serve as input to that same system, a circular process described as a **feedback loop.** Feedback loops are of two types, negative and positive. In a **negative feedback loop** (FIGURE 2.1a), output that results from a system moving in one direction acts as input that moves the system in the other direction. Input and output essentially neutralize one another's effects, stabilizing the system. For instance, a thermostat stabilizes a room's temperature by turning the furnace on when the room gets cold and shutting it off when the room gets hot. Similarly, negative feedback regulates our body temperature. If we get too hot, our sweat glands pump out moisture that evaporates to cool us down, or we move into the shade. If we get too cold, we shiver, creating heat, or we move into the sun. Most systems in nature involve negative

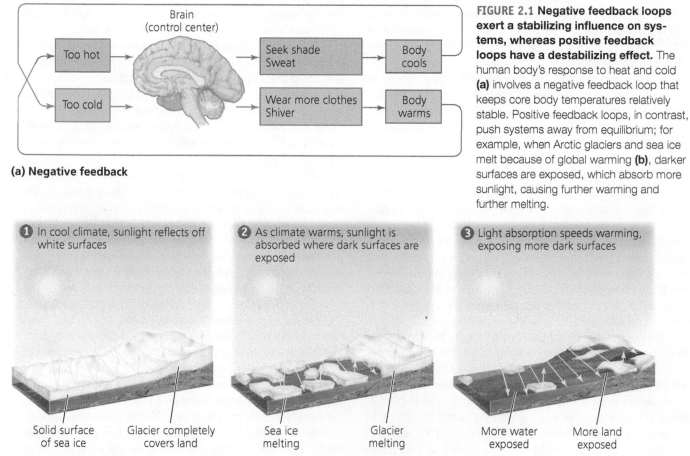

(a) Negative feedback

(b) Positive feedback

FIGURE 2.1 Negative feedback loops exert a stabilizing influence on systems, whereas positive feedback loops have a destabilizing effect. The human body's response to heat and cold **(a)** involves a negative feedback loop that keeps core body temperatures relatively stable. Positive feedback loops, in contrast, push systems away from equilibrium; for example, when Arctic glaciers and sea ice melt because of global warming **(b)**, darker surfaces are exposed, which absorb more sunlight, causing further warming and further melting.

feedback loops. Negative feedback enhances stability, and over time only those systems that are stable will persist.

Positive feedback loops have the opposite effect. Rather than stabilizing a system, they drive it further toward an extreme. In positive feedback, increased output leads to increased input, leading to further increased output. Exponential growth in a population is one such example. The more individuals there are, the more offspring can be produced. Another example is the spread of cancer; as cells multiply out of control, the process is self-accelerating.

One positive feedback cycle of great concern to environmental scientists today involves the melting of glaciers and sea ice in the Arctic as a result of global warming. Ice and snow, being white, reflect sunlight and keep surfaces cool. But if the climate warms enough to melt the ice and snow, darker surfaces of land and water are exposed, and these darker surfaces absorb sunlight. This absorption warms the surface, causing further melting, which in turn exposes more dark surface area, leading to further warming (**FIGURE 2.1b**). Runaway cycles of positive feedback are rare in nature, but they are common in natural systems altered by human impact, and they can destabilize those systems.

FAQ
But isn't positive feedback "good" and negative feedback "bad"?

Understanding negative and positive feedback in systems can be difficult, because it goes against the way we use those terms in everyday language. In daily life, positive feedback (such as a complimentary comment on a writing assignment) is something that makes us feel good, whereas negative feedback (such as criticism on schoolwork) may make us feel bad. In essence, we have been trained to view positive feedback as a stabilizing force ("Keep up the good work, and you'll succeed") and negative feedback as a destabilizing force ("You need to change your approach if you're going to succeed").

In environmental systems, it's the opposite! Negative feedback resists change in systems, and in doing so it enhances stability, typically keeping conditions within ranges beneficial to life. Positive feedback exerts destabilizing effects that push conditions in systems to extremes, threatening organisms adapted to the system's normal conditions. Thus, negative feedback in environmental systems typically aids living things, whereas positive feedback often harms them.

Systems show several defining properties

In a system stabilized by negative feedback, when processes move in opposing directions at equivalent rates so that their effects balance out, they are said to be in **dynamic equilibrium.** Processes in dynamic equilibrium can contribute to **homeostasis,** the tendency of a system to maintain constant or stable internal conditions. A system (such as an organism) in homeostasis keeps its internal conditions within a range that allows it to function. However, the steady state of a homeostatic system may itself change slowly over time. For instance, Earth has experienced gradual changes in atmospheric composition and ocean chemistry over its long history, yet life persists and our planet remains, by most definitions, a homeostatic system.

It is difficult to understand systems fully just by focusing on their individual components because systems can show **emergent properties,** characteristics not evident in the components alone. Stating that systems possess emergent properties is a lot like saying, "The whole is more than the sum of its parts." For example, if you were to reduce a tree to its component parts (leaves, branches, trunk, bark, roots, fruit, and so on) you would not be able to predict the whole tree's emergent properties, which include the role the tree plays as habitat for birds, insects, fungi, and other organisms (**FIGURE 2.2**). You could analyze the tree's chloroplasts (photosynthetic cell organelles), diagram its branch structure, and evaluate the nutritional content of its fruit, but you would still be unable to understand the tree as habitat, as part of a forest landscape, or as a reservoir for carbon storage.

Systems seldom have well-defined boundaries, so deciding where one system ends and another begins can be difficult. Consider a smartphone. It is certainly a system—a network

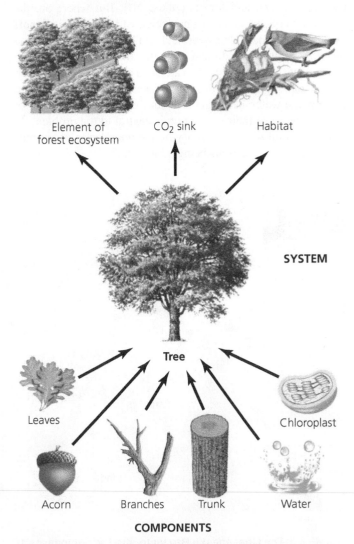

EMERGENT PROPERTIES

Element of forest ecosystem

CO_2 sink

Habitat

SYSTEM

Tree

Leaves

Chloroplast

Acorn

Branches

Trunk

Water

COMPONENTS

FIGURE 2.2 A system's emergent properties are not evident when we break the system down into its component parts. For example, a tree serves as wildlife habitat and plays roles in forest ecology and global climate regulation, but you would not know that from considering the tree only as a collection of leaves, branches, and chloroplasts.

of circuits and parts that interact and exchange energy and information—but where are its boundaries? Is the system merely the phone itself, or does it include the other phones you call, the websites you access on it, and the cellular and Wi-Fi networks that keep it connected? What about the energy grid that recharges the phone's battery, with its transmission lines and distant power plants?

No matter how we attempt to isolate or define a system, we soon see that it has connections to systems larger and smaller than itself. Systems may exchange energy, matter, and information with other systems, and they may contain or be contained within other systems. Thus, where we draw boundaries may depend on the spatial (space) or temporal (time) scale at which we choose to focus.

Environmental systems interact

The Chesapeake Bay and the rivers that empty into it are an example of interacting systems. On a map, these rivers are a branched and braided network of water channels surrounded by farms, cities, and forests (**FIGURE 2.3**). But where are the boundaries of this system? For a scientist interested in **runoff** (precipitation that flows over land and enters waterways) and the flow of water, sediment, or pollutants, it may make the most sense to view the bay's watershed as a system. However, for a scientist interested in the bay's dead zones, it may be best to view the watershed together with the bay as the system of interest, because their interaction is central to the problem. In environmental science, identifying the boundaries of systems depends on the questions being addressed.

The dead zones in the Chesapeake Bay are due to the extremely high levels of nitrogen and phosphorus delivered to its waters from the 6 states in its watershed and the 15 states in its **airshed**—the geographic area that produces air pollutants that are likely to end up in a waterway. In 2007, the bay received an estimated 127 million kg (281 million lb) of nitrogen and 8.3 million kg (18.2 million lb) of phosphorus, with roughly one-third of nitrogen inputs from atmospheric sources. Agriculture was a major source of these nutrients, contributing 40% of the nitrogen (**FIGURE 2.4a**) and 45% of the phosphorus (**FIGURE 2.4b**) entering the bay.

Elevated nitrogen and phosphorus inputs cause phytoplankton in the bay's waters to flourish. High densities lead to elevated mortality in phytoplankton populations, and dead phytoplankton settle to the bottom of the bay. The remains of dead phytoplankton are joined on the bottom by the waste products of zooplankton, tiny creatures that feed on phytoplankton. The abundance of organic material causes an explosion in populations of bacterial decomposers, which deplete the oxygen in bottom waters while consuming this material. Deprived of oxygen, organisms will flee if they can or will suffocate if they cannot. Oxygen replenishes slowly at the bottom because fresh water entering the bay from rivers remains naturally stratified in a layer at the surface and is slow to mix with the denser, saltier bay water. This limits the amount of oxygenated surface water that reaches the bottom-dwelling life that needs it. The process of nutrient overenrichment, blooms of algae, increased production of organic matter, and subsequent ecosystem degradation is known as **eutrophication** (**FIGURE 2.5**).

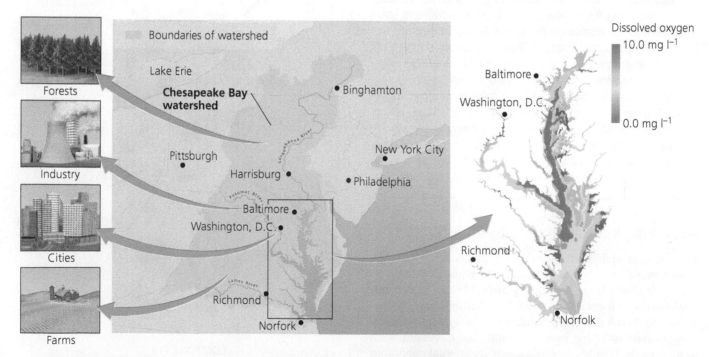

FIGURE 2.3 The Chesapeake Bay watershed encompasses 168,000 km2 (64,000 mi2) of land area in six states and the District of Columbia. Tens of thousands of streams carry water, sediment, and pollutants from a variety of sources downriver to the Chesapeake, where nutrient pollution has given rise to large areas of hypoxic waters. The zoomed-in map (**at right**) shows dissolved oxygen concentrations in the Chesapeake Bay in 2011. Oysters, crabs, and fish typically require a minimum of 3 mg/L of oxygen and are therefore excluded from large portions of the bay where oxygen levels are too low. *Source: Figure at right adapted from Chesapeake Bay Record Dead Zone Map, Chesapeake Bay Foundation.*

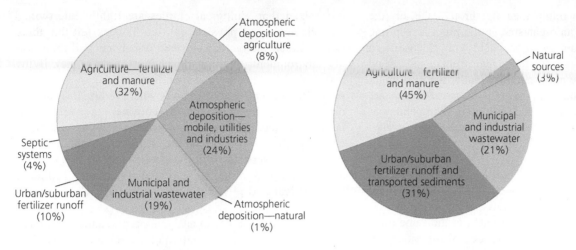

FIGURE 2.4 The Chesapeake Bay receives inputs of nitrogen (a) and phosphorus (b) from many sources in its watershed. *Data from Chesapeake Bay Program Watershed Model Phase 4.3 (Chesapeake Bay Program Office, 2009).*

(a) Sources of nitrogen entering the Chesapeake Bay

(b) Sources of phosphorus entering the Chesapeake Bay

We may perceive Earth's systems in various ways

There are many ways to delineate natural systems. Categorizing environmental systems can help make Earth's dazzling complexity comprehensible to the human brain and accessible to problem solving. For instance, scientists sometimes divide Earth's components into structural spheres. The **lithosphere** is the rock and sediment beneath our feet, the planet's uppermost mantle and crust. The **atmosphere** is composed of the air surrounding our planet. The **hydrosphere** encompasses all water—salt or fresh, liquid, ice, or vapor—in surface bodies, underground, and in the atmosphere. The **biosphere** consists of all the planet's organisms and the abiotic (nonliving) portions of the environment with which they interact.

Picture a robin plucking an earthworm from the ground after a rain. You are witnessing an organism (the robin) consuming another organism (the earthworm) by removing it from part of the lithosphere (the soil) that the earthworm had been modifying, after rain (from the hydrosphere) moistened

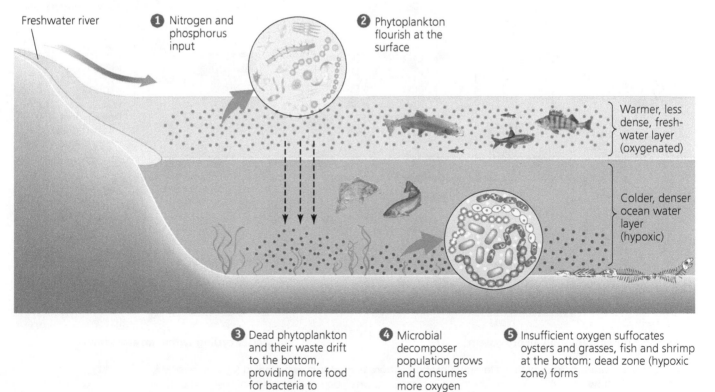

① Nitrogen and phosphorus input

② Phytoplankton flourish at the surface

Warmer, less dense, freshwater layer (oxygenated)

Colder, denser ocean water layer (hypoxic)

③ Dead phytoplankton and their waste drift to the bottom, providing more food for bacteria to decompose

④ Microbial decomposer population grows and consumes more oxygen

⑤ Insufficient oxygen suffocates oysters and grasses, fish and shrimp at the bottom; dead zone (hypoxic zone) forms

FIGURE 2.5 Excess nitrogen and phosphorus causes eutrophication in aquatic systems such as the Chesapeake Bay. Coupled with stratification (layering) of water, eutrophication can severely deplete dissolved oxygen. Nutrients from river water ① boost growth of phytoplankton ②, which die and are decomposed at the bottom by bacteria ③. Stability of the surface layer prevents deeper water from absorbing oxygen to replace oxygen consumed by decomposers ④, and the oxygen depletion suffocates or drives away bottom-dwelling marine life ⑤. This process gives rise to hypoxic zones like those in the bay.

the ground. The robin might then fly through the air (the atmosphere) to a tree (an organism), in the process respiring (combining oxygen from the atmosphere with glucose from the organism, and adding water to the hydrosphere and carbon dioxide and heat to the atmosphere). Finally, the bird might defecate, adding nutrients from the organism to the lithosphere below. The study of such interactions among living and non-living things is a key part of ecology at the ecosystem level.

Ecosystems

An **ecosystem** consists of all organisms and nonliving entities that occur and interact in a particular area at the same time. The ecosystem concept builds on the idea of the biological community, but ecosystems include abiotic components as well as biotic ones. In ecosystems, energy flows and matter cycles among these components.

Ecosystems are systems of interacting living and nonliving entities

The ecosystem concept originated early last century with scientists such as British ecologist Arthur Tansley, who

recognized that biological entities are tightly intertwined with chemical and physical entities. Tansley felt that there was so much interaction between organisms and their abiotic environments that it made the most sense to view living and nonliving elements together. For instance, in the Chesapeake Bay **estuary**—a water body where rivers flow into the ocean, mixing fresh water with saltwater—aquatic organisms are affected by the flow of water, sediment, and nutrients from the rivers that feed the bay and from the land that feeds those rivers. In turn, the photosynthesis, respiration, and decomposition that these organisms conduct influence the chemical and physical conditions of the Chesapeake's waters.

Ecologists soon began analyzing ecosystems as an engineer might analyze the operation of a machine. In this view, ecosystems are systems that receive inputs of energy, process and transform that energy while cycling matter internally, and produce outputs (such as heat, water flow, and animal waste products) that enter other ecosystems.

Energy flows in one direction through ecosystems. Most arrives as radiation from the sun, powers the system, and exits in the form of heat (FIGURE 2.6a). Matter, in contrast, is generally recycled within ecosystems (FIGURE 2.6b). Energy and matter pass among producers, consumers, and decomposers

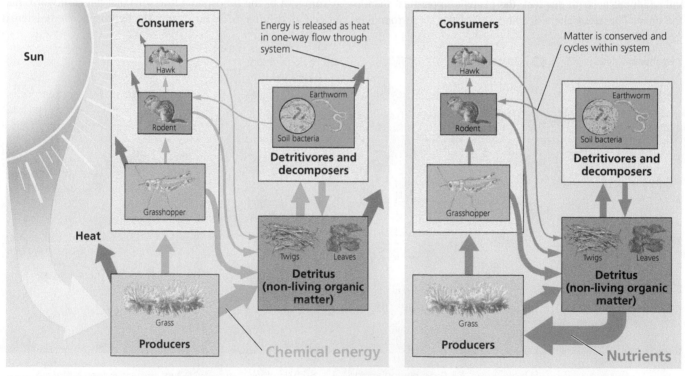

(a) Energy flowing through an ecosystem

(b) Matter cycling within an ecosystem

FIGURE 2.6 In systems, energy flows in one direction, whereas matter is recycled. In **(a)**, light energy from the sun **(yellow arrow)** drives photosynthesis in producers, which begins the transfer of chemical energy **(green arrows)** among trophic levels and detritus. Energy exits the system through respiration in the form of heat **(red arrows)**. In **(b)**, nutrients **(blue arrows)** move among trophic levels and detritus. In both diagrams, box sizes conceptually represent quantities of energy or matter content, and arrow widths represent relative magnitudes of energy or matter transfer. Such values may vary greatly among ecosystems. For simplicity, various abiotic components (such as water, air, and inorganic soil content) of ecosystems have been omitted.

DATA Q Based on the figure, which transfer of chemical energy is the largest in ecosystems? Which transfer is the largest for nutrient cycling in ecosystems?

through food-web relationships. Matter is recycled because when organisms die and decay, their nutrients remain in the system. In contrast, most energy that organisms take in drives cellular respiration and is released as heat.

Energy is converted to biomass

As autotrophs, such as green plants and phytoplankton, convert solar energy to the energy of chemical bonds in sugars through photosynthesis they perform **primary production.** Specifically, the total amount of chemical energy produced by autotrophs is termed **gross primary production.** Autotrophs use most of this production to power their own metabolism by cellular respiration. The energy that remains after respiration and that is used to generate biomass (such as leaves, stems, and roots) ecologists call **net primary production.** Thus, net primary production equals gross primary production minus the energy used in respiration.

Another way to think of net primary production is that it represents the energy or biomass available for consumption by heterotrophs. Some of this plant biomass is eaten by herbivores. Plant matter not eaten by herbivores becomes fodder for detritivores and decomposers once the plant dies or drops its leaves. Heterotrophs use the energy they gain from plant biomass for their own metabolism, growth, and reproduction. Some of this energy is used by heterotrophs to generate biomass in their bodies (such as skin, muscle, or bone), which is termed **secondary production.**

Ecosystems vary in the rate at which autotrophs convert energy to biomass. The rate at which this conversion occurs is termed **productivity,** and ecosystems whose plants convert solar energy to biomass rapidly are said to have high **net primary productivity.** Freshwater wetlands, tropical forests, coral reefs, and algal beds tend to have the highest net primary productivities, whereas deserts, tundra, and open ocean tend to have the lowest (FIGURE 2.7). Variation among ecosystems and among biomes in net primary productivity results in

geographic patterns across the globe (FIGURE 2.8). In terrestrial ecosystems, net primary productivity tends to increase with temperature and precipitation. In aquatic ecosystems, net primary productivity tends to rise with light and the availability of nutrients.

Nutrients influence productivity

Nutrients are elements and compounds that organisms consume and require for survival. Organisms need several dozen naturally occurring nutrients to survive. Elements and compounds required in relatively large amounts (such as nitrogen, carbon, and phosphorus) are called **macronutrients.** Nutrients needed in small amounts are called **micronutrients** (examples include zinc, copper, and iron).

Nutrients stimulate production by plants, and lack of nutrients can limit production. As mentioned earlier, the availability of nitrogen or phosphorus frequently is a limiting factor for plant or algal growth. When these nutrients are added to a system, producers show the greatest response to whichever nutrient has been in shortest supply. Nitrogen tends to be limiting in marine systems, and phosphorus in freshwater systems, though both contribute to eutrophication in all waters. Thus eutrophication in the Chesapeake Bay is driven by excess nitrogen, whereas eutrophication in the freshwater ponds and lakes in the bay's watershed are spurred by increases in phosphorus.

Canadian ecologist David Schindler and others demonstrated the effects of phosphorus on freshwater systems in the 1970s by experimentally manipulating entire lakes. In one experiment, his team bisected a 16-ha (40-acre) lake in Ontario with a plastic barrier. To one half the researchers added carbon, nitrate, and phosphate; to the other they added only carbon and nitrate. Soon after the experiment began, they witnessed a dramatic increase in algae in the half of the lake that received phosphate, whereas the other half (the control for the experiment) continued to host algal levels

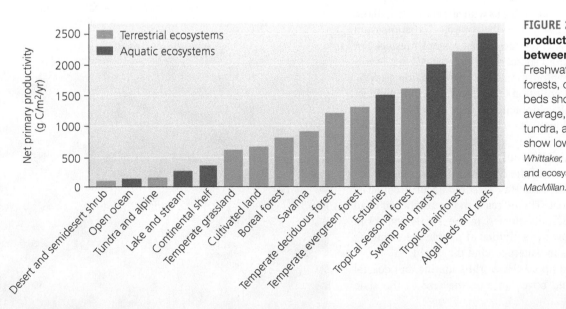

FIGURE 2.7 Net primary productivity varies greatly between ecosystem types. Freshwater wetlands, tropical forests, coral reefs, and algal beds show high values on average, whereas deserts, tundra, and the open ocean show low values. *Data from Whittaker, R.H., 1975.* Communities and ecosystems, *2nd ed. New York: MacMillan.*

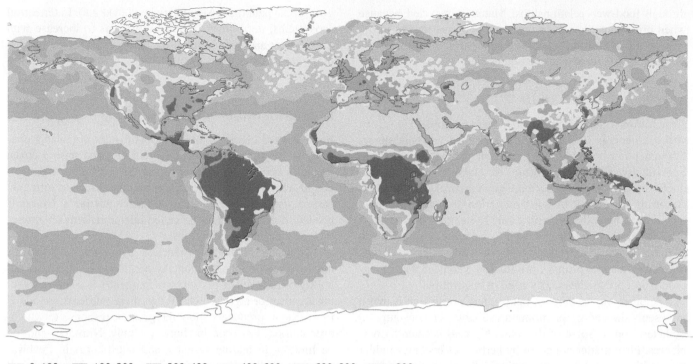

0–100   100–200   200–400   400–600   600–800   >800

FIGURE 2.8 A world map of net primary production based on satellite data shows that on land, net primary production varies geographically with temperature and precipitation. In the world's oceans, net primary production (shown here as grams of carbon fixed per square meter per year) is highest around the margins of continents, where nutrients (of both natural and human origin) run off from land. *Data from Field, C.B., et al., 1998. Primary production of the biosphere: Integrating terrestrial and oceanic components.* Science *281: 237–240. Reprinted with permission from AAAS.*

typical for lakes in the region (FIGURE 2.9). This difference held until shortly after they stopped fertilizing seven years later. At that point, algae decreased to normal levels in the half that had previously received phosphate. Such experiments showed clearly that phosphorus addition can markedly increase primary productivity in freshwater lakes.

Similar experiments in coastal ocean waters show nitrogen to be the more important limiting factor for primary productivity. In experiments in the 1980s and 1990s, Swedish ecologist Edna Granéli took samples of ocean water from the Baltic Sea and added phosphate, nitrate, or nothing. Chlorophyll and phytoplankton increased greatly in the flasks with nitrate, whereas those with phosphate did not differ from the controls. Experiments in Long Island Sound by other researchers show similar results. For open ocean waters far from shore, research indicates that iron is a highly effective nutrient for stimulating phytoplankton growth.

Increased nutrient pollution from farms, cities, and industries has led to the development of over 500 documented hypoxic dead zones globally as of 2010 (FIGURE 2.10), including that of the Chesapeake Bay as well as a large dead zone that forms each year in the Gulf of Mexico off the Louisiana coast near the mouth of the Mississippi River. Some are seasonal (like the Chesapeake Bay's), some occur irregularly, and others are permanent. The increase in the number of dead zones—there were 162 documented in the 1980s and 49 in the 1960s—reflects how the activities of people are changing nutrient concentrations in waters around the world.

If one were to add up all the world's marine and coastal dead zones, they would cover an area the size of the state

of Michigan. Scientists calculate that the amount of marine life missing from the oceans as a result of dead zones likely exceeds the total amount of shellfish harvested each year from the entire United States—a harvest worth over $2 billion.

The good news is that in locations where people have reduced nutrient runoff, dead zones have begun to disappear. In New York City, hypoxic zones at the mouths of the Hudson

FIGURE 2.9 The upper portion of this lake in Ontario was experimentally treated with the addition of phosphate. This treated portion experienced an immediate, dramatic, and prolonged algal bloom, identifiable by its opaque waters.

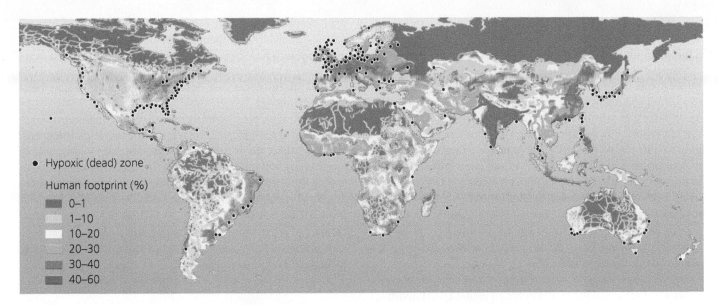

FIGURE 2.10 Over 500 marine dead zones have been recorded across the world. Dead zones as of 2010 (shown by dots on the map) occur mostly offshore from areas of land with the greatest human ecological footprints (here, expressed on a scale of 0 to 100, with higher numbers indicating bigger human footprints). *Data from World Resources Institute, 2010, http://www.wri.org/project/eutrophication/map and Diaz, R., and R. Rosenberg, 2008. Spreading dead zones and consequences for marine ecosystems. Science 321: 926–929. Reprinted with permission from AAAS.*

and East rivers were nearly eliminated once sewage treatment was improved. The Black Sea, which borders Ukraine, Russia, Turkey, and eastern Europe, had long suffered one of the world's worst hypoxic zones. Then in the 1990s, after the Soviet Union collapsed, industrial agriculture in the region declined drastically. With fewer fertilizers draining into it, the Black Sea began to recover, and today fisheries are reviving. However, agricultural collapse is not a strategy anyone would choose to alleviate hypoxia. Rather, scientists are proposing a variety of innovative and economically acceptable ways to reduce nutrient runoff (p. 42).

Ecosystems interact with one another

Whether we stand at a river's mouth or peruse a satellite image, we can conceptualize ecosystems at different scales. An ecosystem can be as small as a puddle of water or as large as a bay, lake, or forest. For some purposes, scientists even view the entire biosphere as a single all-encompassing ecosystem. The term is most often used, however, to refer to systems of moderate geographic extent that are somewhat self-contained. For example, the tidal marshes in the Chesapeake where river water empties into the bay are an ecosystem, as are the sections of the bay dominated by oyster reefs.

Adjacent ecosystems may share components and interact extensively. For instance, a pond ecosystem is very different from a forest ecosystem that surrounds it, but salamanders that develop in the pond live their adult lives under logs on the forest floor until returning to the pond to breed. Rainwater that nourishes forest plants may eventually make its way to the pond, carrying with it nutrients from the forest's leaf litter. Likewise, rivers, tidal marshes, and open waters in estuaries all may interact, as do forests and prairie where they converge. Areas where ecosystems meet may consist of transitional zones called **ecotones,** in which elements of each ecosystem mix.

WEIGHING THE ISSUES

ECOSYSTEMS WHERE YOU LIVE Think about the area where you live, and briefly describe this region's ecosystems. How do these systems interact? For instance, does any water pass from one to another? Describe the boundaries of watersheds in your region. If one ecosystem were greatly modified (say, if a shopping mall were built atop a wetland or amid a forest), what impacts on nearby systems might result? (Note: If you live in a city, realize that urban areas can be thought of as ecosystems, too!)

Landscape ecologists study geographic patterns

Because components of different ecosystems may intermix, ecologists often find it useful to view these systems on a larger geographic scale that encompasses multiple ecosystems. For instance, if you are studying large mammals such as black bears, which move seasonally from mountains to valleys or between mountain ranges, you had better consider the overall landscape that includes all these areas. If you study fish such as salmon, which migrate between marine and freshwater ecosystems, you need to know how these systems interact.

In such a broad-scale approach, called **landscape ecology,** scientists study how landscape structure affects the abundance, distribution, and interaction of organisms. Landscape-level approaches are also helping scientists, citizens, planners, and policymakers to plan for sustainable regional development.

For a landscape ecologist, a landscape is made up of a spatial array of **patches.** Depending on the researcher's perspective, patches may consist of ecosystems or may simply be areas of habitat for a particular organism. Patches are spread spatially over a landscape in a **mosaic.** This metaphor reflects how natural systems often are arrayed across landscapes in complex patterns, like an intricate work of art. Thus, a forest ecologist may refer to a mosaic of forested patches left standing in an agricultural landscape. An amphibian biologist might speak of a mosaic of patches of pond habitat that frogs use for reproduction.

FIGURE 2.11 illustrates a landscape consisting of five ecosystem types, with ecotones along their borders (indicated by thick red lines). At this scale, we perceive a mosaic consisting of four patches and a river. However, we can view a landscape at different scales. The figure's inset shows a magnified view of an ecotone. At this finer resolution, we see that the ecotone consists of patches of forest and grassland in a complex arrangement. The scale at which an ecologist focuses will depend on the questions he or she is interested in, or on the organisms he or she is studying.

Every organism has specific habitat needs, so when its habitat is distributed in patches across a landscape, individuals may need to expend energy and risk predation traveling from one to another. If the patches are far apart, the organism's population may become divided into subpopulations, each occupying a different patch in the mosaic. Such a network of subpopulations, most of whose members stay within their respective patches but some of whom move among patches or mate with members of other patches, is called a **metapopulation.** When patches are still more isolated from one another, individuals may not be able to travel between them at all. In such a case, smaller subpopulations may be at risk of extinction.

Because of this extinction risk, metapopulations and landscape ecology are of great interest to **conservation biologists**, scientists who study the loss, protection, and restoration of biodiversity. Of particular concern is the fragmentation of habitat into small and isolated patches —something that often results from human development pressures. Establishing corridors of habitat (see FIGURE 2.11) to link patches and allow animals to move among them is one approach that conservation biologists pursue as they attempt to maintain biodiversity in the face of human impact.

Remote sensing helps us apply landscape ecology

As more scientists take a landscape perspective, they are benefiting from better and better remote-sensing technologies.

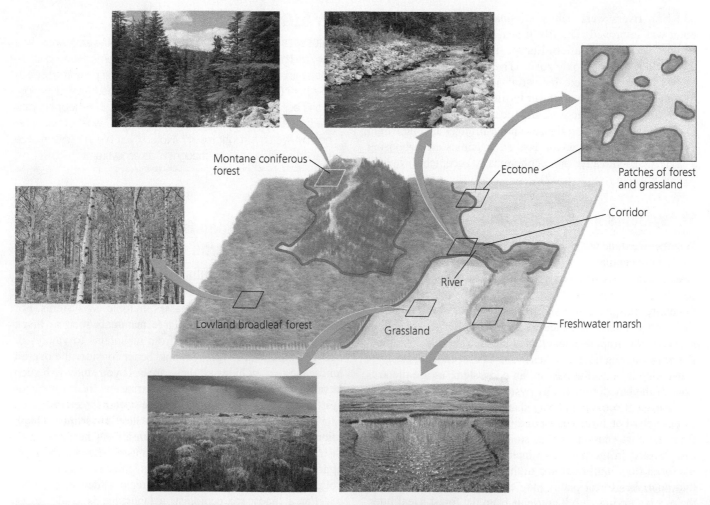

FIGURE 2.11 Landscape ecology deals with spatial patterns above the ecosystem level. This generalized diagram of a landscape shows a mosaic of patches of five ecosystem types (three terrestrial types, a marsh, and a river). Thick red lines indicate ecotones. A stretch of lowland broadleaf forest running along the river serves as a corridor connecting the large region of forest on the left to the smaller patch of forest alongside the marsh. The inset shows a magnified view of the forest-grassland ecotone and how it consists of patches on a smaller scale.

Satellites orbiting Earth are sending us more and better data than ever before on how the surface of our planet looks. By helping us monitor our planet from above, satellite imagery is making vital contributions to modern environmental science.

A common tool for research in landscape ecology is the **geographic information system (GIS).** A GIS consists of computer software that takes multiple types of data (for instance, on geology, hydrology, topography, vegetation, animal populations, and human infrastructure) and combines them on a common set of geographic coordinates. The idea is to create a complete picture of a landscape and to analyze how elements of the different data sets are arrayed spatially and how they may be correlated.

FIGURE 2.12 illustrates in a simplified way how different datasets of a GIS are combined, layer upon layer, to form a composite map. GIS has become a valuable tool used by geographers, landscape ecologists, resource managers, and conservation biologists. Principles of landscape ecology, and tools such as GIS, are increasingly used in regional planning processes.

GIS is being used to guide restoration efforts in the Chesapeake Bay. The *ChesapeakeStat* website, which was launched in 2010, enables scientists, educators, policymakers, and citizens to create customized composite maps that overlay parameters important to the bay's health. This tool is being used to assess the bay's current status, the effects of restoration efforts, and progress toward long-term goals.

Modeling helps ecologists understand systems

Another way in which ecologists seek to make sense of the complex systems they study is by working with models. In science, a **model** is a simplified representation of a complex natural process, designed to help us understand how the process occurs and to make predictions. **Ecological modeling** is the practice of constructing and testing models that aim to explain and predict how ecological systems function.

Because ecological processes (for ecosystems, communities, or populations) involve so many factors, ecological models can be mathematically complicated. However, the general approach of ecological modeling is easy to understand (FIGURE 2.13). Researchers gather data from nature on relationships that interest them and then form a hypothesis about what those relationships are. They construct a model that attempts to explain the relationships in a generalized way so that people can use the model to make predictions about how the system will behave. Modelers test their predictions by gathering new data from natural systems, and they use this new data to refine the model, making it increasingly accurate.

Note that the process illustrated in Figure 2.13 resembles the scientific method; models are essentially hypotheses about how systems function. Accordingly, the use of models is a key part of ecological research and environmental regulation today. As just one example, the National Oceanic and Atmospheric Administration (NOAA) uses the Chesapeake Bay Fisheries Ecosystem model to examine trophic interactions among fish species in the bay, the effects of hypoxia on fish populations, and how the distribution of underwater grasses

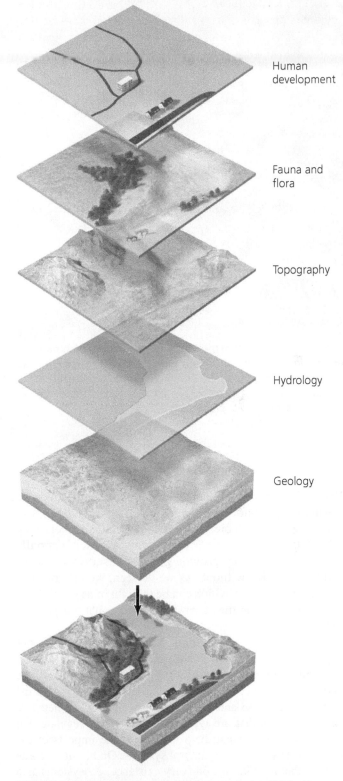

FIGURE 2.12 Geographic information systems (GIS) allow us to layer different types of data on natural landscape features and human land uses so as to produce maps integrating this information. GIS can be used to explore correlations among these data sets and to help in regional planning.

influences blue crab populations. Data from scientific journal articles and direct measurements are used to establish the model's parameters, which are then used to predict the effects of differing fish harvest levels on species and ecosystems in the Chesapeake Bay.

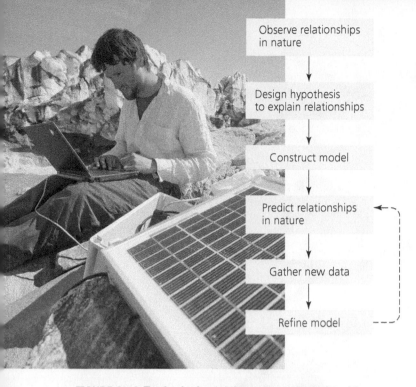

Observe relationships
in nature

↓

Design hypothesis
to explain relationships

↓

Construct model

↓

Predict relationships
in nature

↓

Gather new data

↓

Refine model

FIGURE 2.13 Ecological modelers observe relationships among variables in nature and then construct models to explain those relationships and make predictions. They test and refine the models by gathering new data from nature and seeing how well the models predict those data.

Ecosystem services sustain our world

When scientists try to understand how ecosystems function, it is not simply out of curiosity about the world. They also know that human society depends on healthy, functioning ecosystems. When Earth's ecosystems function normally and undisturbed, they provide goods and services that we could not survive without. As we've seen, we rely not just on natural resources (which can be thought of as goods from nature), but also on the *ecosystem services* that our planet's systems provide. (TABLE 2.1).

Ecological processes form the soil that nourishes our crops, purify the water we drink and the air that we breathe, store and stabilize supplies of water that we use, pollinate the food plants we eat, and receive and break down (some of) the waste we dump and the pollution we emit. The negative feedback cycles that are typical of ecosystems regulate and stabilize the climate and help to dampen the impacts of the disturbances we create in natural systems. On top of all these services that are vital for our very existence, ecosystems also provide services that enhance the quality of our lives, ranging from recreational opportunities to pleasing scenery to inspiration and spiritual renewal. Ecosystem goods and ecosystem services (FIGURE 2.14) support our lives and society in profound and innumerable ways.

One of the most important ecosystem services is the cycling of nutrients. Through the processes that take place within and among ecosystems, the chemical elements and compounds that we need—carbon, nitrogen, phosphorus, water, and many more—cycle through our environment in complex ways.

TABLE 2.1   Ecosystem Services

Ecological processes do many things that benefit us:

- Regulate oxygen, carbon dioxide, stratospheric ozone, and other atmospheric gases
- Regulate temperature and precipitation by means of ocean currents, cloud formation, and so on
- Protect against storms, floods, and droughts, mainly by means of vegetation
- Store and regulate water supplies in watersheds and aquifers
- Prevent soil erosion
- Form soil by weathering rock and accumulating organic material
- Cycle carbon, nitrogen, phosphorus, sulfur, and other nutrients
- Filter waste, remove toxins, recover nutrients, and control pollution
- Pollinate plant crops and wild plants so they reproduce
- Control crop pests with predators and parasites
- Provide habitat for organisms to breed, feed, rest, migrate, and winter
- Produce fish, game, crops, nuts, and fruits that people eat
- Supply lumber, fuel, metals, fodder, and fiber
- Furnish medicines, pets, ornamental plants, and genes for resistance to pathogens and crop pests
- Provide recreation such as ecotourism, fishing, hiking, birding, hunting, and kayaking
- Provide aesthetic, artistic, educational, spiritual, and scientific amenities

FAQ   If we had to pay for the services provided by nature, what would it cost?

Estimating the economic value of all of Earth's ecosystem services is no easy task, but a study published in 1997 by an international team of scientists and economists put a rough dollar figure on the many benefits nature provides us. The team did not examine all of the biosphere's services, but rather focused on 17 key ecosystem services from 16 biomes. The authors defined *ecosystem services* as natural processes (such as nutrient cycling or regulation of the global climate) and renewable natural resources (such as timber or food crops, but not including nonrenewable minerals and fossil fuels) and calculated the economic value of these services.

The study determined that the value of these 17 ecosystem services ranged from $16 to $54 trillion per year, with an average of $33 trillion ($48 billion in 2013 dollars when adjusted for inflation). This is a stunning quantity, especially when one considers that the sum total of the gross national products of every nation in 1997 was only $18 trillion. That is, the ecosystem services provided by nature had a value 1.8 times higher than the entire economic activity of the planet. Such studies are useful because they allow us to more accurately conduct cost-benefit analyses of proposed projects by considering both the expected economic gains from development and the economic costs from the degradation of ecosystem services due to development.

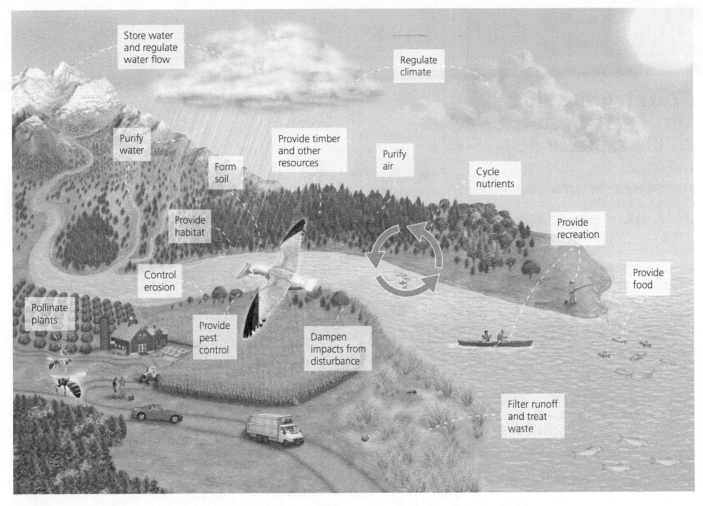

FIGURE 2.14 Ecological processes naturally provide countless services that we call *ecosystem services.* Our society, indeed our very survival, depends on these services.

Biogeochemical Cycles

Just as nitrogen and phosphorus from fertilizer on Pennsylvania corn fields end up in Chesapeake Bay oysters on our dinner plates, all nutrients move through the environment in intricate ways. Whereas energy enters an ecosystem from the sun, flows from organism to organism, and dissipates to the atmosphere as heat, the physical matter of an ecosystem is circulated over and over again.

Nutrients circulate through ecosystems in biogeochemical cycles

Nutrients move through ecosystems in **nutrient cycles,** also known as **biogeochemical cycles.** In these pathways, chemical elements or molecules travel through the atmosphere, hydrosphere, and lithosphere, and from one organism to another, in dynamic equilibrium. A carbon atom in your fingernail today might have helped compose the muscle of a cow a year ago, may have resided in a blade of grass a month before that, and may have been part of a dinosaur's tooth 100 million years ago. After we die, the nutrients in our bodies will spread widely through the environment, eventually being incorporated by an untold number of organisms far into the future.

Nutrients and other materials move from one **pool,** or **reservoir,** to another, remaining for varying amounts of time (the **residence time**) in each. The dinosaur, the grass, the cow, and you are each reservoirs for carbon atoms, as are sedimentary rocks and the atmosphere. The rate at which materials move between reservoirs is termed a **flux,** and the flux between any given reservoirs can change over time. When a reservoir releases more materials than it accepts, it is called a **source,** and when a reservoir accepts more materials than it releases, it is called a **sink.** FIGURE 2.15 illustrates these concepts in a simple manner.

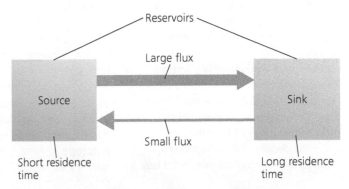

FIGURE 2.15 The main components of a biogeochemical cycle are reservoirs and fluxes. A source releases more materials than it accepts, and a sink accepts more materials than it releases.

"Turning the Tide" for Native Oysters in Chesapeake Bay

In 2001, the Eastern oyster (*Crassostrea virginica*) was in dire trouble in the Chesapeake Bay. Populations had dropped by 99%, and the Chesapeake's oyster industry, once the largest in the world, had collapsed. Poor water quality, reef destruction, virulent diseases spread by transplanted oysters, and 200 years of overharvesting all contributed to the collapse.

Restoration efforts had largely failed. Moreover, when scientists or resource managers proposed to rebuild oyster populations by significantly restricting oyster harvests or establishing oyster reef "sanctuaries," these initiatives were typically defeated by the politically powerful oyster industry. All this had occurred in a place whose very name (derived from the Algonquin word *Chesepiook*) means "great shellfish bay".

With the collapse of the native oyster fishery and with political obstacles blocking restoration projects for native oysters, support grew among the oyster industry, state resource managers, and some scientists for the introduction of Suminoe oysters (*Crassostrea ariakensis*) from Asia. This species seemed well suited for conditions in the bay and showed resistance to the parasitic diseases that were ravaging native oysters. Proponents argued that introducing Suminoe oysters would reestablish thriving oyster populations in the bay and revitalize the oyster fishery.

Introducing oysters would also improve the bay's water quality, proponents said, because as oysters feed, they filter phytoplankton and sediments from the water column.

Filter-feeding by oysters is an important ecological service in the bay

David Schulte, U.S. Army Corps of Engineers

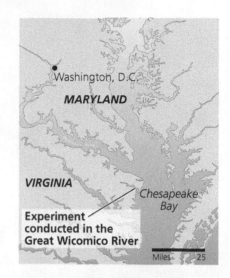

FIGURE 1 Schulte's study was conducted in the Great Wicomico River in Virginia in the lower Chesapeake Bay.

because it reduces phytoplankton densities, clarifies waters, and supports the growth of underwater grasses that provide food and refuge for waterfowl and young crabs. Because introductions of invasive species can have profound ecological impacts, the Army Corps of Engineers was directed to coordinate an environmental impact statement on oyster restoration approaches in the Chesapeake.

It was in this politically charged, high-stakes environment that Dave Schulte, a scientist with the Corps and doctoral student at the College of William and Mary, set out to determine whether there was a viable approach to restoring native oyster populations. The work he and his team began would help turn the tide in favor of native oysters in the bay's restoration efforts.

One of the biggest impacts on native oysters was the destruction of oyster reefs by a century of intensive oyster harvesting. Oysters settle and grow best on the shells of other oysters, and over long periods this process forms reefs (underwater outcrops of living oysters and oyster shells) that solidify and become as

hard as stone. Throughout the bay, massive reefs that at one time had jutted out of the water at low tide had been reduced to rubble on the bottom from a century of repeated scouring by metal dredgers used by oyster harvesting ships. The key, Schulte realized, was to construct artificial reefs like those that once existed, to get oysters off the bottom—away from smothering sediments and hypoxic waters—and up into the plankton-rich upper waters.

Armed with the resources available to the Corps, he opted to take a landscape ecology approach and restore patches of reef habitat on nine complexes of reefs covering a total of 35.3 hectares (87 acres) in an oyster sanctuary near the mouth of the Great Wicomico River (**FIGURE 1**) in the lower Chesapeake Bay. This approach was very different from the smaller-scale restoration efforts of the past.

Artificial reefs of two heights were constructed in 2004 (**FIGURE 2**), and oysters were allowed to colonize the reefs, safe from harvesting. Oyster populations on the constructed reefs were sampled in 2007, and the results were stunning. The reef complex supported an estimated 185 million oysters, a number nearly as large as the wild population of 200 million oysters estimated to live on the remaining degraded habitat in all of Maryland's waters.

Higher reefs supported an average of over 1000 oysters per square meter—four times more than the lower reefs and 170 times more than unrestored bottom (FIGURE 3). Like natural reefs, the constructed reefs began to solidify, providing a firm foundation for the settlement of new oysters. In 2009, Schulte's research made a splash when his team published its findings in the journal *Science*, bringing international attention to their study.

After reviewing eight alternative approaches to oyster restoration that involved one or more oyster species, the Corps advocated an approach that avoided the introduction of non-native oysters. Instead it proposed a combination of native oyster restoration, a temporary moratorium on oyster harvests (accompanied by a compensation program for the oyster industry), and enhanced support for oyster aquaculture in the bay region.

Schulte's restoration project cost roughly $3 million and will require substantial investments if it is to be repeated elsewhere in the bay. This is particularly true in upper portions of the bay, where oyster reproduction levels are lower (requiring restored reefs to be "seeded" with oysters), water conditions are poorer, and oysters are less resistant to disease. Many scientists contend that expanded reef restoration efforts are worth the cost because they enhance oyster populations and provide a vital service to the bay through water filtering.

These efforts are encouraged by the success of the project to date. By summer 2012, the majority of high-relief reef acreage was thriving, despite pressures from poachers and severe anoxic conditions in several years. Moreover, many of the low-relief reefs had accumulated enough shell to now be classified as high-relief reef. The oyster recruitment in 2012 was some of the best Schulte had seen during the project, boding well for the continuance of the reef complexes.

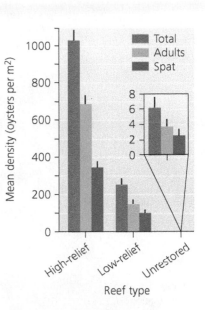

FIGURE 3 **Reef height had a profound effect on the density of adult oysters and spat (newly settled oysters).** Schulte's work suggested that native oyster populations could rebound in portions of Chesapeake Bay if they were provided elevated reefs and were protected from harvest. *Data from Schulte, D.M., R.P. Burke, and R.N. Lipicus, 2009. Unprecedented restoration of a native oyster meta population. Science 325: 1124–1128.*

Some scientists also see value in promoting oyster farming, in which restoration efforts would be supported by businesses instead of taxpayers.

Regardless of how they will be funded, protected sites for oyster restoration efforts are being established. Maryland recently designated 3640 hectares (9000 acres) of new oyster sanctuaries—25% of existing oyster reefs in state waters—where restoration projects like Schulte's could be replicated. This movement toward increased protection for oyster populations, coupled with findings of growing resistance to disease in bay oysters, has given new hope that native oysters may once again thrive in the bay that bears their name. ●

FIGURE 2 **A water cannon blows oyster shells off a barge and onto the river bottom to create an artificial oyster reef for the experiment.**

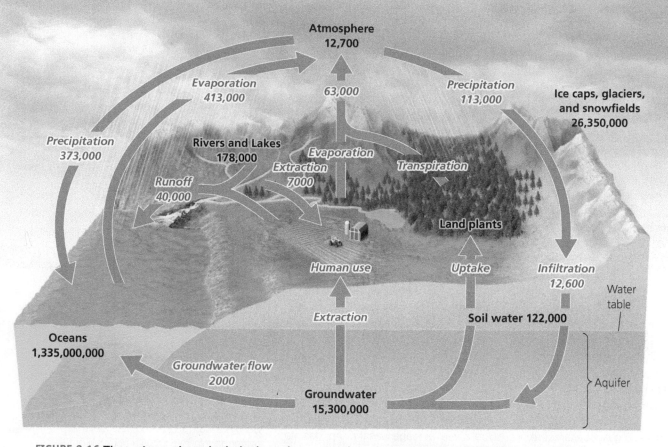

FIGURE 2.16 The water cycle, or hydrologic cycle, summarizes the many routes that water molecules take as they move through the environment. Gray arrows represent fluxes among reservoirs, or pools, for water. Oceans hold 97% of our planet's water, whereas most fresh water resides in groundwater and ice caps. Water vapor in the atmosphere condenses and falls to the surface as precipitation, then evaporates from land and transpires from plants to return to the atmosphere. Water flows downhill into rivers, eventually reaching the oceans. In the figure, pool names are printed in black type, and numbers in black type represent pool sizes expressed in units of cubic kilometers (km^3). Processes, printed in italic red type, give rise to fluxes, printed in italic red type and expressed in km^3 per year. *Data from* Schlesinger, W.H., 2013. Biogeochemistry: An analysis of global change, 3rd ed. Academic Press, London.

Human activity has influenced certain fluxes. We have increased the flux of nitrogen from the atmosphere to reservoirs on Earth's surface, and we have shifted the flux of carbon in the opposite direction. As we discuss biogeochemical cycles, think about how they involve negative feedback loops that promote dynamic equilibrium, and also consider how some human actions can generate destabilizing positive feedback loops.

The water cycle affects all other cycles

Water is so integral to life and to Earth's fundamental processes that we frequently take it for granted. The essential medium for all manner of biochemical reactions, water plays key roles in nearly every environmental system, including each of the nutrient cycles we are about to discuss. Water carries nutrients, sediments, and pollutants from the continents to the oceans via surface runoff, streams, and rivers. These materials can then be carried thousands of miles on ocean currents. Water also carries atmospheric pollutants to the surface when they dissolve in falling rain or snow. The **water cycle**, or **hydrologic cycle** (**FIGURE 2.16**), summarizes how water—in liquid, gaseous, and solid forms—flows through our environment.

The oceans are the main reservoir in the water cycle, holding 97% of all water on Earth. The fresh water we depend on for our survival accounts for less than 3%, and two-thirds of this small amount is tied up in glaciers, snowfields, and ice caps. Thus, considerably less than 1% of the planet's water is in forms that we can readily use—groundwater, surface fresh water, and rain from atmospheric water vapor.

Evaporation and transpiration Water moves from oceans, lakes, ponds, rivers, and moist soil into the atmosphere by **evaporation**, the conversion of a liquid to gaseous form. Warm temperatures and strong winds speed rates of evaporation. A greater degree of exposure has the same effect; an area logged of its forest or converted to agriculture or residential use will lose water more readily than a comparable area that remains vegetated. Water also enters the atmosphere by **transpiration**, the release of water vapor by plants through their leaves, or by evaporation from the surfaces of organisms (such as sweating in humans). Transpiration and evaporation act as natural processes of distillation, because water escaping into the air as a gas leaves behind its dissolved substances.

Precipitation, runoff, and surface water Water returns from the atmosphere to Earth's surface as **precipitation** when water vapor condenses and falls as rain or snow. This moisture may be taken up by plants and used by animals, but much of it flows as runoff into streams, rivers, lakes, ponds, and oceans. Amounts of precipitation vary greatly from region to region, helping give rise to our planet's variety of biomes.

Groundwater Some precipitation and surface water soaks down through soil and rock and becomes **groundwater,** water found beneath layers of soil. Groundwater recharges **aquifers,** spongelike regions of rock and soil that are underground reservoirs of water. The upper limit of groundwater held in an aquifer is referred to as the **water table.** Aquifers can hold groundwater for long periods of time, so the water may be quite ancient. In some cases groundwater can take hundreds or even thousands of years to recharge fully after being depleted. Groundwater becomes surface water when it emerges from springs or flows into streams, rivers, lakes, or the ocean from the soil.

Our impacts on the water cycle are extensive

Human activity affects every aspect of the water cycle. By damming rivers, we slow the movement of water from the land to the sea, and we increase evaporation by holding water in reservoirs. We remove natural vegetation by clear-cutting and developing land, which increases surface runoff, decreases infiltration and transpiration, and promotes soil erosion. Our withdrawals of surface water and groundwater for agriculture, industry, and domestic uses deplete rivers, lakes, and streams and lower water tables. And by emitting into the atmosphere pollutants that dissolve in water droplets, we change the chemical nature of precipitation, in effect sabotaging the natural distillation process that evaporation and transpiration provide. Water shortages have already given rise to conflicts worldwide, from the Middle East to the American West.

WEIGHING **THE ISSUES**

YOUR WATER Has your region faced any water shortages or conflicts over water use? If not, can you describe how such problems affect some other region? What is the quality of your region's water, and what pollution threats does it face? Given your knowledge of the water cycle, what solutions would you propose for water shortages and/or water pollution in your region?

The carbon cycle circulates a vital organic nutrient

As the definitive component of organic molecules, carbon is an ingredient in carbohydrates, fats, and proteins and occurs in the bones, cartilage, and shells of all living things. From DNA to fossil fuels, from plastics to pharmaceuticals, carbon (C) atoms are everywhere. The **carbon cycle** describes the routes that carbon atoms take through the environment (**FIGURE 2.17**).

Photosynthesis, respiration, and food webs Producers—including plants, algae, and cyanobacteria—pull carbon dioxide out of the atmosphere and out of surface water to use in photosynthesis. Photosynthesis breaks the bonds in carbon dioxide (CO_2) and water (H_2O) to produce oxygen (O_2) and carbohydrates (e.g., glucose, $C_6H_{12}O_6$). Autotrophs use some of the carbohydrates to fuel cellular respiration, thereby releasing some of the carbon back into the atmosphere and oceans as CO_2. When producers are eaten by primary consumers, which in turn are eaten by secondary and tertiary consumers, more carbohydrates are broken down in cellular respiration, producing carbon dioxide and water. The same process occurs as decomposers consume waste and dead organic matter. Cellular respiration from all these organisms releases carbon back into the atmosphere and oceans.

Organisms use carbon for structural growth, so a portion of the carbon an organism takes in becomes incorporated into its tissues (such as net primary production in plants; p. 25). The abundance of plants and the fact that they take in so much carbon dioxide for photosynthesis makes plants a major reservoir for carbon. Because CO_2 is a greenhouse gas of primary concern, much research on global climate change is directed toward measuring the amount of CO_2 that plants store. Scientists are working hard to better understand exactly how this portion of the carbon cycle influences Earth's climate (see The Science behind the Story, pp. 38–39).

Sediment storage of carbon As aquatic organisms die, their remains may settle in sediments in ocean basins or freshwater wetlands. As sediment accumulates, older layers are buried more deeply, experiencing high pressure over long periods of time. These conditions can convert soft tissues into fossil fuels—coal, oil, and natural gas (p. 429)—and can turn shells and skeletons into sedimentary rock, such as limestone. Sedimentary rock comprises the largest reservoir in the carbon cycle. Although any given carbon atom spends a relatively short time in the atmosphere, carbon trapped in sedimentary rock may reside there for hundreds of millions of years.

Carbon trapped in sediments and fossil fuel deposits may eventually be released into the oceans or atmosphere by geologic processes such as uplift, erosion, and volcanic eruptions. It also reenters the atmosphere when we extract and burn fossil fuels.

The oceans The world's oceans are the second-largest reservoir in the carbon cycle. They absorb carbon-containing compounds from the atmosphere, from terrestrial runoff, from undersea volcanoes, and from the waste products and detritus of marine organisms. Some carbon atoms absorbed by the oceans—in the form of carbon dioxide, carbonate ions (CO_3^{2-}), and bicarbonate ions (HCO_3^-)—combine with calcium ions (Ca^{2+}) to form calcium carbonate ($CaCO_3$), an essential ingredient in the skeletons and shells of microscopic marine organisms. As these organisms die, their calcium carbonate shells sink to the ocean floor and begin to form sedimentary rock. The rates at which the oceans absorb and release carbon depend on

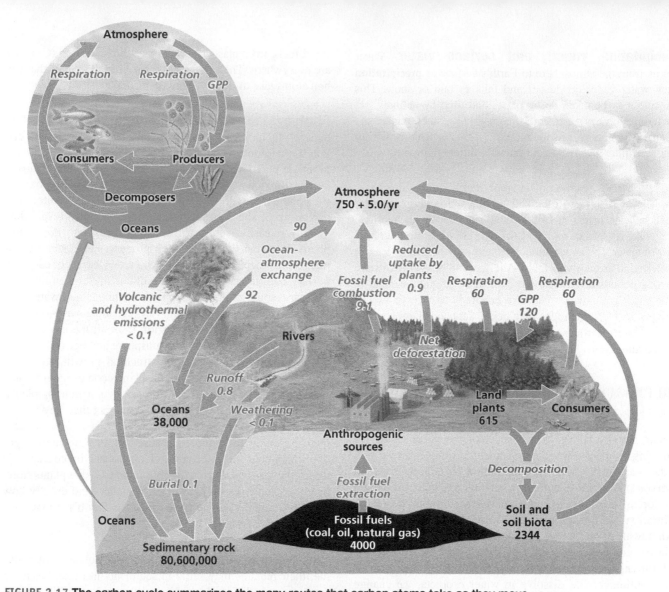

FIGURE 2.17 The carbon cycle summarizes the many routes that carbon atoms take as they move through the environment. Gray arrows represent fluxes among reservoirs, or pools, for carbon. In the carbon cycle, plants use carbon dioxide from the atmosphere for photosynthesis (gross primary production, or "GPP" in the figure). Carbon dioxide is returned to the atmosphere through cellular respiration by plants, their consumers, and decomposers. The oceans sequester carbon in their water and in deep sediments. The vast majority of the planet's carbon is stored in sedimentary rock. In the figure, pool names are printed in black type, and numbers in black type represent pool sizes expressed in petagrams (units of 10^{15} g) of carbon. Processes, printed in italic red type, give rise to fluxes, printed in italic red type and expressed in petagrams of carbon per year. *Data from Schlesinger, W.H., 2013.* Biogeochemistry: An analysis of global change, *3rd ed. Academic Press, London.*

many factors, including temperature and the numbers of marine organisms converting CO_2 into carbohydrates and carbonates.

We are shifting carbon from the lithosphere to the atmosphere

By mining fossil fuel deposits, we are essentially removing carbon from an underground reservoir with a residence time of millions of years. By combusting fossil fuels in our automobiles, homes, and industries, we release carbon dioxide and greatly increase the flux of carbon from the ground to the air. Since the mid-18th century, our fossil fuel combustion has added over 250 billion metric tons (276 billion tons) of carbon to the atmosphere. The movement of CO_2 from the atmosphere back to the hydrosphere, lithosphere, and biosphere has not kept pace.

In addition, cutting down forests removes carbon from the pool of vegetation and releases it to the air. And if less vegetation is left on the surface, there are fewer plants to draw CO_2 back out of the atmosphere.

As a result, scientists estimate that today's atmospheric carbon dioxide reservoir is the largest that Earth has experienced in the past 800,000 years, and likely in the past 20 million years. The ongoing flux of carbon into the atmosphere is the driving force behind today's anthropogenic global climate change.

Some of the excess CO_2 in the atmosphere is now being absorbed by ocean water. This is causing ocean water to become more acidic, leading to problems that threaten many marine organisms.

Our understanding of the carbon cycle is not yet complete. Scientists remain baffled by the so-called missing carbon sink.

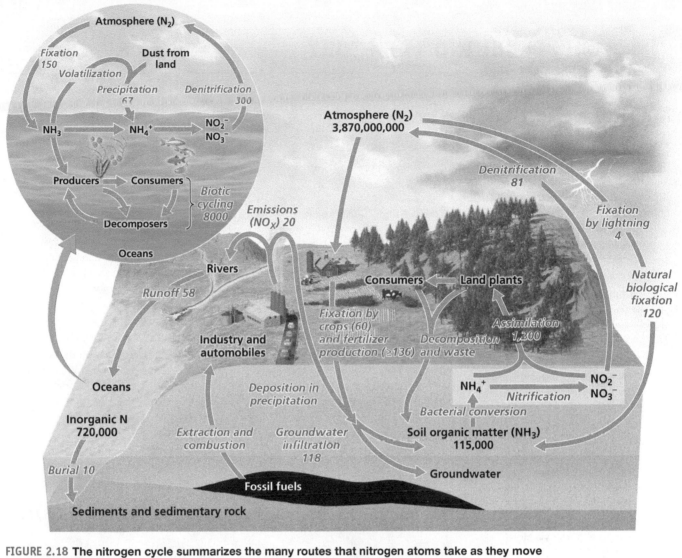

FIGURE 2.18 The nitrogen cycle summarizes the many routes that nitrogen atoms take as they move through the environment. Gray arrows represent fluxes among reservoirs, or pools, for nitrogen. In the nitrogen cycle, specialized bacteria play key roles in "fixing" atmospheric nitrogen and converting it to chemical forms that plants can use. Other types of bacteria convert nitrogen compounds back to the atmospheric gas, N_2. In the oceans, inorganic nitrogen is buried in sediments, whereas nitrogen compounds are cycled through food webs as they are on land. In the figure, pool names are printed in black type, and numbers in black type represent pool sizes expressed in teragrams (units of 10^{12} g) of nitrogen. Processes, printed in italic red type, give rise to fluxes, printed in italic red type and expressed in teragrams of nitrogen per year. *Data from Schlesinger, W.H., 2013.* Biogeochemistry: An analysis of global change, *3rd ed. Academic Press, London.*

Of the carbon dioxide we emit by fossil fuel combustion and deforestation, researchers have measured how much goes into the atmosphere and oceans, but there remain roughly 2.3–2.6 billion metric tons unaccounted for. Many scientists think this CO_2 must be taken up by plants or soils of the temperate and boreal forests. They'd like to know for sure, though, because if certain forests are acting as a major sink for carbon (and thus restraining global climate change), we'd like to be able to keep it that way. For if forests that today are sinks were to turn into sources and begin releasing the "missing" carbon, climate change could accelerate drastically.

The nitrogen cycle involves specialized bacteria

Nitrogen (N) makes up 78% of our atmosphere by mass and is the sixth most abundant element on Earth. It is an essential ingredient in the proteins, DNA, and RNA that build our bodies. Despite its abundance in the air, nitrogen gas (N_2) is chemically inert and cannot cycle out of the atmosphere and into living organisms without assistance from lightning, highly specialized bacteria, or human intervention. For this reason, the element is relatively scarce in the lithosphere and hydrosphere and in organisms. However, once nitrogen undergoes the right kind of chemical change, it becomes biologically active and available to organisms, and it can act as a potent fertilizer. Its scarcity makes biologically active nitrogen a limiting factor for plant growth. For all these reasons the **nitrogen cycle** (FIGURE 2.18) is of vital importance to us and to all other organisms.

Nitrogen fixation To become biologically available, inert nitrogen gas (N_2) must be "fixed," or combined with hydrogen in nature to form ammonia (NH_3), whose water-soluble

FACE-ing a High-CO_2 Future

Can fumigating trees with carbon dioxide tell us what to expect from global climate change? Hundreds of scientists think so, and they are testing plants' responses to atmospheric change at unique outdoor Free-Air CO_2 Enrichment (FACE) facilities.

Our civilization is radically altering Earth's carbon cycle by burning fossil fuels and deforesting landscapes. Today the atmosphere contains over 40% more carbon dioxide (CO_2) than it did just two centuries ago, and the amount is rapidly increasing. Rising CO_2 concentrations are warming our planet, and global climate change brings many unwelcome consequences.

Plants and other autotrophs remove carbon dioxide from the atmosphere to use in photosynthesis, and all organisms add CO_2 to the atmosphere by cellular respiration. Will more CO_2 mean more plant growth, and will more plants be able to absorb and store much of the extra CO_2? Perhaps, but before we rely on forests and phytoplankton to save us from our own emissions, we'd better be sure they can do so.

Historically, if a researcher wanted to measure how plants respond to increased carbon dioxide, he or she would alter gas levels in a small enclosure such as a lab or a greenhouse. But can we really scale up results from such small indoor experiments and trust that they will show how entire forests will behave? Many scientists thought not, so they pioneered Free-Air CO_2 Enrichment. In FACE experiments, ambient levels of CO_2 encompassing areas of forest (or other vegetation) outdoors are precisely controlled. With their large scale and open-air conditions, FACE experiments

Aspen FACE site researcher Dr. Mark Kubiske of the U.S. Forest Service

include most factors that influence a plant community in the wild, such as variation in temperature, sunlight, precipitation, herbivorous insects, disease pathogens, and competition among plants. By measuring how plants respond to changing gas compositions in such real-world conditions, we can better learn how ecosystems may

change in the carbon dioxide–soaked world that awaits us.

Dozens of organizations have sponsored FACE facilities—36 sites in 17 nations so far, including U.S. sites in Arizona, California, Illinois, Minnesota, Nevada, North Carolina, Tennessee, Wisconsin, and Wyoming. The sites cover a variety of ecosystems, from forests to grasslands to rice paddies, and the plots range in size from 1 m to 30 m (3–98 ft) in diameter.

To understand how a typical FACE study works, let's visit the Aspen FACE Experiment at the Harshaw Experimental Forest (where aspen trees are common) near Rhinelander, Wisconsin. Here, tall steel and plastic towers and pipes ring 12 circular plots of forest 30 m (98 ft) in diameter (FIGURE 1). The pipes release CO_2, bathing the plants in an atmosphere 50% richer

FIGURE 1 At the Aspen FACE facility in Wisconsin, tall towers and pipes control the atmospheric composition around selected patches of trees.

in CO_2 than today's (equal to what is expected for the year 2050). Sensors monitor wind conditions, and computers control for the influence of wind by adjusting CO_2 releases, keeping ambient concentrations stable within each plot.

The pipes at the Aspen plots also release tropospheric ozone, and researchers study how this gas and CO_2 affect plant growth, leaf and root conditions, soil carbon content, and much more. Pipes at some plots release normal air, serving as controls for the treatment plots.

Researchers using the Aspen FACE facility have been asking whether forest trees will sequester more carbon as CO_2 levels rise, whether this will change as trees grow, how CO_2 interacts with ozone, and how these gases affect trees' interactions with insects and diseases. They have learned a number of things so far, including:

- Insects and diseases that attack aspen and birch trees increase as atmospheric levels of ozone and CO_2 rise.
- High CO_2 concentrations delay aspen leaf aging, which makes some aspens vulnerable to frost damage in winter.
- Elevated CO_2 levels increase photosynthesis and tree growth—but moderate levels of ozone offset this increased growth (**FIGURE 2**). Because many modelers have not taken ozone into account when estimating how much carbon trees can sequester, the Aspen FACE data suggest that their models may overestimate the amount of CO_2 that trees will pull out of the air.

Together, such results indicate that rising carbon dioxide levels could have a variety of negative impacts on trees

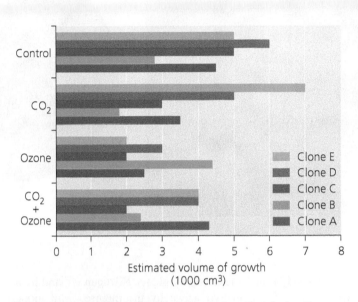

FIGURE 2 **Data from five clones of aspens show that during the study period, trees supplied with carbon dioxide grew more than did the control trees, whereas those supplied with ozone grew less. Trees supplied with both gases did not grow differently from the controls.** *Source: Isebrands, J.G., et al., 2001. Growth responses of* Populus tremuloides *clones to interacting elevated carbon dioxide and tropospheric ozone.* Environmental Pollution *115 (3): 359–371, Fig. 2.*

and forests. Thus, the old expectation that more CO_2 makes for happier plants appears to be an oversimplification. Indeed, research from other FACE sites is showing that increased growth from enhanced CO_2 is often temporary and that growth rates later flatten out or decline. Recent work on crop plants has even shown that high CO_2 makes some crops less nutritious.

Obtaining solid answers to questions like these often takes years or decades, and FACE experiments are designed to monitor plots for the long term as the plants mature. Some FACE sites have been operating for 20 years and are beginning to produce data that could not be gathered in any other way.

Thus, researchers were shocked in 2008 when the U.S. Department of Energy (DOE), which funds Aspen and other major sites, announced it would

cease funding. The DOE advised scientists to cut the trees down and dig up the soil to analyze carbon content. This analysis would provide urgently needed data on carbon sequestration, the DOE said, and then millions of dollars could be shifted toward a new and improved generation of FACE experiments.

The trees at the Aspen site were harvested for analysis in 2009, and researchers are now regrowing forest on the site with funding from the United States Forest Service. The knowledge gains from this project, and other FACE sites in which growth is ongoing, have been substantial. Data from the Aspen FACE project alone has generated more than 180 peer-reviewed scientific articles and is helping scientists today better predict how forest ecosystems will respond to the atmosphere of tomorrow. ●

Root nodules

Nitrogen-fixing bacteria

ions of ammonium (NH_4^+) can be taken up by plants. **Nitrogen fixation** can be accomplished in two ways: by the intense energy of lightning strikes, or when air in the top layer of soil comes in contact with particular types of **nitrogen-fixing bacteria.** These bacteria live in a mutualistic relationship with many types of plants, including soybeans and other legumes, providing them nutrients by converting nitrogen to a usable form. Some farmers nourish soils by planting crops that host nitrogen-fixing bacteria among their roots (**FIGURE 2.19**).

Nitrification and denitrification
Other types of specialized bacteria then perform a process known as **nitrification.** In this process, ammonium ions are first converted into nitrite ions (NO_2^-), then into nitrate ions (NO_3^-). Plants can take up these ions, which also become available after atmospheric deposition on soils or in water or after application of nitrate-based fertilizer.

Animals obtain the nitrogen they need by consuming plants or other animals. Decomposers obtain nitrogen from dead and decaying plant and animal matter and from animal urine and feces. Once decomposers process nitrogen-rich compounds, they release ammonium ions, making these available to nitrifying bacteria to convert again to nitrates and nitrites.

The next step in the nitrogen cycle occurs when **denitrifying bacteria** convert nitrates in soil or water to gaseous nitrogen via a multistep process. Denitrification thereby completes the cycle by releasing nitrogen back into the atmosphere as a gas.

We have greatly influenced the nitrogen cycle

Historically, nitrogen fixation was a **bottleneck,** a step that limited the flux of nitrogen out of the atmosphere. This changed with the research of two German chemists early in the 20th century. Fritz Haber found a way to combine nitrogen and hydrogen gases to synthesize ammonia, a key ingredient in modern explosives and agricultural fertilizers, and Carl Bosch devised methods to produce ammonia on an industrial scale. The **Haber-Bosch process** enabled people to overcome the limits on productivity long imposed by nitrogen scarcity in nature. By enhancing agriculture, the new fertilizers contributed to the past century's enormous increase in human population. Farmers, homeowners, and golf course managers alike all took advantage of fertilizers, dramatically altering the nitrogen cycle. Today, using the Haber-Bosch process, our species is fixing at least as much nitrogen as is being fixed naturally. We have effectively doubled the rate of nitrogen fixation on Earth, overwhelming nature's denitrification abilities.

By fixing atmospheric nitrogen with fertilizers, we increase nitrogen's flux from the atmosphere to Earth's surface. We also enhance this flux by cultivating legume crops whose roots host nitrogen-fixing bacteria. Moreover, we reduce nitrogen's return to the air when we destroy wetlands that filter nutrients; wetland plants host denitrifying bacteria that convert nitrates to nitrogen gas, so wetlands can mop up a great deal of nitrogen pollution.

When our farming practices speed runoff and allow soil erosion, nitrogen flows from farms into terrestrial and aquatic ecosystems, leading to nutrient pollution, eutrophication, and hypoxia. These impacts have become painfully evident to oystermen and scientists in the Chesapeake Bay, but hypoxia in waters is by no means the only human impact on the nitrogen cycle. When we burn forests and fields, we force nitrogen out of soils and vegetation and into the atmosphere. When we burn fossil fuels, we release nitric oxide (NO) into the atmosphere, where it reacts to form nitrogen dioxide (NO_2). This compound is a precursor to nitric acid (HNO_3), a key component of acid precipitation. We introduce another nitrogen-containing gas, nitrous oxide (N_2O), when anaerobic bacteria break down the tremendous volume of animal waste produced in agricultural feedlots. Oddly enough, the overapplication of nitrogen-based fertilizers can strip the soil of other essential nutrients, such as calcium and potassium, because fertilizer flushes them out. As these examples show, human activities have affected the nitrogen cycle in diverse and often far-reaching ways.

The phosphorus cycle circulates a limited nutrient

The element phosphorus (P) is a key component of cell membranes and of several molecules vital for life, including DNA, RNA, ATP, and ADP. Although phosphorus is indispensable for life, the amount of phosphorus in organisms is dwarfed by the vast amounts in rocks, soil, sediments, and the oceans. Unlike the carbon and nitrogen cycles, the **phosphorus cycle** (FIGURE 2.20) has no appreciable atmospheric component besides the transport of tiny amounts in windblown dust and sea spray.

Geology and phosphorus availability The vast majority of Earth's phosphorus is contained within rocks and is released only by weathering, which releases phosphate ions (PO_4^{3-}) into water. Phosphates dissolved in lakes or in the oceans precipitate into solid form, settle to the bottom, and reenter the lithosphere's phosphorus reservoir in sediments.

Because most phosphorus is bound up in rock and only slowly released, environmental concentrations of phosphorus available to organisms tend to be very low. This scarcity explains why phosphorus is frequently a limiting factor for plant growth and why an influx of phosphorus can produce immediate and dramatic effects.

Food webs Aquatic producers take up phosphates from surrounding waters, whereas terrestrial producers take up phosphorus from soil water through their roots. Primary consumers acquire phosphorus from plant tissues and pass it on to secondary and tertiary consumers. Consumers also pass phosphorus to the soil through the excretion of waste. Decomposers break down phosphorus-rich organisms and their wastes and, in so doing, return phosphorus to the soil.

We affect the phosphorus cycle

People increase phosphorus concentrations in surface waters through runoff of the phosphorus-rich fertilizers we apply to lawns and farmlands. A 2008 study determined that an average hectare of land in the Chesapeake Bay region received a

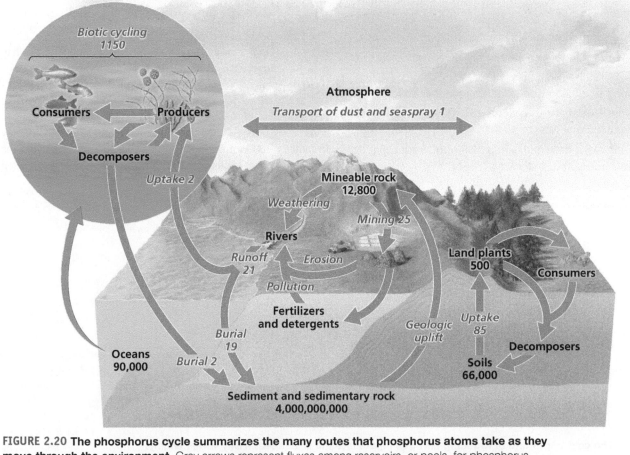

FIGURE 2.20 The phosphorus cycle summarizes the many routes that phosphorus atoms take as they move through the environment. Gray arrows represent fluxes among reservoirs, or pools, for phosphorus. Most phosphorus resides underground in rock and sediment. Rocks containing phosphorus are uplifted geologically and slowly weathered away. Small amounts of phosphorus cycle through food webs, where this nutrient is often a limiting factor for plant growth. In the figure, pool names are printed in black type, and numbers in black type represent pool sizes expressed in teragrams (units of 10^{12} g) of phosphorus. Processes, printed in italic red type, give rise to fluxes, printed in italic red type and expressed in teragrams of phosphorus per year. *Data from Schlesinger, W.H., 2013. Biogeochemistry: An analysis of global change, 3rd ed. Academic Press, London.*

net input of 4.52 kg (10 lb) of phosphorus per year, promoting phosphorus accumulation in soils, runoff into waterways, and phytoplankton blooms and hypoxia in the bay. People also add phosphorus to waterways through releases of treated wastewater rich in phosphates from domestic use of phosphate detergents.

Tackling nutrient enrichment requires diverse approaches

With our reliance on synthetic fertilizers for food production and fossil fuels for energy, nutrient enrichment of ecosystems will be a challenge for many years to come. But there are a number of approaches available to control nutrient pollution in the Chesapeake Bay watershed, Mississippi River watershed, and other waterways affected by eutrophication:

- Reducing fertilizer use on farms and lawns
- Changing the timing of fertilizer application to minimize rainy-season runoff
- More effectively managing manure applications to farmland to reduce nutrient runoff
- Planting and maintaining vegetation "buffers" around streams that trap nutrient and sediment runoff
- Using artificial wetlands to filter stormwater and farm runoff
- Restoring nutrient-absorbing wetlands along waterways
- Improving technologies in sewage treatment plants to enhance nitrogen and phosphorus capture
- Restoring frequently flooded lands to reduce runoff
- Upgrading stormwater systems to capture runoff from roads and parking lots
- Reducing fossil fuel combustion to minimize atmospheric inputs of nitrogen to waterways

These approaches have widely varying costs for the same level of nutrient reduction. For example, embracing approaches such as planting vegetation buffers around streams, restoring wetlands, and practicing sustainable agriculture can reduce nutrient inputs into waterways at a fraction of the cost of other approaches, all while creating habitat for wildlife (FIGURE 2.21). Ultimately, the approaches embraced depend on the major sources of nutrients for a given waterway along with economic considerations.

WEIGHING THE ISSUES

NUTRIENT POLLUTION AND ITS FINANCIAL IMPACTS A sizable amount of the nitrogen and phosphorus that enters the Chesapeake Bay originates from farms and other sources far from the bay, yet it is people living near the bay, such as oystermen and crabbers, who bear many of the negative impacts. Who do you believe should be responsible for addressing this problem? Should environmental policies on this issue be developed and enforced by state governments, the federal government, both, or neither? Explain the reasons for your answer.

A systemic approach to restoration offers hope for the Bay

The Chesapeake Bay finally has prospects for recovery as the federal government and bay states are now managing the bay as a holistic system. Arriving at this endpoint was not easy, though. After 25 years of failed pollution control agreements and nearly $6 billion spent on cleanup efforts, the Chesapeake Bay Foundation (CBF), a nonprofit organization dedicated to conserving the bay, sued the Environmental Protection Agency in January 2009 for failing to use its available powers under the Clean Water Act to clean up the bay. The CBF's lawsuit focused

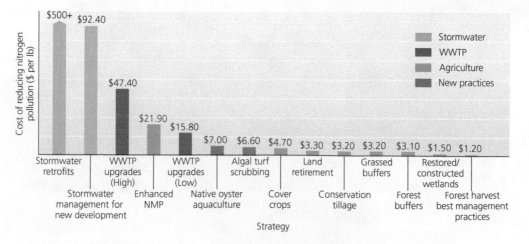

FIGURE 2.21 The cost per pound of reducing nitrogen inputs into the Chesapeake Bay varies widely. Approaches slowing runoff to waterways avoid nitrogen inputs for a few dollars per pound, whereas upgrades to wastewater treatment plants (WWTP), enhanced nutrient management plans (NMP—careful regulation of nutrient applications), and stormwater upgrades can be considerably more expensive.

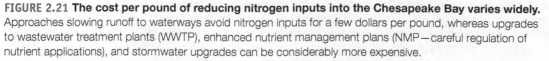

DATA Q For what it costs to remove 1 pound of nitrogen by using enhanced nutrient management programs (NMP), how many pounds of nitrogen could be kept out of waterways by planting forested buffers around streams instead?

media attention on the plight of the bay, its ongoing water quality issues, and its depleted fisheries—and spurred action.

In May 2009, President Obama directed the EPA and other federal agencies through an executive order to establish a comprehensive plan for the restoration of the Chesapeake Bay. One year later, the EPA and the CBF announced a settlement in which the EPA agreed to work with surrounding states to provide aggressive pollution regulation in the bay. In December 2010, a comprehensive "pollution budget" was developed and implemented with the assistance of the District of Columbia, Delaware, Maryland, New York, Pennsylvania, Virginia, and West Virginia.

Existing efforts to reduce nutrient and sediment inputs into the bay and to limit harvests of oysters, crabs, and fish are already leading to modest improvement in some aspects of the bay's health. For example, the CBF's "2012 State of the Bay" report shows the bay's overall health has improved 10% since 2008 and cites recent studies and trends in nutrient concentrations that suggest pollution reduction strategies are working to reduce inputs of nitrogen and phosphorus to bay waters. The Chesapeake Bay remains highly degraded and much work is still needed. Still, the 17 million people living in the Chesapeake Bay watershed have reason to hope that the Chesapeake Bay of tomorrow may be healthier than it is today, thanks to the collaborative efforts of concerned citizens, advocacy organizations, and the federal and bay state governments.

Conclusion

Thinking in terms of systems is important in understanding Earth's dynamics, so that we may learn how to avoid disrupting its processes and how to mitigate any disruptions we cause. By studying the environment from a systems perspective and by integrating scientific findings with the policy process, people who care about the Chesapeake Bay and other waterways are working today to address dead zones around the world.

Earth hosts many interacting systems, and the way one perceives them depends on the questions in which one is interested. Life interacts with its nonliving environment in ecosystems, systems through which energy flows and matter is recycled. Understanding the biogeochemical cycles that describe the movement of nutrients within and among ecosystems is crucial because human activities are causing significant changes in the ways those cycles function.

Unperturbed ecosystems use renewable solar energy, recycle nutrients, and are stabilized by negative feedback loops. The environmental systems we see on Earth today are those that have survived the test of time. Our industrialized civilization is young in comparison. These natural systems therefore provide us a blueprint to mimic as we move towards greater sustainability in modern society.

Reviewing Objectives

You should now be able to:

Describe the nature of environmental systems

- Earth's natural systems are complex, so environmental scientists often take a holistic approach to studying environmental systems. (p. 20)

- Systems are networks of interacting components that generally involve feedback loops, show dynamic equilibrium, and result in emergent properties. (pp. 20–21)

- Negative feedback stabilizes systems, whereas positive feedback destabilizes systems. Positive feedback often results from human disturbance of natural systems. (pp. 20–21)

- Because environmental systems interact and overlap, one's delineation of a system depends on the questions in which one is interested. (p. 22)

- Hypoxia in the Chesapeake Bay, which results from nutrient pollution in the rivers that feed it, illustrates how systems are interrelated. (p. 22)

Define ecosystems and evaluate how living and nonliving entities interact in ecosystem-level ecology

- Ecosystems consist of all organisms and nonliving entities that occur and interact in a particular area at the same time. (pp. 24–25)

- Energy flows in one direction through ecosystems, whereas matter is recycled. (pp. 24–25)

- Energy is converted to biomass, and ecosystems vary in their productivity. (pp. 25–26)

- Input of nutrients can boost productivity, but an excess of nutrients can alter ecosystems and cause severe ecological and economic consequences. (pp. 25–27)

Outline the fundamentals of landscape ecology, GIS, and ecological modeling

- Landscape ecology studies how landscape structure influences organisms. (pp. 27–28)

- Landscapes consist of patches spatially arrayed in a mosaic. Organisms dependent on certain types of patches may occur in metapopulations. (pp. 27–28)

- With the help of remote sensing technology and GIS, landscape ecology is being increasingly used in conservation and regional planning. (pp. 28–29)

- Ecological modeling helps ecologists make sense of the complex systems they study. (pp. 29–30)

Assess ecosystem services and how they benefit our lives

- Ecosystems provide the "goods" we know of as natural resources. (p. 30)

- Ecological processes naturally provide services that we depend on for everyday living. (pp. 30–31)

- **Compare and contrast how water, carbon, nitrogen, and phosphorous cycle through the environment**

- A source is a reservoir that contributes more of a material than it receives, and a sink is one that receives more than it provides. (p. 31)

- Water moves widely through the environment in the water cycle. (pp. 34–35)

- Most carbon is contained in sedimentary rock. Substantial amounts also occur in the oceans and in soil. Carbon flux between organisms and the atmosphere occurs via photosynthesis and respiration. (pp. 35–37)

- Nitrogen is a vital nutrient for plant growth. Most nitrogen is in the atmosphere, so it must be "fixed" by specialized bacteria or lightning before plants can use it. (pp. 37, 40)

- Phosphorus is most abundant in sedimentary rock, with substantial amounts in soil and the oceans. Phosphorus has no appreciable atmospheric reservoir. It is a key nutrient for plant growth. (p. 41)

- **Explain how human impact is affecting biogeochemical cycles**

- People are affecting Earth's biogeochemical cycles by shifting carbon from fossil fuel reservoirs into the atmosphere, shifting nitrogen from the atmosphere to the planet's surface, and depleting groundwater supplies, among other impacts. (pp. 35–42)

- Policy can help us address problems with nutrient pollution. (p. 42)

Testing Your Comprehension

1. Which type of feedback loop is more common in nature, and which more commonly results from human action? How might the emergence of a positive feedback loop affect a system in homeostasis?

2. Describe how hypoxic conditions can develop in ecosystems such as the Chesapeake Bay.

3. What is the difference between an ecosystem and a community?

4. Describe the typical movement of energy through an ecosystem. Now describe the typical movement of matter through an ecosystem.

5. Explain net primary productivity. Name one ecosystem with high net primary productivity and one with low net primary productivity.

6. Why are patches in a landscape mosaic often important to people who are interested in conserving populations of rare animals?

7. What is the difference between evaporation and transpiration? Give examples of how the water cycle interacts with the carbon, phosphorus, and nitrogen cycles.

8. What role does each of the following play in the carbon cycle?
   - Cars
   - Photosynthesis
   - The oceans
   - Earth's crust

9. Distinguish the function performed by nitrogen-fixing bacteria from that performed by denitrifying bacteria.

10. How has human activity altered the carbon cycle? The phosphorus cycle? The nitrogen cycle? What environmental problems have arisen from these changes?

Seeking Solutions

1. Once vegetation is cleared from a riverbank, water begins to erode the bank away. This erosion may dislodge more vegetation. Would you expect this to result in a feedback process? If so, which type—negative or positive? Explain your answer. How might we halt or reverse this process?

2. Consider the ecosystem(s) that surround(s) your campus. Describe one way in which energy flows through and matter is recycled. Now pick one type of nutrient, and briefly describe how it moves through your ecosystem(s). Does the landscape contain patches? Can you describe any ecotones?

3. For a conservation biologist interested in sustaining populations of the organisms below, why would it be helpful to take a landscape ecology perspective? Explain your answer in each case.
   - A forest-breeding warbler that suffers poor nesting success in small, fragmented forest patches
   - A bighorn sheep that must move seasonally between mountains and lowlands
   - A toad that lives in upland areas but travels cross-country to breed in localized pools each spring

4. A simple change in the flux between just two reservoirs in a single nutrient cycle can potentially have major consequences for ecosystems and, indeed, for the entire Earth. Explain how this can be, using one example from the carbon cycle and one example from the nitrogen cycle.

5. How do you think we might solve the problem of eutrophication in the Chesapeake Bay? Assess several possible solutions, your reasons for believing they might work, and the likely hurdles we might face. Explain who should be responsible for implementing these solutions, and why.

6. **THINK IT THROUGH** You are an oysterman in the Chesapeake Bay, and your income is decreasing because the dead zone is making it harder to harvest oysters. One day your senator comes to town, and you have a one-minute audience with her. What steps would you urge her to take in Washington, D.C., to try to help alleviate the dead zone and bring back the oyster fishery?

   Now suppose you are a Pennsylvania farmer who has learned that the government is offering incentives to farmers to help reduce fertilizer runoff into the Chesapeake Bay. What types of approaches described in the text might you be willing to try, and why?

Calculating Ecological Footprints

In the United States, a common dream is to own a suburban home with a weed-free green lawn. Nationwide, Americans tend about 40.5 million acres of lawn grass. But conventional lawn care involves inputs of fertilizers, pesticides, and irrigation water, and using gasoline or electricity for mowing and other care—all of which raise environmental and health concerns. Using the figures for a typical lawn in the table, calculate the total amount of fertilizer, water, and gasoline used in lawn care across the nation each year.

	Acreage of lawn	Fertilizer used (lbs)	Water used (gal)	Gasoline used (gal)
For the typical 1/4-acre lawn	0.25	37	16,000	4.9
For all lawns in your hometown				
For all lawns in the United States	40,500,000			

Data from Chameides, B., 2008. http://www.nicholas.duke.edu/thegreengrok/lawns.

1. How much fertilizer is applied each year on lawns throughout the United States? Where does the nitrogen for this fertilizer come from? What becomes of the nitrogen and phosphorus applied to a suburban lawn that is not taken up by grass?

2. Leaving grass clippings on a lawn decreases the need for fertilizer by 50%. What else might a homeowner do to decrease fertilizer use in a yard and the environmental impacts of nutrient pollution?

3. How much gasoline could Americans save each year if they did not take care of lawns? At today's gas prices, how much money would this save?

Mastering ENVIRONMENTALSCIENCE™

STUDENTS

Go to **MasteringEnvironmentalScience** for assignments, the etext, and the Study Area with practice tests, videos, current events, and activities.

INSTRUCTORS

Go to **MasteringEnvironmentalScience** for automatically graded activities, current events, videos, and reading questions that you can assign to your students, plus Instructor Resources.

CHAPTER 3
The Atomic Nucleus and Radioactivity

THE ATOMIC nucleus and nuclear processes are one of the most misunderstood and controversial areas of science. Distrust of anything *nuclear*, or anything *radioactive*, is much like the fears of electricity more than a century ago. Indeed, electricity can be dangerous, and even lethal, when improperly handled. But with safeguards and well-informed consumers, society has determined that the benefits of electricity outweigh its risks. Today we are making similar decisions about nuclear technology's risks and benefits. The risks became most evident with the 2011 earthquake and tsunami that destroyed Japan's Fukushima Daiichi nuclear power plant. The benefits, however, include the large-scale production of electric energy with no emission of carbon dioxide, which is a potent greenhouse gas. Should society continue to invest in nuclear energy? Now, more than ever, it is important that we "know nukes"!

LEARNING OBJECTIVE
Identify three forms of radioactivity.

3.1 Radioactivity

EXPLAIN THIS Why is it both impractical and impossible to prevent our exposure to radioactivity?

Elements with unstable nuclei are said to be *radioactive*. They eventually break down and eject energetic particles and emit high-frequency electromagnetic radiation. The emission of these particles and radiation is called **radioactivity**. Because the process involves the decay of the atomic nucleus, it is often called *radioactive decay*.

A common misconception is that radioactivity is new in the environment, but it has been around far longer than the human race. Interestingly, the deeper you go below Earth's surface, the hotter it gets. At a depth of only 30 km the temperature is hotter than 500°C. At greater depths it is so hot that rock melts into magma, which can rise to Earth's surface to escape as lava. Superheated subterranean water can escape violently to form geysers or more gently to form a soothing natural hot spring. The main reason it gets hotter down below is that Earth contains an abundance of radioactive isotopes and is heated as it absorbs radiation from these isotopes. So volcanoes, geysers, and hot springs are all powered by radioactivity. Even the drifting of continents (see Chapter 8) is related to Earth's internal radioactivity. Radioactivity is as natural as sunshine and rain.

Alpha, Beta, and Gamma Rays

All isotopes of elements with an atomic number higher than 83 (bismuth) are radioactive. These isotopes, and certain lighter radioactive isotopes, emit three distinct types of radiation, named by the first three letters of the Greek alphabet, α, β, and γ—*alpha*, *beta*, and *gamma*. Alpha rays carry a positive electric charge, beta rays carry a negative charge, and gamma rays carry no charge. The three rays can be separated by placing a magnetic field across their paths (Figure 3.2).

Radioactivity has been around since Earth's beginning.

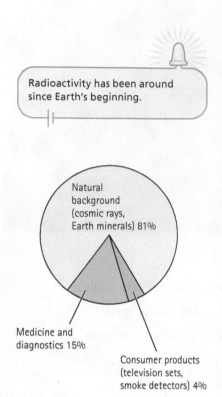

FIGURE 3.1
Sources of radiation exposure for an average individual in the United States.

MasteringPhysics®
TUTORIAL: Radiation and Biological Effects

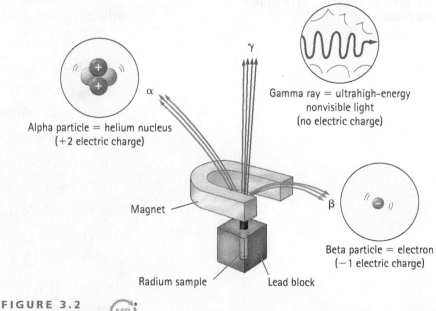

FIGURE 3.2
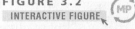

In a magnetic field, alpha rays bend one way, beta rays bend the other way, and gamma rays don't bend at all. Note that the alpha rays bend less than do the beta rays. This is because alpha particles have more inertia (mass) than beta particles.

An **alpha particle** is the combination of two protons and two neutrons (in other words, it is the nucleus of the helium atom, atomic number 2). Alpha particles are relatively easy to shield because of their relatively large size and their double positive charge (+2). For example, they do not normally penetrate through light materials such as paper or clothing. Because of their high kinetic energies, however, alpha particles can cause significant damage to the surface of a material, especially living tissue. When traveling through only a few centimeters of air, alpha particles pick up electrons and become nothing more than harmless helium. As a matter of fact, that's where the helium in a child's balloon comes from—practically all of Earth's helium atoms were at one time energetic alpha particles.

A **beta particle** is an electron ejected from a nucleus. Once ejected, it is indistinguishable from an electron in a cathode ray or electric circuit, or one orbiting the atomic nucleus. The difference is that a beta particle originates inside the nucleus—from a neutron. As we shall soon see, the neutron becomes a proton when it loses the electron that is a beta particle. A beta particle is normally faster than an alpha particle and carries only a single negative charge (−1). Beta particles are not as easy to stop as alpha particles are, and they can penetrate light materials such as paper or clothing. They can penetrate fairly deeply into skin, where they have the potential for harming or killing living cells. But they are not able to penetrate deeply into denser materials such as aluminum. Beta particles, once stopped, simply become part of the material they are in, like any other electron.

Gamma rays are high-frequency electromagnetic radiation emitted by radioactive elements. Like visible light, a gamma ray is pure energy. The amount of energy in a gamma ray, however, is much greater than in visible light, ultraviolet light, or even X-rays. Because they have no mass or electric charge and because of their high energies, gamma rays can penetrate most materials. However, they cannot penetrate unusually dense materials such as lead, which absorbs them. Delicate molecules inside cells throughout our bodies that are zapped by gamma rays suffer structural damage. Hence, gamma rays are generally more harmful to us than alpha or beta particles (unless the alphas or betas are ingested).

FYI Once alpha and beta particles slow down, they combine to form harmless helium. This happens primarily deep underground. As the newly formed helium seeps toward the surface, it becomes concentrated within natural gas deposits. Some natural gas deposits, such as those in Texas, contain as much as 7% helium. This helium is isolated and sold for various applications, such as blimps and helium balloons. Interestingly, natural gas fields within the United States contain about two-thirds of the world's supply of helium.

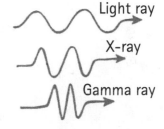

FIGURE 3.3
A gamma ray is simply electromagnetic radiation, much higher in frequency and energy than light and X-rays.

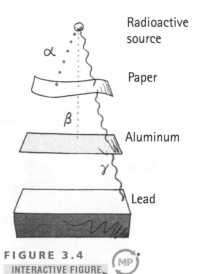

FIGURE 3.4   INTERACTIVE FIGURE   **MP**

Alpha particles are the least penetrating and can be stopped by a few sheets of paper. Beta particles readily pass through paper, but not through a sheet of aluminum. Gamma rays penetrate several centimeters into solid lead.

CHECK YOURSELF
Imagine that you are given three radioactive rocks—one an alpha emitter, one a beta emitter, and one a gamma emitter. You can throw away one, but of the remaining two, you must hold one in your hand and place the other in your pocket. What can you do to minimize your exposure to radiation?

CHECK YOUR ANSWER
Hold the alpha emitter in your hand because the skin on your hand shields you. Put the beta emitter in your pocket because beta particles are likely stopped by the combined thickness of your clothing and skin. Throw away the gamma emitter because gamma rays penetrate your body from either of these locations. Ideally, of course, you should keep as much distance as possible between you and all of the rocks.

FIGURE 3.5
The shelf life of fresh strawberries and other perishables is markedly lengthened when the food is subjected to gamma rays from a radioactive source. The strawberries on the right were treated with gamma radiation, which kills the microorganisms that normally lead to spoilage. The food is only a receiver of radiation and is not transformed into an emitter of radiation, as can be confirmed with a radiation detector.

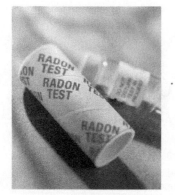

FIGURE 3.6
A commercially available radon test kit for the home. The canister is unsealed in the area to be sampled. Radon seeping into the canister is adsorbed by activated carbon within the canister. After several days, the canister is resealed and sent to a laboratory that determines the radon level by measuring the amount of radiation emitted by the adsorbed radon.

Common rocks and minerals in our environment contain significant quantities of radioactive isotopes because most of them contain trace amounts of uranium. People who live in brick, concrete, or stone buildings are exposed to greater amounts of radiation than people who live in wooden buildings.

The leading source of naturally occurring radiation is radon-222, an inert gas arising from uranium deposits. Radon is a heavy gas that tends to accumulate in basements after it seeps up through cracks in the floor. Levels of radon vary from region to region, depending on local geology. You can check the radon level in your home with a radon detector kit (Figure 3.6). If levels are abnormally high, corrective measures such as sealing the basement floor and walls and maintaining adequate ventilation are recommended.

About one-fifth of our annual exposure to radiation comes from nonnatural sources, primarily medical procedures. Television sets, fallout from nuclear testing, and the coal and nuclear power industries are also contributors. The coal industry far outranks the nuclear power industry as a source of radiation. The global combustion of coal annually releases about 13,000 tons of radioactive thorium and uranium into the atmosphere. Both these minerals are found naturally in coal deposits, so their release is a natural consequence of burning coal. Worldwide, the nuclear power industries generate about 10,000 tons of radioactive waste each year. Most of this waste, however, is contained and *not* released into the environment.

LEARNING OBJECTIVE
Identify the units and biological effects of radioactivity.

 Integrated Science 10A
BIOLOGY

Radiation Dosage

EXPLAIN THIS Why are household smoke detectors radioactive?

Radiation received by living tissue is commonly measured in *rads* (*r*adiation *a*bsorbed *d*ose), a unit of absorbed energy. One **rad** is equal to 0.01 J of radiant energy absorbed per kilogram of tissue. The capacity for nuclear radiation to cause damage to living tissue, however, is not just a function of its level of energy. Some forms of radiation are more harmful than others. For example, suppose you have two arrows, one with a pointed tip and one with a suction cup at its tip. Shoot the two of them at an apple at the same speed and both have the same kinetic energy. The one with the pointed tip, however, invariably does more damage to the apple than the one with the suction cup. Similarly, some forms of radiation cause greater harm than other forms, even when we receive the same number of rads from both forms.

The unit of measure for radiation dosage based on potential damage is the **rem** (*r*oentgen *e*quivalent *m*an).* In calculating the dosage in rems, we multiply the number of rads by a factor that corresponds to different health effects of different types of radiation as determined by clinical studies. For example, 1 rad of alpha particles has the same biological effect as 10 rads of beta particles.** We call both of these dosages 10 rems:

Particle	Radiation Dosage		Factor		Health Effect
alpha	1 rad	×	10	=	10 rems
beta	10 rad	×	1	=	10 rems

CHECK YOURSELF
Would you rather be exposed to 1 rad of alpha particles or 1 rad of beta particles?

CHECK YOUR ANSWER
Multiply these quantities of radiation by the appropriate factor to get the dosages in rems. Alpha: 1 rad × 10 = 10 rems. Beta: 1 rad × 1 = 1 rem. The factors show us that, physiologically speaking, alpha particles are 10 times as damaging as beta particles.

Lethal doses of radiation begin at 500 rems. A person has about a 50% chance of surviving a dose of this magnitude received over a short period of time. During radiation therapy, a patient may receive localized doses in excess of 200 rems each day for a period of weeks (Figure 3.7).

All the radiation we receive from natural sources and from medical procedures is only a fraction of 1 rem. For convenience, the smaller unit *millirem* is used, where 1 millirem (mrem) is 1/1000 of a rem.

The average person in the United States is exposed to about 360 mrem a year, as Table 3.1 indicates. About 80% of this radiation comes from natural sources, such as cosmic rays and Earth itself. A typical chest X-ray exposes a person to 5–30 mrem (0.005–0.030 rem), less than 1/10,000 of the lethal dose. The human body itself is a significant source of natural radiation, primarily from the potassium we ingest. Our bodies contain about 200 g of potassium. Of this quantity, about 20 mg is the radioactive isotope potassium-40, which is a gamma ray emitter. Radiation is indeed everywhere.

When radiation encounters the intricately structured molecules in the watery, ion-rich brine that makes up our cells, the radiation can create chaos on the atomic scale. Some molecules are broken, and this change alters other molecules, which can be harmful to life processes.

Cells can repair most kinds of molecular damage caused by radiation if the radiation is not too severe. A cell can survive an otherwise lethal dose of radiation if the dose is spread over a long period of time to allow intervals for healing. When

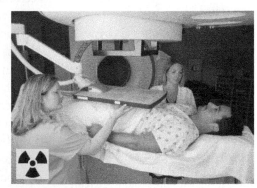

FIGURE 3.7
Nuclear radiation is focused on harmful tissue, such as a cancerous tumor, to selectively kill or shrink the tissue in a technique known as radiation therapy. This application of nuclear radiation has saved millions of lives—a clear-cut example of the benefits of nuclear technology. The inset shows the internationally used symbol to indicate an area where radioactive material is being handled or produced.

---

*This unit is named for the discoverer of X-rays, Wilhelm Roentgen.
**This is true even though beta particles have more penetrating power, as mentioned earlier.

TABLE 3.1 ANNUAL RADIATION EXPOSURE

Source	Typical Amount Received in 1 Year (Millirems)
Natural Origin	
Cosmic radiation	26
Ground	33
Air (radon-222)	198
Human tissues (K-40; Ra-226)	35
Human Origin	
Medical procedures	
Diagnostic X-rays	40
Nuclear medicine	15
TV tubes and other consumer products	11
Weapons-test fallout	1

FIGURE 3.8
The film badges worn by Tammy and Larry contain audible alerts for both radiation surge and accumulated exposure. Information from the individualized badges is periodically downloaded to a database for analysis and storage.

FYI The only element beyond uranium to find a commercial application is americium, Am, which is a key component of almost all household smoke detectors. This element completes an electric circuit by ionizing air within a chamber. Smoke particles interfere with this ionization, thus breaking the circuit and triggering the alarm.

FIGURE 3.9
Tracking fertilizer uptake with a radioactive isotope.

radiation is sufficient to kill cells, the dead cells can be replaced by new ones. Sometimes a radiated cell survives with a damaged DNA molecule. New cells arising from the damaged cell retain the altered genetic information, producing a *mutation*. Usually the effects of a mutation are insignificant, but occasionally the mutation results in cells that do not function as well as unaffected ones, sometimes leading to a cancer. If the damaged DNA is in an individual's reproductive cells, the genetic code of the individual's offspring may retain the mutation.

Radioactive Tracers

Radioactive samples of all the elements have been made in scientific laboratories. This is accomplished by bombardment with neutrons or other particles. Radioactive materials are extremely useful in scientific research and industry. To check the action of a fertilizer, for example, researchers combine a small amount of radioactive material with the fertilizer and then apply the combination to a few plants. The amount of radioactive fertilizer taken up by the plants can be easily measured with radiation detectors. From such measurements, scientists can inform farmers of the proper amount of fertilizer to use. Radioactive isotopes used to trace such pathways are called *tracers*.

In a technique known as medical imaging, tracers are used to diagnose internal disorders. This technique works because the path the tracer takes is influenced only by its physical and chemical properties, not by its radioactivity. The tracer may be introduced alone or along with some other chemical that helps target the tracer to a particular type of tissue in the body.

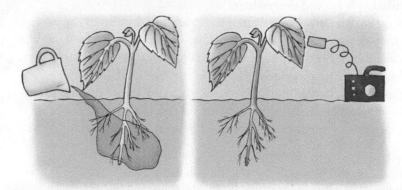

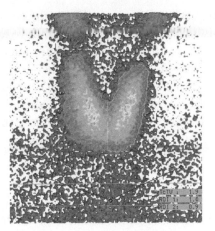

FIGURE 3.10
The thyroid gland, located in the neck, absorbs much of the iodine that enters the body through food and drink. Images of the thyroid gland, such as the one shown here, can be obtained by giving a patient the radioactive isotope iodine-131. These images are useful in diagnosing metabolic disorders.

3.2 The Strong Nuclear Force

EXPLAIN THIS Why are larger nuclei less stable than smaller nuclei?

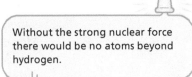

As described the atomic nucleus occupies only a tiny fraction of the volume of an individual atom, leaving most of the atom as empty space. The nucleus is composed of *nucleons*, is the collective name for protons and neutrons.

We know that electric charges of like sign repel one another. So, how do positively charged protons in the nucleus stay clumped together? This question led to the discovery of an attraction called the **strong nuclear force**, which acts between all nucleons. This force is very strong but over only extremely short distances (about 10^{-15} m, the diameter of a typical atomic nucleus). Repulsive electric interactions, on the other hand, are relatively long-ranged. Figure 3.11 suggests a comparison of the strengths of these two forces over distance. For protons that are close together, as in small nuclei, the attractive strong nuclear force easily overcomes the repulsive electric force.

> **LEARNING OBJECTIVE**
> Describe how the strong nuclear force acts to hold nucleons together in the atomic nucleus.

> Without the strong nuclear force there would be no atoms beyond hydrogen.

UNIFYING CONCEPT

● *The Electric Force*
Section 7.1

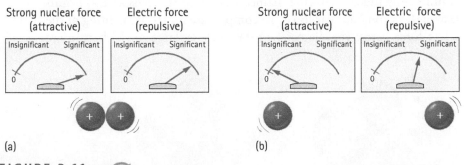

FIGURE 3.11
INTERACTIVE FIGURE (MP)

(a) Two protons near each other experience both an attractive strong nuclear force and a repulsive electric force. At this tiny separation distance, the strong nuclear force overcomes the electric force, and the protons stay together. (b) When the two protons are relatively far from each other, the electric force is more significant and the protons repel each other. This proton–proton repulsion in large atomic nuclei reduces nuclear stability.

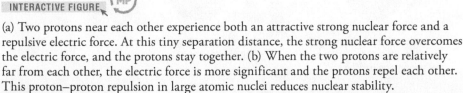

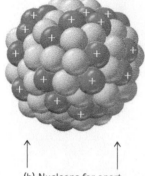

(a) Nucleons close together

(b) Nucleons far apart

FIGURE 3.12
(a) All nucleons in a small atomic nucleus are close to one another; hence, they experience an attractive strong nuclear force. (b) Nucleons on opposite sides of a larger nucleus are not as close to one another, and so the attractive strong nuclear forces holding them together are much weaker. The result is that the large nucleus is less stable.

But for protons that are far apart, such as those on opposite edges of a large nucleus, the attractive strong nuclear force may be weaker than the repulsive electric force.

A large nucleus is not as stable as a small one. In a helium nucleus, which has two protons, each proton feels the repulsive effect of only one other proton. In a uranium nucleus, however, each of the 92 protons feels the repulsive effects of the other 91 protons! The nucleus is unstable. We see that there is a limit to the size of the atomic nucleus. For this reason, all nuclei with more than 83 protons are radioactive.

CHECK YOURSELF
Two protons in the atomic nucleus repel each other, but they are also attracted to each other. Why?

CHECK YOUR ANSWER
Although two protons repel each other by the electric force, they also attract each other by the strong nuclear force. Both of these forces act simultaneously. As long as the attractive strong nuclear force is stronger than the repulsive electric force, the protons remain together. When the electric force overcomes the strong nuclear force, however, the protons fly apart from each other.

Neutrons serve as "nuclear cement" holding the atomic nucleus together. Protons attract both protons and neutrons by the strong nuclear force. Protons also repel other protons by the electric force. Neutrons, on the other hand, have no electric charge and so attract other protons and neutrons only by the strong nuclear force. The presence of neutrons therefore adds to the attraction among nucleons and helps hold the nucleus together (Figure 3.13).

The more protons there are in a nucleus, the more neutrons are needed to help balance the repulsive electric forces. For light elements, it is sufficient to have about as many neutrons as protons. The most common isotope of carbon, C-12, for instance, has equal numbers of each—six protons and six neutrons. For large nuclei, more neutrons than protons are needed. Because the strong nuclear force diminishes rapidly over distance, nucleons must be practically touching in order for the strong nuclear force to be effective. Nucleons on opposite sides of a large atomic nucleus are not as attracted to one another. The electric force, however, does not diminish by much across the diameter of a large nucleus and so begins to win out over the strong nuclear force. To compensate for the weakening of the strong nuclear force across the diameter of the nucleus, large nuclei have more

FIGURE 3.13
The presence of neutrons helps hold the nucleus together by increasing the effect of the strong nuclear force, represented by the single-headed arrows.

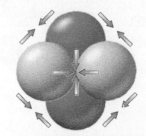

All nucleons, both protons and neutrons, attract one another by the strong nuclear force.

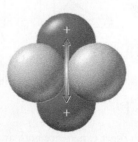

Only protons repel one another by the electric force.

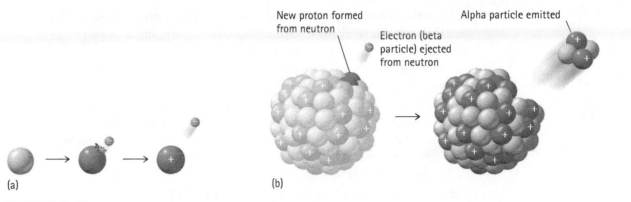

FIGURE 3.14

(a) A neutron near a proton is stable, but a neutron by itself is unstable and decays to a proton by emitting an electron. (b) Destabilized by an increase in the number of protons, the nucleus begins to shed fragments, such as alpha particles.

neutrons than protons. Lead, for example, has about one and a half times as many neutrons as protons.

So, we see that neutrons are stabilizing and large nuclei require an abundance of them. But neutrons are not always successful in keeping a nucleus intact. Interestingly, neutrons are not stable when they are by themselves. A lone neutron is radioactive and spontaneously transforms into a proton and an electron (Figure 3.14a). A neutron seems to need protons around to keep this from happening. After the size of a nucleus reaches a certain point, the neutrons so outnumber the protons that there are not enough protons in the mix to prevent the neutrons from turning into protons. As neutrons in a nucleus change into protons, the stability of the nucleus decreases because the repulsive electric force becomes increasingly significant. The result is that pieces of the nucleus fragment away in the form of radiation, as shown in Figure 3.14b.

CHECK YOURSELF

What role do neutrons serve in the atomic nucleus? What is the fate of a neutron when alone or distant from one or more protons?

CHECK YOUR ANSWERS

Neutrons serve as nuclear cement in nuclei and add to nuclear stability. But when alone or away from protons, a neutron becomes radioactive and spontaneously transforms to a proton and an electron.

3.3 Half-Life and Transmutation

EXPLAIN THIS How is the rate of transmutation related to half-life?

The rate of decay for a radioactive isotope is measured in terms of a characteristic time, the **half-life**. This is the time it takes for half of an original quantity of an element to decay. For example, radium-226 has a half-life of 1620 years, which means that half of a radium-226 sample will be converted into other elements by the end of 1620 years. In the next 1620 years,

LEARNING OBJECTIVE
Recognize how radioactive elements can be identified by the rate at which they decay and how this decay results in the formation of new elements.

MasteringPhysics®
VIDEO: Radioactive Decay
VIDEO: Half-Life

FIGURE 3.15
INTERACTIVE FIGURE

Every 1620 years the amount of radium decreases by half.

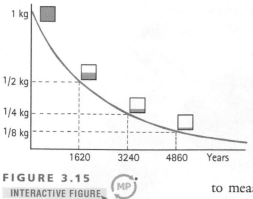

(a)

(b)

FIGURE 3.16
Radiation detectors. (a) A Geiger counter detects incoming radiation by its ionizing effect on enclosed gas in the tube. (b) A scintillation counter detects incoming radiation by flashes of light that are produced when charged particles or gamma rays pass through it.

The radioactive half-life of a material is also the time for its decay rate to reduce to half.

half of the remaining radium will decay, leaving only one-fourth the original amount of radium. (After 20 half-lives, the initial quantity of radium-226 will be diminished by a factor of about 1 million.)

Half-lives are remarkably constant and not affected by external conditions. Some radioactive isotopes have half-lives that are less than a millionth of a second, while others have half-lives longer than a billion years. Uranium-238 has a half-life of 4.5 billion years. All uranium eventually decays in a series of steps to lead. In 4.5 billion years, half the uranium presently in Earth today will be lead.

It is not necessary to wait through the duration of a half-life in order to measure it. The half-life of an element can be calculated at any given moment by measuring the rate of decay of a known quantity. This is easily done using a radiation detector (Figure 3.16). In general, the shorter the half-life of a substance, the faster it disintegrates and the more radioactivity per amount is detected.

CHECK YOURSELF

1. If a radioactive isotope has a half-life of 1 day, how much of an original sample is left at the end of the second day? The third day?
2. Which gives a higher counting rate on a radiation detector—a radioactive material with a short half-life or a radioactive material with a long half-life?

CHECK YOUR ANSWERS

1. One-fourth of the original sample is left at the end of the second day—the three-fourths that underwent decay is then a different element altogether. At the end of three days, one-eighth of the original sample remains.
2. The material with the shorter half-life is more active and shows a higher counting rate on a radiation detector.

When a radioactive nucleus emits an alpha or a beta particle, there is a change in atomic number, which means that a different element is formed. The changing of one chemical element into another is called **transmutation**. Transmutation occurs in natural events and is also initiated artificially in the laboratory.

Natural Transmutation

Consider uranium-238, the nucleus of which contains 92 protons and 146 neutrons. When an alpha particle is ejected, the nucleus loses two protons and two neutrons. Because an element is defined by the number of protons in its nucleus, the 90 protons and 144 neutrons left behind are no longer identified as being uranium. Instead we have the nucleus of a different element—thorium. This transmutation can be written as a nuclear equation:

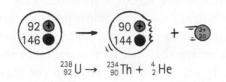

$$^{238}_{92}\text{U} \rightarrow \,^{234}_{90}\text{Th} + \,^{4}_{2}\text{He}$$

We see that $^{238}_{92}U$ transmutes to the two elements written to the right of the arrow. When this transmutation occurs, energy is released, partly in the form of kinetic energy of the alpha particle (^4_2He), partly in the kinetic energy of the thorium atom, and partly in the form of gamma radiation. In this and all such equations, the mass numbers at the top balance ($238 = 234 + 4$) and the atomic numbers at the bottom also balance ($92 = 90 + 2$).

Thorium-234, the product of this reaction, is also radioactive. When it decays, it emits a beta particle. Because a beta particle is an electron, the atomic number of the resulting nucleus is *increased* by 1. So, after beta emission by thorium with 90 protons, the resulting element has 91 protons. It is no longer thorium, but the element protactinium. Although the atomic number has increased by 1 in this process, the mass number (protons + neutrons) remains the same. The nuclear equation is

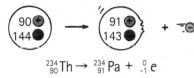

$$^{234}_{90}Th \rightarrow \,^{234}_{91}Pa + \,^{0}_{-1}e$$

We write an electron as $^0_{-1}e$. The superscript 0 indicates that the electron's mass is insignificant relative to that of protons and neutrons. The subscript -1 is the electric charge of the electron.

We see that when an element ejects an alpha particle from its nucleus, the mass number of the resulting atom is decreased by 4 and its atomic number is decreased by 2. The resulting atom is an element two places back in the periodic table of the elements. When an element ejects a beta particle from its nucleus, the mass of the atom is practically unaffected, meaning there is no change in mass number, but its atomic number increases by 1. The resulting atom belongs to an element one place forward in the periodic table. Gamma radiation results in no change in either the mass number or the atomic number. So, we see that radioactive elements can decay backward or forward in the periodic table.

The successions of radioactive decays of $^{238}_{92}U$ to $^{206}_{82}Pb$, an isotope of lead, are shown in Figure 3.17. Each gray arrow shows an alpha decay, and each red arrow shows a beta decay. Notice that some of the nuclei in the series can decay in both ways. This is one of several similar radioactive series that occur in nature.

MasteringPhysics®
TUTORIAL: Nuclear Chemistry
VIDEO: Plutonium

FYI Beta emission is also accompanied by the emission of a neutrino, which is a neutral particle with nearly zero mass that travels at about the speed of light. Neutrinos are hard to detect because they interact very weakly with matter—a piece of lead about 8 light-years thick would be needed to stop half the neutrinos produced in typical nuclear decays. Thousands of neutrinos are flying through you every second of every day because the universe is filled with them. Only occasionally, one or two times a year or so, does a neutrino or two interact with the matter of your body.

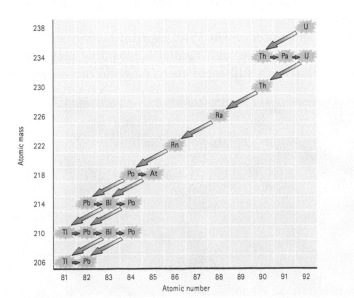

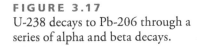

FIGURE 3.17
U-238 decays to Pb-206 through a series of alpha and beta decays.

The alchemists of old tried in vain to cause the transmutation of one element into another. Despite their fervent efforts and rituals, they never came close to succeeding. Ironically, natural transmutations were going on all around them.

CHECK YOURSELF

1. Complete the following nuclear reactions:

   a. $^{226}_{88}\text{Ra} \rightarrow\ ^{?}_{?}? +\ ^{0}_{-1}e$

   b. $^{209}_{84}\text{Po} \rightarrow\ ^{205}_{82}\text{Pb} +\ ^{?}_{?}?$

2. What finally becomes of all the uranium that undergoes radioactive decay?

CHECK YOUR ANSWERS

1. a. $^{226}_{88}\text{Ra} \rightarrow\ ^{226}_{89}\text{Ac} +\ ^{0}_{-1}e$

   b. $^{209}_{84}\text{Po} \rightarrow\ ^{205}_{82}\text{Pb} +\ ^{4}_{2}\text{He}$

2. All uranium ultimately becomes lead. On the way to becoming lead, it exists as a series of elements, as indicated in Figure 3.17.

Artificial Transmutation

Ernest Rutherford, in 1919, was the first of many investigators to succeed in transmuting a chemical element. He bombarded nitrogen gas with alpha particles from a piece of radioactive ore. The impact of an alpha particle on a nitrogen nucleus transmutes nitrogen into oxygen:

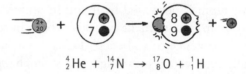

$$^{4}_{2}\text{He} +\ ^{14}_{7}\text{N} \rightarrow\ ^{17}_{8}\text{O} +\ ^{1}_{1}\text{H}$$

Rutherford used a device called a *cloud chamber* to record this event (Figure 3.18). In a cloud chamber, moving charged particles show a trail of ions along their path in a way similar to the ice crystals that show the trails of jet planes high in the sky. From a quarter of a million cloud-chamber tracks photographed on movie film, Rutherford showed seven examples of atomic transmutation. Analysis of tracks bent by a strong external magnetic field showed that when an alpha particle collided with a nitrogen atom, a proton bounced out and the heavy atom recoiled a short distance. The alpha particle disappeared. The alpha particle was absorbed in the process, transforming nitrogen into oxygen.

Since Rutherford's announcement in 1919, experimenters have carried out many other nuclear reactions, first with natural bombarding projectiles from radioactive ores and then with still more energetic projectiles—protons and

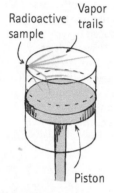

FIGURE 3.18

A cloud chamber. Charged particles moving through supersaturated vapor leave trails. When the chamber is in a strong electric or magnetic field, the bending of the tracks provides information about the charge, mass, and momentum of the particles.

FIGURE 3.19

Tracks of elementary particles in a bubble chamber, a similar yet more complicated device than a cloud chamber. Two particles have been destroyed at the points where the spirals emanate, and four have been created in the collision.

electrons hurled by huge particle accelerators. Artificial transmutation produces the hitherto unknown synthetic elements at the upper end of the periodic table. All of these artificially made elements have short half-lives. If they ever existed naturally when Earth was formed, they have long since decayed.

Integrated Science 10B
BIOLOGY AND EARTH SCIENCE

Radiometric Dating

LEARNING OBJECTIVE
Review how the age of ancient artifacts can be determined by measuring the amounts of remaining radioactivity they contain.

EXPLAIN THIS How does radioactivity enable archaeologists to measure the age of ancient artifacts?

Earth's atmosphere is continuously bombarded by cosmic rays, and this bombardment causes many atoms in the upper atmosphere to transmute. These transmutations result in many protons and neutrons being "sprayed out" into the environment. Most of the protons are stopped as they collide with the atoms of the upper atmosphere, stripping electrons from these atoms to become hydrogen atoms. The neutrons, however, keep going for longer distances because they have no electric charge and therefore do not interact electrically with matter. Eventually, many of them collide with the nuclei in the denser lower atmosphere. A nitrogen nucleus that captures a neutron, for instance, becomes an isotope of carbon by emitting a proton:

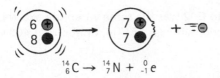

$$_0^1n + {}_7^{14}N \rightarrow {}_6^{14}C + {}_1^1H$$

This carbon-14 isotope, which makes up less than one-millionth of 1% of the carbon in the atmosphere, is radioactive and has eight neutrons. (The most common isotope, carbon-12, has six neutrons and is not radioactive.) Because both carbon-12 and carbon-14 are forms of carbon, they have the same chemical properties. Both these isotopes can chemically react with oxygen to form carbon dioxide, which is taken in by plants. This means that all plants contain a tiny bit of radioactive carbon-14. All animals eat plants (or at least plant-eating animals) and therefore have a little carbon-14 in them. In short, all living things on Earth contain some carbon-14.

Carbon-14 is a beta emitter and decays back to nitrogen by the following reaction:

$$_6^{14}C \rightarrow {}_7^{14}N + {}_{-1}^0e$$

FYI A 1-g sample of carbon from recently living matter contains about 50 trillion billion (5×10^{22}) carbon atoms. Of these carbon atoms, about 65 billion (6.5×10^{10}) are the radioactive C-14 isotope. This gives the carbon a beta disintegration rate of about 13.5 decays per minute.

Because plants continue to take in carbon dioxide as long as they live, any carbon-14 lost by decay is immediately replenished with fresh carbon-14 from the atmosphere. In this way, a radioactive equilibrium is reached at which there is a constant ratio of about one carbon-14 atom to every 100 billion carbon-12 atoms. When a plant dies, replenishment of carbon-14 stops. Then the percentage of carbon-14 decreases

22,920 years ago   17,190 years ago   11,460 years ago   5730 years ago   Present

FIGURE 3.20
The amount of radioactive carbon-14 in the skeleton diminishes by half every 5730 years, with the result that today the skeleton contains only a fraction of the carbon-14 it originally had. The red arrows symbolize relative amounts of carbon-14.

at a constant rate given by its half-life. The longer a plant or other organism is dead, therefore, the less carbon-14 it contains relative to the constant amount of carbon-12.

The half-life of carbon-14 is about 5730 years. This means that half of the carbon-14 atoms that are now present in a plant or animal that dies today will decay over the next 5730 years. Half of the remaining carbon-14 atoms will then decay over the following 5730 years, and so forth.

With this knowledge, scientists can calculate the age of carbon-containing artifacts, such as wooden tools or skeletons, by measuring their current level of radioactivity. This process, known as **carbon-14 dating**, enables us to probe as much as 50,000 years into the past. Beyond this time span, too little carbon-14 remains to permit accurate analysis.

Carbon-14 dating would be an extremely simple and accurate dating method if the amount of radioactive carbon in the atmosphere had been constant over the ages. But it hasn't been. Fluctuations in the Sun's magnetic field as well as changes in the strength of Earth's magnetic field affect cosmic-ray intensities in Earth's atmosphere, which in turn produce fluctuations in the production of C-14. In addition, changes in Earth's climate affect the amount of carbon dioxide in the atmosphere. The oceans are great reservoirs of carbon dioxide. When the oceans are warm, they release more carbon dioxide into the atmosphere than when they are cold.

One ton of ordinary granite contains about 9 g of uranium and 20 g of thorium. Basalt rocks contain 3.5 g and 7.7 g of the same elements, respectively.

CHECK YOURSELF
Suppose an archaeologist extracts a gram of carbon from an ancient axe handle and finds it one-fourth as radioactive as a gram of carbon extracted from a freshly cut tree branch. About how old is the axe handle?

CHECK YOUR ANSWER
Assuming the ratio of C-14 to C-12 was the same when the axe was made, the axe handle is as old as two half-lives of C-14, or about 11,460 years old.

The dating of older, but nonliving, materials is accomplished with radioactive minerals, such as uranium. The naturally occurring isotopes U-238 and U-235 decay very slowly and ultimately become isotopes of lead—but not the common lead isotope Pb-208. For example, U-238 decays through several stages to finally become Pb-206, whereas U-235 finally becomes the isotope Pb-207. Lead isotopes 206 and 207 that now exist were at one time uranium. The older the rock, the higher the percentage of these remnant isotopes.

From the half-lives of uranium isotopes and the percentage of lead isotopes in uranium-bearing rock, it is possible to calculate the date at which the rock was formed. (We'll return to isotopic dating when we investigate Earth's dynamic interior in Chapter 8.)

3.4 Nuclear Fission

EXPLAIN THIS Why isn't it possible for a nuclear power plant to explode like a nuclear bomb?

LEARNING OBJECTIVE
Describe the process by which large atomic nuclei can split in half, leading to the production of energy.

I n 1938, two German scientists, Otto Hahn and Fritz Strassmann, made an accidental discovery that was to change the world. While bombarding a sample of uranium with neutrons in the hope of creating new, heavier elements, they were astonished to find chemical evidence for the production of barium, an element with about half the mass of uranium. Hahn wrote of this news to his former colleague Lise Meitner, who had fled from Nazi Germany to Sweden because of her Jewish ancestry. From Hahn's evidence, Meitner concluded that the uranium nucleus, activated by neutron bombardment, had split in half. Soon thereafter, Meitner, working with her nephew Otto Frisch, also a physicist, published a paper in which the term *nuclear fission* was first coined.

MasteringPhysics®
VIDEO: Nuclear Fission

In the nucleus of every atom is a delicate balance between attractive nuclear forces and repulsive electric forces between protons. In all known nuclei, the nuclear forces dominate. In certain isotopes of uranium, however, this domination is tenuous. If a uranium nucleus stretches into an elongated shape (Figure 3.21), the electric forces may push it into an even more elongated shape. If the elongation passes a certain point, the electric forces overwhelm the strong nuclear forces, and the nucleus splits. This is **nuclear fission**.

The energy released by the fission of one U-235 nucleus is enormous—about 7 million times the energy released by the explosion of one TNT molecule. This energy is mainly in the form of kinetic energy of the fission fragments that fly apart from one another, with some energy given to ejected neutrons and the rest to gamma radiation.

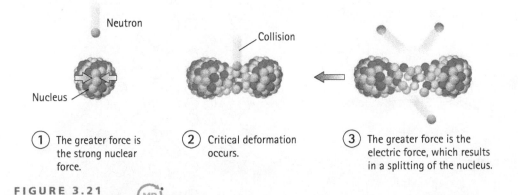

Neutron

Collision

Nucleus

(1) The greater force is the strong nuclear force.

(2) Critical deformation occurs.

(3) The greater force is the electric force, which results in a splitting of the nucleus.

FIGURE 3.21
INTERACTIVE FIGURE MP

Nuclear deformation may result in repulsive electric forces overcoming attractive nuclear forces, in which case fission occurs.

A typical uranium fission reaction is

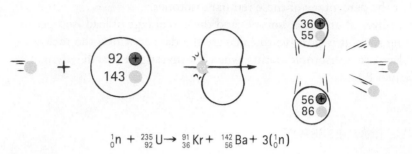

$$_0^1n + {}_{92}^{235}U \rightarrow {}_{36}^{91}Kr + {}_{56}^{142}Ba + 3({}_0^1n)$$

FYI Otto Hahn, rather than Lise Meitner, received the Nobel Prize for the work on nuclear fission. Notoriously, Hahn didn't even acknowledge Meitner's role. See more about this in the readable book *E = mc²* by David Bodanis.

Note in this reaction that 1 neutron starts the fission of a uranium nucleus and that the fission produces 3 neutrons. (A fission reaction may produce fewer or more than 3 neutrons.) These product neutrons can cause the fissioning of 3 other uranium atoms, releasing 9 more neutrons. If each of these 9 neutrons succeeds in splitting a uranium atom, the next step in the reaction produces 27 neutrons, and so on. Such a sequence, illustrated in Figure 3.22, is called a **chain reaction**—a self-sustaining reaction in which the products of one reaction event stimulate further reaction events.

Why don't chain reactions occur in naturally occurring uranium ore deposits? They would if all uranium atoms fissioned so easily. Fission occurs mainly for the rare isotope U-235, which makes up only 0.7% of the uranium in naturally occurring uranium metal. When the more abundant isotope U-238 absorbs neutrons created by fission of U-235, the U-238 typically does not undergo fission. So, any chain reaction is snuffed out by the neutron-absorbing U-238 as well as by the rock in which the ore is imbedded.

UNIFYING CONCEPT

● *Exponential Growth and Decay*
  Appendix D

If a chain reaction occurred in a baseball-size chunk of pure U-235, an enormous explosion would result. If the chain reaction were started in a smaller chunk of pure U-235, however, no explosion would occur. This is because of geometry: The ratio of surface area to mass is higher in a small piece than in a large one (just as there is more skin on six small potatoes with a combined mass of 1 kg than there is on a single 1-kg potato). So there is more surface area on a bunch of small pieces of uranium than on a large piece. In a small piece of U-235, neutrons leak through the surface before an explosion can occur. In a bigger piece, the chain

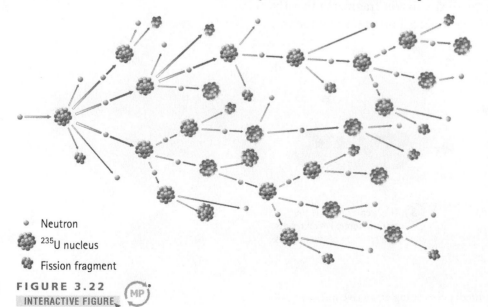

● Neutron
● ²³⁵U nucleus
● Fission fragment

FIGURE 3.22
INTERACTIVE FIGURE **MP**

A chain reaction.

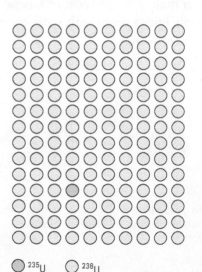

○ ²³⁵U   ○ ²³⁸U

FIGURE 3.23
Only 1 part in 140 of naturally occurring uranium is U-235.

reaction builds up to enormous energies before the neutrons get to the surface and escape (Figure 3.24). For masses greater than a certain minimum amount, called the **critical mass**, an explosion of enormous magnitude may take place.

Consider a large quantity of U-235 divided into two pieces, each with a mass less than critical. The units are *subcritical*. Neutrons in either piece readily reach a surface and escape before a sizable chain reaction builds up. But, if the pieces are suddenly driven together, the total surface area decreases. If the timing is right and the combined mass is greater than critical, a violent explosion takes place. This is what happens in a nuclear fission bomb (Figure 3.25).

Constructing a fission bomb is a formidable task. The difficulty is separating enough U-235 from the more abundant U-238. Scientists took more than two years to extract enough U-235 from uranium ore to make the bomb that was detonated at Hiroshima in 1945. To this day uranium isotope separation remains a difficult process.

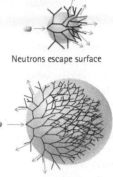

FIGURE 3.24
The exaggerated view shows that a chain reaction in a small piece of pure U-235 runs its course before it can cause a large explosion because neutrons leak from the surface too soon. The surface area of the small piece is large relative to the mass. In a larger piece, more uranium and a smaller surface area are presented to the neutrons.

CHECK YOURSELF
A 1-kg ball of U-235 is at critical mass, but the same ball broken up into small chunks is not. Explain.

CHECK YOUR ANSWER
The small chunks have a larger combined surface area than the ball from which they came (just as the combined surface area of gravel is larger than the surface area of a boulder of the same mass). Neutrons escape via the surface before a sustained chain reaction can build up.

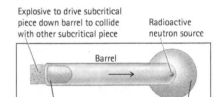

FIGURE 3.25
Simplified diagram of a uranium fission bomb.

Nuclear Fission Reactors

The awesome energy of nuclear fission was introduced to the world in the form of nuclear bombs, and this violent image still colors our thinking about nuclear power, making it difficult for many people to recognize its potential usefulness. Currently, about 20% of electric energy in the United States is generated by *nuclear fission reactors* (whereas in some other countries most of the electric power is nuclear—about 75% in France). These reactors are simply nuclear furnaces. They, like fossil fuel furnaces, do nothing more elegant than boil water to produce steam for a turbine (Figure 3.26). The greatest practical difference is the amount

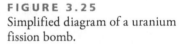
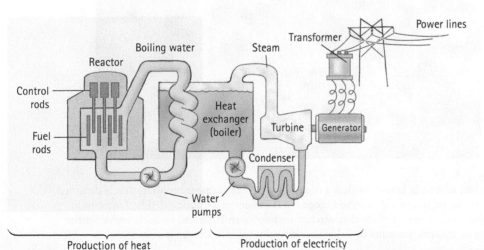

FIGURE 3.26
Diagram of a nuclear fission power plant. Note that the water in contact with the fuel rods is completely contained, and radioactive materials are not involved directly in the generation of electricity.

FYI With the rise of the German Nazis in the 1930s, many scientists, especially those of Jewish ancestry, fled mainland Europe to America. They included dozens of brilliant theoretical physicists who eventually played key roles in the development of nuclear fission. Of these physicists, Leo Szilard (1898–1964) first envisioned the idea of a chain nuclear reaction. With Albert Einstein's consent, Szilard drafted a letter that was signed by Einstein and delivered to President Roosevelt in 1939. This letter outlined the possibility of the chain reaction and its implications for a nuclear bomb. Within six years the first test nuclear bomb was exploded in the desert in New Mexico. In 1945, Szilard generated a petition in which 68 of the scientists involved in the nuclear program asked President Truman not to drop the atomic bomb on a populous Japanese city, such as Nagasaki.

of fuel involved: A mere kilogram of uranium fuel, smaller than a baseball, yields more energy than 30 freight-car loads of coal.

A fission reactor contains four components: nuclear fuel, control rods, moderator (to slow neutrons, which is required for fission), and liquid (usually water) to transfer heat from the reactor to the turbine and generator. The nuclear fuel is primarily U-238 plus about 3% U-235. Because the U-235 isotopes are so highly diluted with U-238, an explosion like that of a nuclear bomb is not possible. The reaction rate, which depends on the number of neutrons that initiate the fission of other U-235 nuclei, is controlled by rods inserted into the reactor. The control rods are made of a neutron-absorbing material, usually the metal cadmium or boron.

Heated water around the nuclear fuel is kept under high pressure to keep it at a high temperature without boiling. It transfers heat to a second lower-pressure water system, which operates the turbine and electric generator in a conventional fashion. In this design, two separate water systems are used so that no radioactivity reaches the turbine or the outside environment.

A significant disadvantage of fission power is the generation of radioactive waste products. Light atomic nuclei are most stable when composed of equal numbers of protons and neutrons, as discussed earlier, and heavy nuclei need more neutrons than protons for stability. For example, U-235 has 143 neutrons but only 92 protons. When uranium fissions into two medium-weight elements, the extra neutrons in their nuclei make them unstable. They are radioactive, most with very short half-lives, but some with half-lives of thousands of years. Safely disposing of these waste products as well as materials made radioactive in the production of nuclear fuels requires special storage casks and procedures. Although fission has been successfully producing electricity for a half century, disposing of radioactive wastes in the United States remains problematic.

The designs for nuclear power plants have progressed over the years. The earliest designs from the 1950s through the 1990s are called the Generation I, II, and III reactors. The safety systems of these reactors are "active" in that they rely on

FIGURE 3.27
The nuclear reactor is housed within a dome-shaped containment building that is designed to prevent the release of radioactive isotopes in the event of an accident. The Soviet-built Chernobyl nuclear power plant that reached meltdown in 1986 had no such containment building, so massive amounts of radiation were released into the environment.

active measures, such as water pumps, to keep the reactor core cool in the event of an accident. Notably, these active measures failed when Japan's Generation II Fukushima Daiichi nuclear plant was hit by a powerful earthquake and tsunami in 2011. Though not yet operational, the latest Generation IV nuclear reactors will have fundamentally different designs. For example, they will incorporate passive safety measures that cause the reactor to shut down by itself in the event of an emergency. The fuel source may be the depleted uranium stockpiled from earlier reactors. Furthermore, these reactors can be built as small modular units that generate between 150 and 600 megawatts of power rather than the 1500 megawatts that is the usual output of today's reactors. Smaller reactors are easier to manage and can be used to build a generating capacity suited to the community being served.

The benefits of fission power include plentiful electricity and the conservation of many billions of tons of fossil fuels. Every year these fuels are turned to heat, smoke, and megatons of poisonous gases such as sulfur oxides. Notably, fossil fuels are far more precious as sources of organic molecules, can be used to create medicines, clothing, automobiles, and much more.

> A nuclear power plant "meltdown" occurs when the fissioning nuclear fuels are no longer submerged within a cooling fluid, such as water. The temperature rises to the point that the solid nuclear fuel, and the reaction vessel itself, melt into a liquid phase that has the potential of penetrating through the floor of the containment building.

> FYI Recent evidence discovered by neutrino research in 2011 indicates that a major source of Earth's internal energy, perhaps half, is due to nuclear fission within Earth's core. This heat-generating process is occurring at great depths beneath your feet right now! Indeed, power from the atomic nuclei is as old as Earth itself.

CHECK YOURSELF
Coal contains tiny quantities of radioactive materials, enough that more environmental radiation surrounds a typical coal-fired power plant than a fission power plant. What does this indicate about the shielding typically surrounding the two types of power plants?

CHECK YOUR ANSWER
Coal-fired power plants are as American as apple pie, with no required (and expensive) shielding to restrict the emissions of radioactive particles. Nukes, on the other hand, are required to have shielding to ensure strict low levels of radioactive emissions.

The Breeder Reactor

One of the fascinating features of fission power is the breeding of fission fuel from nonfissionable U-238. This breeding occurs when small amounts of fissionable isotopes are mixed with U-238 in a reactor. Fission liberates neutrons that convert the relatively abundant nonfissionable U-238 to U-239, which beta-decays to Np-239, which in turn beta-decays to fissionable plutonium—Pu-239. So, in addition to the abundant energy produced, fission fuel is bred from the relatively abundant U-238 in the process.

Breeding occurs to some extent in all fission reactors, but a reactor specifically designed to breed more fissionable fuel than is put into it is called a *breeder reactor*. Using a breeder reactor is like filling your car's gas tank with water, adding some gasoline, then driving the car and having more gasoline after the trip than at the beginning! The basic principle of the breeder reactor is very attractive: After a few years of operation a breeder-reactor power plant can produce vast amounts of power while breeding twice as much fuel as its original fuel.

The downside is the enormous complexity of successful and safe operation. The United States gave up on breeders about two decades ago, and only Russia,

> An average ton of coal contains 1.3 parts per million (ppm) of uranium and 3.2 ppm of thorium. That's why the average coal-burning power plant produces much more airborne radioactive material than a nuclear power plant.

France, Japan, and India are still investing in them. Officials in these countries point out that the supplies of naturally occurring U-235 are limited. At present rates of consumption, all natural sources of U-235 may be depleted within a century. If countries then decide to turn to breeder reactors, they may well find themselves digging up the radioactive wastes they once buried.

3.5 Mass–Energy Equivalence

EXPLAIN THIS Why does it get easier to pull nucleons away from nuclei heavier than iron?

In the early 1900s, Albert Einstein discovered that mass is actually "congealed" energy. Mass and energy are two sides of the same coin, as stated in his celebrated equation $E = mc^2$. In this equation E stands for the energy that any mass has at rest, m stands for the mass, and c is the speed of light. This relationship between energy and mass is the key to understanding why and how energy is released in nuclear reactions.

Is the mass of a nucleon inside a nucleus the same as the mass of the same nucleon outside a nucleus? This question can be answered by considering the work that would be required to separate nucleons from a nucleus. From physics we know that work, which is expended energy, equals *force × distance*. Think of the amount of force required to pull a nucleon out of the nucleus through a sufficient distance to overcome the attractive strong nuclear force, comically indicated in Figure 3.28. Enormous work would be required. This work is energy added to the nucleon that is pulled out.

FIGURE 3.28
Work is required to pull a nucleon from an atomic nucleus. This work increases the energy and hence the mass of the nucleon outside the nucleus.

According to Einstein's equation, this newly acquired energy reveals itself as an increase in the nucleon's mass. The mass of a nucleon outside a nucleus is greater than the mass of the same nucleon locked inside a nucleus. For example, a carbon-12 atom—the nucleus of which is made up of six protons and six neutrons—has a mass of exactly 12.00000 atomic mass units (amu). Therefore on average, each nucleon contributes a mass of 1 amu. However, outside the nucleus, a proton has a mass of 1.00728 amu and a neutron has a mass of 1.00867 amu. Thus we see that the combined mass of six free protons and six free neutrons—(6 × 1.00728) + (6 × 1.00867) = 12.09570—is greater than the mass of one carbon-12 nucleus. The greater mass reflects the energy required to pull the nucleons apart from one another. Thus, what mass a nucleon has depends on where the nucleon is.

A graph of the nuclear masses for the elements from hydrogen through uranium is shown in Figure 3.29. The graph slopes upward with increasing atomic number as expected: Elements are more massive as atomic number increases. The slope curves because there are proportionally more neutrons in the more massive atoms.

A more important graph results from the plot of nuclear mass *per nucleon* from hydrogen through uranium (Figure 3.30). This is perhaps the most important graph in this book because it is the key to understanding the energy associated with nuclear processes.

Note that the masses of the nucleons are different when combined in different nuclei. The greatest mass per nucleon occurs for the proton alone, hydrogen, because it has no binding energy to pull its mass down. Progressing beyond hydrogen, the mass per nucleon is less, and is least for a nucleon in the nucleus of the iron

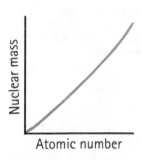

FIGURE 3.29
The plot shows how nuclear mass increases with increasing atomic number.

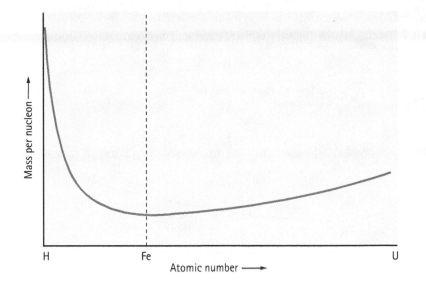

FIGURE 3.30
This graph shows that the average mass of a nucleon depends on which nucleus it is in. Individual nucleons have the greatest mass in the lightest nuclei, the least mass in iron, and intermediate mass in the heaviest nuclei.

atom. Beyond iron, the process reverses itself as nucleons have progressively greater and greater mass in atoms of increasing atomic number. This continues all the way to uranium and elements heavier than uranium.

From Figure 3.30 we can see how energy is released when a uranium nucleus splits into two nuclei of lower atomic number. Uranium, being toward the right-hand side of the graph, is shown to have a relatively large amount of mass per nucleon. When the uranium nucleus splits in half, however, smaller nuclei of lower atomic numbers are formed. As shown in Figure 3.31, these nuclei are lower on the graph than uranium, which means that they have a smaller amount of mass per nucleon. Thus, nucleons lose mass in their transition from being in a uranium nucleus to being in one of its fragments. When this decrease in mass is multiplied by the speed of light squared (c^2 in Einstein's equation), the product is equal to the energy yielded by each uranium nucleus as it undergoes fission.

MasteringPhysics®
VIDEO: Controlling Nuclear Fusion

$E = mc^2$ says that mass is congealed energy. Mass and energy are two sides of the same coin.

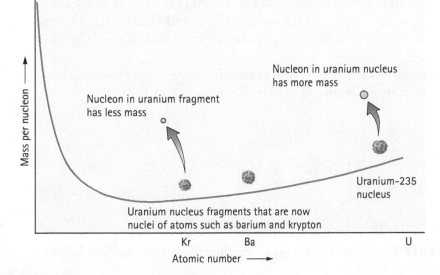

FIGURE 3.31
The mass of each nucleon in a uranium nucleus is greater than the mass of each nucleon in any one of its nuclear fission fragments. This lost mass is mass that has been transformed into energy, which is why nuclear fission is an energy-releasing process.

FIGURE 3.32
INTERACTIVE FIGURE

The mass of each nucleon in a hydrogen-2 nucleus is greater than the mass of each nucleon in a helium-4 nucleus, which results from the fusion of two hydrogen-2 nuclei. This lost mass has been converted into energy, which is why nuclear fusion is an energy-releasing process.

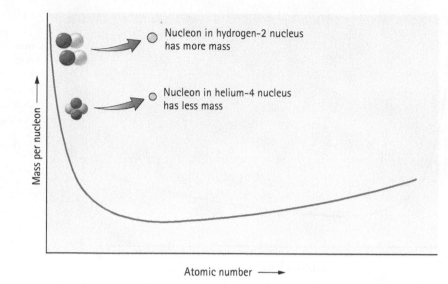

CHECK YOURSELF
Correct the following incorrect statement: When a heavy element such as uranium undergoes fission, there are fewer nucleons after the reaction than before.

CHECK YOUR ANSWER
When a heavy element such as uranium undergoes fission, there aren't fewer nucleons after the reaction. Instead, there's *less mass* in the same number of nucleons.

The graph of Figure 3.30 (and Figures 3.31 and 3.32) reveals the energy of the atomic nucleus, a primary source of energy in the universe—which is why it can be considered the most important graph in this book.

We can think of the mass-per-nucleon graph as an energy valley that starts at hydrogen (the highest point) and slopes steeply to the lowest point (iron), then slopes gradually up to uranium. Iron is at the bottom of the energy valley and is the most stable nucleus. It is also the most tightly bound nucleus; more energy per nucleon is required to separate nucleons from iron's nucleus than from any other nucleus.

All nuclear power today is by way of nuclear fission. A more promising long-range source of energy is found on the left side of the energy valley.

LEARNING OBJECTIVE
Describe the process by which small nuclei can join together, leading to the production of energy such as occurs in the Sun.

Integrated Science 10C
ASTRONOMY

Nuclear Fusion

EXPLAIN THIS How does the energy of gasoline come from nuclear fusion?

 otice in the graph of Figure 3.30 that the steepest part of the energy valley goes from hydrogen to iron. Energy is released as light nuclei combine. This combining of nuclei is **nuclear fusion**—the opposite of nuclear fission. We see from Figure 3.32 that, as we move along the list of elements from hydrogen to iron, the average mass per nucleon decreases. Thus, when two small nuclei fuse—say, two hydrogen isotopes—the mass of the resulting helium-4 nucleus is less than the mass of the two small nuclei before fusion. Energy is released as smaller nuclei fuse.

For a fusion reaction to occur, the nuclei must collide at a very high speed in order to overcome their mutual electric repulsion. The required speeds correspond to the extremely high temperatures found in the core of the Sun and other stars. Fusion brought about by high temperatures is called **thermonuclear fusion**. In the high temperatures of the Sun, approximately 657 million tons of hydrogen are converted into 653 million tons of helium *each second*. The missing 4 million tons of mass are discharged as radiant energy.

Such reactions are, quite literally, nuclear burning. Thermonuclear fusion is analogous to ordinary chemical combustion. In both chemical and nuclear burning, a high temperature starts the reaction; the release of energy by the reaction maintains a high enough temperature to spread the fire. The net result of the chemical reaction is a combination of atoms into more tightly bound molecules. In nuclear fusion reactions, the net result is more tightly bound nuclei.

CHECK YOURSELF

1. Fission and fusion are opposite processes, yet each releases energy. Isn't this contradictory?
2. To get nuclear energy released from the element iron, should iron be fissioned or fused?
3. Predict whether the temperature of the core of a star increases or decreases when iron and elements of higher atomic number than iron in the core are fused.

CHECK YOUR ANSWERS

1. No, no, no! This is contradictory only if the same element is said to release energy by the processes of both fission and fusion. Only the fusion of light elements and the fission of heavy elements result in a decrease in nucleon mass and a release of energy.
2. Neither, because iron is at the very bottom of the "energy valley." Fusing a pair of iron nuclei produces an element to the right of iron on the curve, where the mass per nucleon is greater. If you split an iron nucleus, the products lie to the left of iron on the curve—also a greater mass per nucleon. So no energy is released. For energy release, "decrease mass" is the name of the game—any game, chemical or nuclear.
3. In the fusion of iron and any nuclei beyond, energy is absorbed and the star core cools at this late stage of its evolution. This, however, leads to the star's collapse, which then greatly increases its temperature. Interestingly, elements beyond iron are not manufactured in normal fusion cycles in stellar sources but are manufactured when stars violently explode—supernovae.

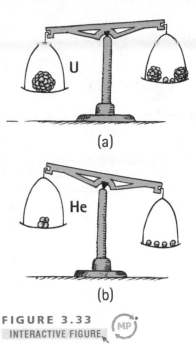

FIGURE 3.33 [MP]
INTERACTIVE FIGURE

The mass of a nucleus is not equal to the sum of the masses of its parts. (a) The fission fragments of a heavy nucleus such as uranium are less massive than the uranium nucleus. (b) Two protons and two neutrons are more massive in their free states than when combined to form a helium nucleus.

FYI A common reaction is the fusion of H-2 and H-3 nuclei to become He-4 plus a neutron. Most of the energy released is in the kinetic energy of the ejected neutron, with the rest of the energy in the kinetic energy of the recoiling He-4 nucleus. Interestingly, without the neutron energy carrier, a fusion reaction won't occur. The intensity of fusion reactions is measured by the accompanying neutron flux.

Before the development of the atomic bomb, the temperatures required to initiate nuclear fusion on Earth were unattainable. When researchers found that the temperature inside an exploding atomic bomb is four to five times the temperature at the center of the Sun, the thermonuclear bomb was but a step

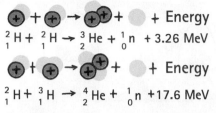

$$^{2}_{1}H + {}^{2}_{1}H \rightarrow {}^{3}_{2}He + {}^{1}_{0}n + 3.26 \text{ MeV}$$

$$^{2}_{1}H + {}^{3}_{1}H \rightarrow {}^{4}_{2}He + {}^{1}_{0}n + 17.6 \text{ MeV}$$

FIGURE 3.34
Fusion reactions of hydrogen isotopes. Most of the energy released is carried by the neutrons, which are ejected at high speeds.

away. This first thermonuclear bomb, a hydrogen bomb, was detonated in 1952. Whereas the critical mass of fissionable material limits the size of a fission bomb (atomic bomb), no such limit is imposed on a fusion bomb (thermonuclear or hydrogen bomb). Just as there is no limit to the size of an oil-storage depot, there is no theoretical limit to the size of a fusion bomb. Like the oil in the storage depot, any amount of fusion fuel can be stored safely until ignited. Although a mere match can ignite an oil depot, nothing less energetic than an atomic bomb can ignite a thermonuclear bomb. We can see that there is no such thing as a "baby" hydrogen bomb. A typical thermonuclear bomb stockpiled by the United States today, for example, is about 1000 times as destructive as the atomic bomb detonated over Hiroshima at the end of World War II.

The hydrogen bomb is another example of a discovery used for destructive rather than constructive purposes. The potential constructive possibility is the controlled release of vast amounts of clean energy.

Controlling Fusion

Carrying out fusion reactions under controlled conditions requires temperatures of millions of degrees. A variety of techniques exist for attaining high temperatures. No matter how the temperature is produced, a problem is that all materials melt and vaporize at the temperatures required for fusion. One solution is to confine the reaction in a nonmaterial container.

A nonmaterial container is a magnetic field that can exist at any temperature and can exert powerful forces on charged particles in motion. "Magnetic walls" of sufficient strength provide a kind of magnetic straitjacket for hot gases called plasmas. Magnetic compression further heats the plasma to fusion temperatures. At this writing, fusion by magnetic confinement has been only partially successful— a sustained and controlled reaction has so far been out of reach.

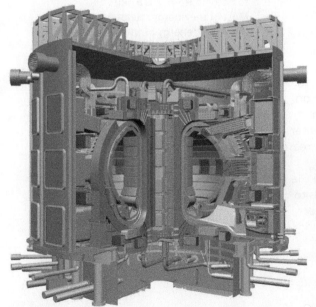

Although no nuclear fusion power plants are currently operating, an international project now exists whose goal is to prove the feasibility of nuclear fusion power in the near future. This fusion power project is the International Thermonuclear Experimental Reactor (ITER). After construction at the chosen site in Cadarache, France, the first sustainable fusion reaction may begin as early as 2015 (Figure 3.35). The reactor will house electrically charged hydrogen gas (plasma) heated to more than 100 million °C, which is hotter than the center of the Sun. In addition to producing about 500 MW of power, the reactor could be the energy source for the creation of hydrogen, H_2, which could be used to power fuel cells such as those incorporated into automobiles.

If people are one day to dart about the universe in the same way we jet about Earth today, their supply of fuel is ensured. The fuel for fusion—hydrogen—is found in every part of the universe, not only in the stars but also in the space between them. About 91% of the atoms in the universe are estimated to be hydrogen. For people of the future, the supply of raw materials is also ensured because all the elements known to exist result from the fusing of more and more hydrogen nuclei. Future humans might synthesize their own elements and produce energy in the process, just as the stars have always done.

FIGURE 3.35
A cross-sectional view of the ITER (rhymes with "fitter") planned to be built and operating in Cadarache, France, before 2020.

For instructor-assigned homework, go to www.masteringphysics.com MP

SUMMARY OF TERMS (KNOWLEDGE)

Alpha particle A subatomic particle made up of the combination of two protons and two neutrons ejected by a radioactive nucleus. The composition of an alpha particle is the same as that of the nucleus of a helium atom.

Beta particle An electron emitted during the radioactive decay of a radioactive nucleus.

Carbon-14 dating The process of estimating the age of once-living material by measuring the amount of radioactive carbon-14 present in the material.

Chain reaction A self-sustaining reaction in which the products of one reaction event initiate further reaction events.

Critical mass The minimum mass of fissionable material needed for a sustainable chain reaction.

Gamma rays High-frequency electromagnetic radiation emitted by radioactive nuclei.

Half-life The time required for half the atoms in a sample of a radioactive isotope to decay.

Nuclear fission The splitting of the atomic nucleus into two smaller halves.

Nuclear fusion The combining of nuclei of light atoms to form heavier nuclei.

Rad A quantity of radiant energy equal to 0.01 J absorbed per kilogram of tissue.

Radioactivity The high-energy particles and electromagnetic radiation emitted by a radioactive substance.

Rem The unit for measuring radiation dosage in humans based on harm to living tissue.

Strong nuclear force The attractive force between all nucleons, effective at only very short distances.

Thermonuclear fusion Nuclear fusion brought about by high temperatures.

Transmutation The changing of an atomic nucleus of one element into an atomic nucleus of another element through a decrease or increase in the number of protons.

READING CHECK QUESTIONS (COMPREHENSION)

3.1 Radioactivity

1. Which type of radiation—alpha, beta, or gamma—results in the greatest change in mass number? The greatest change in atomic number?

2. Which of the three rays—alpha, beta, or gamma—has the greatest penetrating power?

3.2 The Strong Nuclear Force

3. Why doesn't the repulsive electric force of protons in the atomic nucleus cause the protons to fly apart?

4. Which have more neutrons than protons—large nuclei or small nuclei?

5. What role do neutrons play in the atomic nucleus?

3.3 Half-Life and Transmutation

6. In what form is most of the energy released by atomic transmutation?

7. What change in atomic number occurs when a nucleus emits an alpha particle? A beta particle?

8. What is the long-range fate of all the uranium that exists in the world today?

9. What is meant by the half-life of a radioactive sample?

10. What is the half-life of uranium-238?

3.4 Nuclear Fission

11. What happens to the uranium-235 nucleus when it is stretched out?

12. Is a chain reaction more likely to occur in two separate pieces of uranium-235 or in the same pieces stuck together?

13. How is a nuclear reactor similar to a conventional fossil-fuel power plant? How is it different?

3.5 Mass–Energy Equivalence

14. Who discovered that energy and mass are two different forms of the same thing?

15. In which atomic nucleus do nucleons have the least mass?

16. How does the mass per nucleon in uranium compare with the mass per nucleon in the fission fragments of uranium?

THINK INTEGRATED SCIENCE

10A—Radiation Dosage

17. What is the origin of most of the natural radiation we encounter?

18. Which produces more radioactivity in the atmosphere—coal-fired power plants or nuclear power plants?

19. Is radioactivity on Earth something relatively new? Defend your answer.

10B—Radiometric Dating

20. What happens to a nitrogen atom in the atmosphere that captures a neutron?

21. Why is there more carbon-14 in living bones than in once-living ancient bones of the same mass?

22. Why is lead found in all deposits of uranium ores?

10C—Nuclear Fusion

23. How does the mass of a pair of atoms that have fused compare to the sum of their masses before fusion?

24. What kind of containers are used to hold plasmas at temperatures of millions of degrees?

25. What kind of nuclear power is responsible for sunshine?

THINK AND DO (HANDS-ON APPLICATION)

26. Throw ten coins onto a flat surface. Move aside all the coins that landed tails-up. Collect the remaining coins. After tossing them once again, remove all the coins that landed tails-up. Repeat this process until all the coins have been removed. Can you see how this relates to radioactive half-life? In units of "tosses" what is the average half-life of 25 coins? 50 coins? 1 million coins?

27. Repeat Exercise 26 but use 10 dimes and 25 pennies. Let the dimes represent a radioactive isotope, such as carbon-14, while the pennies represent a nonradioactive isotope, such as carbon-12. Remove only the dimes when they land heads-up. Collect all the pennies and add them to the dimes that landed heads-up. Does the number of pennies affect the behavior of the dimes? Someone gives you two sets of coins. The first set contains 10 dimes and 25 pennies. The second set contains 2 dimes and 25 pennies. Which set of coins has gone through a greater number of tosses? Which set provides the most "radioactivity" after a toss? Which set is analogous to a sample of once-living ancient material?

28. Calculate your estimated annual dose of radiation using the EPA's radiation dose calculator available at http://www.epa.gov/radiation/understand/calculate.html.

29. Stand one domino upright so that when it topples it hits two other upright dominos, which also each hit two other upright dominos, and so forth. Arrange as many upright dominos as you can in this fashion so that they fan out as shown in the photograph. Your challenge is to arrange the dominos so that every one of them falls.

Topple the first domino and observe your chain reaction. Focus your attention on the sound.

This dominoes chain reaction occurs on a two-dimensional flat surface. What is the dimensional geometry of a nuclear chain? What would happen if a Ping-Pong ball were tossed into a room in which the floor was covered with thousands of set-to-kill spring-action mouse traps? Such an explosive event can be seen by using the keywords "mouse trap chain reaction" for an Internet video search.

THINK AND COMPARE (ANALYSIS)

30. Rank these three types of radiation by their ability to penetrate a page of a book, from best to worst: (a) alpha particle, (b) beta particle, (c) gamma ray.

31. Consider the atoms C-12, C-14, and N-14. From greatest to least, rank them by the number of (a) protons in the nucleus, (b) neutrons in the nucleus, (c) nucleons in the nucleus.

32. Rank these isotopes in order of their radioactivity, from the most radioactive to the least radioactive: (a) nickel-59, half-life 75,000 years; (b) uranium-238, half-life 4.5 billion years; (c) actinium-225, half-life 10 days.

33. Rank the following in order from the most energy released to the least energy released: (a) uranium-235 splitting into two equal fragments, (b) uranium-235 splitting into three equal fragments, (c) uranium-235 splitting into 92 equal fragments.

THINK AND SOLVE (MATHEMATICAL APPLICATION)

34. Radiation from a point source follows an inverse-square law, where the amount of radiation received is proportional to $1/d^2$, where d is distance. If a Geiger counter that is 1 m away from a small source reads 100 counts per minute, what will be its reading 2 m from the source? 3 m from the source?

35. Consider a radioactive sample with a half-life of one week. How much of the original sample will be left at the end of the second week? The third week? The fourth week?

36. A radioisotope is placed near a radiation detector, which registers 80 counts per second. Eight hours later, the detector registers 5 counts per second. What is the half-life of the radioactive isotope?

37. Uranium-238 absorbs a neutron and then emits a beta particle. Show that the resulting nucleus is neptunium-239.

THINK AND EXPLAIN (SYNTHESIS)

38. Just after an alpha particle leaves the nucleus, would you expect it to speed up? Defend your answer.

39. A pair of protons in an atomic nucleus repel each other, but they are also attracted to each other. Explain.

40. Why do different isotopes of the same element have the same chemical properties?

41. In bombarding atomic nuclei with proton "bullets," why must the protons be given large amounts of kinetic energy in order to make contact with the target nuclei?

42. Why is lead found in all deposits of uranium ores?

43. What do the proportions of lead and uranium in rock tell us about the age of the rock?

44. What are the atomic number and atomic mass of the element formed when $^{218}_{84}Po$ emits a beta particle? What are they if the polonium emits an alpha particle?

45. Elements heavier than uranium in the periodic table do not exist in any appreciable amounts in nature because they have short half-lives. Yet there are several elements below uranium in the periodic table that have equally short half-lives but do exist in appreciable amounts in nature. How can you account for this?

46. People who work around radioactivity wear film badges to monitor the amount of radiation that reaches their bodies. Each badge consists of a small piece of photographic film enclosed in a lightproof wrapper. What kind of radiation do these devices monitor? How can they determine the amount of radiation the people receive?

47. When food is irradiated with gamma rays from a cobalt-60 source, does the food become radioactive? Defend your answer.

48. Radium-226 is a common isotope on Earth, but it has a half-life of about 1620 years. Given that Earth is some 5 billions years old, why is there any radium at all?

49. Is carbon dating advisable for measuring the age of materials a few years old? How about a few thousand years old? A few million years old?

50. Why is carbon-14 dating not accurate for estimating the age of materials more than 50,000 years old?

51. The age of the Dead Sea Scrolls was determined by carbon-14 dating. Could this technique have worked if they had been carved on stone tablets? Explain.

52. If you make an account of 1000 people born in the year 2000 and find that half of them are still living in 2060, does this mean that one-quarter of them will be alive in 2120 and one-eighth of them will be alive in 2180? What is different about the death rates of people and the "death rates" of radioactive atoms?

53. The uranium ores of the Athabasca Basin deposits of Saskatchewan, Canada, are unusually pure, containing up to 70% uranium oxides. Why doesn't this uranium ore undergo an explosive chain reaction?

54. "Strontium-90 is a pure beta source." How could a physicist test this statement?

55. Why will nuclear fission probably never be used directly for powering automobiles? How could it be used indirectly?

56. Why is carbon better than lead as a moderator in nuclear reactors?

57. How does the mass per nucleon in uranium compare with the mass per nucleon in the fission fragments of uranium?

58. Why doesn't iron yield energy if it undergoes fusion or fission?

59. Uranium-235 releases an average of 2.5 neutrons per fission, while plutonium-239 releases an average of 2.7 neutrons per fission. Which of these elements might you therefore expect to have the smaller critical mass?

60. Which process would release energy from gold—fission or fusion? From carbon? From iron?

61. If a uranium nucleus were to fission into three fragments of approximately equal size instead of two, would more energy or less energy be released? Defend your answer using Figure 3.31.

62. Is the mass of an atomic nucleus greater or less than the sum of the masses of the nucleons composing it? Why don't the nucleon masses add up to the total nuclear mass?

63. The original reactor built in 1942 was just "barely" critical because the natural uranium that was used contained less than 1% of the fissionable isotope U-235 (half-life 713 million years). If, in 1942, the Earth had been 9 billion years old instead of 4.5 billion years old, would this reactor have reached critical stage with natural uranium?

64. Heavy nuclei can be made to fuse—for instance, by firing one gold nucleus at another one. Does such a process yield energy or cost energy? Explain.

65. Which produces more energy—the fission of a single uranium nucleus or the fusing of a pair of deuterium nuclei? The fission of a gram of uranium or the fusing of a gram of deuterium? (Why do your answers differ?)

66. If a fusion reaction produces no appreciable radioactive isotopes, why does a hydrogen bomb produce significant radioactive fallout?

67. Explain how radioactive decay has always warmed the Earth from the inside and how nuclear fusion has always warmed the Earth from the outside.

68. What percentage of nuclear power plants in operation today are based on nuclear fusion?

69. Sustained nuclear fusion has yet to be achieved and remains a hope for abundant future energy. Yet the energy that has always sustained us has been the energy of nuclear fusion. Explain.

70. Oxygen and two hydrogen atoms combine to form a water molecule. At the nuclear level, if one oxygen and two hydrogen were fused, what element would be produced?

71. If a pair of carbon nuclei were fused and the product emitted a beta particle, what element would be produced?

72. Ordinary hydrogen is sometimes called a perfect fuel because of its almost unlimited supply on Earth, and when it burns, harmless water is the product of the combustion. So why don't we abandon fission energy and fusion energy, not to mention fossil-fuel energy, and just use hydrogen?

THINK AND DISCUSS (EVALUATION)

73. Why might some people consider it a blessing in disguise that fossil fuels are such a limited resource? Centuries from now, what attitudes about the combustion of fossil fuels are our descendants likely to have?

74. The 1986 accident at Chernobyl, in which dozens of people died and thousands more were exposed to cancer-causing radiation, created fear and outrage worldwide and led some people to call for the closing of all nuclear plants. Yet many people choose to smoke cigarettes in spite of the fact that 2 million people die every year from smoking-related diseases. The risks posed by nuclear power plants are involuntary, risks we must all share like it or not, whereas the risks associated with smoking are voluntary because a person chooses to smoke. Why are we so unaccepting of involuntary risk but accepting of voluntary risk?

75. Your friend Paul says that the helium used to inflate balloons is a product of radioactive decay. Your mutual friend Steve says no way. Then there's your friend Alison, fretful about living near a fission power plant. She wishes to get away from radiation by traveling to the high mountains and sleeping out at night on granite outcroppings. Still another friend, Michele, has journeyed to the mountain foothills to escape the effects of radioactivity altogether. While bathing in the warmth of a natural hot spring, she wonders aloud how the spring gets its heat. What do you tell these friends?

76. Speculate about some worldwide changes that are likely to follow the advent of successful fusion reactors.

READINESS ASSURANCE TEST (RAT)

If you have a good handle on this chapter, then you should be able to score at least 7 out of 10 on this RAT. If you score less than 7, you need to study further before moving on.

Choose the BEST answer to each of the following:

1. Which type of radiation from cosmic sources predominates on the inside of a high-flying commercial airplane?
   (a) alpha
   (b) beta
   (c) gamma
   (d) None of these predominates; all three are abundant.

2. Is it possible for a hydrogen nucleus to emit an alpha particle? Why?
   (a) yes, because alpha particles are the simplest form of radiation
   (b) no, because it would require the nuclear fission of hydrogen, which is impossible
   (c) yes, but it does not occur very frequently
   (d) no, because the nucleus does not contain enough nucleons

3. A sample of radioactive material is usually a little warmer than its surroundings because
   (a) it efficiently absorbs and releases energy from sunlight.
   (b) its atoms are continuously being struck by alpha and beta particles.
   (c) it is radioactive.
   (d) it emits alpha and beta particles.

4. What evidence supports the contention that the strong nuclear force is stronger than the electrical interaction at short internuclear distances?
   (a) Protons are able to exist side by side in an atomic nucleus.
   (b) Neutrons spontaneously decay into protons and electrons.
   (c) Uranium deposits are always slightly warmer than their immediate surroundings.
   (d) Radio interference arises adjacent to any radioactive source.

5. When the isotope bismuth-213 emits an alpha particle, what new element results?
   (a) lead
   (b) platinum
   (c) polonium
   (d) thallium

6. A certain radioactive element has a half-life of 1 hour. If you start with a 1-g sample of the element at noon, how much of this same element will be left at 3:00 PM?
   (a) 0.5 g
   (b) 0.25 g
   (c) 0.125 g
   (d) 0.0625 g

7. The isotope cesium-137, which has a half-life of 30 years, is a product of nuclear power plants. How long will it take for this isotope to decay to about one-half its original amount?
   (a) 0 yr
   (b) 15 yr
   (c) 30 yr
   (d) 60 yr
   (e) 90 yr

8. If uranium were to split into 90 pieces of equal size instead of two, would more energy or less energy be released? Why?
   (a) less energy, because of less mass per nucleon
   (b) less energy, because of greater mass per nucleon
   (c) more energy, because of less mass per nucleon
   (d) more energy, because of greater mass per nucleon

9. Which process would release energy from gold—fission or fusion? From carbon?
   (a) gold: fission; carbon: fusion
   (b) gold: fusion; carbon: fission
   (c) gold: fission; carbon: fission
   (d) gold: fusion; carbon: fusion

10. If an iron nucleus split in two, its fission fragments would have
    (a) greater mass per nucleon.
    (b) less mass per nucleon.
    (c) the same mass per nucleon.
    (d) either greater or less mass per nucleon.

Answers to RAT

1. c, 2. d, 3. b, 4. a, 5. d, 6. c, 7. c, 8. b, 9. a, 10. a

CHAPTER 4
Heat

LAVA HAS an average temperature of about 1000°C—ten times the boiling point of water. White-hot sparks from a Fourth of July sparkler are about 2000°C, twice as hot as typical lava. Why, then, would lava severely burn your skin on contact, but the sparkler's sparks leave you unhurt? Can an object get colder and colder or hotter and hotter forever—or are there limits to coldness and hotness? Why does a tile floor feel colder to bare feet than a carpeted floor at the same temperature? Another question . . . Why does air in a balloon, the concrete of a sidewalk, and almost everything else expand as it warms? Why does ice water do the opposite, contracting instead of expanding as its temperature rises? And why does ice form on the top of a pond rather than at the bottom, thus enabling fish to swim comfortably all winter? This chapter will answer these and other questions relating to heat.

LEARNING OBJECTIVE
Distinguish between the forms of energy that make up thermal energy.

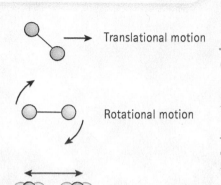

Translational motion

Rotational motion

Vibrational motion

FIGURE 4.1
Types of motion of particles in matter.

LEARNING OBJECTIVE
Distinguish between thermal energy and temperature.

FIGURE 4.2
Can we trust our sense of hot and cold? Will both fingers feel the same temperature when they are put in the warm water? Try this and see (feel) for yourself.

MasteringPhysics®
VIDEO: Low Temperatures with Liquid Nitrogen
VIDEO: How a Thermostat Works

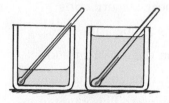

Hot stove

FIGURE 4.3
Although the same quantity of heat is added to both containers, the temperature increases more in the container with the smaller amount of water.

4.1 The Kinetic Theory of Matter

EXPLAIN THIS What is thermal energy?

According to the *kinetic theory of matter*, matter is made up of tiny particles—atoms and molecules. The particles are always moving, and they move in a number of ways. They rotate, vibrate, and move in straight lines between collisions (Figure 4.1).

The energy that atoms and molecules have relates to their motion and their position. They have translational kinetic energy due to their translational (straight-line) motion as well as rotational and vibrational kinetic energy. Also, the particles have potential energy from the attractions between them or from their mutual repulsion when they are at close range. The *total* of all these forms of energy in a particular substance is its **thermal energy**. (Physicists usually refer to thermal energy as *internal energy* because it is internal to a substance.)

4.2 Temperature

EXPLAIN THIS What are two ways to state the freezing point of water?

When you strike a nail with a hammer, the nail becomes warm. Why? Because the hammer's blow makes the nail's atoms move faster. When you put a flame to a liquid, the liquid becomes warmer as its molecules move faster. When you rapidly compress air in a tire pump, the air becomes warmer. In these cases, the molecules are made to race back and forth faster. They gain kinetic energy. In general, the warmer an object, the more kinetic energy its atoms and molecules possess. **Temperature**, the degree of "hotness" or "coldness" of an object, is proportional to the average translational kinetic energy of the atoms or molecules that make up the object. So, the translational motion of particles contributes to the temperature of an object (see Figure 4.1, top).

It is important to note that temperature is not a measure of the total kinetic energy in a substance. For example, there is twice as much molecular kinetic energy in 2 liters of boiling water as in 1 liter of boiling water—but both volumes of water have the same temperature because the *average* kinetic energy per molecule is the same.

We express temperature quantitatively by a number that corresponds to the degree of hotness on some chosen scale. A common thermometer takes advantage of the fact that most substances expand as temperature rises. Such a thermometer measures temperature by comparing the expansion and contraction of a liquid (usually mercury or colored alcohol) to increments on a scale. Some modern thermometers avoid contact and measure temperature by the infrared radiation emitted by substances, as we'll discuss in the section on heat transfer and radiation later in this chapter.

On a worldwide basis, the thermometer most often used is the Celsius thermometer. This thermometer is named in honor of the Swedish astronomer Anders Celsius (1701–1744), who first suggested the scale of 100 degrees between the freezing point and boiling point of water. Zero (0) is assigned to the temperature at which water freezes, and the number 100 is assigned to the temperature at which water boils (at standard atmospheric pressure). In between freezing and boiling temperatures are 100 equal parts called *degrees*.

In the United States, the number 32 is traditionally assigned to the temperature at which water freezes, and the number 212 is assigned to the temperature at which water boils. Such a scale makes up the Fahrenheit thermometer, named after its inventor, the German physicist G. D. Fahrenheit (1686–1736). Although the Fahrenheit scale is the one most commonly used in the United States, the Celsius scale is standard in scientific applications.

Using arithmetic formulas to convert from one temperature scale to the other is common in classroom exams. Because such arithmetic conversions aren't really physics, we won't be concerned with them here. Besides, the conversion between Celsius and Fahrenheit temperatures is closely approximated in the side-by-side scales shown in Figure 4.4.*

It is interesting that a thermometer actually registers its own temperature. When a thermometer is in thermal contact with something whose temperature we wish to know, thermal energy flows between the two until their temperatures are equal. At this point, thermal equilibrium is established. So, when we look at the temperature of the thermometer, we learn about the temperature of the substance with which it reached thermal equilibrium.

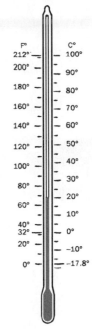

FIGURE 4.4
Fahrenheit and Celsius scales on a thermometer.

4.3 Absolute Zero

EXPLAIN THIS How cold is absolute zero?

LEARNING OBJECTIVE
Describe the meaning of the lowest possible temperature in nature.

In principle, there is no upper limit to temperature. As thermal motion increases, a solid object first melts and then vaporizes. As the temperature is further increased, molecules dissociate into atoms, and atoms lose some or all of their electrons, thereby forming a cloud of electrically charged particles—a plasma. Plasmas exist in stars, where the temperature is many millions of degrees Celsius. Temperature has no upper limit.

In contrast, there is a definite limit at the opposite end of the temperature scale. Gases expand when heated, and they contract when cooled. Nineteenth-century experimenters found that all gases, regardless of their initial pressures or volumes, change by $\frac{1}{273}$ of their volume at 0°C for each drop in temperature of 1 degree Celsius, provided that the pressure is held constant. So, if a gas at 0°C were cooled down by 273°C, it would contract $\frac{273}{273}$ volumes and be reduced to zero volume. Clearly, we cannot have a substance with zero volume (Figure 4.5).

The same is true of pressure. The pressure of a gas of fixed volume decreases by $\frac{1}{273}$ for each drop in temperature of 1 degree Celsius. If it were cooled to 273°C below zero, it would have no pressure at all. In practice, every gas converts to a liquid before becoming this cold. Nevertheless, these decreases by $\frac{1}{273}$ increments suggested the idea of lowest temperature: −273°C. That's the lower limit of temperature, **absolute zero**. At this temperature, molecules have lost all available

---

*Okay, if you really want to know, the formulas for temperature conversion are $C = \frac{5}{9}(F - 32)$ and $F = \frac{9}{5}C + 32$, where C is the Celsius temperature and F is the corresponding Fahrenheit temperature.

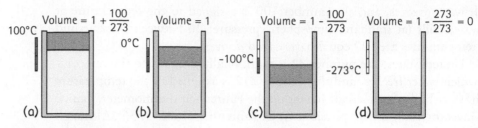

FIGURE 4.5
The gray piston in the vessel goes down as the volume of gas (blue) shrinks. The volume of gas changes by $\frac{1}{273}$ of its volume at 0°C with each 1°C change in temperature when the pressure is held constant. (a) At 100°C, the volume is $\frac{100}{273}$ greater than it is at (b), when its temperature is 0°C. (c) When the temperature is reduced to −100°C, the volume is reduced by $\frac{100}{273}$. (d) At −273°C, the volume of the gas would be reduced by $\frac{273}{273}$ and so would be zero.

kinetic energy.* No more energy can be removed from a substance at absolute zero. It can't get any colder (Figure 4.6).

The absolute temperature scale is called the Kelvin scale, named after the famous British mathematician and physicist William Thomson, First Baron Kelvin. Absolute zero is 0 K (short for "zero kelvin"; note that the word *degrees* is not used with Kelvin temperatures). There are no negative numbers on the Kelvin scale. Its temperature divisions are identical to the divisions on the Celsius scale. Thus, the melting point of ice is 273 K, and the boiling point of water is 373 K.

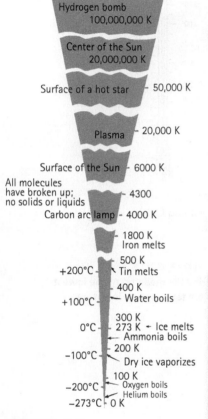

FIGURE 4.6
Some absolute temperatures.

CHECK YOURSELF
1. Which is larger—a Celsius degree or a kelvin?
2. A sample of hydrogen gas has a temperature of 0°C. If the sample were heated until it had twice the thermal energy, what would its temperature be?

CHECK YOUR ANSWERS
1. Neither; they are equal.
2. The 0°C gas has an absolute temperature of 273 K. Twice the thermal energy means that it has twice the absolute temperature, or 2 × 273 K. This would be 546 K, or 273°C.

LEARNING OBJECTIVE
Distinguish between heat and temperature.

4.4 What Is Heat?

EXPLAIN THIS Why do we say that no substances contain heat?

If you touch a hot stove, thermal energy enters your hand because the stove is warmer than your hand. When you touch a piece of ice, however, thermal energy passes out of your hand and into the colder ice. The direction of energy flow is always from a warmer thing to a neighboring cooler thing. A scientist defines **heat** as the thermal energy transferred from one thing to another due to a temperature difference.

Which has a higher temperature—a red-hot tack or a lake? Which has more thermal energy?

*Even at absolute zero, molecules still possess a small amount of kinetic energy, called the zero-point energy. Helium, for example, has enough motion at absolute zero to prevent it from freezing. The explanation for this involves quantum theory.

According to this definition, matter does not contain heat. Matter contains thermal energy, not heat. Heat is the flow of thermal energy due to a temperature difference. Once thermal energy has been transferred to an object or substance, it ceases to be heat. Heat is thermal energy in transit.

For substances in thermal contact, thermal energy flows from the higher-temperature substance to the lower-temperature substance until thermal equilibrium is reached. This does not mean that thermal energy necessarily flows from a substance with more thermal energy into one with less thermal energy. For example, there is more thermal energy in a bowl of warm water than there is in a red-hot thumbtack. If the tack is placed into the water, thermal energy doesn't flow from the warm water to the tack. Instead, it flows from the hot tack to the cooler water. Thermal energy never flows unassisted from a lower-temperature substance to a higher-temperature substance.

If heat is thermal energy that transfers in a direction from hot to cold, what is cold? Does a cold substance contain something opposite to thermal energy? No. An object is not cold because it contains something but because it lacks something. It lacks thermal energy. When outdoors on a near-zero winter day, you feel cold not because something called cold gets to you. You feel cold because you lose heat. That's the purpose of your coat—to slow down the heat flow from your body. Cold is not a thing in itself; it is the result of reduced thermal energy.

FIGURE 4.7
The temperature of the sparks is very high, about 2000°C. That's a lot of thermal energy per molecule of spark. However, because there are few molecules per spark, the thermal energy is safely small. Temperature is one thing; transfer of energy is another.

CHECK YOURSELF

1. **Suppose you apply a flame to 1 liter of water for a certain time and the water's temperature rises by 2°C. If you apply the same flame for the same time to 2 liters of water, by how much will the water's temperature rise?**

2. **If a fast marble hits a random scatter of slow marbles, does the fast marble usually speed up or slow down? Which lose(s) kinetic energy and which gain(s) kinetic energy—the initially fast-moving marble or the initially slow ones? How do these questions relate to the direction of heat flow?**

CHECK YOUR ANSWERS

1. Its temperature will rise by only 1°C, because there are twice as many molecules in 2 liters of water, and each molecule receives only half as much energy on the average. So, the water's average kinetic energy, and thus its temperature, increases by half as much.

2. A fast-moving marble slows when it hits slower-moving marbles. It gives up some of its kinetic energy to the slower ones. Likewise with heat: Molecules with higher kinetic energy that make contact with molecules that have lower kinetic energy give up some of their excess kinetic energy to the slower ones. The direction of energy transfer is from hot to cold. For both the marbles and the molecules, however, the total energy before and after contact is the same.

> Just as dark is the absence of light, cold is the absence of thermal energy.

Quantity of Heat

Heat is a form of energy, and it is measured in joules. It takes about 4.2 joules of heat to change 1 gram of water by 1 Celsius degree. A unit of heat still common in the United States is the **calorie**.* A calorie is defined as the amount of heat

> Temperature is measured in degrees. Heat is measured in joules or calories.

---

*Another common unit of heat is the British thermal unit (Btu). The Btu is defined as the amount of heat required to change the temperature of 1 pound of water by 1 degree Fahrenheit.

FIGURE 4.8
To the weight watcher, the peanut contains 10 Calories; to the physicist, it releases 10,000 calories (or 41,900 joules) of energy when burned or digested.

needed to change the temperature of 1 gram of water by 1 Celsius degree. (The relationship between calories and joules is 1 calorie = 4.19 joules.)

The energy ratings of foods and fuels are measured by the energy released when they are burned. (Metabolism is really "burning" at a slow rate.) The heat unit for labeling food is the kilocalorie, which is 1000 calories (the heat needed to change the temperature of 1 kilogram of water by 1°C). To differentiate this unit and the smaller calorie, the food unit is usually called a Calorie, with a capital C. So, 1 Calorie is really 1000 calories.

CHECK YOURSELF
Which will raise the temperature of water more—adding 4.19 joules or 1 calorie?

CHECK YOUR ANSWER
They are the same. This is like asking which is longer—a 1-mile-long track or a 1.6-kilometer-long track. They're the same length in different units.

LEARNING OBJECTIVE
Describe the three laws of thermodynamics.

4.5 The Laws of Thermodynamics

EXPLAIN THIS How does thermodynamics relate to the conservation of energy?

What we've learned thus far about heat and thermal energy is summed up in the laws of **thermodynamics**. The word *thermodynamics* stems from Greek words meaning "movement of heat." It is the study of heat and its transformation to different forms of energy.

When thermal energy transfers as heat, it does so without net loss or gain. The energy lost in one place is gained in another. When the law of conservation of energy is applied to thermal systems, we have the **first law of thermodynamics**:

Whenever heat flows into or out of a system, the gain or loss of thermal energy equals the amount of heat transferred.

A *system* is any substance, device, or well-defined group of atoms or molecules. The system may be the steam in a steam engine, the entire Earth's atmosphere, or even the body of a living creature. When we add heat to any of these systems, we increase its thermal energy. The added energy enables the system to do work. The first law makes good sense.

The first law is nicely illustrated when you put an airtight can of air on a hot stove and warm it. The energy that is put in increases the thermal energy of the enclosed air, so its temperature rises. If the can is fitted with a movable piston, then the heated air can do *mechanical work* as it expands and pushes the piston outward. This ability to do mechanical work is energy that comes from the energy you put in to begin with. The first law says you don't get energy from nothing.

The **second law of thermodynamics** restates what we've learned about the direction of heat flow:

Heat never spontaneously flows from a lower-temperature substance to a higher-temperature substance.

FIGURE 4.9
When Pete pushes down on the piston, he does work on the air inside. What happens to the air's temperature?

When heat flow is spontaneous—that is, when no external work is done—the direction of flow is always from hot to cold. In winter, heat flows from inside a warm home to the cold air outside. In summer, heat flows from the hot air outside into the cooler interior. Heat can be made to flow the other way only when work is done on the system or when energy is added from another source. This occurs with heat pumps and air conditioners. In these devices, thermal energy is pumped from a cooler to a warmer region. But without external effort, the direction of heat flow is from hot to cold. The second law, like the first law, makes logical sense.*

The **third law of thermodynamics** restates what we've learned about the lowest limit of temperature:

No system can reach absolute zero.

As investigators attempt to reach this lowest temperature, it becomes more difficult to get closer to it. Physicists have been able to record temperatures that are less than a millionth of 1 kelvin, but never as low as 0 K.

 Integrated Science 6A
CHEMISTRY AND BIOLOGY

Entropy

LEARNING OBJECTIVE
Relate the dispersal of energy to the concept of entropy.

EXPLAIN THIS When does entropy decrease in a system?

Energy tends to disperse. It flows from where it is localized to where it is spread out. For example, consider a hot pan once you have taken it off the stove. The pan's thermal energy doesn't stay localized in the pan. Instead, it disperses outward, away from the pan into its surroundings. As the pan is heated, energetic molecules transfer energy to the air by molecular collisions as well as by radiation. Consider a second example: The chemical energy in gasoline burns explosively in a car engine when the molecules combust. Some of this energy disperses through the transmission to get the car moving. The rest of the energy disperses as heat into the metal of the engine, into the coolant that flows through the engine and the radiator, and into the gases that flow through the engine and out the exhaust pipe. The energy, once localized in the small volume of the gasoline, is now spread out through a larger volume of space. Or, witness the dispersion of energy when you pick up an object—a marble, for example—and drop it. When you lift the marble, you give it potential energy. Drop it and that potential energy converts to kinetic energy, pushing air aside as it falls (therefore spreading out the marble's kinetic energy a bit), before hitting the ground. When the marble hits, it disperses energy as sound and as heat (when it heats the ground a bit). The potential energy you put into the marble by lifting it, which was once localized in the marble, is now spread out and dispersed in a little air movement plus the heating of the air and ground. The marble bounces before it finally comes to rest; in each bounce, energy spreads out from the marble to its surroundings.

---

* The laws of thermodynamics were all the rage back in the 1800s. At that time, horses and buggies were yielding to steam-driven locomotives. There is the story of the engineer who explained the operation of a steam engine to a peasant. The engineer cited in detail the operation of the steam cycle—how expanding steam drives a piston that in turn rotates the wheels. After some thought, the peasant said, "Yes, I understand all that. But where's the horse?" This story illustrates how hard it is to abandon our way of thinking about the world when a newer method comes along to replace established ways. Are we any different today?

The tendency of energy to spread out is one of the central driving forces of nature. Processes that disperse energy tend to occur spontaneously—they are favored. The opposite holds true as well. Processes that result in the concentration of energy tend not to occur—they are not favored. Heat from the room doesn't spontaneously flow into the frying pan to heat it up. Likewise, the lower-energy molecules of a car's exhaust won't on their own come back together to re-form the higher-energy molecules of gasoline. And, needless to say, dropped marbles don't jump back into your hand. The natural flow of energy is always a one-way trip from where it is concentrated to where it is spread out. The second law of thermodynamics states this principle for heat flow. But now we can see that the second law of thermodynamics can be generalized and stated this way:

Natural systems tend to disperse from concentrated and organized-energy states toward diffuse and disorganized states.

The least concentrated form of energy is thermal energy. So, since organized forms of energy tend to become less organized, they ultimately degrade into the environment as thermal energy. Further, when energy is dispersed, it is less able to do useful work than when it was concentrated—in effect, it becomes diluted. So, thermal energy is the graveyard of useful energy.

The measure of energy dispersal is a quantity known as **entropy**.* More entropy means more degradation of energy. Since energy tends to degrade and disperse with time, the total amount of entropy in any system tends to increase with time. Things wear down (Figure 4.10). The same is true for the largest system, the universe. The net entropy in the universe is continuously increasing (the universe is continuously running "downhill").

We say *net* entropy because there are some regions where energy is actually being organized and concentrated. Work input from outside of an isolated system can decrease entropy in the system, with energy proceeding toward organization and concentration in that system. For example, diffuse thermal energy in the air can be concentrated in a heat pump. And living things seem to defy the second law of thermodynamics with their highly organized and concentrated energy. But, on closer examination, the orderliness we observe among life forms is a result of energy input. Ultimately, the energy that builds and maintains orderly biological systems comes mostly from the Sun when plants build energy-rich sugar molecules from disorderly gases and liquids during photosynthesis. The *spontaneous* processes that occur within organisms actually do increase entropy—consider, for example, the diffusion of nutrients across a cell membrane. Without some outside energy input, processes in which entropy decreases are not observed in nature (Figure 4.11).

Interestingly, the direction of time's passage is linked to increasing entropy; examples are a leaf falling from a tree, wood burning in a fire, and even the hands of a clock moving. As these occur, energy is dispersed, and we gain the sense that time moves forward. To put it another way, consider the likelihood of a burned log in a fire becoming whole, or a leaf on the ground spontaneously moving upward to join the branch from which it came. These cases involve the opposite of the dispersion of energy, which would be perceived as time moving backward. Hence, entropy is both a gauge for the dispersal of energy and time's arrow.

FIGURE 4.10
Entropy: Order in nature tends to progress to disorder.

Here's another way of stating the laws of thermodynamics: You can't win (because you can't get any more energy out of a system than you put into it), you can't break even (because you can't get as much useful energy out as you put in), and you can't get out of the game (entropy in the universe is always increasing).

---

*Entropy can be expressed mathematically. The increase in entropy ΔS of a thermodynamic system is equal to the amount of heat added to the system ΔQ divided by the temperature T at which the heat is added: $\Delta S = \Delta Q/T$.

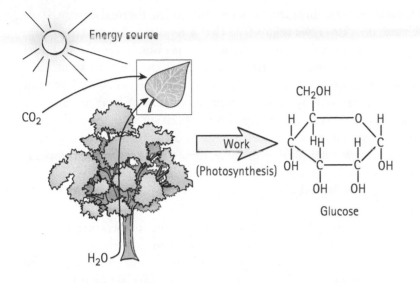

CH₂OH

Glucose

FIGURE 4.11
Work is needed to transform a state of disorderly, diffuse energy into a state of more concentrated energy. The Sun supplies the energy to do this work when plants transform liquids and vapors into sugar molecules—a plant's storehouse of usable, concentrated energy.

CHECK YOURSELF

1. As energy disperses, where does it ultimately go?
2. Which has greater entropy—the molecules of perfume in a closed perfume bottle or the molecules of perfume when the perfume bottle is opened?
3. In the formation of molecular hydrogen H_2 from atomic hydrogen H, there is a net increase in entropy. Will this chemical reaction proceed on its own? Justify your answer.
4. A tree takes in carbon dioxide from the air, water from the soil, and a small amount of water vapor from the air. Structures in the tree's leaves, called chloroplasts, convert these disorderly building materials into sugar molecules, which are highly concentrated forms of energy. Does this violate the second law of thermodynamics? Explain your answer.

CHECK YOUR ANSWERS

1. Ultimately the energy disperses into thermal energy.
2. The molecules diffuse when the bottle is opened, spreading their thermal energy over a larger volume of space. Entropy is increased.
3. Yes; by the second law of thermodynamics, processes that increase entropy are favored.
4. No; the radiant energy of the Sun provides the energy input needed to convert less-concentrated energy into a more concentrated, usable form.

4.6 Specific Heat Capacity

LEARNING OBJECTIVE
Relate the specific heat capacity of substances to thermal inertia.

EXPLAIN THIS Why does a hot frying pan cool faster than the same mass of equally hot water?

You've likely noticed that some foods remain hotter much longer than others. Whereas the filling of a hot apple pie can burn your tongue, the crust does not, even when the pie has just been removed from the oven (Figure 4.12). Or a piece of toast may be comfortably eaten a few seconds after coming from the hot toaster, whereas you must wait several minutes before eating soup that initially had the same temperature.

FIGURE 4.12
The filling of a hot apple pie may be too hot to eat, even though the crust is not.

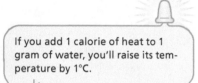

If you add 1 calorie of heat to 1 gram of water, you'll raise its temperature by 1°C.

Different substances have different capacities for storing thermal energy. If we heat a pot of water on a stove, we might find that it requires 15 minutes to raise it from room temperature to its boiling temperature. But if we put an equal mass of iron on the same stove, we'd find it would rise through the same temperature range in only about 2 minutes. For silver, the time would be less than a minute. Different materials require different quantities of heat to raise the temperature of a given mass of the material by a specified number of degrees. This is because different materials absorb energy in different ways. The energy may increase the translational motion of molecules, which raises the temperature; or it may increase the amount of internal vibration or rotation within the molecules and go into potential energy, which does not raise the temperature. Generally, there is a combination of both.

A gram of water requires 1 calorie of energy to raise the temperature 1 degree Celsius. It takes only about one-eighth as much energy to raise the temperature of a gram of iron by the same amount. Water absorbs more heat than iron for the same change in temperature. We say water has a higher **specific heat capacity** (sometimes called *specific heat*).

The specific heat capacity of any substance is the quantity of heat required to change the temperature of a unit mass of the substance by 1 degree Celsius.

We can think of specific heat capacity as thermal inertia. Recall that *inertia* is a term used in mechanics to signify the resistance of an object to a change in its state of motion. Specific heat capacity is like thermal inertia because it signifies the resistance of a substance to a change in temperature.

CHECK YOURSELF
Which has a higher specific heat capacity—water or sand? In other words, which takes longer to warm in sunlight (or longer to cool at night)?

CHECK YOUR ANSWER
Water has the higher specific heat capacity. In the same sunlight, the temperature of water increases more slowly than the temperature of sand. And water will cool more slowly at night. The low specific heat capacity of sand and soil, as evidenced by how quickly they warm in the morning Sun and how quickly they cool at night, affects local climates.

Water has a much higher capacity for storing energy than almost all other substances. A lot of heat energy is needed to change the temperature of water. This explains why water is very useful in the cooling systems of automobiles and other engines. It absorbs a great quantity of heat for small increases in temperature. Water also takes longer to cool.

FIGURE 4.13
Because water has a high specific heat capacity and is transparent, it takes more energy to warm a body of water than to warm the land. Solar energy incident on the land is concentrated at the surface, but solar energy hitting the water extends beneath the surface and is diluted.

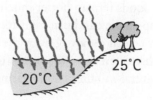

Integrated Science 6B
EARTH SCIENCE

Specific Heat Capacity and Earth's Climate

EXPLAIN THIS Relate specific heat capacity to the oceans.

Water's high specific heat capacity affects the world's climate. Look at a globe or a map of the Northern Hemisphere and notice the high latitude of Europe. Water's high specific heat keeps Europe's climate appreciably milder than regions of the same latitude in northeastern Canada. Both Europe and Canada receive about the same amount of sunlight per square kilometer. What happens is that the Atlantic Ocean current known as the Gulf Stream carries warm water northeastward from the Caribbean Sea. The water retains much of its thermal energy long enough to reach the North Atlantic Ocean off the coast of Europe. Then it cools, releasing 4.19 joules of energy for each gram of water that cools by 1°C. The released energy is carried by westerly winds over the European continent.

MATH CONNECTION

The Heat-Transfer Equation

We can use specific heat capacity to write a formula for the quantity of heat Q involved when a mass m of a substance undergoes a change in temperature: $Q = cm\Delta T$. In words, heat transferred into or out of a substance = specific heat capacity of the substance × mass of the substance × the substance's temperature change. This equation is valid for a substance that gets warmer as well as for one that cools. When a substance is warming up, the heat transferred into it, Q, is positive. When a substance is cooling off, Q has a minus sign.

Let's apply this equation to a few examples.

Problems

1. A 2.0-kg aluminum pan is heated on the stove from 20°C to 110°C. How much heat had to be transferred to the aluminum? The specific heat capacity of aluminum is 900 J/kg·°C.
2. What will be the final temperature of a mixture of 50 g of 20°C water and 50 g of 40°C water?
3. What will be the final temperature when 100 g of 25°C water is mixed with 75 g of 40°C water?
4. Radioactive decay of granite and other rocks in Earth's interior provides enough energy to keep the interior hot, to produce magma, and to provide warmth to natural hot springs. This is due to the average release of about 0.03 J per kilogram each year. How many years are required for a chunk of thermally insulated granite to increase 500°C in temperature, assuming that the specific heat of granite is 800 J/kg·°C?

Solutions

1. $Q = cm\Delta T = (900 \text{ J/kg} \cdot °\text{C}) (2.0 \text{ kg})(110°\text{C} - 20°\text{C})$
   $= 1.62 \times 10^5$ J. The sign of Q is positive because the pan is absorbing heat.

2. The heat gained by the cooler water = the heat lost by the warmer water. Since the masses of the water are the same, the final temperature is midway between the two, 30°C. So, we'll end up with 100 g of 30°C water.

3. Here we have different masses of water that are mixed together. We equate the heat gained by the cool water to the heat lost by the warm water. We can express this equation formally, and then we can let the expressed terms lead to a solution:

   Heat gained by cool water = heat lost by warm water

   $$cm_1\Delta T_1 = cm_2\Delta T_2$$

   ΔT_1 doesn't equal ΔT_2 as in Problem 2 because of different masses of water. We can see that ΔT_1 will be the final temperature T minus 25°C, since T will be greater than 25°C; ΔT_2 is 40°C minus T, because T will be less than 40°C. Then, showing magnitude only, we see

   $$c(100)(T - 25) = c(75)(40 - T)$$

   $$100T - 2500 = 3000 - 75T$$

   $$T = 31.4°\text{C}$$

4. Here, we switch to rock, but the same concept applies. No particular mass is specified, so we'll work with quantity of heat/mass (our answer should be the same for a small chunk of rock or a huge chunk). From $Q = cm\Delta T$,

   $$\frac{Q}{m} = c\Delta T = (800 \text{ J/kg} \cdot °\text{C}) \times (500°\text{C}) = 400,000 \text{ J/kg}.$$

   The time required is (400,000 J/kg)/(0.03 J/kg·yr) = 13.3 million years. Small wonder it remains hot down there!

FIGURE 4.14
Many ocean currents, shown in blue, distribute heat from the warmer equatorial regions to the colder polar regions.

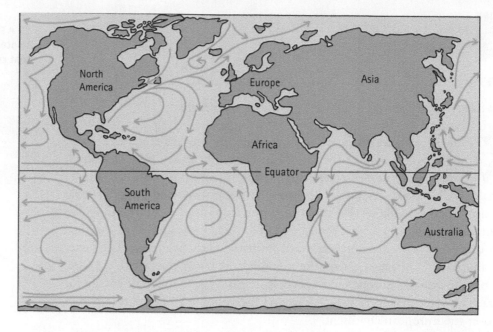

A similar effect occurs in the United States. The winds in North America are mostly westerly. On the West Coast, air moves from the Pacific Ocean to the land. In winter months, the ocean water is warmer than the air. Air blows over the warm water and then moves over the coastal regions. This produces a warmer climate. In summer, the opposite occurs. The water cools the air, and the coastal regions are cooled. The East Coast does not benefit from the moderating effects of water because the direction of the prevailing wind is eastward from the land to the Atlantic Ocean. Land, with a lower specific heat capacity, gets hot in the summer but cools rapidly in the winter.

Islands and peninsulas do not have the extremes of temperatures that are common in the interior regions of a continent. The high summer and low winter temperatures common in Manitoba and the Dakotas, for example, are largely due to the absence of large bodies of water. Europeans, islanders, and people living near ocean air currents should be glad that water has such a high specific heat capacity. San Franciscans certainly are!

See Chapter 10 on weather for more discussion of the effects of ocean currents on global climate.

CHECK YOURSELF

1. **Bermuda is close to North Carolina, but, unlike North Carolina, it has a tropical climate year-round. Why?**
2. **How is the thermal energy that is given up by the northern Atlantic Ocean off the coast of Europe carried to the European continent?**
3. **If the winds at the latitude of San Francisco and Washington, DC, were from the east rather than from the west, why might cherry trees grow in San Francisco and palm trees grow in Washington, DC?**

CHECK YOUR ANSWERS

1. Bermuda is an island. The surrounding water warms it when it might otherwise be too cold, and cools it when it might otherwise be too warm.

2. Thermal energy moves from the Atlantic Ocean into the air and is carried over Europe by westerly winds.

3. As the ocean off the coast of San Francisco cools in the winter, the heat it loses warms the atmosphere it comes in contact with. This warmed air blows over the California coastline to produce a relatively warm climate. If the winds were easterly instead of westerly, the climate of San Francisco would be chilled by winter winds from dry and cold Nevada. The climate would also be reversed in Washington, DC, because air warmed by the Atlantic Ocean would blow over Washington, DC, and produce a warmer climate there in the winter.

4.7 Thermal Expansion

EXPLAIN THIS Why does ice float?

LEARNING OBJECTIVE
Relate the open crystalline structure of ice to water's maximum density at 4°C.

Molecules in a hot substance jiggle faster and move farther apart than molecules in a colder substance. The result is thermal expansion. Most substances expand when heated and contract when cooled. Sometimes the changes aren't noticed, and sometimes they are. Telephone wires are longer and sag more on a hot summer day than they do in winter. Railroad tracks laid on cold winter days tend to expand and buckle during the hot summer (Figure 4.15). Metal lids on glass fruit jars can often be loosened by heating them under hot water. If one part of a piece of glass is heated or cooled more rapidly than adjacent parts, the resulting expansion or contraction may break the glass. This is especially true of thick glass. Pyrex glass is an exception because it is specially formulated to expand very little with increasing temperature.

Thermal expansion must be taken into account in structures and devices of all kinds. A dentist uses filling material that has the same rate of expansion as teeth. A civil engineer uses reinforcing steel that has the same expansion rate as concrete. A long steel bridge usually has one end anchored while the other rests on rockers (Figure 4.16). Notice also that many bridges have tongue-and-groove gaps called expansion joints (Figure 4.17). Similarly, concrete roadways and sidewalks are intersected by gaps, which are sometimes filled with tar, so that the concrete can expand freely in summer and contract in winter.

FIGURE 4.15
Thermal expansion gone wild. Extreme heat on a July day caused the buckling of these railroad tracks.

FIGURE 4.16
One end of the bridge rides on rockers to allow for thermal expansion. The other end (not shown) is anchored.

FIGURE 4.17
The gap in the roadway of a bridge is called an expansion joint. It allows the bridge to expand and contract. (Was this photo taken on a warm day or a cold day?)

Thermal expansion accounts for the creaky noises often heard in the attics of old houses on cold nights. The construction materials expand during the day and contract at night, creaking as they grow and shrink.

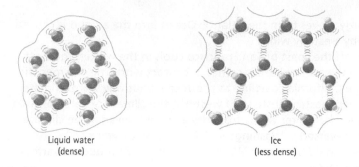

FIGURE 4.18
Liquid water is more dense than ice because water molecules in a liquid are closer together than water molecules frozen in ice, where they have an open crystalline structure.

With increases in temperature, liquids expand more than solids. We notice this when gasoline overflows from a car's tank on a hot day. If the tank and its contents expanded at the same rate, the gas would not overflow. This is why you shouldn't "top off" a gas tank when you fill it, especially on a hot day.

Expansion of Water

Water, like most substances, expands when it is heated, except in the temperature range between 0°C and 4°C. Something fascinating happens in this range. Ice has a crystalline structure, with open-structured crystals. Water molecules in this open structure occupy a greater volume than they do in the liquid phase (Figures 4.18 and 4.19). This means that ice is less dense than water.

When ice melts, not all the six-sided crystals collapse. Some of them remain in the ice-water mixture, making up a microscopic slush that slightly "bloats" the water, increasing its volume (Figure 4.20). This results in ice water being less dense than slightly warmer water. As the temperature of water at 0°C is increased, more of the remaining ice crystals collapse. This further decreases the volume of the water. This contraction occurs only up to 4°C. That's because two things occur at the same time—contraction and expansion. Volume tends to decrease as ice crystals collapse, while volume tends to increase due to greater molecular motion. The collapsing effect dominates until the temperature reaches 4°C. After that, expansion overrides contraction because most of the ice crystals have melted (Figure 4.21).

FIGURE 4.19
The six-sided structure of a snowflake is a result of the six-sided ice crystals that make it up.

FIGURE 4.20
Close to 0°C, liquid water contains crystals of ice. The open structure of these crystals increases the volume of the water slightly.

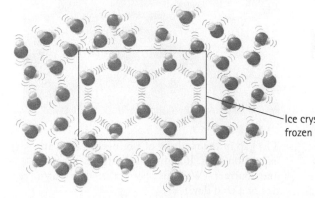

Ice crystals in nearly frozen liquid water

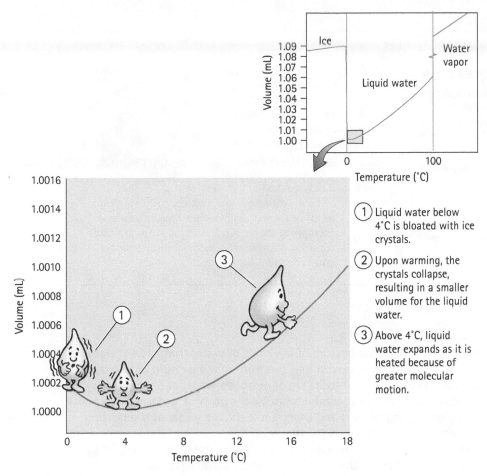

FIGURE 4.21
Between 0°C and 4°C, the volume of liquid water decreases as temperature increases. Above 4°C, water behaves the way other substances do. Its volume increases as its temperature increases. The volumes shown here are for a 1-gram sample.

1 Liquid water below 4°C is bloated with ice crystals.

2 Upon warming, the crystals collapse, resulting in a smaller volume for the liquid water.

3 Above 4°C, liquid water expands as it is heated because of greater molecular motion.

When ice water freezes to become solid ice, its volume increases tremendously—and its density is therefore much lower. That's why ice floats on water. Like most other substances, solid ice contracts without further cooling. This behavior of water is very important in nature. If water were most dense at 0°C, it would settle to the bottom of a lake or pond. Because water at 0°C is less dense, it floats at the surface. That's why ice forms at the surface (Figure 4.22).

UNIFYING CONCEPT

● *Density*
Section 2.3

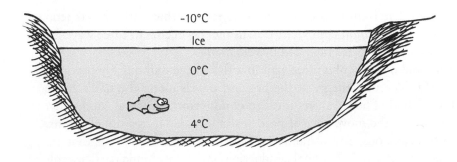

FIGURE 4.22
As water cools, it sinks until the entire lake is 4°C. Then, as the water at the surface is cooled further, it floats on top and can freeze. Once ice is formed, temperatures lower than 4°C can extend down into the lake.

CHECK YOURSELF

1. **What was the precise temperature at the bottom of Lake Michigan on New Year's Eve in 1901?**

2. **What's inside the open spaces of the ice crystals shown in Figure 4.20? Is it air, water vapor, or nothing?**

TECHNOLOGY

Engineering for Thermal Expansion

An illustration of the fact that different substances expand at different rates is provided by a bimetallic strip. This device is made of two strips of different metals welded together, one of brass and the other of iron. When the strip is heated, the greater expansion of the brass bends the strip. This bending may be used to turn a pointer, to regulate a valve, or to close a switch.

A practical application of a bimetallic strip wrapped into a coil is the thermostat that predates modern electronic ones. When a room becomes too warm, the bimetallic coil expands and the drop of liquid mercury rolls away from the electrical contacts and breaks the electrical circuit.

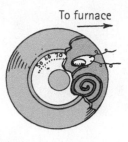
To furnace

When the room is too cool, the coil contracts and the mercury rolls against the contacts and completes the circuit. Bimetallic strips are used in oven thermometers, refrigerators, electric toasters, and other devices.

Brass / Iron — Room temperature — Brass / Iron

Can ice be colder than 0°C?

CHECK YOUR ANSWERS

1. The temperature at the bottom of any body of water that has 4°C water in it is 4°C, for the same reason that rocks are at the bottom of a body of water. Both 4°C water and rocks are denser than water at any temperature. Water is a poor heat conductor, so, if the body of water is deep and in a region of long winters and short summers, the water at the bottom is likely to remain a constant 4°C year round.

2. There's nothing at all in the open spaces. It's empty space—a void. If air or water vapor were in the open spaces, the illustration should show molecules there—oxygen and nitrogen for air and H_2O for water vapor.

LEARNING OBJECTIVE
Describe the nature of conduction in solids.

4.8 Heat Transfer: Conduction

EXPLAIN THIS Why does a tile floor feel colder to your feet than a rug of the same temperature?

FIGURE 4.23
The tile floor feels colder than the wooden floor, even though both floor materials are at the same temperature. This is because tile is a better conductor of heat than wood, and so heat is more readily conducted out of the foot touching the tile.

MasteringPhysics®
VIDEO: The Secret to Walking on Hot Coals
VIDEO: Air is a Poor Conductor

Heat transfers from warmer to cooler objects, so that both objects tend to reach a common temperature. This process occurs in three ways: by *conduction*, by *convection*, and by *radiation*.

When you hold one end of an iron nail in a flame, the nail quickly becomes too hot to hold. Thermal energy at the hot end travels along the nail's entire length. This method of heat transfer is called **conduction**. Thermal conduction occurs by means of the movement of particles in a material, mainly electrons. Every atom has electrons, and metal atoms have loosely held electrons that are free to migrate in the metal. Thermal conduction occurs by atomic particles colliding inside the heated object.

Solids whose atoms or molecules have loosely held electrons are good conductors of heat. Metals have the loosest electrons, and they are excellent conductors of heat. Silver is the best, copper is next, and then, among the common metals, aluminum and iron. Poor conductors include wool, wood, paper, cork, and plastic foam. Molecules in these materials have electrons that are firmly attached to them. Poor conductors are called *insulators*.

FIGURE 4.25
When you touch a nail stuck in ice, does cold flow from the ice to your hand, or does energy flow from your hand to the ice?

Wood is a great insulator, and it is often used for cookware handles. Even when a pot is hot, you can briefly grasp the wooden handle with your bare hand without harm. An iron handle of the same temperature would surely burn your hand. Wood is a good insulator even when it's red hot. This explains how fire-walking coauthor John Suchocki can walk barefoot on red-hot wood coals without burning his feet (Figure 4.24). (Caution: Don't try this on your own; even experienced fire walkers sometimes receive bad burns when conditions aren't just right.) The main factor here is the poor conductivity of wood—even red-hot wood. Although its temperature is high, very little energy is conducted to the feet. A fire walker must be careful that no iron nails or other good conductors are among the hot coals. Ouch!

Air is a very poor conductor as well. You can briefly put your hand into a hot pizza oven without harm. The hot air doesn't conduct thermal energy well. But don't touch the metal in the hot oven. Ouch again! The good insulating properties of such things as wool, fur, and feathers are largely due to the air spaces they contain. Porous substances are also good insulators because of their many small air spaces. Be glad that air is a poor conductor; if it weren't, you'd feel quite chilly on a 20°C (68°F) day!

Snow is a poor conductor of thermal energy. Snowflakes are formed of crystals that trap air and provide insulation. That's why a blanket of snow keeps the ground warm in winter. Animals in the forest find shelter from the cold in snow banks and in holes in the snow. The snow doesn't provide them with thermal energy—it simply slows down the loss of body heat generated by the animals. Then there are igloos, Arctic dwellings built from compacted snow to shield those inside from the bitter cold of Arctic winters.

FIGURE 4.26
Snow patterns on the roof of a house show areas of conduction and insulation. Bare parts show where heat from inside has leaked through the roof and melted the snow.

4.9 Heat Transfer: Convection

LEARNING OBJECTIVE
Describe the nature of convection in fluids.

EXPLAIN THIS Why does warm air rise?

Liquids and gases transfer thermal energy mainly by **convection**, which is heat transfer due to the actual motion of the fluid itself. Unlike conduction (in which heat is transferred by successive collisions of electrons and atoms), convection involves the motion of a fluid—currents. Convection occurs in all fluids, whether liquids or gases. Whether we heat water in a pan or heat

Convection ovens are simply ovens with a fan inside. Cooking is speeded up by the circulation of heated air.

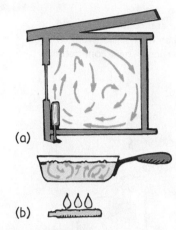

FIGURE 4.27
(a) Convection currents in air.
(b) Convection currents in liquid.

FIGURE 4.28
Blow warm air onto your hand from your wide-open mouth. Now reduce the opening between your lips so that the air expands as you blow. Try it now. Do you notice a difference in the air temperature?

FIGURE 4.29
The hot steam expands from the pressure cooker and is cool to Millie's touch.

As something expands, it spreads its energy over a greater area and therefore it cools.

air in a room, the process is the same (Figure 4.27). As the fluid is heated from below, the molecules at the bottom move faster, spread apart more, become less dense, and are buoyed upward. Denser, cooler fluid moves in to take their place. In this way, convection currents keep the fluid stirred up as it heats—warmer fluid moving away from the heat source and cooler fluid moving toward the heat source.

We can see why warm air rises. When warmed, it expands, becomes less dense, and is buoyed upward in the cooler surrounding air like a balloon buoyed upward. When the rising air reaches an altitude at which the air density is the same, it no longer rises. We see this occurring when smoke from a fire rises and then settles off as it cools and its density matches that of the surrounding air. To see for yourself that expanding air cools, right now do the experiment shown in Figure 4.28. Expanding air really does cool.*

A dramatic example of cooling by expansion occurs when steam expands through the nozzle of a pressure cooker (Figure 4.29). The combined cooling effects of expansion and rapid mixing with cooler air will allow you to hold your hand comfortably in the jet of condensed vapor. (Caution: If you try this, be sure to place your hand high above the nozzle at first and then lower it slowly to a comfortable distance above the nozzle. If you put your hand directly at the nozzle where no steam is visible, watch out! Steam is invisible and is clear of the nozzle before it expands and cools. The cloud of "steam" you see is actually condensed water vapor, which is much cooler than live steam.)

Cooling by expansion is the opposite of what occurs when air is compressed. If you've ever compressed air with a tire pump, you probably noticed that both air and pump became quite hot. Compression of hot air warms it.

Convection currents stir the atmosphere and produce winds. Some parts of Earth's surface absorb thermal energy from the Sun more readily than others. This results in uneven heating of the air near the ground. We see this effect at the seashore, as Figure 4.30 shows. In the daytime, the ground warms up more than the water. Then the warmed air close to the ground rises and is replaced by cooler air that moves in from above the water. The result is a sea breeze. At night, the process reverses because the shore cools off more quickly than the water, and then the warmer air is over the sea. If you build a fire on the beach, you'll see that the smoke sweeps inland during the day and then seaward at night.

*Where does the energy go in this case? It goes to work done on the surrounding air as the expanding air pushes outward.

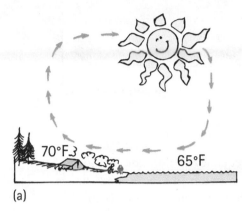 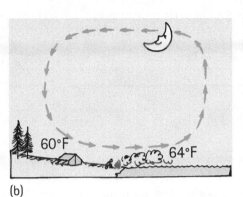

FIGURE 4.30
Convection currents produced by unequal heating of land and water. (a) During the day, warm air above the land rises, and cooler air over the water moves in to replace it. (b) At night, the direction of the airflow is reversed because now the water is warmer than the land.

(a)   (b)

UNIFYING CONCEPT

● *Convection*

CHECK YOURSELF
Explain why you can hold your fingers beside the candle flame without harm, but not above the flame.

CHECK YOUR ANSWER
Thermal energy travels upward by convection. Since air is a poor conductor, very little energy travels sideways to your fingers.

4.10 Heat Transfer: Radiation

LEARNING OBJECTIVE
Describe the nature of radiant energy.

EXPLAIN THIS How do we know the temperatures of stars?

Thermal radiation from the Sun travels through space and then through Earth's atmosphere and warms Earth's surface. This energy cannot pass through the empty space between the Sun and Earth by conduction or convection because there is no medium for doing so. Energy must be transmitted some other way—by **radiation**.* The energy so radiated is called radiant energy.

Radiant energy exists in the form of electromagnetic waves. It includes a wide span of waves, ranging from longest to shortest: radio waves, microwaves, infrared waves (invisible waves below red in the visible spectrum), visible waves, then to waves that can't be seen by the eye, including ultraviolet waves, X-rays, and gamma rays.

FIGURE 4.31
Types of radiant energy (electromagnetic waves).

*The radiation we are talking about here is electromagnetic radiation, including visible light. Don't confuse this with radioactivity, a process of the atomic nucleus that we'll discuss in Chapter 3.

FIGURE 4.32
A wave of long wavelength is produced when the rope is shaken gently (at a low frequency). When it is shaken more vigorously (at a high frequency), a wave of shorter wavelength is produced.

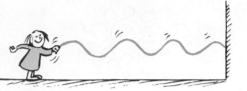

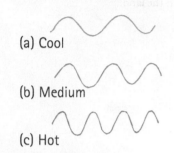

(a) Cool

(b) Medium

(c) Hot

FIGURE 4.33
(a) A low-temperature (cool) source emits primarily low-frequency, long-wavelength waves. (b) A medium-temperature source emits primarily medium-frequency, medium-wavelength waves. (c) A high-temperature (hot) source emits primarily high-frequency, short-wavelength waves.

The wavelength of radiation is related to the frequency of vibration. Frequency is the rate of vibration of a wave source. Nellie Newton in Figure 4.32 shakes a rope at both a low frequency (left) and a higher frequency (right). Note that shaking at a low frequency produces a long, lazy wave, and the higher-frequency shake produces shorter waves. This is also true with electromagnetic waves. Low-frequency vibrations produce long waves, and high-frequency vibrations produce shorter waves (Figure 4.33).

Emission of Radiant Energy

All substances at any temperature above absolute zero emit radiant energy. The average frequency f of the radiant energy is directly proportional to the absolute temperature T of the emitter: $f \sim T$.

Figure 4.34 shows radiation curves for an object at three sample temperatures. At these temperatures, the peak radiation frequencies are in the infrared part of the electromagnetic spectrum.

The fact that all objects in our environment continuously emit infrared radiation underlies the increasingly common infrared thermometers (Figure 4.35). Quite remarkably, you simply point the thermometer at something whose temperature you want, press a button, and a digital temperature reading appears. There is no need to touch the thermometer to whatever is being measured. The radiation it emits provides the reading. Typical classroom infrared thermometers operate in the range of about −30°C to 200°C.

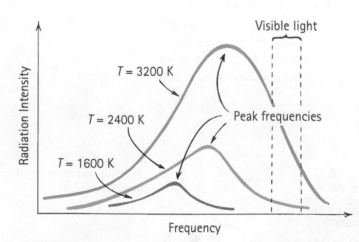

FIGURE 4.34
Radiation curves for different temperatures. The peak frequency of radiant energy is directly proportional to the absolute temperature of the emitter.

FIGURE 4.35
An infrared thermometer measures the infrared radiant energy emitted by a body and converts it into temperature.

If an object is hot enough, some of the radiant energy it emits is in the range of visible light. At a temperature of about 500°C, an object begins to emit the longest waves we can see, red light. Higher temperatures produce a yellowish light. At about 1200°C all the different waves to which the eye is sensitive are emitted and we see an object as "white hot." A blue-hot star is hotter than a white-hot star, and a red-hot star is less hot. Since a blue-hot star has twice the light frequency of a red-hot star, it therefore has twice the surface temperature of a red-hot star.

The surface of the Sun has a high temperature (by earthly standards) and therefore emits radiant energy at a high frequency—much of it in the visible portion of the electromagnetic spectrum. Earth's surface, by comparison, is relatively cool, and so the radiant energy it emits has a frequency lower than that of visible light. The radiation emitted by Earth is in the form of infrared waves—below our threshold of sight. Radiant energy emitted by Earth is called *terrestrial radiation*.

Radiant energy is emitted by both the Sun and Earth, and it differs only in the range of frequencies and the amount (Figure 4.36). When we study meteorology, we'll learn how the atmosphere is transparent to the high-frequency solar radiation but opaque to much of the lower-frequency terrestrial radiation. This produces the greenhouse effect, which plays a role in global warming.

All objects—you, your instructor, and everything in your surroundings—continuously emit radiant energy in a mixture of frequencies (because temperature corresponds to a mixture of different molecular kinetic energies). Objects with everyday temperatures mostly emit low-frequency infrared waves. When your skin absorbs the higher-frequency infrared waves, you feel the sensation of heat. So it is common to refer to infrared radiation as heat radiation.

Common infrared sources that give the sensation of heat are the burning embers in a fireplace, a lamp filament, and the Sun. All of these sources emit both infrared radiation and visible light. When this radiant energy falls on other objects, it is partly reflected and partly absorbed. The part that is absorbed increases the thermal energy of the objects on which it falls.

FIGURE 4.36
Both the Sun and Earth emit the same kind of radiant energy. The Sun's glow consists of longer waves and isn't visible to the eye.

CHECK YOURSELF
Which of these do not emit radiant energy: (a) the Sun, (b) lava from a volcano, (c) red-hot coals, (d) this textbook?

CHECK YOUR ANSWER
All emit radiant energy—even your textbook, which, like the other substances, has a temperature. According to the relation $f \sim T$, the book emits radiation whose average frequency f is quite low compared with the radiation frequencies emitted by the other substances. Everything with any temperature above absolute zero emits radiant energy. That's right—everything!

Absorption of Radiant Energy

If everything is radiating energy, why doesn't everything finally run out of energy? The answer is that everything is also absorbing energy. Good emitters of radiant energy are also good absorbers; poor emitters are poor absorbers. For

Everything around you both radiates and absorbs energy continuously.

FIGURE 4.37
When the black, rough-surfaced container and the shiny, polished one are filled with hot (or cold) water, the blackened one cools (or warms) faster.

A hot pizza put outside on a winter day is a net emitter. The same pizza placed in a hotter oven is a net absorber.

example, a radio dish antenna constructed to be a good emitter of radio waves is also, by its very design, a good receiver (absorber) of them. A poorly designed transmitting antenna is also a poor receiver.

It's interesting to note that, if a good absorber were not also a good emitter, black objects would remain warmer than lighter-colored objects, and the two would never reach a common temperature. Objects in thermal contact, given sufficient time, will reach the same temperature. A blacktop pavement may remain hotter than the surroundings on a hot day, but, at nightfall, it cools faster. Sooner or later, all objects come to thermal equilibrium. So, a dark object that absorbs a lot of radiant energy must emit a lot as well (Figure 4.37).

The surface of any material, hot or cold, both absorbs and emits radiant energy. If the surface absorbs more energy than it emits, it is a net absorber and its temperature rises. If it emits more than it absorbs, it is a net emitter and its temperature drops. Whether a surface plays the role of net absorber or net emitter depends on whether its temperature is higher or lower than that of its surroundings. In short, if it's hotter than its surroundings, the surface will be a net emitter and will cool; if it's colder than its surroundings, it will be a net absorber and will warm.

CHECK YOURSELF
1. If a good absorber of radiant energy were a poor emitter, how would its temperature compare with the temperature of its surroundings?
2. A farmer turns on the propane burner in his barn on a cold morning and heats the air to 20°C (68°F). Why does he still feel cold?

CHECK YOUR ANSWERS
1. If a good radiator were not also a good emitter, there would be a net absorption of radiant energy and the temperature of the absorber would remain higher than the temperature of the surroundings. Things around us approach a common temperature only because good absorbers are, by their very nature, also good emitters.
2. The walls of the barn are still cold. The farmer radiates more energy to the walls than the walls radiate back at him, and he feels chilly. (On a winter day, you are comfortable inside your home or classroom only if the walls are warm—not just the air.)

For instructor-assigned homework, go to www.masteringphysics.com **MP**

SUMMARY OF TERMS (KNOWLEDGE)

Absolute zero The lowest possible temperature that a substance may have—the temperature at which molecules of the substance have their minimum kinetic energy.

Calorie The amount of heat needed to change the temperature of 1 gram of water by 1 Celsius degree.

Conduction The transfer of thermal energy by molecular and electronic collisions within a substance (especially within a solid).

Convection The transfer of thermal energy in a gas or liquid by means of currents in the heated fluid. The fluid flows, carrying energy with it.

Entropy The measure of the energy dispersal of a system. Whenever energy freely transforms from one form into another, the direction of transformation is toward a state of greater disorder and, therefore, toward greater entropy.

First law of thermodynamics A restatement of the law of energy conservation, usually as it applies to systems involving changes in temperature: Whenever heat flows into or out of a system, the gain or loss of thermal energy equals the amount of heat transferred.

Heat The thermal energy that flows from a substance of higher temperature to a substance of lower temperature, commonly measured in calories or joules.

Radiation The transfer of energy by means of electromagnetic waves.

Second law of thermodynamics Heat never spontaneously flows from a lower-temperature substance to a higher-temperature substance. Also, all systems tend to become more and more disordered as time goes by.

Specific heat capacity The quantity of heat required to raise the temperature of a unit mass of a substance by 1 degree Celsius.

Temperature A measure of the hotness or coldness of substances, related to the average translational kinetic energy per molecule in a substance; measured in degrees Celsius, in degrees Fahrenheit, or in kelvins.

Thermal energy The total energy (kinetic plus potential) of the submicroscopic particles that make up a substance (often called *internal energy*).

Thermodynamics The study of heat and its transformation into different forms of energy.

Third law of thermodynamics No system can reach absolute zero.

READING CHECK QUESTIONS (COMPREHENSION)

4.1 The Kinetic Theory of Matter

1. What kinds of particle motion account for thermal energy?
2. Why does a penny become warmer when it is struck by a hammer?

4.2 Temperature

3. What are the temperatures for freezing water on the Celsius and Fahrenheit scales? What are the temperatures for boiling water on those scales?
4. Is the temperature of an object a measure of the total translational kinetic energy of the molecules in the object or a measure of the average translational kinetic energy per molecule in the object?
5. What is meant by this statement: "A thermometer measures its own temperature"?

4.3 Absolute Zero

6. What pressure would you expect in a rigid container of 0°C gas if you cooled it by 273 Celsius degrees?
7. How much energy can be taken from a system at a temperature of 0 K?

4.4 What Is Heat?

8. When you touch a cold surface, does cold travel from the surface to your hand or does energy travel from your hand to the cold surface? Explain.
9. (a) Distinguish between temperature and heat.
   (b) Distinguish between heat and thermal energy.
10. What determines the direction of heat flow?
11. Distinguish between a calorie and a Calorie, and between a calorie and a joule.

4.5 The Laws of Thermodynamics

12. How does the law of conservation of energy relate to the first law of thermodynamics?
13. What happens to the thermal energy of a system when mechanical work is done on the system? What happens to the temperature of the system?
14. How does the second law of thermodynamics relate to the direction of heat flow?

4.6 Specific Heat Capacity

15. Which warms up faster when heat is applied—iron or silver?
16. Does a substance that heats up quickly have a high or low specific heat capacity?
17. How does the specific heat capacity of water compare with the specific heat capacities of other common materials?

4.7 Thermal Expansion

18. Which generally expands more for an equal increase in temperature—solids or liquids?
19. What is the reason ice is less dense than water?
20. Why does ice form at the surface of a pond instead of at the bottom?

4.8 Heat Transfer: Conduction

21. What is the role of "loose" electrons in heat conduction?
22. Distinguish between a heat conductor and a heat insulator.
23. Why is a barefoot fire walker able to walk safely on red-hot wooden coals?
24. Why are such materials as wood, fur, and feathers—and even snow—good insulators?

4.9 Heat Transfer: Convection

25. Describe how convection transfers heat.
26. What happens to the temperature of air when it expands?
27. Why does the direction of coastal winds change from day to night?

4.10 Heat Transfer: Radiation

28. (a) What exactly is radiant energy? (b) What is heat radiation?
29. How does the frequency of radiant energy relate to the absolute temperature of the radiating source?
30. Since all objects continuously radiate energy to their surroundings, why don't the temperatures of all objects continuously decrease?

THINK INTEGRATED SCIENCE

6A—Entropy

31. What does it mean to say that energy becomes less useful when it is transformed?

32. What is the physicist's term for the measure of energy dispersal?

33. Consider the decomposition of water (H_2O) to form hydrogen (H_2) and oxygen (O_2). At room temperature, the products of this reaction have less entropy than the reactants. Is this reaction thermodynamically favored? Justify your answer.

34. A deer is a more concentrated form of energy than the grass it feeds on. Does this imply that the second law of thermodynamics is violated as the deer converts its food into tissue? Explain.

6B—Specific Heat Capacity and Earth's Climate

35. Northeastern Canada and much of Europe receive about the same amount of sunlight per unit area. Why, then, is Europe generally warmer in the winter months?

36. Iceland, so named to discourage conquest by expanding empires, is not ice-covered like Greenland and parts of Siberia, even though it is nearly on the Arctic Circle. The average winter temperature of Iceland is considerably higher than the temperatures of regions at the same latitude in eastern Greenland and central Siberia. Why is this so?

37. Why does the presence of large bodies of water tend to moderate the climate of nearby land—to make it warmer in cold weather and cooler in warm weather?

THINK AND DO (HANDS-ON APPLICATION)

38. Hold the bottom end of a test tube full of cold water in your hand. Heat the top part in a flame until the water boils. The fact that you can still hold the bottom shows that water is a poor conductor of heat. This is even more dramatic when you wedge chunks of ice at the bottom; then the water above can be brought to a boil without melting the ice. Try it and see.

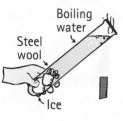

39. Wrap a piece of paper around a thick metal bar and place it in a flame. Note that the paper will not catch fire. Can you figure out why? (Paper will generally not ignite until its temperature reaches 233°C.)

40. Watch the spout of a teakettle of boiling water. Notice that you cannot see the steam that issues from the spout. The cloud that you see farther away from the spout is not steam but condensed water droplets. Now hold the flame of a candle in the cloud of condensed steam. Can you explain your observations?

PLUG AND CHUG (FORMULA FAMILIARIZATION)

$$Q = cm\Delta T$$

41. Show that 5000 cal is required to increase the temperature of 50 g of water from 0°C to 100°C. The specific heat capacity of water is 1 cal/g·°C.

42. Calculate the quantity of heat absorbed by 20 g of water that warms from 30°C to 90°C.

THINK AND COMPARE (ANALYSIS)

43. Rank the magnitudes of these units of thermal energy from greatest to least: (a) 1 calorie, (b) 1 Calorie, (c) 1 joule.

44. The precise volume of water in a beaker depends on the temperature of the water. Rank from greatest to least the volumes of water at these temperatures: (a) 0°C, (b) 4°C, (c) 10°C.

45. From best to worst, rank these materials as heat conductors: (a) copper wire, (b) snow, (c) a glass rod.

46. From greatest to least, rank the frequencies of radiation of these emitters of radiant energy: (a) red-hot star, (b) blue-hot star, (c) the Sun.

THINK AND SOLVE (MATHEMATICAL APPLICATION)

47. Pounding a nail into wood makes the nail warmer. Consider a 5-g steel nail 6 cm long and a hammer that exerts an average force of 500 N on the nail when it is being driven into a piece of wood. Show that the increase in the nail's temperature will be 13.3°C. (Assume that the specific heat capacity of steel is 450 J/kg·°C.)

48. If you wish to warm 100 kg of water by 20°C for your bath, show that 8370 kJ of heat is required.

49. The specific heat capacity of copper is 0.092 calorie per gram per degree Celsius. Show that the heat required to raise the temperature of a 10-g piece of copper from 0°C to 100°C is 92 calories.

50. When 100 g of 40°C iron nails is submerged in 100 g of 20°C water, show that the final temperature of the water will be 22.1°C. (The specific heat capacity of iron is 0.12 J/kg·°C. Here, you should equate the heat gained by the water to the heat lost by the nails.)

51. A 10-kg iron ball is dropped onto a pavement from a height of 100 m. If half the heat generated goes into warming the ball, show that the temperature increase of the ball will be 1.1°C. (In SI units, the specific heat capacity of iron is 450 J/kg·°C.) Why is the answer the same for an iron ball of any mass?

THINK AND EXPLAIN (SYNTHESIS)

52. Which is greater—an increase in temperature of 1°C or an increase of 1°F?

53. Which has the greater amount of thermal energy—an iceberg or a hot cup of coffee? Explain.

54. When air is rapidly compressed, why does its temperature increase?

55. What happens to the gas pressure within a sealed gallon can when it is heated? What happens to the pressure when the can is cooled? Why?

56. After a car has been driven for some distance, why does the air pressure in the tires increase?

57. Why doesn't adding the same amount of heat to two different objects necessarily produce the same increase in temperature?

58. Why will a watermelon stay cool for a longer time than sandwiches when both are removed from a cooler on a hot day?

59. Cite an exception to the claim that all substances expand when heated.

60. An old method for breaking boulders was to put them into a hot fire and then douse them with cold water. Why does this fracture the boulders?

61. A metal ball is just able to pass through a metal ring. When the ball is heated, however, it will not pass through the ring. What would happen if the ring, rather than the ball,

were heated? Would the size of the hole increase, stay the same, or decrease?

62. After a machinist very quickly slips a hot, snugly fitting iron ring over a very cold glass cylinder, there is no way that the two can be separated intact. Why is this so?

63. Suppose you cut a small gap in a metal ring. If you heat the ring, will the gap become wider or narrower?

64. Why is it important to protect water pipes so that they don't freeze?

65. If you wrap a fur coat around a thermometer, will its temperature rise?

66. If you hold one end of a nail against a piece of ice, the end in your hand soon becomes cold. Does cold flow from the ice to your hand? Explain.

67. From the rules that a good absorber of radiation is a good radiator and a good reflector is a poor absorber, state a rule relating the reflecting and radiating properties of a surface.

68. Suppose that, at a restaurant, you are served coffee before you are ready to drink it. So that it will be as warm as possible when you are ready to drink it, would you be wiser to add cream right away or to add it just before you are ready to drink it?

THINK AND DISCUSS (EVALUATION)

69. In your room, there are tables, chairs, other people, and other things. Discuss which of these things has a temperature (1) lower than, (2) higher than, (3) equal to the temperature of the air.

70. Discuss why you can't establish whether you are running a high temperature by touching your own forehead.

71. Use the laws of thermodynamics to defend the statement that 100% of the electrical energy that goes into lighting an incandescent lamp is converted into thermal energy.

72. If you drop a hot rock into a pail of water, the temperature of the rock and the water will change until both are equal. The rock will cool and the water will warm. Does

this hold true if the hot rock is dropped into the Atlantic Ocean? Discuss.

73. On cold winter nights in the old days it was common to bring a hot object to bed. Which would do a better job of keeping you warm through the cold night—a 10-kg iron brick or a 10-kg jug of hot water at the same temperature? Discuss.

74. Would you or the gas company gain by having gas warmed before it passes through your gas meter? Discuss.

75. Suppose that water instead of mercury is used in a thermometer. If the temperature is at 4°C and then changes, why can't the thermometer indicate whether the temperature is rising or falling?

76. In terms of physics, speculate as to why some restaurants serve baked potatoes wrapped in aluminum foil.

77. Wood is a better insulator than glass, yet fiberglass is commonly used as an insulator in wooden buildings. Discuss.

78. Visit a snow-covered cemetery and note that the snow does not slope upward against the gravestones but, instead, forms depressions around them, as shown. Can you think of a reason for this?

79. Why is it that you can safely hold your bare hand in a hot pizza oven for a few seconds, but, if you were to touch the metal inside, you'd burn yourself?

80. In a still room, smoke from a candle will sometimes rise only so far, not reaching the ceiling. Discuss.

81. After boiling a bit of water in a gallon can and then sealing the can when water vapor has driven out most of the air, Dan Johnson and his class watch the can slowly crumple. Discuss the role of condensation of water vapor inside the can. What does the crumpling?

READINESS ASSURANCE TEST (RAT)

If you have a good handle on this chapter, then you should be able to score at least 7 out of 10 on this RAT. If you score less than 7, you need to study further before moving on.

Choose the BEST answer to each of the following:

1. When scientists discuss kinetic energy per molecule, the concept being discussed is
   (a) temperature.
   (b) heat.
   (c) thermal energy.
   (d) entropy.

2. In a mixture of hydrogen gas, oxygen gas, and nitrogen gas, the molecules with the greatest average speed are those of
   (a) hydrogen.
   (b) oxygen.
   (c) nitrogen.
   (d) All have the same speed.

3. Your garage gets messier every day. In this case entropy is
   (a) decreasing.
   (b) increasing.
   (c) holding steady.
   (d) none of these

4. The specific heat capacity of aluminum is more than twice that of copper. If equal quantities of heat are added to equal masses of aluminum and copper, the metal that more rapidly increases in temperature is
   (a) aluminum.
   (b) copper.
   (c) Both increase at the same rate.
   (d) none of these

5. A bimetallic strip used in thermostats relies on the fact that different metals have different
   (a) specific heat capacities.
   (b) thermal energies at different temperatures.
   (c) rates of thermal expansion.
   (d) all of these

6. Water at 4°C will expand when it is
   (a) slightly cooled.
   (b) slightly warmed.
   (c) both cooled and warmed.
   (d) neither cooled nor warmed.

7. The principal reason one can walk barefoot on red-hot wood coals without burning the feet has to do with
   (a) the low temperature of the coals.
   (b) the low thermal conductivity of the coals.
   (c) mind-over-matter techniques.
   (d) none of these

8. Thermal convection is linked mostly to
   (a) radiant energy.
   (b) fluids.
   (c) insulators.
   (d) all of these

9. Which of these electromagnetic waves has the lowest frequency?
   (a) infrared
   (b) visible
   (c) ultraviolet
   (d) gamma rays

10. Compared with terrestrial radiation, the radiation from the Sun has
    (a) a longer wavelength.
    (b) a lower frequency.
    (c) both a longer wavelength and a lower frequency.
    (d) neither a longer wavelength nor a lower frequency.

Answers to RAT

1. a, 2. a, 3. b, 4. b, 5. c, 6. c, 7. b, 8. b, 9. a, 10. d

CHAPTER 5
The Universe

O N A moonless night and away from city lights the unaided eye sees no more than 3000 stars, horizon to horizon. Many more stars become visible with a telescope, especially when the telescope is pointed toward a cloudlike band of light that stretches north to south. The ancient Greeks called this diffuse band of light the Milky Way.

Today we know that the Milky Way is a vast collection of more than 100 billion stars. When viewed from afar, all of these stars—along with our own star, the Sun—appear as a great swirl of stars known as a *galaxy*.

In this chapter we will explore the nature of stars—how they form, how they die, and how they are organized within galaxies. We will explore how there are many different types of stars, just as there are many different types of galaxies. We will conclude with a discussion of cosmology, in which we attempt to answer such questions as How did the universe come into being? and What might be its ultimate fate?

5.1   Observing the Night Sky

EXPLAIN THIS   When can winter constellations be seen in the summer?

Early astronomers divided the night sky into groups of stars called *constellations*. The names of the constellations today carry over mainly from the names assigned to them by early Greek, Babylonian, and Egyptian astronomers. The Greeks, for example, included the stars of the Big Dipper in a larger group of stars that outlined a bear. The large constellation Ursa Major (the Great Bear) is illustrated in Figure 5.1. The groupings of stars and the significance given to them have varied from culture to culture. To some cultures, the constellations stimulated storytelling and the making of great myths; to other cultures, the constellations honored great heroes, such as Hercules and Orion; to yet others, they served as navigational aids for travelers and sailors. To many cultures, including the African Bushmen and Masai, the constellations provided a guide for planting and harvesting crops because they were seen to move in the sky in concert with the seasons. Charts of this periodic movement became some of the first calendars. We can see in Figure 5.2 why the background of stars varies throughout the year.

The stars are at different distances from Earth. However, because all the stars are so far away, they appear equally remote. This illusion led the ancient Greeks and others to conceive of the stars as being attached to a gigantic sphere surrounding Earth, called the **celestial sphere**. Though we know it is imaginary, the celestial sphere is still a useful construction for visualizing the motions of the stars (Figure 5.3).

The stars appear to turn around an imaginary north–south axis. This is the *diurnal motion* of the stars. Diurnal motion is easy to visualize as a rotation of the celestial sphere from east to west. This motion is a consequence of the daily counterclockwise rotation of Earth on its axis. When we speak of the diurnal motion of the stars, we are referring to the motions of celestial objects as a

LEARNING OBJECTIVE
Distinguish between the diurnal and intrinsic motions of celestial objects, and express the vast distances in space in units of light-years.

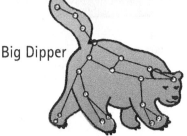

FIGURE 5.1
The constellation Ursa Major, the Great Bear. The seven stars in the tail and back of Ursa Major form the Big Dipper.

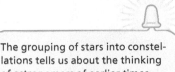

The grouping of stars into constellations tells us about the thinking of astronomers of earlier times, but it tells us nothing about the stars themselves.

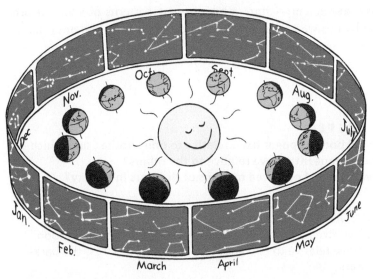

FIGURE 5.2
The night side of Earth always faces away from the Sun. As Earth circles the Sun, different parts of the universe are seen in the nighttime sky. Here the circle, representing 1 year, is divided into 12 parts—the monthly constellations. The stars in the nighttime sky change in a yearly cycle.

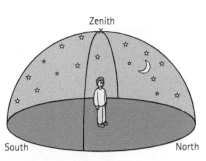

FIGURE 5.3
The celestial sphere is an imaginary sphere to which the stars are attached. We see no more than half of the celestial sphere at any given time. The point directly over your head at any time is called the *zenith*.

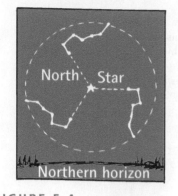

FIGURE 5.4
The pair of stars in the end of the Big Dipper's bowl point to the North Star. Earth rotates about its axis and therefore about the North Star, so over a 24-hour period the Big Dipper (and other surrounding star groups) makes a complete revolution.

FIGURE 5.5
A time exposure of the northern night sky.

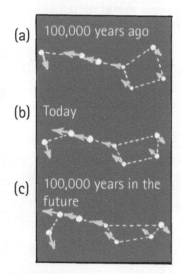

FIGURE 5.6
The present pattern of the Big Dipper is temporary. Here we can see its pattern (a) 100,000 years ago; (b) as it appears at present; and (c) as it will appear in the future, about 100,000 years from now.

whole; this motion does not change the relative positions of objects. Figure 5.4 shows the diurnal motion of the stars making up the Big Dipper. Time-exposure photographs show that the Big Dipper appears to move in circles around the North Star (Figure 5.5). The North Star appears nearly stationary as the celestial sphere rotates because it lies very close to the projection of Earth's rotational axis.

In addition to the diurnal motion of the sky, there is *intrinsic motion* of certain bodies that change their positions with respect to the stars. The Sun, the Moon, and planets, called "wanderers" by ancient astronomers, appear to migrate across the fixed backdrop of the celestial sphere. Interestingly, the stars themselves have intrinsic motion. They are so far away, however, that this motion is not apparent on the time scale of a human life. As shown in Figure 5.6, over thousands of years, the intrinsic movement of stars results in new patterns of stars. In other words, the constellations we see today are quite different from the ones that appeared to our earliest ancestors.

CHECK YOURSELF
1. **Which celestial bodies appear fixed relative to one another, and which celestial bodies appear to move relative to the others?**
2. **What are two types of observed motions of the stars in the sky?**

CHECK YOUR ANSWERS
1. The stars appear fixed as they move across the sky. The Sun, the Moon, and planets move relative to one another as they move across the backdrop of the stars.
2. One type of motion of the stars is their nightly rotation as if they were painted on a rotating celestial sphere; this is due to Earth's rotation on its own axis. Stars also appear to undergo a yearly cycle around the Sun because of Earth's revolution about the Sun.

Some stars on the celestial sphere are actually much farther away than others from Earth. Astronomers measure the vast distances between Earth and the stars using *light-years*. One **light-year** is the distance that light travels in 1 year, nearly 10 trillion km. For perspective, the diameter of Neptune's orbit is about 0.001 light-year. The distance from the Sun to the outer edges of the Oort cloud (the full radius of our solar system) is about 0.8 light-year. The star closest to our Sun, Proxima Centauri, is about 4.2 light-years away. The diameter of the Milky Way galaxy is about 100,000 light-years. The next closest major galaxy, the Andromeda galaxy, is about 2.3 million light-years distant. Figure 5.7 shows the distances to the seven stars making up the Big Dipper in light-years.

The speed of light is 3×10^8 m/s. Although this is very fast, it nevertheless takes light appreciable time to travel large distances. And so, when you see the light emitted by a very distant object, you are actually seeing the light it emitted long ago—you are looking back in time. Consider the example of Supernova 1987a (a supernova is the explosion of a star, as you will learn more about in Section 5.4). This supernova occurred in a galaxy 190,000 light-years from Earth. Although we witnessed the supernova in 1987, the light from this explosion took 190,000 years to reach our planet, so the explosion actually occurred 190,000 years earlier. "News" of the supernova took 190,000 years to reach Earth!

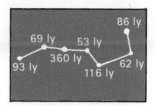

FIGURE 5.7
The seven stars of the Big Dipper are at distances from Earth. Note their distances in light-years (ly).

5.2 The Brightness and Color of Stars

EXPLAIN THIS How do astronomers gauge the temperature of a star?

Stars are born from clouds of interstellar dust with roughly the same chemical composition as the Sun (see Chapter 6). About three-fourths of the interstellar material from which a star forms is hydrogen; one-fourth is helium; and no more than 2% of the material from which a star forms consists of heavier chemical elements. Stars shine brilliantly for millions or billions of years because of the nuclear fusion reactions that occur in their cores. And all stars, the Sun included, ultimately exhaust their nuclear fuel and die. Yet not all stars are the same. If you look into the night sky, you will see that stars differ in two very visible ways: brightness and color.

Brightness relates to how much energy a star produces. However, although a star's brightness is related to its energy output, its brightness also depends on how far away it is from Earth. Recall from earlier chapters inverse-square laws; in this case, the intensity of light diminishes as the reciprocal of the square of the distance from the source. For example, the stars Betelgeuse and Procyon appear equally bright even though Betelgeuse emits about 5000 times as much light as Procyon. The reason? Procyon is much closer to Earth than Betelgeuse is.

To avoid confusing brightness with energy output, astronomers clearly distinguish between apparent brightness and the more important property, *luminosity*. Apparent brightness is the brightness of a star as it appears to our eyes. Luminosity, on the other hand, is the total amount of light energy that a star emits into space. Luminosity is usually expressed relative to the Sun's luminosity, which is noted L_{Sun}. For example, the luminosity of Betelgeuse is 38,000 L_{Sun}. This indicates that Betelgeuse is a very luminous star emitting about 38,000 times as much energy each second into space as the Sun. On the other hand, Proxima Centauri is quite dim, with a luminosity of 0.00006 L_{Sun}. Astronomers have

LEARNING OBJECTIVE
Distinguish between a star's apparent brightness and its luminosity, and identify its temperature by its color.

FIGURE 5.8
Most of the stars in this photograph are approximately the same distance—2000 light-years—from the center of the Milky Way galaxy. A star's color indicates its surface temperature—a blue star is hotter than a yellow star, and a yellow star is hotter than a red star. This photo was taken by the Hubble Telescope.

measured the luminosity of many stars and found that stars vary greatly in this respect. The Sun is somewhere in the middle of the luminosity range. The most luminous stars are about a million times as luminous as the Sun, while the dimmest stars produce about 1/10,000 as much energy per second as the Sun.

Besides apparent brightness, color is another property that varies widely among stars. Figure 5.8, a photograph of stars taken with the Hubble Telescope, shows that stars come in every color of the rainbow. A star's color directly tells you about its surface temperature—for example, a blue star is hotter than a yellow star, and a yellow star is hotter than a red star. In fact, astronomers use color to measure the temperatures of stars. Why is it that a star's color corresponds to its temperature?

Radiation Curves of Stars

As you learned in Chapters 4, all objects that have a temperature emit energy in the form of electromagnetic radiation. The peak frequency $\overline{f}$ of the radiation is directly proportional to the absolute temperature T of the emitter:

$$\overline{f} \sim T$$

Stars have different colors because they emit different frequencies of electromagnetic waves in the visible range. Our eyes sense different frequencies of visible radiation as different colors. Figure 5.9 shows the radiation curves, which are graphs of the intensity of emitted radiation versus wavelength, for two stars of the same size with different temperatures. The radiation curves show that the hotter a star is, the shorter the wavelength of its peak frequency and the bluer it looks. So the blue stars in the night sky have higher temperatures than the red ones. The Sun, for example, with its approximately 5800 K surface temperature, emits most strongly in the middle of the visible spectrum and so appears yellow.

FYI Interestingly, the Earth's atmosphere is transparent to a narrow band of light centered upon the Sun's peak frequency. Creatures here on Earth's surface evolved to be sensitive to these most abundant frequencies, which we now perceive as visible light. Within the spectrum of visible light we are most sensitive to a greenish-yellow, which is why many emergency vehicles are commonly painted greenish-yellow.

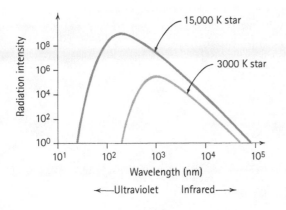

FIGURE 5.9
These radiation curves for stars of the same size and different surface temperatures show two important facts: (1) hotter stars emit radiation with higher average frequency than cooler stars, and (2) hotter stars emit more radiation per unit surface area at every frequency than cooler stars.

Betelgeuse, on the other hand, appears red because of its cooler surface temperature (about 3400 K). Betelgeuse emits more red light than blue light.

Notice also from Figure 5.9 that the hotter a star is, the more radiant energy it emits. Thus we see that hot blue stars are more luminous than cooler red stars of the same size.

CHECK YOURSELF
The temperature of Sirius is about 9400 K. What color is this star—and why?

CHECK YOUR ANSWER
Sirius has a slightly blue color. It emits more blue light than red light because of its high surface temperature.

5.3   The Hertzsprung–Russell Diagram

EXPLAIN THIS When is a cool star larger than a hot star?

When you compare the luminosity of stars to their temperature, interesting patterns emerge. Early in the 20th century, Danish astronomer Ejnar Hertzsprung and American astronomer Henry Norris Russell did just this. They produced a diagram known as the **Hertzsprung–Russell diagram**, or **H–R diagram**, which is of key importance in astronomy (Figure 5.10). The H–R diagram is a plot of the luminosity versus surface temperature of stars. Luminous stars are near the top of the diagram, and dim stars are toward the bottom. Hot bluish stars are toward the left side of the diagram, and cool reddish stars are toward the right side.

The H–R diagram shows several distinct regions of stars. Most stars are plotted on the band that stretches diagonally across the diagram. This band is called the **main sequence**. Stars on the main sequence, including our Sun, generate energy by fusing hydrogen to helium. As we would expect, the hottest main-sequence stars are the brightest and bluest stars and the coolest main-sequence

LEARNING OBJECTIVE
Describe the relationship between stellar luminosity and surface temperature as portrayed in the Hertzsprung–Russell diagram.

Because the giants and supergiants are so luminous, they are easy to see in the night sky even if they are not close to Earth. You can often identify them by their reddish color.

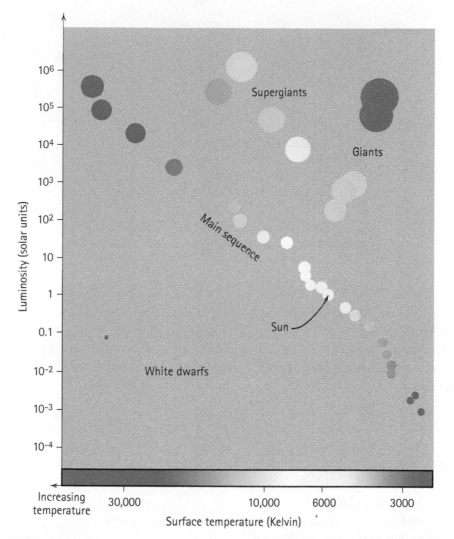

FIGURE 5.10

The H–R diagram shows a star's surface temperature on the horizontal axis and its luminosity on the vertical axis. The giant and supergiant stars shown here as circles are not drawn to scale. The red supergiant, Antares, for example, is so large that, if drawn to scale, it would reach the ceiling of your classroom. Interestingly, although the radius of Antares is 700 times that of our Sun, its mass is only about 15 times greater. So, Antares is much larger, but it is also much less dense.

FYI The H–R diagram is to astro-physicists what the periodic table is to chemists—an extremely important tool. A star's position on the H–R diagram can reveal its age. The age of our galaxy can be estimated by looking at the positions of our oldest stars and their white-dwarf remnants.

stars are the most dim and red stars. Take a moment to locate the Sun on the H–R diagram. Can you see that the Sun is a roughly average main-sequence star in terms of its luminosity and temperature?

Toward the upper right of the diagram is a distinct group of stars—the **giant stars**. These stars clearly do not follow the pattern of the hydrogen-burning main-sequence stars. Because these stars are red, we know they must have low surface temperatures. If they were main-sequence stars, the giants would be dim. Yet notice how high the giants are on the luminosity scale—they are very bright. The fact that the giants are both much cooler and much brighter than the Sun tells us that these stars must also be much larger than the Sun. (Hence the name *giant*.) Above the giants on the H–R diagram are a few rare stars, the *supergiants*. The supergiants are even larger and brighter than the giants. As you will see in the next section, the giants and supergiants are stars nearing the end of their lives because the fuel in their cores is running out.

Toward the lower left are some stars that are so dim they cannot be seen with the unaided eye. The surfaces of these stars can be hotter than the Sun, which makes them blue or white. Yet their luminosities are quite low—on the order of $0.1L_{Sun}$ to $0.0001L_{Sun}$. To be so hot and radiate so little light, these stars must be very small—they are called the **white dwarfs**. White dwarfs are typically the size of Earth or even smaller, yet they have mass comparable to the Sun. The density (or mass per volume) of a white dwarf is thus extremely high—about a million g/cm^3. For comparison, gold has a density of about 19 g/cm^3, while the average density of Earth is about 5.4 g/cm^3. As you will learn in the next section, white dwarfs are dead stars, the remnants of stars that have exhausted their nuclear fuel.

CHECK YOURSELF

1. What characteristic do all main-sequence stars share?
2. Giant stars have cool surface temperatures yet are highly luminous. Does this mean that the frequency of light emitted by a giant star does not depend on its surface temperature as described by Figure 5.9?

CHECK YOUR ANSWERS

1. All main-sequence stars generate energy by the nuclear fusion of hydrogen to helium.
2. No, radiation curves hold for a giant star as for any other radiating body. Giants do have a relatively low energy output per unit surface area; they are highly luminous only because they are very large.

SCIENCE AND SOCIETY

Astrology

There is more than one way to view the cosmos and its processes—astronomy is one and astrology is another. Astrology is a belief system that began more than 2000 years ago in Babylonia. Astrology has survived nearly unchanged since the second century AD, when some revisions were made by Egyptians and Greeks who believed that their gods moved heavenly bodies to influence the lives of people on Earth. Astrology today holds that the position of Earth in its orbit around the Sun at the time of birth, combined with the relative positions of the planets, has some influence over one's personal life. The stars and planets are said to affect such personal things as one's character, marriage, friendships, wealth, and death.

Could the force of gravity exerted by these celestial bodies be a legitimate factor in human affairs? After all, the ocean tides are the result of the Moon's and Sun's positions, and the gravitational pulls between the planets perturb one another's orbits. Because slight variations in gravity produce these effects, might not slight variations in the planetary positions at the time of birth affect a newborn? If the influence of stars and planets is gravitational, then credit must also be given to the effect of the gravitational pull between the newborn and Earth itself. This pull is enormously greater than the combined pull of all the planets, even when lined up in a row (as occasionally happens). The gravitational influence of the hospital building on the newborn far exceeds that of the distant planets. So planetary gravitation cannot be an underlying agent for astrology.

Astrology is not a science because it doesn't change with new information as science does, nor are its predictions borne out by experiment. Rather, its predictions depend on coincidence and also on the tendency of many people to seek external explanations for their fates or personal behaviors. Astrological beliefs are built on anecdotal evidence that is neither reproducible nor testable. Astrology means different things to different people, but in any case, it is outside the realm of science. It is a pseudoscience lying within the realm of superstition.

LEARNING OBJECTIVE
Use the Hertzsprung–Russell diagram to summarize the stages of stellar development from initial formation to an ultimate fate, such as supernovae.

MasteringPhysics®
TUTORIAL: Stellar Evolution
VIDEO: Lives of Stars

UNIFYING CONCEPT
● *The Gravitational Force*
  Section 5.3

FIGURE 5.11
This image of the Trifid Nebula was obtained by the Spitzer Space Telescope. This nebula is located 5400 light-years from Earth in the constellation Sagittarius. Within each of the red dust clouds are developing stars.

5.4   The Life Cycles of Stars

EXPLAIN THIS Why doesn't a neutron star emit beta particles?

In Chapter 6, we discussed the nebular theory, which explains how the Sun formed from an expansive, low-density cloud of gas and dust called a *nebula* (Figure 5.11). Other stars are also thought to form in the same way. That is, over time, a nebula flattens, heats, and spins more rapidly as it gravitationally contracts. Furthermore, the center of the nebula becomes dense enough to trap infrared radiation so that this energy is no longer radiated away. The hot central bulge of a nebula is called a *protostar*.

Mutual gravitation between the gaseous particles in a protostar results in an overall contraction of this huge ball of gas, and its density increases still further as matter is crunched together, with an accompanying rise in pressure and temperature. When the central temperature reaches about 10 million K, hydrogen nuclei begin fusing to form helium nuclei. This thermonuclear reaction, converting hydrogen into helium, releases an enormous amount of radiant and thermal energy, as discussed in Chapter 6. The ignition of nuclear fuel marks the change from protostar to star. Outward-moving radiant energy and the gas accompanying it exert an outward pressure called *thermal pressure* on the contracting matter. When nuclear fusion occurs fast enough, thermal pressure becomes strong enough to halt the gravitational contraction. At this point, outward thermal pressure balances inward gravitational pressure, and the star's size stabilizes.

CHECK YOURSELF
What do the processes of thermonuclear fusion and gravitational contraction have to do with the physical size of a star?

CHECK YOUR ANSWER
The size of a star is the result of these two continually competing processes. Energy from thermonuclear fusion tends to blow the star outward like a hydrogen bomb explosion, and gravitation tends to contract its matter in an implosion. The outward thermonuclear expansion and inward gravitational contraction produce an equilibrium that accounts for the star's size.

Though all stars are born in the same way from contracting nebulae, they do not all progress through their lives in the same way. A star's mass determines the stages a star will go through from birth to death. There are limits on the mass that a star can attain. A protostar with a mass less than 0.08 times the mass of the Sun (0.08 M_{Sun}) never reaches the 10 million K threshold needed for sustained fusion of hydrogen. On the other hand, stars with masses above 100 M_{Sun} would undergo fusion at such a furious rate that gravity could not resist thermal pressure and the star would explode. So stars exist within the limits of about a tenth of the mass of the Sun and 100 times the solar mass.*

---

*One solar mass, $1M_{Sun}$, is a unit of mass equivalent to that of the Sun: 2×10^{30} kg.

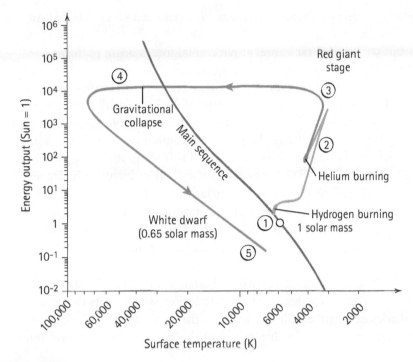

FIGURE 5.12

The stages of the Sun's life cycle are plotted on this H–R diagram. The short segment labeled Hydrogen burning lasts about 10 billion years. The later segments are much shorter.

Most stars have masses not very different from that of the Sun. Such stars inhabit a central place on the main sequence of the H–R diagram. If you plot the life-cycle stages of average stars on an H–R diagram, they trace a curve similar to the one for our Sun, which is shown in Figure 5.12. The Sun was born about 4.5 billion years ago at position 1, when the fusion of hydrogen ignited. The Sun will spend most of its lifetime—some 10 billion years—on the main sequence, with thermal pressure keeping gravity at bay. Speaking more generally, a star's hydrogen-burning lifetime lasts for a period of a few million to 50 billion years, depending on its mass.

More-massive stars have shorter lives than less-massive stars. This may sound counterintuitive, because if stars have more mass, they have more fuel to burn longer, right? High-mass stars, however, are more luminous than low-mass stars, meaning that they burn their hydrogen fusion fuel at a faster rate. Massive stars *must* be more luminous than small-mass stars so that the outward pressure of their nuclear fusion can offset the greater gravitational force of their contraction. Massive stars start out with more hydrogen fuel than small-mass stars, but they consume their fuel so much faster that they die billions of years younger than smaller stars.

No star lasts forever. In the old age of an average-mass star like our Sun, the nuclear fusion within the core eventually comes to a halt. This happens because the core has run out of hydrogen, which has been transformed into helium. But might this helium within the core start fusing to form heavier elements? The answer is no, because the temperatures within the core are not yet hot enough. Recall that each helium nucleus has two positively charged protons. Helium nuclei repel each other much more strongly than hydrogen

A star's life cycle depends on its mass. The lowest-mass stars are brown dwarfs, dim but long-lived stars. Medium-mass stars progress from main-sequence stars to red giants or supergiants, then to white dwarfs. Very massive stars have short lives and die in massive explosions called *supernovae*.

nuclei. Much higher temperatures, therefore, are required to enable helium atoms to start fusing.

As fusion stops within the star's core, gravitational forces begin to dominate, and this causes the star to contract. This contraction, however, soon heats up the hydrogen that was lying outside the core to temperatures sufficient for nuclear fusion. The result is a star with a core of helium "ash" surrounded by a shell of fusing hydrogen. It is interesting that the rate of fusion within this shell is quite high, which causes the star to become more luminous. This pushes the star off of the main sequence of the H–R diagram, as shown by the green line in Figure 5.12. Furthermore, as the shell of burning hydrogen grows outward, the size of the star begins to inflate dramatically, creating what is called a red giant (position 2). When our Sun reaches this giant stage about 5 billion years from now, its swelling and increased energy output will elevate Earth's temperature. Earth will be stripped of its atmosphere and the oceans boiled dry. Ouch!

Eventually, the fusion of hydrogen within the red giant begins to diminish. This allows gravity to dominate, leading to a contraction, which heats the core to a temperature sufficient to ignite helium burning—the fusion of helium to carbon. This causes another increase in the luminosity of the star, as shown by position 3 in Figure 5.12.

For a star like our Sun, as helium fusion continues, carbon accumulates in the core, but temperatures will never become hot enough to allow the carbon to undergo fusion. Instead, carbon "ash" accumulates inside the star and fusion gradually tapers off. Then gravity predominates and the star contracts, which boosts its temperature. With higher temperatures, the color of the shrinking Sun will shift from red to blue and its position will shift to the left in the H–R diagram (position 4).

When our Sun turns into a red giant billions of years from now, its diameter will encompass the orbit of Venus.

CHECK YOURSELF
Why does a star shrink when its core runs out of nuclear fuel?

CHECK YOUR ANSWER
Outward thermal expansion and inward gravitational contraction produce an equilibrium that accounts for the star's size. As the heat from the inner thermonuclear reactions begins to die down, gravity predominates and the star shrinks. Upon shrinking, matter becomes compressed, which is an additional source of heat to ignite further nuclear fusion. For a star the size of our Sun, compression raises the temperature enough to fuse elements to carbon. The fusion of heavier elements in our Sun, however, is not possible.

Astronomers have found evidence suggesting that the carbon within the center of many white dwarfs crystallizes into diamond. They expect that when our Sun transforms into a white dwarf 5 billion years from now, its ember core will crystallize as well, leaving a planet-sized diamond at the center of our solar system.

Our fuel-exhausted Sun will continue to shrink until the electrons within the Sun are so squeezed that they resist any further compression. Having spent all of its nuclear fuel, our dead Sun, now quite small, will no longer be producing energy (position 5).

As our Sun goes through this final collapse, the layers of plasma and gas surrounding the core will be ejected in a brilliant display, forming what is called a **planetary nebula** (Figure 5.13). Despite its name, a planetary nebula has nothing to do with planets. The name is derived from the fact that the planetary nebula looks like a nebula from which planets could form. The planetary nebula, however, will disperse within a million years, leaving the Sun's cooling carbon core behind as a white dwarf. White dwarfs have the mass of a star but the volume of a planet, and are thus far more dense than anything on Earth. Because the nuclear fires of a white dwarf have burned out, it is not actually a star anymore, but is more accurately called a *stellar remnant*. In any case, a white dwarf cools for eons in space until it becomes too cold to radiate visible light (Figure 5.14).

Novae and Supernovae

There is another possible fate for a white dwarf, if it is part of a *binary star*. A binary star is a double star—a system of two stars that revolve about a common center, just as Earth and the Moon revolve about each other. If a white dwarf is a binary and close enough to its partner, the white dwarf may gravitationally pull hydrogen from its companion star. It then deposits this material on its own surface as a very dense hydrogen layer. Continued compacting increases the temperature of this layer, which ignites to embroil the white dwarf's surface in a thermonuclear blast that we see as a **nova**, which appears in the nighttime sky as a new star (*nova* is Latin for "new"). A nova is an event, not a stellar object. After a while, a nova subsides until enough matter accumulates to repeat the event. A given nova flares up at irregular intervals that may range from decades to hundreds of thousands of years.

Although low- and medium-mass stars become white dwarfs, the fate of stars more massive than about 10 M_{Sun} is quite different. When such a massive star contracts after its giant or supergiant phase, more heat is generated than in the contraction of a small star. Such a star does not shrink to become a white dwarf. Instead, carbon nuclei in its core fuse and liberate energy while synthesizing heavier elements, such as neon and magnesium. Thermal pressure halts further gravitational contraction until all the carbon is fused. Then the core of the star contracts again to produce even higher temperatures, and a new fusion series produces even heavier elements. The fusion cycles repeat until the element iron is formed.

Fusion of elements with atomic numbers higher than those of iron consumes energy rather than liberating energy. (The reason for this, as you may recall from Chapter 3, is that the average mass per nucleon is lower for iron than for any other element.) Once nuclei transform into iron, the fusion process stops. Thermal expansion that pushes against gravity, therefore, also stops. Gravity thus predominates and the entire star begins its final contraction.

Recall that with a dying medium-sized star, such as our Sun, contraction continues until gravity is counteracted by the resistance of electrons. With a supermassive supergiant, however, the gravitational forces are strong enough to overcome this resistance. The electrons, however, do not merge into one another. Instead, they combine with protons to form neutrons. What happens next is an astounding event called a **supernova**. Within minutes, the supergiant's iron core, about the size of Earth, collapses into a ball of neutrons only several kilometers in diameter. Massive amounts of energy are released—enough to outshine an entire galaxy. During this brief time of abundant energy, the heavy elements beyond iron are synthesized, as protons and neutrons outside the core mash into other nuclei to produce such elements as silver, gold, and uranium. These heavy elements are less abundant than the lighter elements because of the brief time available for synthesizing them.

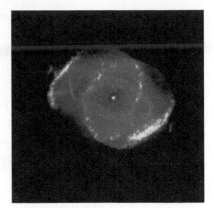

FIGURE 5.13
The Cat's Eye planetary nebula, seen here with the Hubble Space Telescope, measures about 1.2 light-years across, which is about a thousand times the diameter of Neptune's orbit. This planetary nebula is about 3000 light-years away, which places it within our galaxy. Clearly visible are the hot gases exploding away from the central Sun-sized star, which is in the process of transforming into a white dwarf.

FIGURE 5.14
A white dwarf, shown here in an artist's sketch, is the final stage in the evolution of low- and medium-mass stars. After a star has used all its nuclear fuel, its outer layers escape into space, leaving the dense core behind as a white dwarf. The strong gravitational field of a white dwarf causes it to attract matter from surrounding space to form an accretion disk. The disk is heated by friction where it meets the star, causing it to glow brightly.

FYI Do planets also orbit other stars? The answer is a resounding yes. These "exoplanets" reveal themselves by causing slight but detectable wobbles in the star they orbit. In some cases, the exoplanet transits in front of the star, which causes the star to become slightly dimmer, again at detectable levels. More than a thousand exoplanets have so far been discovered. Most are Jupiter-sized planets, but some near-Earth-sized planets have also been detected, such as Gliese 581g, which is about 20 light-years distant.

Most of the energy during the collapse of the iron core is released in the form of *neutrinos*—nearly massless subatomic particles that rarely interact with matter. Concentrations of neutrinos released from the collapse of the iron core are great enough to blow the outer shells of the star outward at speeds in excess of 10,000 km/s, which is fast enough to travel 1 AU in about four hours. Over time, this supernova wind of heavy elements spreads to far reaches of the galaxy where the elements are taken in by nebulae destined to become new stars. The gold and platinum we wear for jewelry here on Earth, as well as the bulk of Earth itself, are dust from supernovae that exploded many years before our solar system came to be.

CHECK YOURSELF

A star can undergo a nova more than once. Can a star also go through multiple supernovae? Why or why not?

CHECK YOUR ANSWER

A nova is a thermonuclear explosion that occurs when a white dwarf collects sufficient mass from a very close neighboring star. As long as the neighboring star provides mass, this explosion can be repeated multiple times. A supernova is such an energetic release of energy that it is an end-all event occurring never more than once for a particular supergiant star.

A supernova flares up to millions of times its former brightness. In AD 1054, Chinese astronomers recorded their observation of a star so bright that it could be seen by day as well as by night. This was a supernova (a "super new star"), its glowing plasma remnants now making up the spectacular Crab Nebula, shown in Figure 5.15. A less spectacular but more recent supernova was witnessed in 1987. The progress of this supernova, shown in Figure 5.16, has been very carefully monitored by modern scientific equipment.

FIGURE 5.15
The Crab Nebula is the remnant of a supernova explosion first observed on Earth in AD 1054. The explosion took place within our galaxy at a distance of about 7000 light-years from Earth. Had the blast occurred within 50 light-years, most life on Earth would have likely gone extinct. Is there any nemesis star right now within this limit ready to supernova? We know of none now, but check the Internet for information about Betelgeuse, which lies some 500 light-years away.

The superdense neutron core that remains after the supernova is called a **neutron star**. In accord with the law of conservation of angular momentum, these tiny bodies, with densities hundreds of millions times greater than those of white dwarfs, can spin at fantastic speeds. Neutron stars provide an explanation for the existence of *pulsars*. **Pulsars**, thought to be neutron stars, are rapidly varying sources of low-frequency radio emissions. As a pulsar spins, the beam of radiation it emits sweeps across the sky. If the beam sweeps over Earth, we detect its pulses. Of the approximately 300 known pulsars, only a few have been found emitting X-rays or visible light. One is in the center of the Crab Nebula (Figure 5.17). It has one of the highest rotational speeds of any pulsar studied, rotating more than 30 times per second. This thousand-year-old pulsar is relatively young. It is theorized that X-rays and visible light are emitted only during a pulsar's early history.

We saw earlier that a medium-sized star, such as our Sun, can collapse no further than a white dwarf because the force of gravity is not strong enough to overcome the resistance of electrons, which refuse to trespass into the quantum states of neighboring electrons. Similarly, a neutron star stops collapsing because neutrons, like electrons, resist trespassing into their neighboring neutrons. For a dying star, however, the bigger they are, the harder they fall. When the collapsing star is the biggest of the big, gravitational forces can be strong enough to overcome even the resistance of neutrons. The collapse continues beyond the stage of a neutron star, and the star disappears altogether from the observable universe. What is left is a *black hole*.

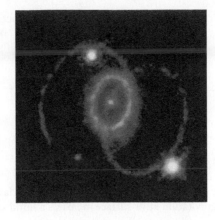

FIGURE 5.16
This image of the 1987A supernova was captured by the Hubble Telescope about 20 years after the initial explosion was sighted. Note the development of the ring systems, which continue to expand outward. This supernova occurred safely outside the Milky Way galaxy some 160,000 light-years away within a nearby smaller galaxy called the Large Magellanic Cloud. Some of its neutrinos were detected on Earth.

UNIFYING CONCEPT

● *The Law of Conservation of Momentum*
Section 4.4

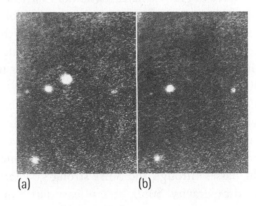

(a)   (b)

FIGURE 5.17
The pulsar in the Crab Nebula rotates like a searchlight, beaming visible light and X-rays toward Earth about 30 times per second, blinking on and off: (a) pulsar on, (b) pulsar off.

A neutron star is a kilometer-sized atomic nucleus!

5.5 Black Holes

EXPLAIN THIS What happens to a light beam bouncing between two upright and perfectly parallel mirrors here on Earth?

A **black hole** is the remains of a supergiant star that has collapsed into itself. Upon this collapse, the force of gravity at the surface increases dramatically. Consider this from the perspective of Newton's law of gravity. According to this law, as discussed in Section 5.3, the force of gravity depends on the inverse square of the distance. If a star collapses to a tenth of its original size, the distance between the surface and the center of the star is one-tenth as much. The inverse square of one-tenth $(1/0.1^2)$ equals 100. The

LEARNING OBJECTIVE
Identify the major attributes of black holes, such as the photon sphere, event horizon, and singularity.

MasteringPhysics®
TUTORIAL: Black Holes

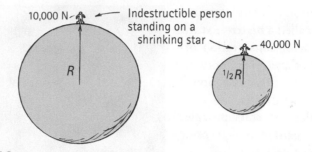

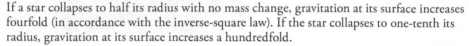

FIGURE 5.18
If a star collapses to half its radius with no mass change, gravitation at its surface increases fourfold (in accordance with the inverse-square law). If the star collapses to one-tenth its radius, gravitation at its surface increases a hundredfold.

FYI Contrary to stories about black holes, they're nonaggressive and don't reach out and swallow objects at a distance. Their gravitational fields are no stronger than the original fields about the stars before their collapse—except at distances less than the radius of the original star. If they don't get too close, black holes shouldn't worry future astronauts.

weight at the surface, therefore, is 100 times as much, as suggested in Figure 5.18. So the gravitational force at the surface of a collapsing star increases because the star is getting smaller.

As the force of gravity increases, so does the *escape speed*. For planet Earth, the escape speed is 11.2 km/s. This means that an object shot outward at 11.2 km/s (about 25,000 mi/h) will never fall back to Earth. The escape speed from the surface of our Sun is 618 km/s. For a supergiant star that has collapsed past the neutron star stage, the escape speed increases to the speed of light, which is 300,000 km/s.

In the early 20th century, Einstein proposed that light, like matter, is affected by gravity. We don't normally witness light being affected by gravity because light moves so fast, but with careful observations the influence is quite measurable. Starlight grazing the eclipsed Sun, for example, is seen to bend inward as the light passes through the Sun's strong gravitational field. So light is pulled downward by gravity. Sunlight can leave our Sun because the speed of light is much greater than the escape velocity. If a star such as our Sun, however, were to collapse to a radius of 3 km, the escape velocity from its surface would exceed the speed of light, and nothing—not even light—could escape. The Sun would be invisible. It would be a black hole.

The Sun, in fact, has too little mass to experience such a collapse, but when some stars with core masses over 40 times greater than the mass of the Sun reach the end of their nuclear resources, they undergo collapse; their collapse continues until the stars reach infinite densities. Gravitation near the surfaces of these shrunken stars is so enormous that light cannot escape from them. They have crushed themselves out of visible existence.

Except for material blown away during its formation, a black hole has the same amount of mass after its collapse as before its collapse. So, the gravitational field in regions at and beyond the star's original radius is no greater than before the star's collapse. An orbiting planet would keep on orbiting as though nothing happened. But closer distances near the vicinity of a black hole, beneath the star's original radius, are nothing less than the collapse of space itself, with a surrounding warp into which anything that passes too close—light, dust, or a spaceship—is drawn (Figure 5.19). Astronauts in a powerful spaceship could enter the fringes of this warp and still escape. At closer than a certain distance, however, they could not, and they would disappear from the observable universe.

FIGURE 5.19
A rendering of a black hole stealing matter from a companion star.

CHECK YOURSELF

If the Sun somehow suddenly collapsed to a black hole, what change would occur in the orbital speed of Earth?

CHECK YOUR ANSWER

None. This is best understood classically; nothing in Newton's law of gravitation, $F = G\frac{mM}{d^2}$, changes. The fact that the Sun is compressed doesn't change its mass, M, or its distance, d, from Earth. Because Earth's mass, m, and G don't change either, the force, F, holding Earth in its orbit does not change.

Black Hole Geometry

As shown in Figure 5.20, a black hole can either deflect light or capture it. Also, there is one particular distance from the hole at which light can orbit in a circle. This distance is called the *photon sphere*. Light orbiting at that distance is highly unstable. The slightest disturbance will send it off into space or spiraling into the black hole.*

An indestructible astronaut with a powerful enough spaceship could venture into the photon sphere of a black hole and come out again. While inside the photon sphere, she could still send beams of light back into the outside universe as shown in Figure 5.21. If she directed her flashlight sideways and toward the black hole, the light would quickly spiral into the black hole, but light directed vertically and at angles close to the vertical would still escape. As she drew closer and closer to the black hole, however, she would need to shine the light beams closer and closer to the vertical for escape. Moving closer still, our astronaut would find a particular distance where *no* light can escape. No matter in what direction the flashlight pointed, all the beams would be deflected into the black hole. Our unfortunate astronaut would have passed within the **event horizon**, the boundary where no light within can escape. Once inside the event horizon, she could no longer communicate with the outside universe; neither light waves, radio waves, nor any matter could escape from inside the event horizon. Our astronaut would have performed her last experiment in the universe as we conceive it.

The event horizon surrounding a black hole is often called the *surface* of the black hole, the diameter of which depends on the mass of the hole. For example,

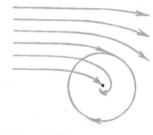

FIGURE 5.20
Light rays deflected by the gravitational field around a black hole. Light aimed far from the black hole is slightly deflected. Light aimed close to the black hole is drawn into the hole. In between, there is a particular radius at which photons can orbit the black hole.

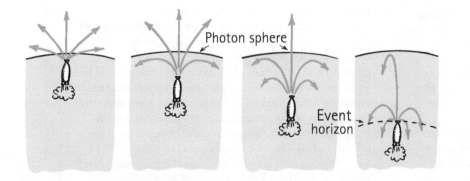

FIGURE 5.21
Just beneath the photon sphere, an astronaut can still shine light to the outside. But as she gets closer to the black hole, only light directed nearer to the vertical gets out, until finally even vertically directed light is trapped. This occurs at a distance called the event horizon.

*This discussion applies to a nonrotating black hole. The situation for a rotating one is more complicated.

TABLE 5.1	CALCULATED RADII OF EVENT HORIZONS FOR NONROTATING BLACK HOLES OF VARIOUS MASSES
Mass of Black Hole	**Radius of Event Horizon**
1 Earth mass	0.8 cm
1 Jupiter mass	2.8 m
1 solar mass	3 km
2 solar masses	6 km
3 solar masses	9 km
5 solar masses	15 km
10 solar masses	30 km
50 solar masses	148 km
100 solar masses	296 km
1000 solar masses	2961 km

a black hole resulting from the collapse of a star 10 times as massive as the Sun has an event-horizon diameter of about 30 km. Calculated radii of event horizons for black holes of various masses are shown in Table 5.1. The event horizon is not a physical surface. Falling objects pass right through it. The event horizon is simply the boundary of no return.

SCIENCE AND SOCIETY

Falling into a Black Hole

Imagine yourself exploring a black hole on some futuristic scientific mission. Your spacecraft is cruising within a safe orbit around the black hole. Your first experiment is to launch a clock-bearing probe toward the black hole. The clock consists of a large LED display of blue lights. Through a telescope you watch as the probe descends. Remarkably, the closer the probe gets to the black hole, the slower the clock appears to run. Furthermore, the light coming from the clock shifts from blue to a lower-frequency red. As the probe gets closer still, the clock runs even slower. Soon you can't make out the clock at all because it has shifted to the infrared. So you switch to your infrared telescope and see that as the probe gets closer to the black hole its clock slows to a creep. Furthermore, the probe seems to be taking an unusually long time to descend. Eventually, the light from the clock is visible only with your microwave telescope, followed by your radio telescope as the frequency of the light from the clock gets lower and lower. Ultimately, just as the clock disappears completely, emitting no light whatsoever, you note that the clock has frozen in time. To get to this point, however, would take, from your point of view, forever.

But you don't have forever, and you soon grow tired of watching the ultraslow clock as it creeps ever so slowly toward the black hole. So you decide to move on to the second experiment, for which you have volunteered to place yourself within a second probe equipped with a blue clock and an array of telescopes. As you descend toward the black hole you note that your clock runs perfectly normally without changing color. The clock on the mother ship, however, is running rather fast. Furthermore, its color is shifting toward ultraviolet and beyond. Your old shipmates are moving rather fast as well. As you descend even deeper, their peculiar speed grows even faster. Soon they grow impatient waiting for you and they leave you behind for dead. Before you know it, the remaining visible stars quickly pass through their life spans, their light coming to you in a flash of ultrahigh frequencies but through a narrowing field of view. And then there is nothing. At that moment you pass through the event horizon, which is a mathematical boundary, not a physical one. Singularity is still kilometers beneath you, but you are caught within its unrelenting grip. The universe you left behind has run through infinite time and exists no longer.

Unfortunately, such a fall through the event horizon of a regular-sized black hole would not be survivable. As you come closer, the gravitational pull on your feet would far exceed that on your head. As a result, your body would be stretched. You would be "ripped" of the opportunity to experience what it would be like inside the event horizon. Furthermore, as you continued to fall toward the black-hole singularity, your atoms would be compressed to an infinitely small size, which you would not survive. What would happen next is only conjecture. Perhaps your mass would explode like a Big Bang into another universe. Perhaps what happens to the mass that falls into the singularity is even stranger than we're capable of imagining. Maybe one day we crafty humans will come to understand such processes. If our species lasts that long!

When a collapsing star contracts within its own event horizon, the star still has substantial size. No known forces, however, can stop the continued contraction, and the star quickly shrinks until finally it is crushed, presumably to the size of a pinhead, then to the size of a microbe, and finally to a realm of size smaller than ever measured by humans. At this point, according to theory, what remains has infinite density. This point is the **black-hole singularity.**

Locating black holes is very difficult. One way to find them is to look for a binary system in which a single luminous star appears to orbit about an invisible companion, as was illustrated in Figure 5.19. If they are closely situated, matter ejected by the normal companion and accelerating into the neighboring black hole should emit X-rays. The first convincing candidate for a black hole, the X-ray star Cygnus X-1, was discovered in 1971. Many additional black hole candidates have since been found, which suggests that black holes are common. Studies of the center of our galaxy strongly suggest the presence of a black hole some 6 billion km in diameter, which is as large as our solar system! The origin of this mega black hole is likely related to the formation of the galaxy itself. It is currently thought that most, if not all, large galaxies contain central mega-sized black holes.

CHECK YOURSELF
What determines whether a star becomes a white dwarf, a neutron star, or a black hole?

CHECK YOUR ANSWER
The mass of a star is the principal factor that determines its fate. Stars that are about as massive as the Sun, and those that are less massive, evolve to become white dwarfs; stars with masses of $10M_{Sun}$ or greater evolve to become neutron stars; the most massive stars of about $40M_{Sun}$ or greater ultimately become black holes.

5.6 Galaxies

LEARNING OBJECTIVE
Describe the discovery of galaxies; their classification as elliptical, spiral, or irregular; and how they are organized into superclusters.

EXPLAIN THIS All the celestial objects discussed so far are located in what galaxy?

Look up into the clear nighttime sky away from the city lights and you will see plenty of stars. In between the stars you'll also see plenty of black. Before the early 20th century, the abundance of black in the night sky led many people to conclude that the universe consisted of an island of millions of stars nestled within a vast sea of emptiness. In addition to stars, however, are the cloudlike nebulae, some of them with a distinct spiral-shaped structure. As early as the 1750s, the German philosopher Immanuel Kant proposed that these spiral clouds were other islands of stars called *galaxies.* But without powerful telescopes, there was no way to tell whether that was true.

The debate about whether the universe consisted of one or many islands of stars was settled by the American astronomer Edwin Hubble. In 1927, working with the newly built largest telescope in the world at Mt. Wilson in California, Hubble made out individual stars within the Andromeda spiral nebula (Figure 5.22). Some of these stars he noticed to be *Cepheids,* which are stars that change their

FIGURE 5.22
Hubble showed that the great spiral nebula within the Andromeda constellation was not just a swirling cloud of gas, but a neighboring galaxy of stars, which is now called the Andromeda galaxy and cataloged as M31. You can see the Andromeda galaxy for yourself by looking between the constellations of Cassiopeia and Pegasus in the late fall nighttime sky. The galaxy appears huge, covering an area six times that of the full Moon. It is, of course, much dimmer than the Moon. Best viewing comes with a good pair of binoculars far away from city lights.

FYI Galaxies are cataloged by two systems. The first catalog is based on the work of Charles Messier, who in 1781 published a list of heavenly structures, such as galaxies, that are relatively easy to observe with small telescopes. The Andromeda galaxy, for example, is the 31st entry of this catalog and is thus listed as M31. A "New General Catalog" was begun in 1888 that was subsequently used to identify all structures, including the many more that became visible with the advent of more powerful telescopes. Under this system, the Andromeda galaxy is cataloged as NGC 224. You can use these catalog numbers in your Internet search engine to learn more about these objects, including their locations in the nighttime sky.

luminosity over short periods of time. Using photos of Cepheid variables in the Magellanic Clouds, Henrietta Leavitt had earlier discovered a relationship between Cepheids' periods and their luminosities. So, by measuring the rate at which they changed luminosity, Hubble estimated their distance, which he found to be much farther away than any star within our own galaxy. Spiral nebulae were not simply clouds—they were neighboring islands of stars within a vast emptiness that potentially extended forever.

But Hubble took his research a step further and discovered something even more amazing. He knew that the color of light emitted by a star or galaxy receding away from us shifts to the red because of the Doppler effect. The degree of redshift could be measured quantitatively by focusing on the line spectrum of hydrogen. The greater the shift in the lines of hydrogen's spectrum, the faster the receding speed. Using Cepheid variables and stellar spectra, Hubble's research team determined both the distances and redshifts of numerous galaxies and discovered that the farther the galaxy, the greater the redshift. This meant that the galaxies were not static islands. Rather, they were receding from us in every direction, which meant that the universe itself was expanding.

If distant galaxies were all moving away from one another, that could only mean that they were once much closer together. Running the cosmic movie backward would inevitably lead to a moment when all the galaxies were gathered together, perhaps within a single point. The universe as we know it, therefore, had a beginning. This moment has come to be known as the **Big Bang**, which we will discuss in more detail in Section 5.7. Now, however, we will describe the different kinds of galaxies and how they are organized within the observable universe.

A **galaxy** consists of a large assemblage of stars, interstellar gas, and dust. Galaxies are the breeding grounds of stars. Our own star, the Sun, is an ordinary star among more than 100 billion others in an ordinary galaxy known as the Milky Way galaxy (Figure 5.23). With unaided eyes, we see the Milky Way as a faint band of light that

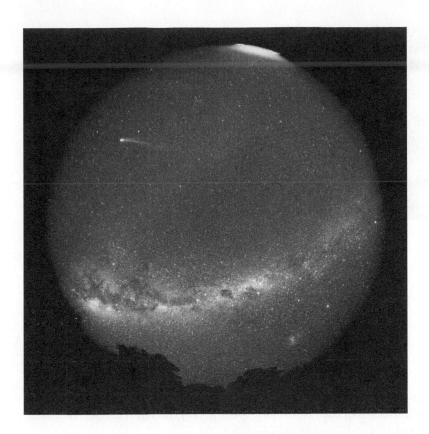

FIGURE 5.23
A wide-angle photograph of the Milky Way, which appears as a north–south cloudlike band of light. The dark lanes and blotches are interstellar gas and dust obscuring the light from the galactic center. If it weren't for this dust, the Milky Way would be a much more spectacular nighttime display. This photograph also shows Comet Hyakutake, which appeared in 1996.

stretches across the sky. The early Greeks called it the "milky circle" and the Romans called it the "milky road" or "milky way." The latter name has stuck.

The masses of galaxies range from about a millionth the mass of our galaxy to some 50 times more. Galaxies are calculated to have much more mass than can be seen with the telescope. A small proportion of the invisible mass is simply matter that has grown so cold that it doesn't emit enough light for us to see. The bulk of the invisible mass, however, is likely an unknown form of matter, called *dark matter*, that does not absorb or emit light. It does, however, possess mass and so its gravitational effects are quite measurable. In Section 5.8 we will describe how dark matter likely played a key role in the formation and distribution of galaxies.

Elliptical, Spiral, and Irregular Galaxies

The millions of galaxies visible in photographs can be separated into three main classes—elliptical, spiral, and irregular. *Elliptical galaxies* are the most common galaxies in the universe. They are spherical, with the stars more crowded toward the center. Most contain little gas and dust, which makes them easy to see through. They also tend to be yellow, which tells us that they consist primarily of older stars—older stars are yellow, while hot young stars tend to be blue. Most ellipticals are small, consisting of fewer than a billion stars (Figure 5.24). An exception is the giant elliptical galaxy M87 (Figure 5.25). The largest ellipticals are about 5 times as large as our galaxy, and the smallest are 1/100 as large.

FIGURE 5.24
This small elliptical galaxy, Leo I, found within the constellation Leo, is only about 2500 light-years in diameter. For comparison, the diameter of our Milky Way galaxy is about 100,000 light-years.

FIGURE 5.25
The giant elliptical galaxy M87, one of the most luminous galaxies in the sky, is located near the center of the Virgo cluster, some 50 million light-years from Earth. It is about 120,000 light-years across and about 40 times as massive as our own galaxy, the Milky Way.

FIGURE 5.26
The Sombrero galaxy, cataloged as M104, is about 80,000 light-years in diameter and about 32 million light-years from Earth. At its center is one of the most supermassive black holes measured in any nearby galaxy.

FYI The Andromeda galaxy is our closest spiral neighbor, being only some 2.3 million light-years away. It contains many more stars than the Milky Way, which makes it more luminescent. Also, its diameter is about 220,000 light-years, compared to the Milky Way's 100,000 light-years. Thus, our view of the Andromeda is likely more spectacular than the Andromeda's view of us.

Spiral galaxies, such as the Andromeda galaxy, shown in Figure 5.22, are perhaps the most beautiful arrangements of stars. Some spirals, such as the Sombrero galaxy of Figure 5.26, have a spheroid central hub. Others, like the one shown in Figure 5.27, have a hub shaped like a bar. The Milky Way galaxy is thought to look much like the NGC 6744 spiral galaxy, which is an intermediate between a barred and unbarred spiral (Figure 5.28).

Elliptical and spiral galaxies sometimes cross paths or even collide. In such cases, gravity causes the shape of the galaxy to become distorted. These distorted looking galaxies are called *irregular galaxies*. Most irregular galaxies are small and faint and are difficult to detect. They tend to contain large clouds of gas and dust mixed with both young (blue) and old (yellow) stars. The irregular galaxy first described by the navigator on Magellan's voyage around the world in 1521 is our nearest neighboring galaxy—the Magellanic Clouds. This galaxy consists of two "clouds," called the Large Magellanic Cloud (LMC) and the Small

FIGURE 5.27
The beautiful barred spiral galaxy NGC 1300 is about 100,000 light-years across and some 70 million light-years away.

FIGURE 5.28
The NGC 6744 galaxy is an intermediate between a barred and unbarred spiral galaxy. Studies of the Milky Way suggest that it too is an intermediate spiral. In other words, this is what we may look like from afar.

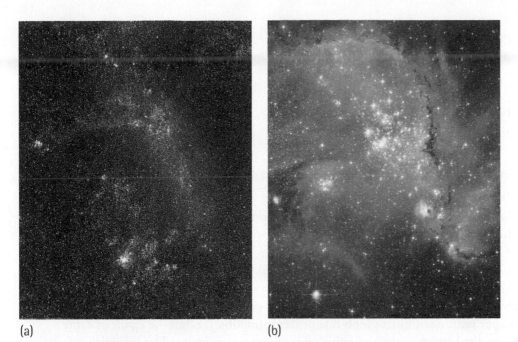

(a)   (b)

FIGURE 5.29
(a) The Large Magellanic Cloud and (b) the neighboring Small Magellanic Cloud are a
pair of irregular galaxies. The Magellanic Clouds are our closest galactic neighbors, about
150,000 light-years distant. They likely orbit the Milky Way.

Magellanic Cloud (SMC), both of which are slowly being pulled into the Milky
Way. The LMC is dotted with hot young stars with a combined mass of some
20 billion solar masses, and the SMC contains stars with a combined mass of
about 2 billion solar masses (Figure 5.29). Some irregular galaxies, such as NGC
4038 shown in Figure 5.30, are the aftermaths of galactic collisions.

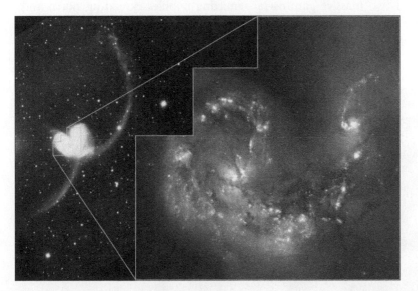

FIGURE 5.30
Shown in black and white is the ground-telescope view of an irregular galaxy resulting
from the collision of two galaxies. Note the remnant arms that suggest two former spiral
galaxies. The inset shows a close-up color view taken by the Hubble Telescope. Evident is
the rapid formation of new stars (blue) occurring as the two galaxies combined.

CHECK YOURSELF
Is it possible for one type of galaxy to turn into another?

CHECK YOUR ANSWER
Yes, and this occurs as two symmetrically shaped galaxies collide to form an asymmetrically shaped irregular galaxy.

Active Galaxies

Galaxies differ greatly in the activity going on inside them. This activity may include star formation, supernova, or energy-releasing processes at the galactic core. Those galaxies with notable activity are sometimes called *active galaxies*.

When it comes to star formation, our Milky Way is a relatively calm place, producing on average about one new star per year. By comparison, one type of active galaxy, known as a **starburst galaxy**, can produce more than 100 new stars per year. A starburst's high rate of star formation is often the result of some violent disturbance, such as a collision between two galaxies. The irregular galaxy shown in Figure 5.30 is an example of a starburst galaxy. Another example is the Cigar galaxy, M82, which is being deformed by the tidal forces from its much larger neighbor, M81 (Figure 5.31). A starburst tends to die down once the disturbance is removed or after the starburst galaxy consumes all its interstellar fuel. Many elliptical galaxies are thought to be former starburst galaxies because of their low abundance of interstellar dust and gases.

Other active galaxies are active by virtue of their galactic core, which hosts a black hole more massive than millions or even billions of Suns. The event horizons of these black holes are about as large as our solar system! Most large galaxies, including the Milky Way, have such black holes in their centers, and these massive black holes can be a source of much activity.

For example, in 2010, using NASA's Fermi gamma-ray space telescope, astronomers discovered two massive gamma-ray–emitting bubbles extending north and south from the center of our galactic disk, as shown in Figure 5.32. Together, these bubbles, known as *Fermi bubbles*, extend about 50,000 light-years, which is about

FIGURE 5.31
The Cigar galaxy, M82, is a spiral galaxy tilted away from us so that we see it from an edge-on view. Tidal forces from the nearby M81 galaxy disturb the distribution of matter within M82, which clumps, allowing for the formation of many new stars, as evidenced by M82's remarkable blue color. The red gases above and below the galactic plane are primarily hydrogen being pushed out by abundant stellar wind.

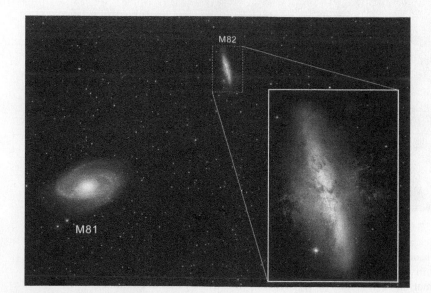

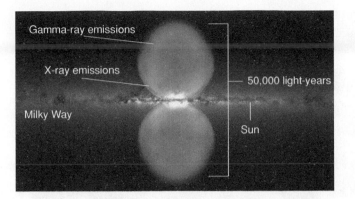

Gamma-ray emissions

X-ray emissions

50,000 light-years

Milky Way

Sun

FIGURE 5.32
Vast gamma-ray–emitting bubbles, known as Fermi bubbles, extend north and south from the center of our galaxy. Though invisible to the naked eye, these bubbles span over half the sky when viewed from Earth through gamma-ray detectors.

half the diameter of our galaxy. Their edges are well defined (not diffuse), which suggests they are a fairly recent occurrence, perhaps arising only several million years ago. Their nature and origin are not yet fully understood. One model suggests they arose from large amounts of material falling into our galaxy's mega-size central black hole. Alternatively, they may have resulted from the outgassing of a brief but intense period of starburst activity occurring at the galactic core.

The Milky Way's Fermi bubbles, however, are minor compared to the activity we see arising from the centers of other large galaxies. In such cases, supermassive amounts of matter are likely falling into central supermassive black holes. Before falling into the black hole, the doomed mass forms a rapidly spinning disk, called an *accretion disk*, around the equator of the black hole. Charged particles in this hyperspinning disk create a narrow yet ultrastrong magnetic field that rises from the black hole's poles. Rather than falling into the black hole, some of the charged particles, such as electrons, are accelerated outward through these magnetic fields to nearly the speed of light. This results in two extremely long streams of particles, called *jets*, extending more than 100,000 light-years away from the galactic center, which is called an **active galactic nucleus** (AGN).

A relatively close AGN is found within the large elliptical galaxy M87, which was shown in Figure 5.25. High-resolution images of this galaxy, as shown in Figure 5.33, reveal a jet of material streaming away from the center of this galaxy. Interestingly, the jet is angled toward us. This plus the great speed of the jet (99.5% of the speed of light) helps make the jet appear more luminous. The opposite "counterjet" receding away from us at such great speeds is barely visible.

Nearby active galactic nuclei, such as that of M87, give us a clue as to the possible nature of the most energetic galaxies of all—the *quasars*. Starting in the 1960s, astronomers began discovering extremely energetic bodies hundreds of times more luminous than our own galaxy, yet farther away than any observed object. Because they looked like radio-emitting stars, they were dubbed "quasi-stellar radio sources," which was shortened to **quasars**. Because all quasars are so very far away, they occurred a very long time ago—up to 13 billion years ago, which was close to the beginning of the universe. As we look to quasars, therefore, we are peering into the early lives of galaxies (Figure 5.34). During this galactic youth, it is thought that much material was still falling into the supermassive black holes found within their galactic cores. The dynamics of

FIGURE 5.33
Material falling into the supermassive black hole in the center of M87 generates powerful jets that shoot out at near light speed.

FIGURE 5.34
Each disk in this deep-space image taken by the Hubble Telescope is a galaxy. The quasar shown in the center is billions of light-years behind this cluster of galaxies. Interestingly, the cluster's gravity has bent the light from the quasar like a lens so that multiple images of the quasar are also seen.

this process allow for an efficient conversion of mass into energy, which would provide for colossal jets of highly energetic particles and light. When one of these ancient jets faces our direction, the result is an unusually brilliant display of energy we call a *blazar*.

CHECK YOURSELF

Are there any quasars within the Milky Way galaxy?

CHECK YOUR ANSWER

No. A quasar is the active galactic nucleus of a galaxy as it appeared toward the beginning of the universe. All quasars are billions of light-years away from our galaxy.

Clusters and Superclusters

Galaxies are not the largest structures in the universe; they tend to cluster into distinguishable groups. Our Milky Way galaxy, for example, is part of a cluster of local galaxies that includes two other major spiral galaxies—namely, the Andromeda galaxy and the Triangulum galaxy. Also included are more than a dozen smaller elliptical galaxies, including the Leo I galaxy shown in Figure 5.24, and a few irregular galaxies, such as the Large Magellanic Cloud. Altogether this cluster of galaxies is called the **Local Group**. Their approximate distributions are shown in Figure 5.35. If drawn correctly to scale, Andromeda is only about 20 Milky Way diameters away from the Milky Way.

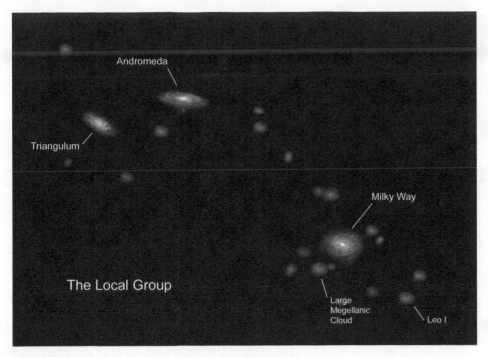

FIGURE 5.35
This two-dimensional composition shows the approximate relative distances between the members of our Local Group of galaxies. These galaxies are all moving toward each other and will one day collide into a larger supergalaxy.

The Triangulum galaxy, so named because it completes a triangle between the spirals, is even closer to Andromeda, but farther away from us.

Our Local Group of galaxies is also under the gravitational influence of neighboring galactic clusters. Our cluster plus all these other clusters make up what is called a *supercluster*, which is a cluster of galactic clusters. Our Local Group is actually a rather minor component of our **Local Supercluster**, as is illustrated in Figure 5.36.

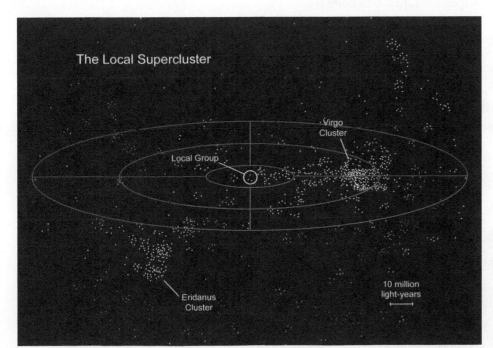

FIGURE 5.36
A supercluster is a cluster of galactic clusters. Each dot represents a galaxy. Note that our Local Group is found midway between two much larger clusters, the Virgo and Eridanus clusters.

FIGURE 5.37
Each cloud represents a supercluster.
Note that the superclusters are strung
together as though on the surface of
a foam.

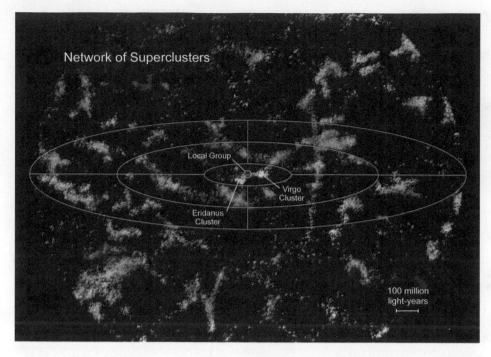

Our Local Supercluster is tied in with an elaborate network of many other superclusters, as shown in Figure 5.37. Together, these superclusters appear as though they reside on the surface of a foam inside which are large voids of empty space. Zooming out farther we find that the network of superclusters extends to the edges of the *observable universe*, as illustrated in Figure 5.38. By "observable universe" we mean all that we are able to see given the fact that the universe is only about 14 billion years old.

Polls show that about half of American adults do not know that it takes one year for Earth to go around the Sun. Many of us, therefore, are still struggling with scientific ideas of 400 years ago. Your knowledge is much greater, and being aware of the amazing possibilities that science continues to reveal puts you in a very privileged minority. Celebrate that!

FIGURE 5.38
The network of superclusters extends
to the edges of the observable
universe, which is no farther than
14 billion light-years away. This
illustration, however, shows a
hypothetical bird's-eye view of this
observable universe fully matured to
the present moment, which, because
of cosmic expansion, would place
those most distant objects now some
42 billion light-years away.

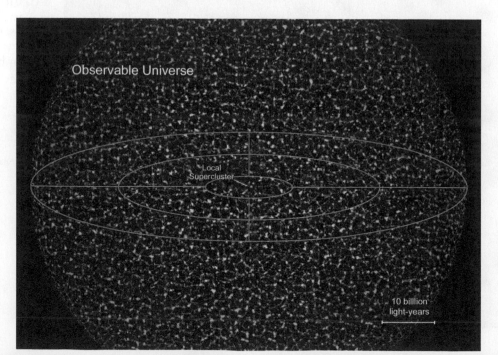

MATH CONNECTION

The Scale of the Galaxy

Problem Earth is about 0.000016 light-year from the Sun and about 4.2 light-years from the next nearest star, which is Proxima Centauri. How far away is Proxima Centauri in Earth–Sun distances?

Solution Divide our distance from Proxima Centauri by our distance to the Sun:

$$\frac{4.2 \text{ light-years}}{0.000016 \text{ light-year}} = 262,500$$

So the nearest star is about 260,000 times as far from us as the Sun is.

Problem Our distance from the center of the Milky Way galaxy is about 26,000 light-years. How many Earth–Proxima Centauri distances is that?

Solution Divide the distance to the center of the galaxy by the distance to Proxima Centauri:

$$\frac{26,000 \text{ light-years}}{4.2 \text{ light-years}} = 6190$$

So the center of our galaxy is about 6200 times as far away as the nearest star.

Problem The Milky Way and Andromeda galaxies are about 2,300,000 light-years apart. The diameter of the Milky Way galaxy is about 100,000 light-years. How many Milky Way diameters distant is the Andromeda galaxy?

Solution Divide the distance to the Andromeda galaxy by the diameter of the Milky Way galaxy:

$$\frac{2,300,00 \text{ light-years}}{100,000 \text{ light-years}} = 23$$

So the Andromeda galaxy is about 23 Milky Way galaxy diameters away.

Problem The Andromeda galaxy is moving toward the Milky Way galaxy at a rate of about 300,000 mi/h. In how many years will these two galaxies collide?

Solution Convert 300,000 mi/h to light-years per year. First convert the 300,000 mi to light-years:

$$(300,000 \text{ mi})(1.61 \text{ km}/1 \text{ mi}) \times$$
$$(1 \text{ light-year}/9,460,000,000,000 \text{ km})$$
$$= 4.79 \times 10^{-8} \text{ light-year}$$

Second, convert hours to years:

$$(1 \text{ h})(1 \text{ day}/24 \text{ h})(1 \text{ yr}/365.25 \text{ days})$$
$$= 1.14 \times 10^{-4} \text{ year}$$

Put the two converted values together:

$$300,000 \text{ mi/h}$$
$$= 4.79 \times 10^{-8} \text{ light-year}/1.14 \times 10^{-4} \text{ yr}$$
$$= 4.20 \times 10^{-4} \text{ light-year/yr}$$

Use this equation for speed:

$$\text{Speed} = \text{distance/time}$$
$$4.20 \times 10^{-4} \text{ light-year/yr}$$
$$= 2,300,000 \text{ light-years}/x \text{ yr}$$

Solve for x:

$$x = 5,470,000,000 \text{ yr}$$

So in roughly 5.47 billion years, the Andromeda and Milky Way galaxies will collide. By this time our Sun will have exhausted almost all of its nuclear fuel, so this is not something we Earthlings will be around to witness. Collisions between galaxies, however, are fairly common, and astronomers have photographed many such occurrences now in progress.

CHECK YOURSELF

Which is greater—the number of stars in our galaxy or the number of galaxies in the observable universe?

CHECK YOUR ANSWER

There are far more galaxies in the entire universe than there are stars in our galaxy. Recall from the beginning of this chapter that astronomers estimate that there are about 100 billion stars in our galaxy and about 100 billion galaxies in our observable universe. If true, that means there are about 10^{22} stars in our observable universe, which is about the number of water molecules in a drop of water. As large as the observable universe is large is as small as the fundamental building blocks of our body are small. As humans we are nicely situated between these two extremes.

Integrated Science 29A
BIOLOGY

The Drake Equation

EXPLAIN THIS: How would finding microbial extraterrestrial life on Jupiter's moon Europa affect the value of N in the Drake equation?

The search for extraterrestrial intelligence (SETI) dates back to 1959, when physicists from Cornell University suggested that radio waves could be used for interstellar communication. The idea is that since human civilization leaks radio messages into space, the inhabitants of other planets might be doing the same thing. Large radio telescopes on Earth could detect such radio leaks from civilizations in nearby star systems, as well as stronger signals dispatched from planets thousands of light-years away. The young astronomer Frank Drake (who later became president of the SETI Institute) was the first to conduct a radio search throughout the galaxy. Although SETI telescopes have been analyzing signals for decades, the antenna have not yet picked up any unique frequencies that could signal distant civilizations, but there is plenty of sky yet to be searched.

Is it logical to search for extraterrestrial civilizations? What are the odds that such civilizations exist, and if they do, what are the chances that we could contact them? Frank Drake's answer to this question is the Drake equation. Since its introduction in 1961, this tool has framed the debate. The Drake equation estimates the odds of our ever making contact with another intelligent civilization by multiplying seven variables related to the possibility of life. The Drake equation is

$$N = R \times F \times Ne \times Fl \times Fi \times Fc \times L$$

where

R = the rate of formation of suitable stars—stars like the Sun—in our galaxy per year
F = the fraction of these stars that have planets
Ne = the number of Earth-like planets—meaning planets that have liquid water—within each planetary system
Fl = the fraction of Earth-like planets where life develops
Fi = the fraction of life sites where intelligent life develops
Fc = the fraction of intelligent life sites where communication develops
L = the "lifetime" (in years) of a communicative civilization
N = the number of civilizations with which we could possibly communicate

A problem with Drake's equation, however, is that we don't know the value of any of the terms! We can make rough estimates of some of them: Astronomers believe that the product $R \times F \times Ne$, which would give us the number of habitable planets in the Milky Way, may be in the neighborhood of 100 billion. The technology for detecting extrasolar planets—planets that orbit stars beyond our solar system—is rapidly advancing. Today, more than 1000 extrasolar planets have been found and new ones are rapidly being discovered.

But presently there is no way to know how many of these 100 billion hypothetical planets have produced life. Life arose quickly on Earth (see Chapter 13), which suggests that life develops fairly easily under the right conditions, but this is not definitive—N could be anywhere between 1 (if Earth is the only planet in the Milky Way with life) and 100 billion (if they all have life). The fact that life flourished on Earth some 4 billion years before humans developed suggests that the development of intelligent life is much more tenuous than the rise of microbial life. But how much more difficult? As to the fraction of intelligent life sites, there could be intelligent beings who haven't yet invented radio telescopes. (We humans belonged to this category until the 20th century.) Or, there could be other civilizations that have the means to communicate but don't—perhaps because they are not interested or they fear that they might endanger themselves by advertising where they live. And L, the lifetime of an intelligent, communicative civilization? Well, humans have been communicative for fewer than 100 years. Do you think we, or the average intelligent species, will remain willing and able to communicate with other star systems for a century? A thousand years? A million? If organizations of intelligent beings—civilizations—last long enough, the Milky Way may now be brimming with communicative, advanced beings. One day, we just may make contact with them.

5.7 Looking Back in Time

EXPLAIN THIS Where did the Big Bang occur?

LEARNING OBJECTIVE
Describe the Big Bang and three lines of evidence that support it.

Imagine some fantastic optical instrument through which we can see the actual history of human civilization. Tune into some 40,000 years ago and you are able to witness the migration of humans into the Australian subcontinent. Re-focus to some 4500 years ago and see the building of the Egyptian pyramids. With such a device we would have an amazing window into our past. The accuracy of history books would be assured.

When it comes to the history of the universe, we have exactly such a device. It is called the *telescope*. The speed of light is fast, but the universe is exceedingly large. The light from our nearest star, Proxima Centauri, takes 4.2 years to reach us. Thus, as we view this star, we are literally looking at the star as it appeared 4.2 years ago. Similarly, the Andromeda galaxy we see today is the Andromeda galaxy as it appeared 2.3 million years ago.

Want to see the history of our universe? All we need to do is look through our telescopes. The farther away the object, the older it is. Start cataloging the past as we see it today, and soon we come to an appreciable understanding of how the universe itself formed. The study of the overall structure and evolution of the universe is called **cosmology**. With the advent of modern technology, especially with the development of space telescopes, the field of cosmology is currently in a golden era of discovery.

In this section we will present some of the more well-established findings of cosmology. To provide a sense of the current excitement, we also dip into some speculations, such as the possible final fate of the universe. But because our discussions here are brief, you should consider exploring the latest news as it happens through online resources such as those listed in Table 5.2.

MasteringPhysics®
TUTORIAL: Hubble's Law
VIDEO: From the Big Bang to Galaxies

UNIFYING CONCEPT
● *The Scientific Method*
Section 1.3

TABLE 5.2   WEB RESOURCES FOR COSMOLOGY

- The Harvard-Smithsonian Center for Astrophysics
  http://www.cfa.harvard.edu
- The Hubble Space Telescope
  http://Hubblesite.org
- The Wilkinson Microwave Anisotropy Probe
  http://map.gsfc.nasa.gov

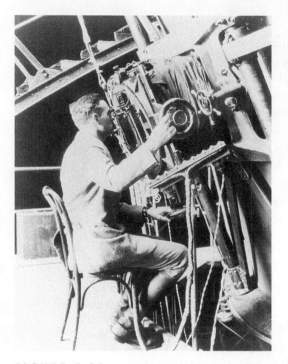

FIGURE 5.39
Edwin Hubble (1889–1953), astronomer and cosmologist, is shown here in 1923 using the 100-inch telescope at the Mt. Wilson Observatory, where he worked for most of his life. In 1929, he announced Hubble's law, which states that the farther apart galaxies are, the faster they move.

FIGURE 5.40   (MP)

INTERACTIVE FIGURE

Every ant on the expanding balloon sees all other ants moving farther away. Each ant may therefore think that it is at the center of the expansion. Not so! There is no center to the surface of the balloon, just as there are no edges.

The Big Bang

Not so long ago it was commonly thought that our Milky Way galaxy made up the whole universe. Then, in the early 1920s, the astronomer Edwin Hubble, using the new Mt. Wilson telescope, discovered that the Andromeda "nebula" was, in fact, a separate galaxy farther away than the outermost stars of the Milky Way (Figure 5.39). This was a monumental discovery, but Hubble didn't stop there. As discussed earlier in this chapter, Hubble identified and measured the distances to numerous other galaxies. What he discovered next was astonishing—the galaxies are almost all receding from one another. Furthermore, the farther away the galaxy, the greater the velocity with which it is receding.

Hubble's observations had two major implications. The first was that the universe arose from an infinitesimal point that expanded rapidly in an event called the Big Bang. The second major implication was that the universe is not contained within a region of space. Rather, space is *in* the universe and expanding. This is peculiar because you may first think that the Big Bang occurred within an already existing infinite space and that matter and energy flew outward from this Big Bang to occupy this space. If this were the case, however, the distribution of galaxies we observe today and their relative motions would be quite different. To reemphasize this often confused concept: When we talk about the expansion of the universe, we are referring to an expansion of the very structure of space itself. A useful analogy is a group of ants on a balloon that is expanding, as shown in Figure 5.40. As the balloon is inflated, every ant sees every other ant moving farther away. Likewise, in an expanding universe, any observer sees all other galaxies moving away. So the Big Bang marked not only the beginning of time but also the beginning of space.

Hubble suggested a simple relationship between the distance of an object from Earth and its velocity of recession. This relationship, which has been confirmed by numerous measurements over many decades, is known as **Hubble's law**:

$$\text{Hubble's law: } v = H \times d$$

where v is the velocity of a galaxy, H is a constant known as Hubble's constant, and d is the distance of the galaxy from Earth. This law tells us, for example, that if one galaxy is twice as far away as another, the farther galaxy recedes twice as fast from us. Furthermore, if a galaxy were to move from where we are now to its present location with a velocity v, then the time of this trip would be the distance it travels divided by its velocity:

$$t = \frac{d}{v}$$

We use Hubble's law to substitute for v:

$$t = \frac{d}{H \times d} = \frac{1}{H}$$

When we enter the value of H into this equation, we have an estimate of the interval of time for the expansion. Said another way, we have determined the age of the universe. Plugging the currently accepted value of H into the equation indicates that the universe is nearly 14 billion years old. Wow!

CHECK YOURSELF
Draw three dots equally spaced along the length of a rubber band. Assume the distance between these dots is 5 mm. In 1 s stretch the rubber band to 10 times its original length.

1. Show that the second dot recedes from the first dot with a speed of 45 mm/s. (*Hint*: Speed = distance/time.)
2. Show that the third dot recedes from the first dot with a speed of 90 mm/s.
3. Why do farther galaxies recede from us at faster rates?

CHECK YOUR ANSWERS
1. The original distance was 5 mm, which stretched to 50 mm. The change in distance, therefore, was 45 mm over a time of 1 s. So the speed equals 45 mm/s.
2. The difference between 100 mm and 10 mm is 90 mm over a time of 1 s, which equals 90 mm/s, or twice the speed of 45 mm/s.
3. For an expanding rubber band, we see that a dot twice as far away travels twice as fast. The same goes with the universe: A galaxy twice as far away from us is moving twice as fast. The reason for these receding velocities is the expansion of space itself. (A few nearby galaxies, including Andromeda, buck the trend and move toward us.)

Cosmic Background Radiation

In addition to the expansion of the universe, a second line of evidence supporting the Big Bang theory is *cosmic background radiation*. In 1964, scientists Arno Penzias and Robert W. Wilson, working at Bell Labs in New Jersey, used a simple radio receiver to survey the heavens for radio signals (Figure 5.41). No matter which way they directed their receiver, they detected microwaves with a wavelength of 7.35 cm coming toward Earth. Penzias and Wilson were puzzled. With no specific source of the radiation, where were the microwaves coming from and why?

Remember that any object above absolute zero emits energy in the form of electromagnetic radiation. The frequency of this radiation is proportional to

> Light from a distant galaxy is the light from glowing elements, which emit spectra of particular frequencies. An examination of the full spectrum of a galaxy's light shows a pattern of peaks that are the sum of the spectra of all of the many glowing elements, primarily hydrogen and helium. If these peaks are shifted toward the red, then we know the galaxy must be receding away from us. The amount of redshift tells us how fast that galaxy is receding.

> Where exactly did the Big Bang occur? Was it at some now far distant point from which we have long since traveled? The answer is an astounding NO! Rather, every point in the universe was present at the Big Bang. It's just that all of these points are now quite far away from one another. So if you want to point to the location of the Big Bang, just point your finger to the tip of your nose, or anywhere for that matter. You can't miss.

FIGURE 5.41
Arno Penzias and Robert Wilson in front of the microwave receiver they used to detect the afterglow of the Big Bang.

FIGURE 5.42
This all-sky map of the cosmic background radiation taken by the Wilkinson Microwave Anisotropy Probe (WMAP) satellite reveals an average temperature of about 2.73 K everywhere. This is the cooled-off remnants of the Big Bang. The color shows minor temperature variation on the order of ± 0.0001 K.

the absolute temperature of the emitter. Theorists at Princeton, working around the same time as Penzias and Wilson, showed that if the universe began in a primordial explosion as described by the Big Bang, it would still be cooling off. Further, they showed that the temperature of the early universe would have cooled by today to an average of about 3 K. A universe of this temperature would be expected to emit microwave radiation of just the frequency observed by Penzias and Wilson. Thus the influx of microwave radiation that initially puzzled Penzias and Wilson was found to be emitted by the cooling universe itself. This faint microwave radiation is now referred to as **cosmic background radiation** and is taken as strong evidence of the Big Bang (Figure 5.42).

The Abundance of Hydrogen and Helium

The Big Bang answers another cosmic mystery involving the element helium. Measurements show that matter in the universe is about 75% hydrogen and 25% helium. (Heavier elements such as those found on Earth are very minor contributors to the total amount of matter in the universe.) Hydrogen is the simplest of all elements, consisting of a single proton nucleus. It makes sense that hydrogen was the original element. Helium, however, is a more complex element containing a nucleus of two protons and two neutrons. We know that helium is produced from the fusion of hydrogen in stars. But the number of stars is insufficient to account for all the observed helium—not more than 10% of the observed helium could have originated in stars. Most of the helium observed in the universe must have been created elsewhere. As described in the Science and Society box, the Big Bang model predicts that the early universe

SCIENCE AND SOCIETY

Big Bang Helium

As the universe expands, it cools. The cosmic background microwave radiation tells us that it has cooled to an average of about 3 K. Working backward from the present, scientists estimate a temperature in excess of 100 billion K within a few seconds after the Big Bang. At this extreme temperature, protons would be turning into neutrons and neutrons would be turning into protons. The rates of these transformations would be about the same, meaning the ratio of protons to neutrons in this super early universe would be about 1:1.

Over the next three minutes, the temperature dropped to less than 100 billion K, which favored the formation of protons.* Soon protons outnumbered neutrons. By the time the ratio of protons to neutrons was 7:1, the universe would have *cooled enough* to allow for nuclear fusion. We say "cooled enough" because the universe was still quite hot, but not as hot as before. At this point, the protons and neutrons would have begun fusing into deuterium nuclei (consisting of one proton and one neutron). Deuterium nuclei would have then

fused to form helium. They would continue doing so until the deuterium grew sparse. (Incidentally, this explains why deuterium is such a rare isotope today.) Continued cooling would prevent the further fusion of helium into heavier elements, such as carbon. By the time the three minutes of helium synthesis were over, the universe would be left with about 75% hydrogen and 25% helium, which is what we observe in the universe today. The Milky Way is actually about 28% helium. The 3% excess helium is likely from the fusion of hydrogen in the stars. No galaxy detected so far, however, has a helium abundance of less than 25%, just as predicted by the Big Bang theory.

*Neutrons are slightly more massive than protons. The transformation of a proton into a neutron, therefore, requires a slightly greater input of energy in accordance with $E = mc^2$. At temperatures below 100 billion K, there is insufficient energy to allow this transformation. The conversion of neutrons into protons, however, releases energy at lower temperatures in accordance with the second law of thermodynamics.

would have been favorable to the formation of helium, but not the formation of other elements. A more detailed analysis shows that the amount of helium created just after the Big Bang should be about the same as the amount we observe in the universe today.

In summary, three major lines of evidence strongly support the Big Bang theory. The first is the current expansion of space, which causes galaxies to recede from one another. The second is the discovery of cosmic background radiation, which is thought to be the Big Bang's afterglow. The third is the Big Bang's ability to explain the observed proportions of elements. Because of these and other similar lines of evidence, the Big Bang has come to be widely accepted by the scientific community as the most viable explanation for the beginning of our universe.

An antenna-fed television (not cable or satellite) tuned into a channel with no local station shows a screen of static "snow." Interestingly, about 1% of this snow is due to photons from the cosmic background radiation.

5.8 Dark Matter and Dark Energy

EXPLAIN THIS How is it possible to detect something in space that we can't see through our telescopes?

LEARNING OBJECTIVE
Describe the evidence for dark matter and dark energy and their role in the evolution of the universe.

Evidence now suggests that the Big Bang generated matter in at least two different forms—one that we can see and another that we can't. The visible form of matter is the "ordinary matter" made of subatomic particles such as protons, neutrons, and electrons. As you learned in earlier chapters, these particles combine to make the atoms of the periodic table. Atoms then combine to make molecules, such as those that make our bodies. This matter we can touch. We interact with it directly. You, the planets, and the stars are made of this form of matter, which we will from here on refer to as **ordinary matter.**

The second form of matter generated from the Big Bang is quite unlike ordinary matter. This form of matter does not recognize the strong nuclear force, which means it cannot clump to form atomic nuclei. Neither does this second form of matter recognize the electromagnetic force, which makes it invisible to light as well as to our sense of touch. The electromagnetic force is responsible for the repulsion between electrons. The reason you can't walk through a wall is because of the repulsions between the electrons in your body and the electrons in the wall. If the wall were made of this invisible matter you would be able to walk right through it. Of course, you wouldn't be able to see the wall either. This invisible form of matter that we cannot see or touch is known as **dark matter.**

So, if dark matter is invisible to us, how do we know it's there? The answer is that this ghostly form of matter gives itself away by its gravitational effects. One of the first clues came to us as we were mapping the speeds at which stars orbit our galactic center. According to the laws of gravity, orbital speed is a function of the force of gravity between the orbiting object and the object being orbited—the greater the force of gravity, the greater the orbital speed. The inner planets of our solar system, for example, orbit the Sun much faster than the outer planets because they are closer to the Sun and experience stronger gravitational forces. Relative to our galaxy, we might expect the same trend—stars closest to the galactic center should have faster orbital speeds than stars farther out. Interestingly, that's not what we observe! Instead, stars closer to the galactic center and those farther out orbit with about the same speed. How can this be?

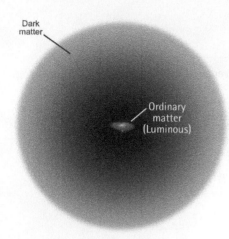

Dark matter

Ordinary matter (Luminous)

FIGURE 5.43
As large as a galaxy is, its diffuse halo of dark matter is much larger. This halo may measure up to 10 times the diameter of the luminous galaxy and be about six times as massive.

FYI An alternative theory to dark matter is Modified Newtonian Dynamics (MOND), proposed by the physicist Mordehai Milgrom in the early 1980s. According to MOND, Newton's equation $a = F/m$ fails when the force is exceedingly weak, perhaps because of quantum effects. A modified version of this equation was thus created to account for the observed orbital velocities of stars within galaxies. The theory is controversial. To date, most astronomers find the dark matter theory to be more acceptable.

For a solar system, planets orbit as they do because most of the solar system's mass is concentrated within the central sun. For a galaxy such as the Milky Way or Andromeda, it sure looks as though most of the mass is concentrated within the central bulge. The measured orbital speeds of stars, however, tell us that the bulk of the galaxy's mass lies outside the galaxy itself within a diffuse yet massive invisible halo many times the diameter of the visible galaxy, as shown in Figure 5.43. We know it's invisible because all of our telescopes see right through it! But something must be there affecting stellar orbital speeds.

Another bit of evidence for dark matter comes from measuring the speeds of galaxies as they orbit one another within clusters. The measured speeds tell us that the masses of these galaxies are many times greater than the total mass of all their stars.

Last, we know that the path of light is bent by gravity much as it is bent by an optical lens. A cluster of galaxies, therefore, can bend the light from an even farther cluster lying directly behind it—we say the foreground cluster behaves as a *gravitational lens*. Such a gravitational lensing effect was shown in Figure 5.34. The degree to which the light from the distant cluster bends is a function of the mass of the foreground cluster. Once again, the degree of light bending tells us that the mass of the closer cluster far exceeds the mass we would expect based solely on the cluster's luminosity. So, by carefully studying the bending of light from distant galaxies, we can build a map of the dark matter's distribution. Such a study using the Hubble Space Telescope is illustrated in Figure 5.44.

So the evidence for dark matter is strong. Our current problem, however, is trying to figure out exactly what dark matter is made of. It's clear that dark matter is not simply ordinary matter, such as expired stars, that has gotten so cold that it emits no light. Although numerous theories abound about the fundamental nature of dark matter, no dark matter particles have been detected. Until that happens, we are left with yet another fascinating mystery of our universe.

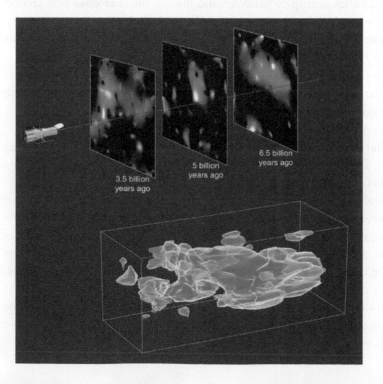

3.5 billion years ago

5 billion years ago

6.5 billion years ago

FIGURE 5.44
Images of dark matter, shown in blue, were created through the Hubble Space Telescope's Cosmic Evolution Survey. Of course, the dark matter is not blue. This graphic, however, shows dark matter's distribution over a narrow region of the sky back to about 6.5 billion years ago.

Galaxy Formation

We can speculate that when the universe formed, ordinary matter plus an even greater amount of dark matter was produced. Held together by gravity, the ordinary matter and dark matter would have been strewn outward in a clumpy fashion. Within a clump, ordinary and dark matter may initially have been uniformly mixed together. These two forms of matter differ significantly in that when ordinary matter collides with ordinary matter, energy is released. With this loss of energy, the ordinary matter loses orbital speed and thus falls closer to the center of the clump. Over time, while all dark matter stayed distributed throughout the clump, the ordinary matter became concentrated at the center (Figure 5.45). This concentration of ordinary matter at the center of the clump allowed for the formation of stars. Also, as ordinary matter congregated toward the center, the rate of rotation would increase—angular momentum would have been conserved. If the original clump of ordinary and dark matter was just barely spinning, then the stars forming at the center would take on the form of an elliptical galaxy. If the original clump was spinning a bit faster, then the new stars would be spinning fast enough to flatten the galaxy, much like a rapidly spinning ball of pizza dough. The resulting disk would take on the form of a spiral galaxy. So from a clump of ordinary and dark matter, ordinary matter condensed to form a central galaxy. The dark matter remained diffuse, forming an invisible halo surrounding the newly formed galaxy.

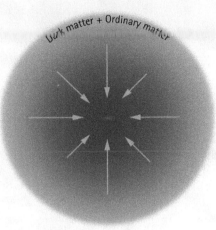

FIGURE 5.45
Ordinary matter condensed out of a mixture of dark and ordinary matter.

Dark Energy

In the years just before Hubble's discovery of the expansion of the universe, Einstein was struggling to understand why gravity wasn't causing the universe to collapse in a Big Crunch. He was thinking of the universe as static, neither collapsing nor expanding. But, in order for the universe to remain static against the inward force of gravity, there would need to be another fundamental outward force counteracting gravity. In other words, if gravity is the "pull inward," there should be a phenomenon that creates a "push outward." To allow for such a balance, he introduced into his equations a factor that he called the *cosmological constant*. He had no proof for the existence of such a phenomenon. Rather, he just postulated it to account for the apparent stability of the universe.

About 10 years later, Hubble announced that the universe was *not* stable but very dynamic and expanding. Einstein later remarked that his own failure to predict a dynamic universe was the "greatest blunder of his life." Subsequent workings of Einstein's equations showed that a static universe would not be stable. Just the slightest push this way or that would cause it to either collapse or expand. Einstein abandoned his notion of a cosmological constant, which for the next 75 years remained a historical curiosity.

Then in the 1990s, some 40 years after Einstein's death, two teams of astronomers made a startling discovery. High-resolution data from very distant galaxies showed that space, beginning about 7.5 billion years ago, started to accelerate in its expansion. Galaxies are not simply coasting away from each other and slowing down. Rather, some unknown form of energy is causing an increase in the rate at which galaxies are receding. Here was a phenomenon that acted as the opposite of gravity, possible evidence of Einstein's once-proposed cosmological constant.

There remains much speculation about how these findings affect the fate of the universe. This form of unknown energy is generally described as

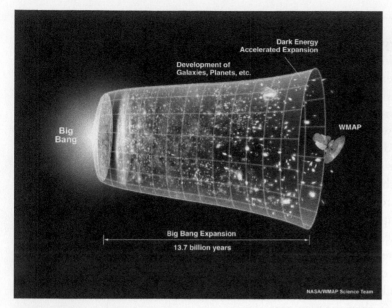

FIGURE 5.46
The expansion of space started to accelerate about 7.5 billion years ago, which is shown on this diagram as a gradual widening just after the development of galaxies. The cause of this accelerated expansion has been given the name *dark energy*. But just because we can name something doesn't mean we understand it. Such is the case with dark energy.

FYI The space through which our planets orbit contains about 100 hydrogen atoms per liter. The space between the stars of our galaxy contains about 2 hydrogen atoms per liter. If you want really empty space, you'll need to travel to the vast voids that separate the superclusters, as was shown in Figure 5.36. It's only from these regions that dark energy appears to be taking hold. The space within and between our local galaxies is too dense!

dark energy (Figure 5.46). Theorists have various ideas about the nature of dark energy, including the possibility that the effects of dark energy may be embodied by Einstein's famed cosmological constant.

Some current models suggest that dark energy originates within the emptiness of space. Matter has the effect of pulling space together so that it contracts. The classic example is what happens upon the formation of a black hole—space contracts to a point of zero volume (and infinite density). In the absence of matter—within a perfect vacuum—empty space seethes with an energy that creates an opposite curvature, which allows space to expand. As more empty space is created, the *vacuum energy* becomes more predominant, which accelerates the formation of even more empty space. Distant galaxies are thus seen to be accelerating from each other. It is as though gravity and dark energy are diametrically opposed. When gravity gains full rein, the result is infinite density—a black hole. When dark energy gains full rein, the result may be an infinite vacuum—a region of truly empty space.

Many other intriguing models attempt to explain the nature of dark energy. Which model is best can be determined only after more evidence is collected. Stay tuned for science news reports. In particular, the European Space Agency's *Planck Surveyor* may answer many of our current questions. However, this powerful space telescope and its many successors will, no doubt, also raise more questions than they answer. One thing is for sure: The universe holds no shortage of mysteries.

The Fate of the Universe

The universe is expanding. Matter, however, has the effect of reversing this expansion. Might enough matter exist within the universe to halt or even reverse this expansion? Before the discovery of dark energy and dark matter, astronomers had calculated that the ordinary matter in the universe was only 4% of the mass needed to halt the expansion. Dark matter was then discovered to be about six times as abundant as ordinary matter, making up about 23% of the mass needed to halt the expansion. If the remaining $100\% - (4\% + 23\%) = 73\%$ of matter could be accounted for, then the mass of the universe would be sufficient to one day halt the expansion.

Then came the discovery of dark energy. Recall that matter and energy are related by Einstein's equation $E = mc^2$. Both dark matter and dark energy, therefore, need to be included in tabulations of the total composition of the universe. The abundance of dark energy then fits the bill for making up the remaining 73% of the composition of the observable universe, as shown in Figure 5.47. There's a twist, however, in that dark energy causes the *expansion* of space, not contraction. The current thinking of most cosmologists, therefore, is that our universe is destined for an eternal expansion. This gives rise to a select number of possible scenarios for the fate of our universe.

In one scenario, called **heat death**, the universe will continue to expand, approaching absolute zero and a state of maximum entropy. After 10^{14} years, all stars will have exhausted all possible fuel. The universe will be fully dark. After 10^{16} years, planets and stars will be flung from their orbits because of random collisions, most then falling into supermassive black holes and the rest forming scattered stellar debris. After 10^{40} years, all protons and neutrons will have decayed, leaving behind gamma radiation and *leptons*, of which the electron is an example. From this time to about 10^{100} years in the future, supermassive black holes will likely be the dominant form of mass in the universe. But by the passing of 10^{150} years, they too will depart as they evaporate into photons and leptons. From then to perhaps 10^{1000} years in the future, the wavelengths of photons as well as all other remaining particles will be stretched to the lowest energy states possible. Entropy will have won supreme victory.

A second scenario, known as the **Big Rip**, recognizes that the influence of dark energy may grow stronger over time (Figure 5.48). As the universe expands exponentially, clusters of galaxies will be pulled farther apart, past the point of being visible to each other. Neighboring galaxies will then be pulled out of each other's sight. About 60 million years before the end, stars within galaxies will fly off in every direction. Some three months before the end, solar systems will disperse. In the last few minutes, stars and planets will become unbound. Then in the last instant, all atoms will be ripped apart, followed by their subatomic particles. The timeframe for the Big Rip is estimated to be about 35 billion years after the Big Bang, which would be about 21 billion years from now. And where will all the matter fly off to? Good question. Perhaps to subsequent Big Bangs?

Alan Guth, one of the early developers of modern cosmology, supports the idea that the universe will not end everywhere at once. Some 14 billion years ago, a tiny patch of primordial material inflated to form our own observable universe. But this inflation will keep on going for other patches of this primordial material and will continue to do so eternally. So, while our region of the universe expands

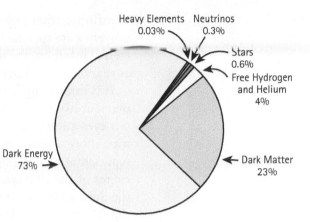

FIGURE 5.47
Ordinary matter, the stuff from which we and the galaxies we live in are made, makes up not more than 4% of the composition of the universe. The remainder is primarily dark matter (23%) and dark energy (73%), both of which we know very little about.

Although *dark energy* and *dark matter* both begin with the word *dark*, they are uniquely different. One is a form of matter; the other is a form of energy. Both are still mysterious and their existence may yet be disproven by new evidence or alternative explanations. By the next edition of this textbook, the picture may look quite different!

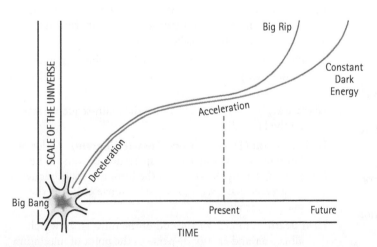

FIGURE 5.48
If the strength of dark energy remains constant, we can expect our universe to suffer heat death. If dark energy gains strength, then the ultimate demise of our universe may be the Big Rip.

to infinity, other regions are just being born. This scenario, in which observable universes are spawned on a perpetual basis, is known as **eternal inflation**. With eternal inflation, the ultimate fate of our own observable universe is not the same as that of the universe as a whole.

It is interesting how the focus of our speculations has been narrowing down over our history. In the beginning, anything seemed possible. But as we opened our eyes and minds to the natural universe, we learned that some speculations were more worthy than others. We once viewed the constellations as heavenly representations of gods. Of course, it was once thought that Earth was the center of the universe. Then we realized that Earth was just a planet orbiting the Sun, which itself was a medium-sized star among many. Our universe was the Milky Way galaxy until Hubble pointed out otherwise. When galaxies were found to be receding, many hypothesized that gravity might be strong enough to pull them back together in a Big Crunch. This possibility has since been discredited. Now we are at the point of wondering what might happen after eternal expansion. Our current speculations are just that—speculations. But they are highly refined speculations based on a great deal of collected evidence. As we continue to look at the natural universe with ever more powerful telescopes and a host of other devices, we can expect that our speculations will become ever more refined. This is the mind-opening art of science, which seeks to learn the nature of the universe for what it is—not for what we might wish it to be. Stay tuned.

For instructor-assigned homework, go to www.mastering phyics.com (MP)

SUMMARY OF TERMS (KNOWLEDGE)

Active galactic nucleus The central region of a galaxy in which matter is falling into a supermassive black hole and emitting huge amounts of energy.

Big Bang The primordial creation and expansion of space at the beginning of time.

Big Rip A model for the end of the universe in which dark energy grows stronger over time and causes all matter to rip apart.

Black hole The remains of a supergiant star that has collapsed into itself. It is so dense, and has a gravitational field so intense, that light itself cannot escape from it.

Black-hole singularity The object of zero radius into which the matter of a black hole is compressed.

Celestial sphere An imaginary sphere surrounding Earth to which the stars are attached.

Cosmic background radiation The faint microwave radiation emanating from all directions that is the remnant heat of the Big Bang.

Cosmology The study of the overall structure and evolution of the universe.

Dark energy An unknown form of energy that appears to be causing an acceleration of the expansion of space; thought to be associated with the energy exuded by a perfect vacuum.

Dark matter Invisible matter that has made its presence known so far only through its gravitational effects.

Eternal inflation A model of the universe in which cosmic inflation is not a one-time event but rather progresses to continuously spawn an infinite number of observable universes in its wake.

Event horizon The boundary region of a black hole from which no radiation can escape. Any events within the event horizon are invisible to distant observers.

Galaxy A large assemblage of stars, interstellar gas, and dust, usually categorized by its shape: elliptical, spiral, or irregular.

Giant stars Cool giant stars above the main-sequence stars on the H–R diagram.

H–R diagram (Hertzsprung–Russell diagram) A plot of luminosity versus surface temperature for stars. When so plotted, stars' positions take the form of a main sequence for average stars, with exotic stars above or below the main sequence.

Heat death A model for the end of the universe in which all matter and energy disperse to the point of maximum entropy.

Hubble's law The farther away a galaxy is from Earth, the more rapidly it is moving away from us: $v = H \times d$.

Light-year The distance light travels in one year.

Local Group Our immediate cluster of galaxies, including the Milky Way, Andromeda, and Triangulum spiral galaxies plus a few dozen smaller elliptical and irregular galaxies.

Local Supercluster The cluster of galactic clusters in which our Local Group resides.

Main sequence The diagonal band of stars on an H–R diagram; such stars generate energy by fusing hydrogen to helium.

Neutron star A small, extremely dense star composed of tightly packed neutrons formed by the welding of protons and electrons.

Nova An event in which a white dwarf suddenly brightens and appears as a "new" star.

Ordinary matter Matter that responds to the strong nuclear, weak nuclear, electromagnetic, and gravitational forces. This is matter made of protons, neutrons, and electrons, which includes the atoms and molecules that make us and our immediate environment.

Planetary nebula An expanding shell of gas ejected from a low-mass star during the latter stages of its evolution.

Pulsar A celestial object (most likely a neutron star) that spins rapidly, sending out short, precisely timed bursts of electromagnetic radiation.

Quasar The core of a distant galaxy early in its life span when its central black hole has not yet swept much matter from its vicinity, leading to a rate of radiation higher than that from entire older galaxies.

Starburst galaxy A galaxy in which stars are forming at an unusually fast rate.

Supernova The explosion of a massive star caused by gravitational collapse with the emission of enormous quantities of matter and radiation.

White dwarf A dying star that has collapsed to the size of Earth and is slowly cooling off; located at the lower left on the H–R diagram.

READING CHECK (COMPREHENSION)

5.1 Observing the Night Sky

1. What are constellations?

2. Why does an observer at a given location see one set of constellations in the winter and a different set of constellations in the summer?

3. Why do the stars appear to turn on an imaginary north–south axis about once every 24 hours?

4. Is the light-year a measurement of time or distance?

5.2 The Brightness and Color of Stars

5. Which is hotter—a red star or a blue star?

6. What is the difference between apparent brightness and luminosity?

5.3 The Hertzsprung–Russell Diagram

7. What is an H–R diagram?

8. Where are the great majority of stars plotted on an H–R diagram?

9. Where does our Sun reside on an H–R diagram?

10. Among stars originating from the main sequence, which are larger—red stars or yellow stars?

5.4 The Life Cycles of Stars

11. What event changes a protostar into a full-fledged star?

12. What are the outward and inward forces that act on a star?

13. Is the lifetime of a high-mass star longer or shorter than that of a low-mass star?

14. What is the relationship between the heavy elements that we find on Earth today and supernovae?

15. What is the relationship between a supernova and a neutron star?

5.5 Black Holes

16. What is the relationship between a supergiant star and a black hole?

17. Why don't we think the Sun will eventually become a black hole?

18. If black holes are invisible, what is the evidence for their existence?

19. Is a black hole's event horizon a physical or mathematical boundary?

5.6 Galaxies

20. What type of galaxy is the Milky Way?

21. What is a starburst galaxy?

22. How many spiral galaxies are in the Local Group?

23. Name three galactic clusters found in our Local Supercluster.

5.7 Looking Back in Time

24. Is the universe in space or is space in the universe?

25. Which depends on distance—a star's brightness or its luminosity?

26. What is the approximate age of the universe?

5.8 Dark Matter and Dark Energy

27. If we can't see dark matter, how do we know it is there?

28. Is dark matter found mostly within or just outside a galaxy?

29. According to recent evidence, how long ago did the expansion of the universe start accelerating?

30. What does WMAP stand for?

31. Which is more abundant—dark matter or ordinary matter?

32. What does the Big Rip scenario assume about dark energy?

THINK INTEGRATED SCIENCE

29A—The Drake Equation

33. What is SETI? Was it a mistake for Congress to cut its funding? Why or why not?

34. The total number of stars in the universe is much greater than the number of grains of sand on all the beaches of Earth. Given this, do you think it's possible that there are other civilizations in the universe?

THINK AND DO (HANDS-ON APPLICATION)

35. To observe the daily diurnal motion of the stars, go star watching tonight. Pick a star or constellation that lines up with a stationary landmark such as a tree or house. Then come back in an hour or so and you will see that the star has moved away from the landmark but remains in place relative to the other stars. In what direction has that star moved? To the east? West? Southwest? Northwest? Where will the star be when the Sun rises? Will it be in the same location in 24 hours?

36. To observe the revolutionary motion of Earth around the Sun, go star watching and make note of the stars directly above you. Sketch their pattern on a piece of paper and write down the date and time at which you make this observation. If these stars are not already a well-known constellation, make up a new constellation and give it a creative name. After a month has passed, look for this same constellation at the same time of night. Why isn't it still directly above you? In what direction has your constellation shifted? Why?

THINK AND COMPARE (ANALYSIS)

37. Rank the appearance of the North Star in order of increasing height from the horizon as seen from (a) Alaska, (b) Florida, (c) Vermont.

38. Rank the objects in order of increasing intrinsic motion as viewed from Earth: (a) the Moon, (b) Venus, (c) the North Star.

39. Rank the following stars in order of increasing radius:

	Star A	Star B	Star C
Surface temperature (K):	6,000	4,000	30,000
Luminosity (solar units):	1	100	0.01

40. Rank these stages of stellar development from earliest to latest: (a) white dwarf, (b) nova, (c) red giant.

41. Rank the nuclear fuels in order of being consumed, from first to last: (a) carbon, (b) helium, (c) hydrogen.

42. Rank in order of increasing size: (a) solar system, (b) Local Group, (c) galaxy.

43. Rank these elements in order of increasing abundance in the universe: (a) helium, (b) hydrogen, (c) carbon.

44. Rank the following in order of increasing abundance in the universe: (a) dark matter, (b) ordinary matter, (c) dark energy.

THINK AND SOLVE (MATHEMATICAL APPLICATION)

45. Suppose Star A is four times as luminous as Star B. If these stars are both 500 light-years away from Earth, how will their apparent brightness compare? How will the apparent brightness of these stars compare if Star A is twice as far away as Star B?

46. If you were to travel straight up from the core of our galaxy and then look back, you would have a grand view of the Milky Way's spiral shape. If the distance from the core to the outer edges was 50,000 light-years, how much surface area are you looking at? Assume the galaxy is a circle whose area can be found by the equation Area $= \pi r^2$.

47. Assume the Milky Way contains 100 billion stars evenly distributed with none concentrated toward the center. What would be the surface area density of stars? Use the equation Surface area density $=$ number of stars/surface area.

48. Use the information in the preceding problem to figure out the average area around a single star in units of AU. (Note: 1 light-year = 63,000 AU.)

49. From your answer to the preceding problem, would it be possible for two galaxies with stars evenly distributed to pass right through each other?

THINK AND EXPLAIN (SYNTHESIS)

50. Is any star bright enough for us to see on a sunny day?

51. On the Moon, stars other than the Sun can be seen during the daytime. Why?

52. We see the constellations as distinct groups of stars. Discuss why they would look entirely different from some other location in the universe, far distant from Earth.

53. Distinguish between the diurnal and intrinsic motions of celestial objects.

54. Which moves faster from horizon to horizon—the Sun or the Moon? Explain.

55. What is the relationship between a planetary nebula and a white dwarf?

56. What do the outward and inward forces acting on a star have to do with its size?

57. What is the relationship between a white dwarf and a nova?

58. What does the color of a star tell you about the star?

59. What is expected to happen to the Sun in its old age?

60. In what sense are we all made of star dust?

61. Would you expect metals to be more abundant in old stars or in new stars? Defend your answer.

62. What is the evidence for believing our Sun is a relatively young star in the universe?

63. Why are massive stars generally shorter lived than low-mass stars?

64. Why are supermassive stars relatively rare?

65. What does the spin rate of a star have to do with whether or not it has a system of planets?

66. With respect to stellar evolution, what is meant by the statement, "The bigger they are, the harder they fall"?

67. Why isn't the Sun able to fuse carbon nuclei in its core?

68. Which has the highest surface temperature—a red star, white star, or blue star?

69. In terms of the life cycle of the Sun, explain why life on Earth cannot last forever.

70. What happens to the radial distance of the event horizon as more and more mass falls into the black hole? Explain.

71. Will the Sun become a supernova? A black hole? Defend your answer.

72. Are there galaxies other than the Milky Way that can be seen with the unaided eye? Discuss.

73. Does the Milky Way galaxy contain an active galactic nucleus?

74. When was most of the helium in the universe created?

75. What does the expansion of space do to light passing through it?

76. What is the relationship between dark energy and Einstein's cosmological constant?

77. The average temperature of the universe right now is about 2.73 K. Will this temperature likely go up or down over the next billion years?

78. If the initial universe remained hotter for a longer period of time, would there likely be more or less helium?

79. Are astronomers able to point their telescopes in the direction of where the Big Bang occurred?

80. True or false: A helium balloon here on Earth pops, releasing direct remnants of the Big Bang. Explain.

81. If we are made of stardust, what are stars made of?

82. Why doesn't dark matter clump together as effectively as ordinary matter?

83. What is one important difference between dark matter and dark energy?

84. Why isn't dark energy called the dark force?

85. If there are so many stars and galaxies, why do we see so much darkness in the clear night sky?

86. If we can't even predict the weather, how can we ever expect to predict the fate of the universe?

THINK AND DISCUSS (EVALUATION)

87. Compare and contrast astronomy and astrology.

88. Project what human civilization would be like if our Sun were hidden in a dusty part of the galaxy such that no stars were ever visible to us at night.

89. It takes an infinite amount of time to watch an object fall through a black hole's event horizon. In what sense, therefore, can it be said that black-hole singularity does not exist?

90. Why is it important to have a science-based understanding of the structure of our universe? Try condensing your answer into a single philosophical sentence.

READINESS ASSURANCE TEST (RAT)

If you have a good handle on this chapter, if you really do, then you should be able to score 7 out of 10 on this RAT. If you score less than 7, you need to study further before moving on.

Choose the BEST answer to each of the following:

1. Summer and winter constellations are different because
   (a) of the spin of Earth about its polar axis.
   (b) the night sky faces in opposite directions in summer and winter.
   (c) of the tilt of Earth's polar axis.
   (d) the universe is symmetrical and harmonious.

2. Polaris is always directly over
   (a) the North Pole.
   (b) any location north of the equator.
   (c) the equator.
   (d) the South Pole.

3. What is the star nearest Earth?
   (a) Proxima Centauri
   (b) Polaris
   (c) Mercury
   (d) the Sun

4. The property of a star that relates to the amount of energy per unit time it is producing is its
   (a) luminosity.
   (b) apparent brightness.
   (c) color.
   (d) volume.
   (e) mass.

5. The longest-lived stars are those of
   (a) low mass.
   (b) high mass.
   (c) intermediate mass.
   (d) infinite mass.

6. After our Sun burns all the hydrogen in its core, it will become a
   (a) white dwarf.
   (b) black dwarf.
   (c) black hole.
   (d) red giant.
   (e) blue giant.

7. The shape of an active starburst galaxy tends to be
   (a) elliptical.
   (b) spiral.
   (c) irregular.
   (d) all of these

8. Scientists estimate the age of our universe to be about
   (a) 5000 years old.
   (b) 1 billion years old.
   (c) 14 billion years old.
   (d) 42 billion years old.

9. Which of the following is not accepted evidence for the Big Bang?
   (a) cosmic background radiation
   (b) homogeneity of the temperature of the universe
   (c) the abundance of helium
   (d) dark energy

10. Dark matter is
    (a) ordinary matter that is no longer emitting light.
    (b) affecting the orbits of stars.
    (c) a dense form of dark energy.
    (d) repelled by ordinary matter.

Answers to RAT

1. b, 2. a, 3. d, 4. a, 5. a, 6. d, 7. c, 8. c, 9. d, 10. b

6
CHAPTER 6
The Solar System

How does the Sun produce so much energy? How are the planets similar, and how are they different? How did our Moon form, and how does it go through phases? Why do we see only one side of the Moon? What are solar and lunar eclipses, and why are they rare? What are meteors, asteroids, and comets? How frequently do they collide with our planet, and why does a comet's tail always point away from the Sun?

For thousands of years, people have gazed into the night sky and pondered such questions. Thanks to scientific advances over the past century, however, the answers to these and other basic questions about the universe are now available to us. This chapter focuses on what we know about our solar system, which on a cosmic scale is Earth's own backyard. In the next chapter, we expand our view to galaxies and beyond, where deeper mysteries still remain.

6.1 The Solar System and Its Formation

EXPLAIN THIS How is gravity responsible for solar energy?

LEARNING OBJECTIVE
Describe how nebular theory accounts for the main attributes of our solar system.

Our solar system is the collection of objects gravitationally bound to the Sun. Along with the Sun itself, the solar system contains at least eight **planets**, which are large orbiting bodies massive enough for their gravity to make them spherical but small enough to avoid having nuclear fusion in their cores. The planets also have successfully cleared all debris from their orbital paths, which all lie roughly in the same plane. This plane, called the **ecliptic**, is defined as the plane of Earth's orbit. Within the solar system are also numerous moons (objects orbiting planets), asteroids (small, rocky bodies), comets (small, icy bodies), and a collection of miniature planets known as dwarf planets that orbit on the outer edges of the solar system. The most well-known dwarf planet is Pluto, which was downgraded from planet status in 2006. The planets and all these other objects are quite small compared to the Sun. Figure 6.1 shows the sizes of the planets relative to the Sun, which contains a whopping 99.86% of the solar system's mass.

The vast distances between the Sun and the objects orbiting it can be grasped by imagining the Sun reduced to the size of a large beach ball 1 m in diameter. The closest planet, Mercury, would be an apple seed located about 40 m (130 ft) away. The next closest planet, Venus, would be the size of a pea about 80 m (255 ft) distant. Earth, also about the size of a pea, would be about 110 m away, which is greater than the length of a football field. The next planet, Mars, which is only a bit larger than Mercury, would be an apple seed almost two football field lengths away from our solar beach ball.

These first four planets—Mercury, Venus, Earth, and Mars—are called the **inner planets** because of their relatively close proximity to the Sun. All the inner planets are solid rocky planets. The **outer planets** are larger gaseous planets located much farther away. The first outer planet is Jupiter, which on the scale mentioned would be the size of a softball more than half a kilometer away. The second outer planet, Saturn, famous for its extensive ring system, would be the size of a baseball more than a kilometer away. Planets Uranus and Neptune would both be about the size of Ping-Pong balls located 2 and 3 km away, respectively. We see that solar system objects are mere specks in the vastness of the space about the Sun.

MasteringPhysics®
TUTORIAL: Formation of the Solar System
VIDEO: History of the Solar System
VIDEO: Orbits in the Solar System

The ancients could tell the difference between planets and stars because of the difference in their movements in the sky. The stars remain relatively fixed in their patterns in the sky, but the planets wander. The term *planet* is derived from the Greek for "wandering star."

FIGURE 6.1
This illustration shows the order and relative sizes of planets. Moving away from the Sun, we have in order: Mercury, Venus, Earth, Mars, Jupiter, Saturn, Uranus, and Neptune. The planets range greatly in size, but the Sun dwarfs them all—containing more than 99% of the mass in the solar system. *Note:* Distances are not to scale in this illustration. If they were, Earth would be placed over 8 meters away. Neptune would be over 240 meters away!

TABLE 6.1 PLANETARY DATA

	Mean Distance from Sun (Earth distances, AU)	Orbital Period (years)	Diameter		Mass		Density (g/cm³)	Inclination to Ecliptic
			(km)	(Earth = 1)	(kg)	(Earth = 1)		
Sun			1,392,000	109.1	1.99×10^{30}	3.3×10^{5}	1.41	
Terrestrial								
Mercury	0.39	0.24	4,880	0.38	3.3×10^{23}	0.06	5.4	7.0°
Venus	0.72	0.62	12,100	0.95	4.9×10^{24}	0.81	5.2	3.4°
Earth	1.00	1.00	12,760	1.00	6.0×10^{24}	1.00	5.5	0.0°
Mars	1.52	1.88	6,800	0.53	6.4×10^{23}	0.11	3.9	1.9°
Jovian								
Jupiter	5.20	11.86	142,800	11.19	1.90×10^{27}	317.73	1.3	1.3°
Saturn	9.54	29.46	120,700	9.44	5.7×10^{26}	95.15	0.7	2.5°
Uranus	19.18	84.0	50,800	3.98	8.7×10^{25}	14.65	1.3	0.8°
Neptune	30.06	164.79	49,600	3.88	1.0×10^{26}	17.23	1.7	1.8°
Dwarf Planets								
Pluto	39.44	247.70	2,300	0.18	1.3×10^{22}	0.002	1.9	17°
Eris	67.67	557	2,400	0.19	1.6×10^{22}	0.002	1.9	44°

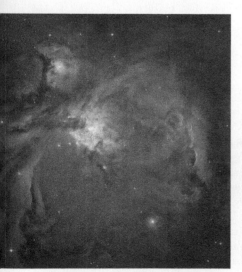

FIGURE 6.2
This photograph, provided by the Hubble Telescope, shows the Orion Nebula. The Orion Nebula, like the nebula from which our solar system formed, is an interstellar cloud of gas and dust and the birthplace of stars.

Because of these vast interplanetary distances, astronomers use the *astronomical unit* to measure them. One **astronomical unit (AU)** is about 1.5×10^{8} km (about 9.3×10^{7} mi) or the distance from Earth to the Sun. Table 6.1 gives the distances of planets from the Sun in AU. The data in Table 6.1 also show the division of the planets into two groups with similar properties. The inner planets—Mercury, Venus, Earth, and Mars—are solid and relatively small and dense. They are called the *terrestrial planets*. The outer planets are large, have many rings and satellites, and are composed primarily of hydrogen and helium gas. These are called the *jovian planets* because their large sizes and gaseous compositions resemble those of Jupiter.

Nebular Theory

Any theory of solar system formation must be able to explain two major regularities: (1) *the motions among large bodies of the solar system* and (2) *the division of planets into two main types*—terrestrial *and* jovian. Further, a viable theory of solar system formation must explain other known features of the solar system, including the existence of asteroids, comets, and moons.

The modern scientific theory that satisfies these requirements is called the **nebular theory**, which holds that the Sun and planets formed together from a cloud of gas and dust, a *nebula* (Latin for "cloud"). According to the theory, the solar system began to condense from the cloud of gas and dust about 5 billion years ago. The cloud would have been very diffuse and large, with a diameter thousands of times larger than Pluto's orbit. A nebula currently visible within the constellation of Orion is shown in Figure 6.2.

Within the nebula from which our solar system formed, the gravitational pull on particles exceeded the tendency of gas to disperse and fill all available space. Once the gravitational collapse of a cloud begins, gravity ensures that it continues. The universal law of gravity is an inverse-square law: The strength of the gravitational force increases dramatically as the particles become closer.

MATH CONNECTION

The Scale of the Solar System

Astronomical distances are mind-boggling. Try the following problems to better appreciate the sizes of bodies in the solar system and the distances between them. (Use the distance formula: distance = speed × time and data from Table 6.1.)

Problem The distance between Earth and the Moon is 384,401 km. How many Earth diameters would fit between Earth and the Moon?

Solution:

$$\frac{384,401 \text{ km}}{12,760 \text{ km}} \approx 30$$

About 30 Earth-sized planets would fit in the distance between Earth and the Moon.

Problem How long would it take to drive from Earth to the Moon if you drive at 55 mi/h? State your answer in years.

Solution: $d = vt \rightarrow t = \dfrac{d}{v}$

Convert all units to metric:
(55 mi/h) (1 km/0.62 mi) ≈ 89 km/h.
Then t = 384,401 km/89 km/h =
4319 h (1 day/24 h) (1 yr/365 days) ≈ 0.5 yr.
It would take about one-half year to drive to the Moon traveling at freeway speeds.

Problem If you could fly to the Sun on a jet that moves at 1000 km/h, how long would it take? State your answer in years.

Solution:

$$t = \frac{d}{v} = \frac{1.5 \times 10^8 \text{ km}}{1000 \text{ km/h}}$$

$$= 1.5 \times 10^5 \text{ h}$$

To convert to years, multiply by the following conversion factors:

$$(1.5 \times 10^5 \text{ h})\left(\frac{1 \text{ day}}{24 \text{ h}}\right)\left(\frac{1 \text{ yr}}{365 \text{ days}}\right) = 17 \text{ yr}$$

So if you could fly to the Sun in a jet without becoming vaporized, it would take about 17 years.

Problem The diameter of the Sun is 1,390,000 km. What is its diameter in AU? How much greater is the mean distance between Earth and the Sun compared to the diameter of the Sun?

Solution:

$$(1.39 \times 10^6 \text{ km}) \times (1 \text{ AU}/1.5 \times 10^8 \text{ km}) \approx 0.01 \text{ AU}$$

$$\frac{1 \text{ AU}}{0.01 \text{ AU}} = 100$$

The diameter of the Sun is approximately equal to 0.01 AU, so the distance between Earth and the Sun is about 100 times the diameter of the Sun. Big as the Sun is, the solar system is mostly empty space.

The cloud maintained a constant mass as it shrank, but gravitational forces grew ever stronger, and the cloud came together, taking on a spherical shape.

This nebula must also have had a slight net rotation, possibly due to the rotation of the galaxy itself. As the nebula shrank, it spun faster and faster (because of the *conservation of angular momentum* discussed in Appendix B). As any spinning object contracts, the speed of its spin increases such that angular momentum is conserved. A familiar example is an ice skater whose spin rate increases when her extended arms are pulled inward. A nebula does the same, as shown in Figure 6.3.

What happens to the shape of a sphere as it spins faster and faster? The answer is that it flattens. A familiar example is the chef who turns a ball of pizza dough into a disk by spinning it on his hands. Even planet Earth is a slightly "flattened" sphere because of its daily spin. Saturn, with a faster spin, noticeably departs from a purely spherical shape. So the initially spherical nebula progressed to a spinning disk, the center of which became the *protosun*.

UNIFYING CONCEPT

● *The Gravitational Force*
   Section 5.3

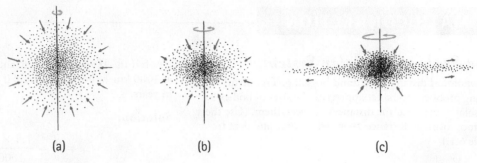

(a) (b) (c)

FIGURE 6.3
(a) The nebula from which the solar system formed was originally a large, diffuse cloud that rotated quite slowly. The cloud began to collapse under the influence of gravity.
(b) As the cloud collapsed, it heated up as gravitational potential energy converted to heat. It spun faster by the conservation of angular momentum. (c) The cloud flattened into a disk as a result of its fast rotation. A spinning, flattened disk was produced whose mass was concentrated at its hot center.

UNIFYING CONCEPT
● *The Scientific Method*
Section 1.3

The formation of the spinning disk explains the motions of our solar system today. All planets orbit the Sun in nearly the same plane because they formed from that same flat nebular disk. The direction in which the disk was spinning became the direction of the Sun's rotation and the orbits of planets.

CHECK YOURSELF
As a nebula contracts, its rate of spin increases. What rule of nature is at play here?

CHECK YOUR ANSWER
The rule that applies to all spinning bodies is the *conservation of angular momentum*. That rule and the conservation of energy are dominant players in the universe.

The surrounding disk was the source of material that became the planets. In the spinning disk, matter collected in some regions more densely than in others. Perhaps small particles of gas and dust stuck together via gravity or electrostatic attraction. Because of their extra mass, these clumps exerted a stronger gravitational force on one another than on neighboring regions of the disk, and so they pulled in even more material to them. This led to the accretion of the nebular disk into small objects called *planetesimals*, which ranged in size from boulders to objects several kilometers in diameter. Planetesimals grew larger through countless collisions until they gravitationally dominated surrounding matter and finally became full-grown planets.

All the while, compression due to gravity caused a rise in temperature, especially within the central portions of the solar nebula, which developed into a hot ball of gas called the *protosun*. The protosun transformed into the Sun once the temperature became sufficient to ignite thermonuclear fusion. Once thermonuclear fusion occurred and the Sun began to radiate energy, the nebular disk warmed, with the inner portions reaching higher temperatures than the outer portions. As a result, the inner and outer planets developed differently. The inner planets formed from materials that remained solid at high temperatures; hence, the inner planets are rocky. The outer planets, by contrast, consist mainly of hydrogen and helium gas that coalesced in the cold regions of the solar system far from the Sun. Thus, we can see that the nebular theory accounts for the formation of the planets and the neat division of them into two groups.

6.2   The Sun

EXPLAIN THIS   Why is the Sun's surface much cooler than its inner core?

LEARNING OBJECTIVE
Recognize the features of the Sun, including its interior, photosphere, sunspots, solar cycle, chromosphere, and corona.

The Sun has a mass of about a trillion quadrillion tons (2×10^{30} kg). It produces energy from the thermonuclear fusion of hydrogen into helium. Each second, approximately 657 million tons of hydrogen is fused to 653 million tons of helium. The 4 million tons of mass lost is discharged as radiant energy. This conversion of hydrogen into helium in the Sun has been going on since it formed nearly 5 billion years ago, and it is expected to continue for another 5 billion years. A tiny fraction of the Sun's energy reaches Earth and is converted by photosynthesizing organisms into chemical energy stored in large molecules. These energy-rich molecules are the primary energy source for almost all the organisms of this planet. The Sun, Earth's nearest star, is the solar system's power supply.

MasteringPhysics®
TUTORIAL: The Sun

Solar energy is generated deep within the core of the Sun. The solar core constitutes about 10% of the Sun's total volume. It is very hot—more than 15,000,000 K. The core is also very dense, with more than 12 times the density of solid lead. Pressure in the core is 340 billion times Earth's atmospheric pressure! Because of these intense conditions, the hydrogen, helium, and minute quantities of other elements exist in the plasma state. *Plasma*, recall, is the phase of matter beyond gas, consisting of ions and electrons rather than atoms—electrons have been stripped from atoms by high energies. The nuclei of this plasma move fast enough to undergo nuclear fusion, (Integrated Science 10C). The energy released from this nuclear fusion rises to the surface, where it causes gases to emit a broad spectrum of electromagnetic radiation, centered in the visible region.

The Sun's surface is a layer of glowing 5800 K plasma, which is much cooler than the Sun's core but hot enough to generate lots of light. This layer, called the *photosphere* (sphere of light), is about 500 km deep. Within the photosphere are relatively cool regions that appear as **sunspots** when viewed from Earth. Sunspots are cooler and darker than the rest of the photosphere and are caused by magnetic fields that impede hot gases from rising to the surface. As shown in Figure 6.4, sunspots can be seen by focusing the image of the Sun from a telescope or pair of binoculars onto a flat white surface. Sunspots are typically twice the size of Earth, move around because of the Sun's rotation, and

FIGURE 6.4
Never directly look at the Sun! Instead, you can get a nice view of the Sun by focusing the image of the Sun from a pair of binoculars onto a white surface. If the Sun is eclipsed by the Moon, which is a rare event, the Sun is seen as a crescent. More commonly, the Sun's image may reveal sunspots.

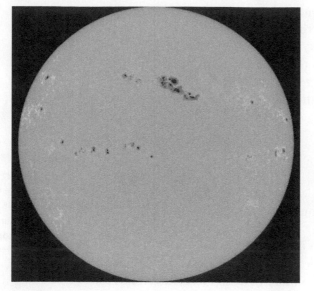

FIGURE 6.5

Sunspots on the solar surface are relatively cool regions. We say relatively cool because they are hotter than 4000 K. They look dark only in contrast with their 5800 K surroundings.

FIGURE 6.6

The pink chromosphere becomes visible when the Moon blocks most of the light from the photosphere during a solar eclipse.

FIGURE 6.7

The pearly white solar corona is visible only during a solar eclipse. Notice how this exceptional photo of the corona also captures some of the pink of the chromosphere as well as the face of the new Moon, which is faintly illuminated by light reflected from the full Earth. In other words, if you were standing on the Moon when this photo was taken, you would see your faint shadow cast by the fully lit Earth shining above you.

last about a week or so. Often, they cluster in groups as shown in Figure 6.5.

The Sun spins slowly on its axis. Because the Sun is a fluid rather than a solid, different latitudes of the Sun spin at different rates. Equatorial regions spin once in 25 days, but higher latitudes take up to 36 days to make a complete rotation. This differential spin means the surface near the equator pulls ahead of the surface farther north or south. The Sun's differential spin wraps and distorts the solar magnetic field, which bursts out to form the sunspots mentioned earlier. A reversal of magnetic poles occurs every 11 years, and the number of sunspots also reaches a maximum every 11 years (currently). The complete cycle of solar activity is 22 years.

Above the Sun's photosphere is a transparent 10,000-km-thick shell called the *chromosphere* (sphere of color), seen during an eclipse as a pinkish glow surrounding the eclipsed Sun. The chromosphere is hotter than the photosphere, reaching temperatures of about 10,000 K. Its beautiful pink color, as shown in Figure 6.6, arises from the emission of light from hydrogen atoms.

Beyond the chromosphere are streamers and filaments of outward-moving, high-temperature plasmas curved by the Sun's magnetic field. This outermost region of the Sun's atmosphere is the *corona*, which extends out several million kilometers (Figure 6.7). The temperature of the corona is amazingly high—on the order of 1 million K—and it is where most of the Sun's powerful X-rays are generated. Because the corona is not very dense, its brightness is not as intense as the Sun's surface, which makes the corona safe to observe during (and only during) a total solar eclipse. High-speed protons and electrons are cast outward from the corona to generate the *solar wind*, which powers the aurora on Earth and produces the tails of comets.

CHECK YOURSELF

1. **Was the Sun more massive 1000 years ago than it is today? Defend your answer.**
2. **Of the photosphere, chromosphere, and corona, which is thinnest? Which is hottest? Which is between the other two?**

CHECK YOUR ANSWER

1. Yes, although slightly compared with its great mass. The Sun loses mass as hydrogen nuclei combine to make helium nuclei.
2. The photosphere is the thinnest. The corona is the hottest. The chromosphere is the pinkish layer above the photosphere and below the vast corona.

FYI We have seven days in a week because ancient Europeans decided to name days after the seven wandering celestial objects they could observe. The English day names were derived from the language of the Teutonic tribes who lived in the region that is now Germany. In Teutonic, the Sun is *Sun* (Sunday), the Moon is *Moon* (Monday), Mars is *Tiw* (Tuesday), Mercury is *Woden* (Wednesday), Jupiter is *Thor* (Thursday), Venus is *Fria* (Friday), and Saturn is *Saturn* (Saturday).

6.3 The Inner Planets

EXPLAIN THIS Why does Venus, not Mercury, have the hottest surface of any planet in the solar system?

LEARNING OBJECTIVE
Identify the major properties of the four inner planets: Mercury, Venus, Earth, and Mars.

Compared with the outer planets, the four planets nearest the Sun are close together. These are Mercury, Venus, Earth, and Mars. Each of these rocky planets has a mineral-containing solid crust.

Mercury

Mercury (Figure 6.8) is about 1.4 times larger than Earth's Moon and similar in appearance. It is the closest planet to the Sun. Because of this closeness it is the fastest planet, circling the Sun in only 88 Earth days—which thus equals one Mercury "year." Mercury spins about its axis only three times for each two revolutions about the Sun. This makes its daytime very long and very hot, with temperatures as high as 430°C.

Because of Mercury's small size and weak gravitational field, it holds very little atmosphere. Mercury's atmosphere is only about a trillionth as dense as Earth's atmosphere—it's a better vacuum than laboratories on Earth can produce. So without a blanket of atmosphere, and because there are no winds to transfer heat from one region to another, nighttime on Mercury is very cold, about −170°C. Mercury is a fairly bright object in the nighttime sky and is best seen as an evening "star" during March and April or as a morning star during September and October. It is seen near the Sun at sunup or sunset.

FIGURE 6.8
Mercury is heavily cratered from the impacts of many meteorites. Mercury is a small planet, with only about 6% of the volume and mass of Earth. This photo was taken by the *Messenger* spacecraft, which was launched from Earth in 2004 and reached orbit around planet Mercury in 2011.

Venus

Venus is the second planet from the Sun and, like Mercury, has no moon. Venus is frequently the first starlike object to appear after the Sun sets, so it is often called the evening "star," as illustrated in Figure 6.9. Compared with other planets, Venus most closely resembles Earth in size, density, and distance from the Sun

FIGURE 6.9
Because the orbits of Mercury and Venus lie inside the orbit of Earth, they are always near the Sun in our sky. Near sunset (or sunrise) they are visible as "evening stars" or "morning stars."

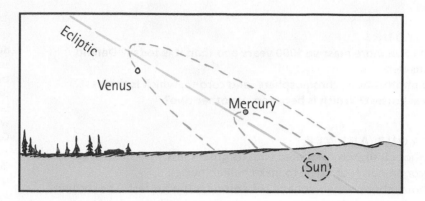

FIGURE 6.10
Venus is an Earth-sized planet barren of any oceans. The surface of Venus was first mapped in the early 1990s by the spacecraft *Magellan*, which used microwave radar ranging to "see through" the planet's thick atmosphere of carbon dioxide and sulfuric acid clouds.

FYI Ancient American cultures ran their lives using three calendars. Their secular calendar, which told them when to plant seeds and so forth, followed the 365-day orbit of Earth. Their religious calendar centered on the roughly 260-day orbit of Venus. Both of these calendars were cyclical and couldn't account for succeeding years. For that purpose they developed the "long count" calendar, which, interestingly enough, employed the concept of zero. They did this centuries before the concept of zero was recognized by accountants in India.

(Figure 6.10). However, Venus has a very dense atmosphere and opaque cloud cover that generate high surface temperatures (470°C)—too hot for oceans. The atmosphere of Venus is about 96% CO_2. Remember from Chapter 10 that carbon dioxide is a "greenhouse gas." By this we mean that CO_2 blocks the escape of infrared radiation from Earth's surface and contributes to the warming of our planet. The thick blanket of CO_2 surrounding Venus effectively traps heat near the Venusian surface. This and Venus's proximity to the Sun make Venus the hottest planet in the solar system.

Another difference between Venus and Earth is the way the two planets spin about their axes. Venus takes 243 Earth days to make one full spin and only 225 Earth days to make one revolution around the Sun. Furthermore, Venus spins in a direction opposite to the direction of Earth's spin. So, on Venus, the Sun rises in the west and sets in the east. But, because the cloud cover is so dense, a Venusian sunrise or sunset is never visible from its surface.

The slow spin of Venus means that the atmosphere is not disturbed by the Coriolis effect described in Chapter 10. As a result, there is very little wind and weather on the surface of Venus. Instead, the stifling hot dense air sits still throughout its long days and nights.

In recent years, 17 probes have landed on the surface of Venus. There have been 18 flyby spacecraft (notably *Pioneer Venus* in 1978 and *Magellan* in 1993). From spacecraft data, scientists have been able to account for why the atmospheres of Venus and Earth are so different. According to the generally accepted model, when the two planets first formed they had similar amounts of water. Venus, however, is a bit closer to the Sun than Earth is. It also rotates much more slowly. These two factors combined to make the Sun-facing side of Venus significantly warmer than Earth. With greater warmth, more of Venus's water evaporated into its atmosphere. Like carbon dioxide, water vapor is a powerful greenhouse gas. So more water vapor in the atmosphere caused even more warming, which caused more of the oceans to evaporate, causing further warming—runaway global warming! Venus's early oceans contained massive amounts of dissolved carbonates, just as on Earth. As the oceans evaporated, these carbonates transformed into carbon dioxide and moved into the atmosphere, increasing the intensity of the greenhouse effect. Water vapor in the early Venusian atmosphere was subject to the Sun's ultraviolet rays, which broke the water down into hydrogen and oxygen. The hydrogen escaped into space while the oxygen chemically reacted with minerals on the surface. In the end, the planet's supply of water was forever lost. All that remains we see today as a thick atmosphere of heat-trapping carbon dioxide, as well as other compounds, most notably, sulfuric acid, H_2SO_4.

CHECK YOURSELF

As the Sun gets older it also gets hotter. How will this affect the amount of water vapor in our atmosphere?

CHECK YOUR ANSWER

Initially, the additional heat from the Sun will increase the rate at which Earth's oceans evaporate. More water vapor in the atmosphere will then enhance the greenhouse effect, causing even warmer temperatures, which will provide for even more evaporation. As the oceans disappear, carbon dioxide levels will also rise dramatically, ensuring that the greenhouse effect keeps the water vaporized. Ultraviolet light from the Sun, however, will zap this water from the atmosphere. So, in the end, as the Sun gets hotter, the amount of water vapor in the atmosphere will drop to near nothing. We will share the same fate as our sister planet Venus. You can breathe a bit easy because the timeframe for this is about a billion years.

FYI Not all of the Venusian water was lost to space. Some instead reacted with volcano-generated sulfur dioxide to form sulfuric acid, which now laces the upper levels of the Venusian atmosphere. The water that stayed behind to react with sulfur dioxide was predominately water containing the heavier isotope of hydrogen, known as deuterium. This has been confirmed with direct measurements from space probes, which show an unusually high proportion of deuterium. This, in turn, supports the theory that Venus lost its water because of a runaway greenhouse effect. Without the greenhouse effect, the proportion of deuterium in the atmosphere would remain similar to that currently found on Earth.

Earth

Our home planet Earth resides within the Sun's *habitable zone*, which is a region not too close and not too far from the Sun so that water can exist predominately in the liquid phase, as shown in Figure 6.11. Earth has an abundant supply of liquid water covering about 70% of Earth's surface, which makes our planet the blue planet (Figure 6.12).

Earth's oceans support the *carbon dioxide cycle*, which acts as a thermostat to keep global temperatures from reaching harsh extremes. For example, if Earth froze over completely, carbon dioxide released by volcanoes would no longer be absorbed by the oceans. Instead the carbon dioxide would build up in the atmosphere, which would warm the atmosphere and hence melt the frozen Earth. Conversely, if Earth became hotter and hotter, more water would evaporate. This would lead to more precipitation, which would remove carbon dioxide from the atmosphere. With less carbon dioxide in the atmosphere, the greenhouse effect would be minimized and Earth would cool. So not only are we a nice distance from the Sun, but our atmosphere contains just enough water vapor and carbon dioxide to keep temperatures favorable for life. Furthermore, our relatively high daily spin rate allows only a brief and small lowering of temperature on the nighttime side of Earth. So temperature extremes of day and night are also kept moderate.

Moreover, that movements within Earth's molten core generate a strong magnetic field around our planet. This magnetic field, called the *magnetosphere*, extends thousands of kilometers into space and shields the Earth from *solar wind*, which is a flow of charged particles emanating from the Sun. This form of cosmic radiation is harmful to living organisms. Furthermore, solar wind is capable of stripping a planet of its atmosphere. Planet Earth is indeed a sanctuary for life in an otherwise inhospitable universe.

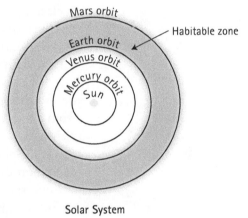

Solar System

FIGURE 6.11

Earth resides on the inner side of the Sun's habitable zone, which is where conditions are favorable for life as we know it.

FIGURE 6.12

Earth, the blue planet. This famous photo was taken by *Apollo 17* astronauts as they returned from the last manned mission to the Moon in 1972. It is the only existing photo of the full Earth from an appreciable distance. Can you see that it was taken in the summer months of the Southern Hemisphere?

CHECK YOURSELF
If Venus was also once protected by the carbon dioxide cycle, what went wrong?

CHECK YOUR ANSWER
The carbon dioxide cycle requires water. The Venusian carbon dioxide cycle, therefore, broke down as the Venusian water was split apart by the Sun's ultraviolet rays.

Mars

Mars captures our fancy as another world, perhaps even as a world with life because it resides on the outer fringes of the habitable zone. Mars is a little more than half Earth's size; its mass is about one-ninth that of Earth; and it has a core, a mantle, a crust, and a thin, nearly cloudless atmosphere. It has polar ice caps and seasons that are nearly twice as long as Earth's because Mars takes nearly two Earth years to orbit the Sun. Mars and Earth spin on their axes at about the same rate, which means the lengths of their days are about the same. When Mars is closest to Earth, a situation that occurs once every 15 to 17 years, its bright, ruddy color outshines the brightest stars.

The Martian atmosphere is about 95% carbon dioxide, with only about 0.15% oxygen. Yet because the Martian atmosphere is relatively thin, it doesn't trap heat via the greenhouse effect as much as Earth's and Venus's atmospheres do. So the temperatures on Mars are generally colder than on Earth, ranging from about 30°C in the day at the equator to a frigid −130°C at night. If you visit Mars, never mind your raincoat, for there is far too little water vapor in the atmosphere for rain. Even the ice at the planet's poles consists primarily of carbon dioxide. And don't give a second thought to waterproof footwear because the very low atmospheric pressure doesn't allow any puddles or lakes to form.

(a)   (b)

FIGURE 6.13
(a) A model of NASA's Mars Exploration Rover, *Spirit*, with cameras mounted on the white mast. (b) *Spirit* took photographs in June 2004 for this composite, true-color image of the region named Columbia Hills on Mars. The vehicle later traveled to the hills to analyze their composition.

Surface features on Mars, such as channels, indicate that liquid water was once abundant on this planet. This implies a distant past that was much warmer—a situation likely made possible by the greenhouse effect of a thicker atmosphere.

What happened to this thicker atmosphere? A currently accepted model is that because Mars is such a small planet, its molten core cooled down and solidified relatively fast—within a billion years of formation. This would have had at least two major consequences. The first is a decrease in the activity of volcanoes, which are a prime source of atmospheric gases. The second is the loss of the planet's magnetosphere. Without a magnetosphere, the bulk of the early Martian atmosphere—no longer replaced by volcanoes—was carried away into space by solar winds.

Today, landings on Mars show it to be a very dry and windy place. Because the Martian atmosphere has a very low density, its winds are about 10 times as fast as winds on Earth.

In 2004, spacecraft orbiting Mars detected signs of the organic compound methane, CH_4, in the atmosphere. This is unusual because methane decomposes fairly rapidly, which tells us that this compound is currently being produced. The likely source is ongoing residual volcanic activity, which could potentially melt underground ice into liquid water. Indeed, scientists have found evidence of the leakage of underground liquid water onto the surface occurring since we started surveying Mars from space. Once on the surface, this water would evaporate or freeze and sublime away. Underground pools of volcanically warmed liquid water, however, may harbor microscopic life forms.

Mars has two small moons—Phobos, the inner one, and Deimos, the outer. Both are potato-shaped and have cratered surfaces. Also, both orbit in the same easterly direction in which Mars spins (like our Moon). The eastward orbit of Phobos, however, is so fast that from the Martian surface, this moon is seen to rise in the west and set in the east. The slower moving and much more distant Deimos is only about half the size of Phobos and from the Martian surface appears as a barely visible point of light.

Why are planets round? All parts of a forming planet pull close together by mutual gravitation. No "corners" form because they're simply pulled in. So gravity is the cause of the spherical shapes of planets and other celestial bodies.

FYI Jupiter is near the point at which the addition of more matter would cause the size of this planet to contract. This is analogous to a stack of pillows. Start stacking pillows and the stack gets taller. Eventually, however, a point is reached at which the weight of upper pillows pushes down on lower pillows such that the column of pillows gets shorter. Interestingly, Jupiter is *larger* than the smallest stars, which, though smaller than Jupiter, are about 80 times as massive.

6.4   The Outer Planets

EXPLAIN THIS The exteriors of the outer planets are gaseous, but their interiors are mostly liquid. Why?

LEARNING OBJECTIVE
Identify the major properties of the four outer planets: Jupiter, Saturn, Uranus, and Neptune.

The outer planets—Jupiter, Saturn, Uranus, and Neptune—are gigantic, gaseous, low-density worlds. Each of them formed from rocky and metallic cores that were much more massive than the terrestrial planets. The gravitational forces of these cores were strong enough to sweep up gases of the early planetary nebula, primarily hydrogen and helium. The cores continued to collect gases until the Sun ignited and the solar wind blew away the remaining interplanetary gases. The core of Jupiter was the first to develop, and hence it had the longest time to collect gas before solar ignition. This is why Jupiter is the largest of the outer planets. Another commonality is that they all have ring systems, Saturn's being the most prominent. We will explore the outer planets in the order of their distance from the Sun.

FIGURE 6.14
Jupiter, with its moons Io (orange dot over planet) and Europa (white dot to right of planet), as seen from the *Voyager 1* spacecraft. The Great Red Spot (lower left), larger than Earth, is a cyclonic weather pattern.

FIGURE 6.15
This artist's rendering shows aurorae (pink) in the polar atmosphere of Jupiter. Aurorae, like the northern lights on Earth, are caused by charged particles from the solar wind exciting gas molecules in the upper atmosphere.

FIGURE 6.16
Galileo was the first to study the heavens with a telescope. He noted the changing positions of Jupiter's four largest moons and concluded they were orbiting Jupiter, which was a violation of the then widely held belief that all heavenly objects orbited Earth. In his honor, these four moons are known as the Galilean moons—from left to right starting with top row: Ganymede, Callisto, Io, and Europa.

Jupiter

Jupiter is the largest of all the planets. Its yellow light in our night sky is brighter than that of any star. Jupiter spins rapidly about its axis in about 10 hours, a speed that flattens it so that its equatorial diameter is about 6% greater than its polar diameter. As with the Sun, all parts do not rotate in unison. Equatorial regions complete a full revolution several minutes before nearby regions in higher and lower latitudes. This results in a pattern of stripes running parallel to the equator. The atmospheric pressure deep within Jupiter is more than a million times the atmospheric pressure of Earth. Jupiter's atmosphere is about 82% hydrogen, 17% helium, and 1% methane, ammonia, and other molecules.

Jupiter's average diameter is about 11 times Earth's, which means Jupiter's volume is more than 1000 times Earth's. Jupiter's mass is greater than the combined masses of all the other planets. Because of its low density, however—about one-fourth of Earth's—Jupiter's mass is more than 300 times Earth's. Investigations of Jupiter tell us that its core is a solid sphere about 15 times as massive as the entire Earth, and it is composed of iron, nickel, and other minerals.

More than half of Jupiter's volume is an ocean of liquid hydrogen. Beneath the hydrogen ocean lies an inner layer of hydrogen compressed into a liquid metallic state. In it are abundant conduction electrons that flow to produce Jupiter's enormous magnetic field.

Jupiter has more than 60 moons in addition to a faint ring. The four largest moons were discovered by Galileo in 1610; Io and Europa are about the size of our Moon, and Ganymede and Callisto are about as large as Mercury (Figure 6.16). Jupiter's moon Io has more volcanic activity than any other body in the solar system. Perhaps most intriguing of all, however, are Ganymede and Europa, whose surfaces are made of frozen water. As shown in Figure 6.17, deep beneath this ice is likely an ocean of water kept warm by the strong tidal forces from nearby Jupiter.

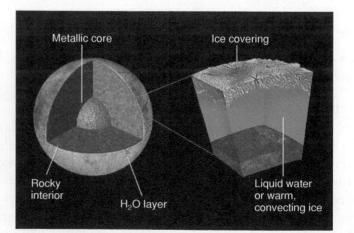

FIGURE 6.17
A model of the interior of Europa with a zoomed-in view of its ice-capped ocean, which, according to magnetic measurements, likely covers the entire sphere.

Saturn

Saturn is one of the most remarkable objects in the sky, with its rings clearly visible through a small telescope. It is quite bright—brighter than all but two stars—and it is second only to Jupiter in mass and size. Saturn is twice as far from Earth as Jupiter is. Its diameter, not counting its ring system, is nearly 10 times that of Earth, and its mass is nearly 100 times Earth's. It is composed primarily of hydrogen and helium, and it has the lowest density of any planet, only 0.7 times the density of water. These characteristics mean that Saturn would easily float in a bathtub, if the bathtub were large enough. Its low density and its 10.2-hour rapid spin produce more polar flattening than can be seen in the other planets. Notice its oblong shape in Figure 6.18.

FIGURE 6.18
Saturn surrounded by its famous rings, which are composed of rocks and ice.

Saturn's rings, only a few kilometers thick, lie in a plane coincident with Saturn's equator. Four concentric rings have been known for many years, and spacecraft missions have detected many others. The rings are composed of chunks of frozen water and rocks, believed to be the material of a moon that never formed or the remnants of a moon torn apart by tidal forces. All the rocks and bits of matter that make up the rings pursue independent orbits about Saturn. The inner parts of the ring travel faster than the outer parts, just as any satellite near a planet travels faster than a more distant satellite.

Saturn has about 50 moons beyond its rings. The largest is Titan, 1.6 times as large as our Moon and even larger than Mercury. It spins once every 16 days and has a methane atmosphere with atmospheric pressure that is likely greater than Earth's. Its surface temperature is cold, roughly −170°C. A space probe built by NASA and the European Space Agency landed on Titan in 2005. Remarkably, photos revealed a landscape similar to Earth's despite the fact that the materials are completely different (Figure 6.19). Lakes and streams are filled with not water but liquid methane. Rocks are made of ice. Instead of lava, Titan has a flowing slush of ice and liquid ammonia. No life is expected to be found on this moon because of the intensely cold temperatures. Titan, however, holds an intriguing soup of organic molecules whose chemistry may provide a clue to what Earth was like during the time before life arose here.

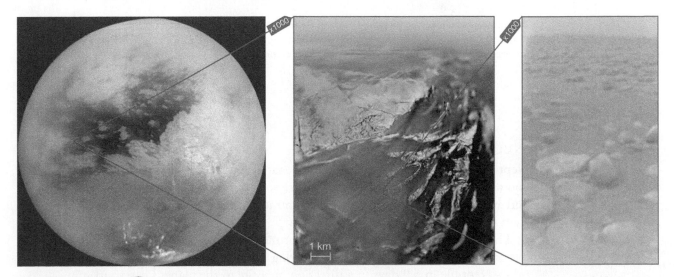

FIGURE 6.19
INTERACTIVE FIGURE (MP)

Images from Saturn's largest moon, Titan, taken by the *Cassini* spacecraft and its space probe, the *Huygens*, which successfully descended to the surface.

Uranus

Uranus ("YUR-uh-nus," accent on the first syllable) is twice as far from Earth as Saturn is, and it can barely be seen with the naked eye. Uranus was unknown to ancient astronomers and not discovered as a planet until 1781. The *Voyager 2* spacecraft first visited this planet in 1986. Uranus has a diameter four times that of Earth and a density slightly greater than that of water. So, if you could place Uranus in a giant bathtub, it would sink. The most unusual feature of Uranus is its tilt. Its axis is tilted 98° to the perpendicular of its orbital plane, so it lies on its side (Figure 6.20). Unlike Jupiter and Saturn, it appears to have no appreciable internal source of heat. Uranus is a cold place.

Uranus has at least 27 moons, in addition to a complicated faint ring system. Perturbations in the planet Uranus led to the discovery in 1846 of a farther planet, Neptune.

FIGURE 6.20
Astronomers believe the rotational axis of Uranus is tilted as a result of a collision it had with a large body early in the solar system's history. Methane in the upper atmosphere absorbs red light, giving Uranus its blue-green color.

Neptune

Neptune has a diameter about 3.9 times that of Earth, a mass 17 times as great, and a mean density about a third of Earth's. Its atmosphere is mainly hydrogen and helium, with some methane and ammonia, which makes Neptune bluer than Uranus (Figure 6.21).

The *Voyager 2* spacecraft flew by Neptune in 1989. It showed that Neptune has at least 13 moons in addition to a ring system. The largest moon, Triton, orbits Neptune in 5.9 days in a direction opposite to the planet's eastward spin. This suggests that Triton is a captured object. Triton's diameter is three-quarters of our Moon's diameter, and yet Triton is twice as massive as Earth's Moon. It has bright polar caps and geysers of liquid nitrogen.

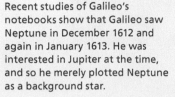
Recent studies of Galileo's notebooks show that Galileo saw Neptune in December 1612 and again in January 1613. He was interested in Jupiter at the time, and so he merely plotted Neptune as a background star.

FIGURE 6.21
Cyclonic disturbances on Neptune in 1989 produced a great dark spot, which was even larger than Earth and similar to Jupiter's Great Red Spot. The spot has now disappeared. The gray horizon in the foreground of this computer-generated montage is a close-up of Neptune's moon Triton, which has a composition and size similar to those of Pluto.

 Integrated Science 28A
BIOLOGY

What Makes a Planet Suitable for Life?

LEARNING OBJECTIVE
Describe the conditions required for extraterrestrial life.

EXPLAIN THIS Jupiter's major moons keep getting stretched in different directions by tidal forces. What force causes these moons to become warm?

What does a planet need in order to support life? Astrobiologists, scientists who study the origin and distribution of life in the universe, have a number of ideas about what planetary characteristics are conducive to the evolution of life. First, most familiar life on Earth is carbon-based, and there are good reasons to expect life elsewhere to be carbon-based as well. Carbon has the unusual ability to bind to as many as four other atoms at a time, which enables it to serve as the basis for a wide variety of complex molecules. This versatility is probably necessary for life. So, the first attribute of a habitable planet is that it contain abundant amounts of carbon along with certain other elements such as hydrogen, nitrogen, and oxygen that combine with carbon to make biomolecules. Second, living things require energy. This energy can come from sunlight or from chemical reactions that take place on or inside planets or even tidal forces. Third, the evolution of life probably requires the presence of a liquid medium such as water. Molecules can move around and react with one another in liquids, and this is probably essential for any life form. The fourth condition needed is stability so that there is sufficient time for the life forms to develop and evolve.

Given these requirements, where in the solar system should we look for life? It is interesting that the first two conditions—the need for the right elements and the need for an energy source—are satisfied by most planetary bodies in the solar system. In contrast, the presence of water is relatively rare. There is abundant geologic evidence, however, that the planet Mars once had liquid water. Parts of the Martian surface appear to have been produced by flowing water, resembling floodplains or dry riverbeds, and the Martian poles are still covered with water ice. The one-time presence of liquid water also implies that Mars used to be significantly warmer. Mars almost certainly was habitable in the past. But was it inhabited? The discovery of bacteria-like "fossils" in a Martian meteorite (see Chapter 13) fueled speculation that Mars not only was inhabited but also was the source of life on Earth. However, these supposed bacteria are much tinier than any organisms found on Earth, and perhaps too tiny to contain all the cellular structures a bacterium needs to function. The question of whether life existed—or even exists—on Mars is still open, and further exploration is needed to provide definitive answers.

Other possible locations for extraterrestrial life in our solar system include the jovian moons Europa and Ganymede, which, as discussed in Section 6.4, may contain an ocean of liquid water beneath their icy surfaces. Any life on either of these moons may have originated adjacent to volcanic thermal vents on the ocean floor. Such extraterrestrial life forms may be similar to the bizarre forms of life recently discovered adjacent to deep thermal vents on Earth's ocean floor. Alternatively, they may be single-celled organisms, such as bacteria. Then again, there may be nothing. The European Space Agency is planning to develop a satellite scheduled to launch by 2022 and reach Jupiter's moons by 2030. Its mission is to probe beneath the surfaces of these moons with radar and other technologies. It will fly by Europa and Callisto before settling into orbit around Ganymede.

So, is life rare or common in this universe? The answer may be waiting for us in our own galactic backyard. Stay tuned.

CHECK YOURSELF
Many scientists believe that life is most likely to evolve on planets that contain liquid in their environments. One of the perceived advantages of water over other potential liquids (such as ammonia, methane, or ethane) is that frozen water—ice—floats. Why might this be important for life?

CHECK YOUR ANSWER
On Earth, a layer of floating ice insulates the underlying water and allows it to remain liquid. If ice sank, it would expose more liquid water to the environment, which would then also freeze and sink. In a cold period, lakes and oceans would eventually freeze solid—this is not good for the organisms living in them.

6.5 Earth's Moon

EXPLAIN THIS When the Moon rises at sunset, its phase is always full. Why?

Earth's Moon is puzzling. It is close to the size of Mercury, which is a planet and *not* a moon. The composition of Earth's Moon is nearly the same as Earth's mantle. Furthermore, the Moon possesses a rather small iron core. To explain these and a multitude of other facts about the Moon, scientists have pieced together the following possible scenario for its origin.

During the early history of the solar system, the young Earth had a Mercury-sized companion form within an orbit close to that of Earth. Normally, if the companion's orbit were a bit closer to the Sun, then it would orbit faster than Earth and move ahead of Earth. Upon passing through a special point, known as the *Lagrangian point*, however, the object would find that the gravitational pull of Earth was strong enough to hold it back so that it orbited with Earth in unison. So early Earth may have had a twin that paraded with Earth around the Sun much like two horses running side by side on a circular track.

Eventually, a random event, such as the passing of an asteroid or comet, caused our companion to sway from the Lagrangian point and fall toward and collide

We see the aftermath of meteoroid bombardment on the Moon because it wears no makeup. Similar bombardment on Earth has been long erased by erosion.

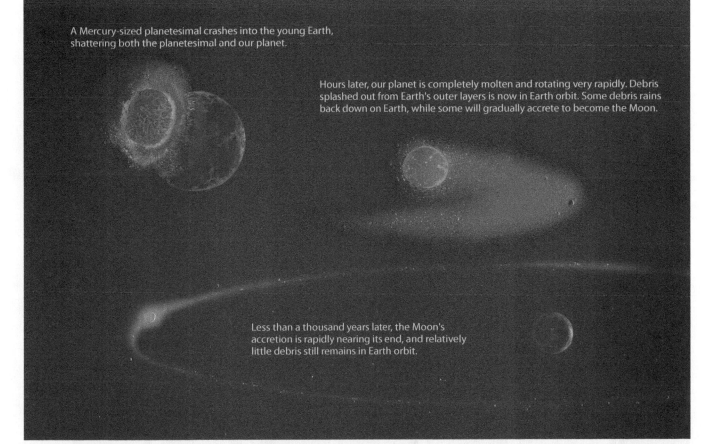

A Mercury-sized planetesimal crashes into the young Earth, shattering both the planetesimal and our planet.

Hours later, our planet is completely molten and rotating very rapidly. Debris splashed out from Earth's outer layers is now in Earth orbit. Some debris rains back down on Earth, while some will gradually accrete to become the Moon.

Less than a thousand years later, the Moon's accretion is rapidly nearing its end, and relatively little debris still remains in Earth orbit.

FIGURE 6.22
Three steps in the formation of Earth's Moon. A Mercury-sized object collides with Earth, which turns molten. Debris collects in a ring that accretes into the Moon, which is quite close to the rapidly rotating Earth. Over the next billion years tidal forces slow the rate of Earth's rotation while also causing the Moon to move farther away.

UNIFYING CONCEPT

● *The Scientific Method*
Section 1.3

FIGURE 6.23
Earth and the Moon as photographed in 1977 from the *Voyager 1* spacecraft on its way to Jupiter and Saturn.

Most planets wobble significantly as they spin about their axes. The Moon, however, helps keep Earth's wobble to a minimum. As a result, our weather patterns are fairly consistent through the ages, which makes our planet even more favorable for the development of life. Thank you, Moon!

with Earth. The collision would have been massively spectacular, spewing debris everywhere while turning Earth fully molten. Hitting askew, the impact sent Earth into a wild spin rotating once every five hours. The debris soon collected as a ring around Earth, and then, within about 1000 years, the ring coalesced into the Moon. This scenario is known as the *giant impact theory* of the origin of Earth's Moon. It explains why the Moon is so large (we started out as twin planets), why its composition is similar to Earth's (it formed from our mantle and our mantle formed from it), why it has such a small iron core (Earth's iron core had already differentiated and was not sent up with the debris), and much more. This impact theory is still the subject of much research and is thus being continually refined. Although it was developed within only the past couple decades, scientists are excited by its explanatory powers.

From a distance, Earth and the Moon still resemble a twin planet system, as you can see in Figure 6.23. Compared to Earth, however, the Moon is relatively small, with a diameter of about the distance from San Francisco to New York City. It once had a molten surface, but it cooled too rapidly for the establishment of moving crustal plates, like those of Earth. In its early history, it was intensely bombarded by meteoroids (as was Earth). A little more than 3 billion years ago, meteoroid bombardment and volcanic activity filled basins with lava to produce its present surface. It has undergone very little change since then. Its igneous crust is thicker than Earth's. The Moon is too small with too little gravitational pull to have an atmosphere. Without weather, the only significant eroding agents have been meteoroid impacts.

The Phases of the Moon

Sunshine always illuminates half of the Moon's surface. The Moon shows us different amounts of its sunlit half as it circles Earth each month. These changes are the **Moon phases** (Figure 6.24). The Moon cycle begins with the **new Moon**. In this phase, its dark side faces us and we see darkness. This occurs when the Moon is between Earth and the Sun (position 1 in Figure 6.25).

During the next seven days, we see more and more of the Moon's sunlit side (position 2 in Figure 6.25). The Moon is going though its waxing crescent phase (*waxing* means "increasing"). At the first quarter, the angle between the Sun, the Moon, and Earth is 90°. At this time, we see half the sunlit part of the Moon (position 3 in Figure 6.25).

During the next week, we see more and more of the sunlit part. The Moon is going through its waxing gibbous phase (position 4 in Figure 6.25). (*Gibbous* means "more than half.") We see a **full Moon** when the sunlit side of the Moon faces us squarely (position 5 in Figure 6.25). At this time, the Sun, Earth, and the Moon are lined up, with Earth in between. To view this full Moon you need

FIGURE 6.24
The Moon in its various phases.

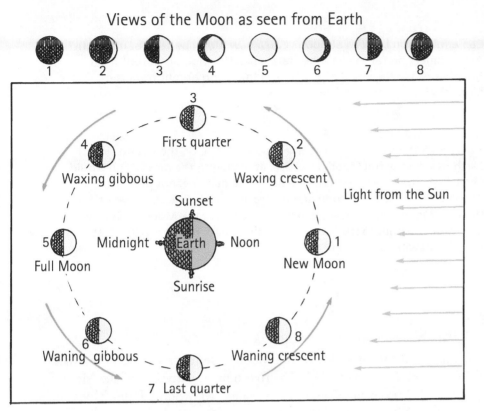

Views of the Moon as seen from Earth

FIGURE 6.25
Sunlight always illuminates half of the Moon. As the Moon orbits Earth, we see varying amounts of its sunlit side. One lunar phase cycle takes 29.5 days.

FYI During the time of the dinosaurs, a day was only about 19 hours. Today our days are about 24 hours. Billions of years from now, as Earth continues to slow down, a day will last about 47 hours. At that time, Earth and the Moon will be gravity locked such that the Moon will always appear in one location in the sky. To see the Moon, you will need to be on the Moon side of the planet, where perhaps real estate prices will be higher because of the view. One huge problem, however, is that by then, our Sun will have already gone through its dying phases, through which Earth will be subject to the fate of Venus, where it is forever cloudy. Nothing is permanent.

to be on the nighttime side of Earth, at sunset when the full Moon rises from the east, or at sunrise when it sets in the west.

The cycle reverses during the following two weeks, as we see less and less of the sunlit side while the Moon continues in its orbit. This movement produces the waning gibbous, last quarter, and waning crescent phases. (*Waning* means "shrinking.") The time for one complete cycle is about 29.5 days.*

*The Moon actually orbits Earth once every 27.3 days relative to the stars. The 29.5-day cycle is relative to the Sun and is due to the motion of the Earth–Moon system as it revolves about the Sun.

FIGURE 6.26
Edwin E. Aldrin, Jr., one of the three *Apollo 11* astronauts, stands on the dusty lunar surface. To date, 12 people have stood on the Moon.

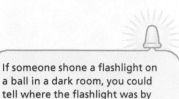

If someone shone a flashlight on a ball in a dark room, you could tell where the flashlight was by looking at the illumination on the ball. The Moon is similarly lit by the Sun.

CHECK YOURSELF

1. Can a full Moon be seen at noon? Can a new Moon be seen at midnight?
2. Astronomers prefer to view the stars when the Moon is absent from the night sky. When, and how often, is the Moon absent from the night sky?

CHECK YOUR ANSWERS

1. Figure 6.25 shows that at noontime, you would be on the wrong side of Earth to view the full Moon. Likewise, at midnight, the new Moon would be absent. The new Moon is in the sky in the daytime, not at night.
2. At the time of the new Moon and during the week on either side of the new Moon, the night sky can be seen without the Moon. Unless an astronomer wishes to study the Moon, these dark nights are the best time for viewing other objects.

Why One Side Always Faces Us

The first images of the back side of the Moon were taken by the unmanned Russian spacecraft *Lunik 3* in 1959. The first human witnesses of the Moon's back were *Apollo 8* astronauts, who orbited the Moon in 1968. From Earth, we see only a single lunar side. The familiar facial features of the "man in the Moon" are always turned toward us on Earth. Does this mean that the Moon doesn't spin about its axis as Earth does daily? No, but, relative to the stars, the Moon in fact does spin, although quite slowly—about once every 27 days. This monthly rate of spin matches the rate at which the Moon revolves about Earth. This explains why the same side of the Moon always faces Earth (Figure 6.27). The matching of monthly spin rate and orbital revolution rate is not a coincidence. After you answer the following question, we'll explore why.

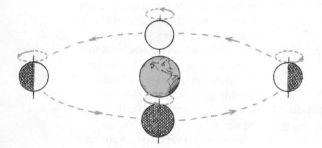

FIGURE 6.27
The Moon spins about its own polar axis just as often as it circles Earth. So as the Moon circles Earth, it spins so that the same side (shown in yellow) always faces Earth. In each of the four successive positions shown here, the Moon has spun one-quarter of a turn.

CHECK YOURSELF

A friend says that the Moon does not spin about its axis, and evidence for a nonspinning Moon is the fact that its same side always faces Earth. What do you say?

CHECK YOUR ANSWER

Place a quarter and a penny on a table. Pretend the quarter is Earth and the penny is the Moon. Keeping the quarter fixed, revolve the penny around it in such a way that Lincoln's head is always pointed to the center of the quarter. Ask your friend to count how many rotations the penny makes in one revolution (orbit) around the quarter. He or she will see that it rotates once with each revolution. The key concept is that the Moon takes the same amount of time to complete one rotation as it does to revolve around Earth.

Think of a compass needle that lines up with a magnetic field. This lineup is caused by a *torque*—a "turning force with leverage" (like that produced by the weight of a child at the end of a seesaw). The compass needle on the left in Figure 6.28 rotates because of a pair of torques. The needle rotates counterclockwise until it aligns with the magnetic field. In a similar manner, the Moon aligns with Earth's gravitational field.

We know from the law of universal gravitation that gravity weakens with the inverse square of distance, so the side of the Moon nearer to Earth is gravitationally pulled more than the farther side. This stretches the Moon out slightly toward a football shape. (The Moon does the same to Earth and gives us tides.) If its long axis doesn't line up with Earth's gravitational field, a torque acts on it as shown in Figure 6.29. Like a compass in a magnetic field, it turns into alignment. So the Moon lines up with Earth in its monthly orbit. One hemisphere always faces us. It's interesting to note that for many moons orbiting other planets, a single hemisphere faces the planet. We say these moons are "tidally locked."

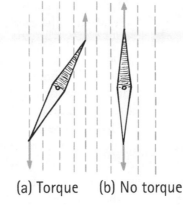

(a) Torque   (b) No torque

FIGURE 6.28
(a) When the compass needle is not aligned with the magnetic field (dashed lines), the forces represented by the blue arrows at either end produce a pair of torques that rotate the needle. (b) When the needle is aligned with the magnetic field, the forces no longer produce torques.

FIGURE 6.29
When the long axis of the Moon is not aligned with Earth's gravitational field, Earth exerts a torque that rotates the Moon into alignment.

Eclipses

Although the Sun is 400 times as large in diameter as the Moon, it is also 400 times as far away. So, from Earth, both the Sun and Moon measure the same angle (0.5°) and appear to be the same size in the sky. This coincidence allows us to see solar eclipses.

Both Earth and the Moon cast shadows from the sunlight shining on them. When the path of either of these bodies crosses into the shadow cast by the other, an eclipse occurs. A **solar eclipse** occurs when the Moon's shadow falls on Earth. Because of the large size of the Sun, the rays taper to provide an umbra and a surrounding penumbra, as shown in Figures 6.30 and 6.31.

An observer in the umbra part of the shadow experiences darkness during the day—a total eclipse, *totality*. Totality begins when the Sun disappears behind the

FIGURE 6.30
A solar eclipse occurs when the Moon passes in front of the Sun as seen from Earth. The Moon's shadow has two portions: a dark, central umbra that the Moon blocks completely from sunlight, surrounded by a lighter penumbra from which sunlight is only partly blocked. A total eclipse is seen from within the umbra and may last several minutes.

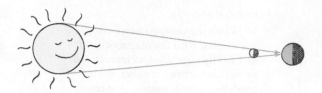

FIGURE 6.31
Geometry of a solar eclipse. During a solar eclipse, the Moon is directly between the Sun and Earth and the Moon's shadow is cast on Earth. Because of the small size of the Moon and tapering of the solar rays, a total solar eclipse occurs only on a small area of Earth.

Because of the large size of the Sun compared to the Moon, the umbra of the Moon's shadow is a cone about as long as the distance from the Moon to Earth. As a result, when the Moon is farthest away from Earth in its orbit, the umbra doesn't quite reach Earth's surface. Then no total eclipse occurs. Instead, at mid-eclipse one sees a ring of Sun surrounding the dark moon, an *annular eclipse*.

Moon, and ends when the Sun reappears on the other edge of the Moon. The average time of totality at any location is about 2 or 3 minutes, with a maximum no longer than 7.5 minutes. The eclipse time in any location is brief because of the Moon's motion. During totality, what appears in the sky is an eerie black disk surrounded by the pearly white streams of the corona, as was shown in Figure 6.7. It is an experience one can never forget. With binoculars, the features of the Moon can be seen because they are lit by the sunlight reflected from Earth. Pink flares from the chromosphere may also appear. But great caution is advised when viewing the totality, which must be a totality of 100%. The moment the first edges of the photosphere appear, which is the moment you now have 99.99% totality, is the very moment when you can seriously damage your eyes if you continue to look.* At that moment you have entered the penumbra, where the eclipse is partial. An ideal way to view the partial solar eclipse is to focus the light of the eclipse onto a white surface, as was shown in Figure 6.4. Alternatively, you can view the crescent Sun under the shade of a tree, which casts pinhole images of the Sun onto the ground, as shown in Figure 6.32. Check the map shown in Figure 6.33 to see if a solar eclipse is coming to your area soon. Many solar eclipse enthusiasts travel the world to view this inspiring natural phenomenon.

The alignment of Earth, the Moon, and the Sun also produces a **lunar eclipse** when the Moon passes into the shadow of Earth, as shown in Figure 6.34. Usually a lunar eclipse precedes or follows a solar eclipse by two weeks. Just as all

*People are cautioned not to look at the Sun at the time of a solar eclipse because the brightness and the ultraviolet light of direct sunlight damage the eyes. This good advice is often misunderstood by those who then think that sunlight is more damaging at this special time. However, staring at the Sun when it is high in the sky is harmful whether or not an eclipse occurs. In fact, staring at the bare Sun is more harmful than when part of the Moon blocks it. The reason for special caution at the time of an eclipse is simply that more people are interested in looking at the Sun during this time.

(a)　　　　　　　　(b)　　　　　　　　(c)

FIGURE 6.32
(a) The spots of light on the wall and the ground, as well as on lab manual author Dean Baird, are pinhole images of the Sun cast through small openings between leaves on nearby trees. The spots are round because the Sun is round. (b) During a partial solar eclipse, the solar images are crescents because the Sun is then crescent shaped, as the Moon covers part of the Sun in the sky. (c) During an annular eclipse the Moon aligns with but doesn't fully cover the Sun, which results in the rarely seen Sun circles as demonstrated by Paul Doherty during the 2012 annular eclipse that passed over the western United States.

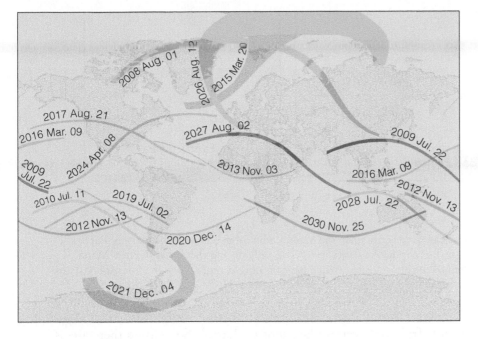

FIGURE 6.33
This map shows the paths of total solar eclipses from 2006 through 2030. More details about these and other future solar eclipses can be found on NASA's eclipse Web site, http://sunearth.gsfc.nasa.gov/eclipse/eclipse.html. If you live in the United States, August 21, 2017, is your special day.

solar eclipses involve a new Moon, all lunar eclipses involve a full Moon. They may be partial or total. All observers on the dark side of Earth see a lunar eclipse at the same time. Interestingly enough, when the Moon is fully eclipsed, it is still visible as is shown and discussed in Figure 6.35.

Why are eclipses relatively rare events? This has to do with the different orbital planes of Earth and the Moon. Earth revolves around the Sun in a flat planar orbit. The Moon similarly revolves about Earth in a flat planar orbit. But the planes are slightly tipped with respect to each other—a 5.2° tilt, as shown in Figure 6.36. If the planes weren't tipped, eclipses would occur monthly. Because of the tip, eclipses occur only when the Moon intersects the Earth–Sun plane at the time of a three-body alignment (Figure 6.37). This occurs about two times per year, which is why there are at least two solar eclipses

FIGURE 6.34
A lunar eclipse occurs when Earth is directly between the Moon and the Sun and Earth's shadow is cast on the Moon.

FIGURE 6.35
A fully eclipsed Moon is not completely dark in the shadow of Earth but is quite visible. This is because Earth's atmosphere acts as a lens and refracts light into the shadow region—sufficient light to faintly illuminate the Moon.

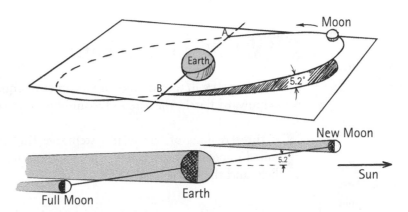

FIGURE 6.36
The Moon orbits Earth in a plane tipped 5.2° relative to the plane of Earth's orbit around the Sun. A solar or lunar eclipse occurs only when the Moon intersects the Earth–Sun plane (points A and B) at the precise time of a three-body alignment. Otherwise, the shadows are not aligned, as shown in the lower drawing.

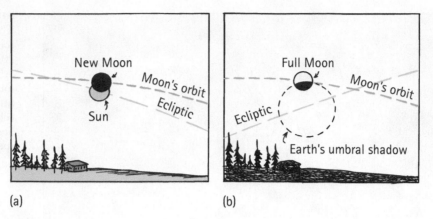

(a)   (b)

FIGURE 6.37
A total eclipse can occur only when the Moon's orbit intersects with the plane of Earth's orbit, which is the ecliptic. A solar eclipse occurs only during the day as the new Moon passes in front of the Sun. A lunar eclipse happens only at night when the full Moon passes through Earth's shadow.

per year (visible from only certain locations on Earth). Sometimes there are as many as seven solar and lunar eclipses in a year.

CHECK YOURSELF
1. **Does a solar eclipse occur at the time of a full Moon or a new Moon?**
2. **Does a lunar eclipse occur at the time of a full Moon or a new Moon?**

CHECK YOUR ANSWERS
1. A solar eclipse occurs at the time of a new Moon, when the Moon is directly in front of the Sun. Then the shadow of the Moon falls on part of Earth.
2. A lunar eclipse occurs at the time of a full Moon, when the Moon and Sun are on opposite sides of Earth. Then the shadow of Earth falls on the full Moon.

LEARNING OBJECTIVE
Compare and contrast asteroids, Kuiper belt objects, and the Oort cloud.

Meteorites fall all over our planet, but the easiest place to find them is on the icy white surfaces found in polar regions. Do you want to collect your own meteorites? Head south to Antarctica!

6.6 Failed Planet Formation

EXPLAIN THIS If an asteroid and a comet of equal mass were on a collision course toward Earth, the asteroid would be easier to deflect. Why?

In three regions of our solar system, we find the remains of material that failed to collect into planets. These regions are the asteroid belt, the Kuiper belt, and the Oort cloud.

The Asteroid Belt and Meteors

The **asteroid belt** is a collection of rocks located between the orbits of Mars and Jupiter. More than 150,000 asteroids have been cataloged so far, but many more no doubt have yet to be discovered. They come in all shapes and sizes, but the largest asteroid, Ceres, is just less than a thousand kilometers in diameter.

Although Ceres is large enough to be fairly round, most asteroids are shaped more like a potato, as shown in Figure 6.38.

Evidence suggests that when the solar system was forming, the asteroid belt held much more mass than it does today. Massive Jupiter likely disrupted the orbits of this material, sending it off in many directions, including toward the inner planets and out of the solar system. The two moons of Mars, for example, may be former asteroids. What remains of the asteroid belt is small. If all the presently remaining asteroids were scrunched together, they would make a sphere less than half the size of our Moon.

Jupiter also causes the collisions of asteroids with asteroids, which then break apart into smaller fragments. So rather than building into a planet, this material is slowly ground down and pushed off course. Asteroid fragments known as **meteoroids** frequently find their way to Earth, where they are heated white-hot by friction with the atmosphere. As they descend with a fiery glow, they are called **meteors** (Figure 6.39).

If the meteoroid is large enough, it may survive to reach the surface, where it is called a **meteorite**. Most meteoroids, meteors, and meteorites are from asteroids, but many are also from comets, as we discuss later. Fortunately, smaller meteorites hit us more frequently than larger ones do. About 200 tons of small meteorites strike Earth every day. Every 10,000 years or so we are hit with a meteorite big enough to create a large crater, such as the one shown in Figure 6.40. Every 100 million years or so we are hit with one big enough—about 10 km in diameter—to cause a mass extinction, as occurred 65 million years ago at the end of the Cretaceous period discussed in Chapter 11. Accordingly, one of NASA's goals is to detect up to 90% of all large, near-Earth objects. If we can detect a dangerous space fragment early enough, we can take actions to alter its orbital path sufficiently to avoid impending disaster.

The Kuiper Belt and Dwarf Planets

Beyond Neptune at a distance from about 30 to 50 AU is a region known as the **Kuiper belt** ("KI-pur," rhymes with *hyper*). The Kuiper belt is occupied by many rocky, ice-covered objects. The most well-known Kuiper belt object is Pluto, which until recently was classified as a planet. Since its discovery in 1930, however, astronomers knew that Pluto was quite different from all the other known planets. For example, Pluto orbits at an angle to the plane of Earth's orbit—the ecliptic. Also, Pluto is quite small, being only one-seventh as massive as our Moon. Then, starting in the 1990s, astronomers began discovering many more Kuiper belt objects, some as large as or larger than Pluto. So in 2006 these Pluto-sized Kuiper belt objects were officially classified as **dwarf planets**. The main reason they do not meet full planet status is that they have yet to accrete all the material in their orbital paths. In the outer edges of our solar system, however, matter is simply too sparse for that to happen. Interestingly, if the Kuiper belt were more dense with material, then these dwarf planets could have served as cores for additional jovian planets. But that never happened, and so the Kuiper belt is another zone of failed planet formation.

Space probes have yet to visit any of the dwarf planets of the Kuiper belt. Pluto and its moon, Charon, however, are due to be visited by the *New Horizons*

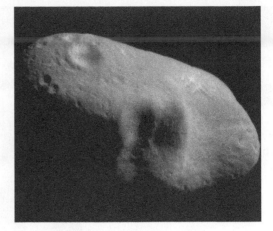

FIGURE 6.38
The asteroid Eros is about 40 km long, and like other small objects in the solar system, it is not spherical.

FIGURE 6.39
A meteor is produced when a meteoroid, usually about 80 km high, enters Earth's atmosphere. Most are sand-sized grains, which are seen as "falling" or "shooting" stars.

FIGURE 6.40
The Barringer Crater in Arizona, made 25,000 years ago by an iron meteorite with a diameter of about 50 m. The crater extends 1.2 km across and reaches 200 m deep.

FIGURE 6.41
This infrared image of Pluto being orbited by its moon, Charon, is fuzzy because of the small size of these bodies and their great distance from Earth.

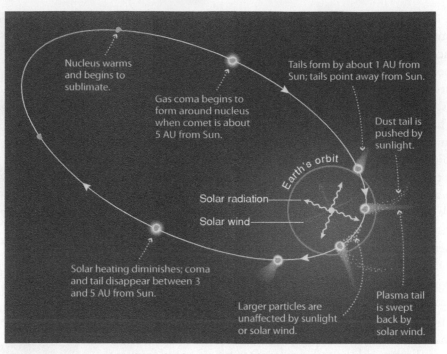

FIGURE 6.42
A comet warms as it gets closer to the Sun and initially develops a coma, which is a halo of gases surrounding the comet nucleus. From this coma arises the tail, which is blown outward by the solar wind. Note how the tail always extends away from the Sun. Most Kuiper belt objects never make this journey and instead remain perpetually frozen within the outer reaches of our solar system.

spacecraft in 2015. We may have already had a preview, however, when the *Voyager 2* spacecraft took pictures of Neptune's moon Triton. Astronomers now suspect that Triton is a Kuiper belt dwarf planet pulled off course and captured into orbit around Neptune.

The larger Kuiper belt objects, such as Pluto, have a fair amount of inertia and so are not so easily thrown off course. Lighter Kuiper belt objects, however, are thrown off course quite frequently. Sometimes they are thrown toward the Sun, where the added heat and solar wind cause the ice and other volatile materials to be ejected, always in a direction away from the Sun. We see these objects as **comets**, which are characterized by their long and sometimes quite brilliant tails. Comets that come from the Kuiper belt tend to have orbital periods of less than 200 years. An example is Comet Halley, which returns to the inner solar system every 76 years—once in an average lifetime (Figure 6.43). Its next scheduled return is in 2061.

Comets apparently reside in at least two regions. The first is the Kuiper belt, which lies roughly within the same plane of the solar system. The second region lies much farther out and surrounds our entire solar system—like a cloud.

The Oort Cloud and Comets

As the jovian planets grew, their gravitational pulls became stronger, which made them even more effective at pulling in additional interplanetary debris. Not all debris, however, was pulled fully into the jovian planets. In many cases, a chunk of rock or ice just missing a planet was instead whipped around the planet and

FIGURE 6.43
Observations of Comet Halley have been recorded for thousands of years. Although it usually provides a brilliant display, its last visit in 1986 was not so spectacular when viewed from Earth. We were ready, though, with space probes that flew close enough to Halley to capture dramatic images of its nucleus.

then flung violently outward in some direction. Over billions of years this created a sphere of far-out objects just barely held to our solar system. We refer to this collection of far-out objects as the **Oort cloud** (*Oort* rhymes with *court*). Evidence suggests that the Oort cloud consists of trillions of objects extending as far out as 50,000 AU, which brings the cloud about a quarter of the way to the nearest star. A few of these objects occasionally fall toward and then around the Sun, where they appear as comets. The orbital periods of comets originating from the Oort cloud are on the order of thousands or even millions of years. They come from nearly any angle.

Whether the comet comes from the Kuiper belt or the Oort cloud, it still has the potential for colliding with a planet. In 1994, Comet Shoemaker-Levy

Most comets usually last only a couple of orbits before they break up. But if the solar system is billions of years old, shouldn't they be depleted by now? This very question led to the idea of the Oort cloud, which provides a continual supply of new comets, replacing those that are destroyed.

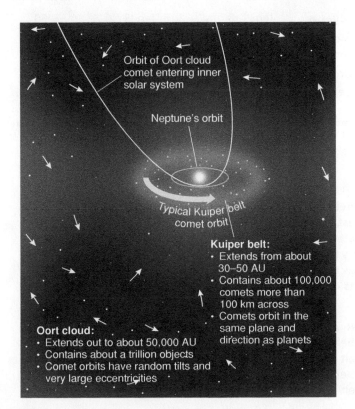

Orbit of Oort cloud comet entering inner solar system

Neptune's orbit

Typical Kuiper belt comet orbit

Kuiper belt:
· Extends from about 30–50 AU
· Contains about 100,000 comets more than 100 km across
· Comets orbit in the same plane and direction as planets

Oort cloud:
· Extends out to about 50,000 AU
· Contains about a trillion objects
· Comet orbits have random tilts and very large eccentricities

FIGURE 6.44
There are two major sources for comets: the Kuiper belt and the Oort cloud.

FIGURE 6.45
Comet Shoemaker-Levy was already broken up into a string of objects just before it collided with Jupiter in 1994. The image in part (a) is an infrared view of the collision, which produced much heat as well as visible scars (the black dots), as shown in the photograph in part (b).

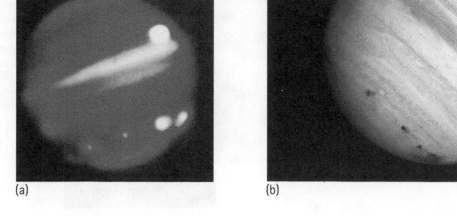
(a)   (b)

FIGURE 6.46
When the orbiting Earth intercepts the debris from a comet, we see a meteor shower.

collided spectacularly with Jupiter, as shown in Figure 6.45. Also, the large meteorite that collided with Earth 65 million years ago causing the mass extinction of the dinosaurs may have been a comet.

The tail of the comet leaves behind a wide trail of particles. Each year Earth passes through the remnants of comet tails that create annual meteor showers, as indicated in Table 6.2. Just go outside, look up at the sky, and with good eyesight every minute or so you will see a shooting star. Each streak is a tiny chip of a comet, once so very far away, that has fallen into Earth's neighborhood (Figure 6.46).

TABLE 6.2	**METEOR SHOWER DATA**			
Shower Name	**Radiant***	**Dates**	**Peak Dates**	**Meteors per Hour**
Quadrantids	Pegasus	Jan. 1–6	Jan. 3	60
Eta Aquarids	Aquarius	May 1–10	May 6	35
Perseids	Perseus	Jul. 23–Aug. 20	Aug. 12	75
Orionids	Orion	Oct. 16–27	Oct. 22	25
Geminids	Gemini	Dec. 7–15	Dec. 13	75

*Meteors appear to radiate from a certain region of the sky, appropriately called a *radiant*. Radiants refer to constellations. See Chapter 5 for more on where the various constellations are located in the night sky.

CHECK YOURSELF
Of the asteroid belt, the Kuiper belt, and the Oort cloud:
1. Which is closest to the Sun?
2. Which generates comets?
3. Which gives us the most meteorites?
4. Which gives us the brightest meteor showers?
5. Which consists of fragments that never coalesced into planets?

CHECK YOUR ANSWERS
1. The asteroid belt
2. The Kuiper belt and the Oort cloud
3. The asteroid belt
4. The Kuiper belt and the Oort cloud
5. All of them

For instructor-assigned homework, go to www.masteringphysics.com (MP)

SUMMARY OF TERMS (KNOWLEDGE)

Asteroid belt A region between the orbits of Mars and Jupiter that contains small, rocky, planet-like fragments that orbit the Sun. These fragments are called *asteroids* ("small star" in Latin).

Astronomical unit (AU) The average distance between Earth and the Sun; about 1.5×10^8 km (about 9.3×10^7 mi).

Comet A body composed of ice and dust that orbits the Sun, usually in a very eccentric orbit, and that casts a luminous tail produced by solar radiation pressure when close to the Sun.

Dwarf planet A relatively large icy body, such as Pluto, that originated within the Kuiper belt.

Ecliptic The plane of Earth's orbit around the Sun. All major objects of the solar system orbit roughly within this same plane.

Full Moon The phase of the Moon when its sunlit side faces Earth.

Inner planets The four planets orbiting within 2 AU of the Sun: Mercury, Venus, Earth, and Mars — all are rocky and known as the *terrestrial* planets.

Kuiper belt The disk-shaped region of the sky beyond Neptune populated by many icy bodies and a source of short-period comets.

Lunar eclipse The phenomenon in which the shadow of Earth falls on the Moon, producing the relative darkness of the full Moon.

Meteor The streak of light produced by a meteoroid burning in Earth's atmosphere; a "shooting star."

Meteorite A meteoroid, or a part of a meteoroid, that has survived passage through Earth's atmosphere to reach the ground.

Meteoroid A small rock in interplanetary space, which can include a fragment of an asteroid or comet.

Moon phases The cycles of change of the "face" of the Moon, changing from *new*, to *waxing*, to *full*, to *waning*, and back to *new*.

Nebular theory The idea that the Sun and planets formed together from a cloud of gas and dust, a *nebula*.

New Moon The phase of the Moon when darkness covers the side facing Earth.

Oort cloud The region beyond the Kuiper belt populated by trillions of icy bodies and a source of long-period comets.

Outer planets The four planets orbiting beyond 2 AU of the Sun, Jupiter, Saturn, Uranus, and Neptune—all are gaseous and known as the *jovian* planets.

Planets The major bodies orbiting the Sun that are massive enough for their gravity to make them spherical and small enough to avoid having nuclear fusion in their cores. They also have successfully cleared all debris from their orbital paths.

Solar eclipse The phenomenon in which the shadow of the Moon falls on Earth, producing a region of darkness in the daytime.

Sunspots Temporary, relatively cool and dark regions on the Sun's surface.

READING CHECK (COMPREHENSION)

6.1 The Solar System and Its Formation

1. How many known planets are in our solar system?
2. What dwarf planet was downgraded from planetary status in 2006?
3. How are the outer planets different from the inner planets aside from their location?
4. Why does a nebula spin faster as it contracts?
5. According to the nebular theory, did the planets start forming before or after the Sun ignited?

6.2 The Sun

6. What happens to the amount of the Sun's mass as it "burns"?
7. What are sunspots?
8. What is the solar wind?
9. How does the rotation of the Sun differ from the rotation of a solid body?
10. What is the age of the Sun?

6.3 The Inner Planets

11. Why are the days on Mercury very hot and the nights very cold?
12. What two planets are evening or morning "stars"?
13. Why is Earth called "the blue planet"?
14. What gas makes up most of the Martian atmosphere?
15. What evidence tells us that Mars was at one time wetter than it presently is?

6.4 The Outer Planets

16. What surface feature do Jupiter and the Sun have in common?
17. Which move faster—Saturn's inner rings or the outer rings?
18. How tilted is Uranus's axis?
19. Why is Neptune bluer than Uranus?

6.5 Earth's Moon

20. Why doesn't the Moon have an atmosphere?
21. Where is the Sun located when you view a full Moon?
22. Where are the Sun and the Moon located at the time of a new Moon?
23. Why don't eclipses occur monthly, or nearly monthly?
24. How does the Moon's rate of rotation about its own axis compare with its rate of revolution around Earth?

6.6 Failed Planet Formation

25. Between the orbits of what two planets is the asteroid belt located?
26. What is the difference between a meteor and a meteorite?
27. What is the Kuiper belt?
28. What is the Oort cloud, and what is it noted for?
29. What is a falling star?
30. What causes comet tails to point away from the Sun?

THINK INTEGRATED SCIENCE

28A—What Makes a Planet Suitable for Life?

31. Why is carbon such a special atom?

32. Why does the evolution of life probably require the presence of a liquid on a planet?

THINK AND DO (HANDS-ON APPLICATION)

33. Find a Ping-Pong ball on the next clear day when the Moon is out. Hold the Ping-Pong ball with your arm stretched out toward where the Moon is so that the ball overlaps the Moon. Look carefully at how the ball is lit by the Sun. Notice that this is the same way the Moon is lit by the Sun! For an example, see the photograph accompanying Exercise 69. To see the different phases that the Moon would have if it were elsewhere in the sky, move your Ping-Pong ball around. Note that as you bring the ball closer to the Sun, the crescent on the ball gets thinner. The same thing happens with the Moon. This activity is a great way of really experiencing the roundness of the Moon.

34. Simulate the lunar phases. Insert a pencil into a Styrofoam ball. This will be the Moon. Position a lamp (representing the Sun) in another room near the doorway. Hold the ball in front and slightly above yourself. Slowly turn yourself around, keeping the ball in front of you as you move. Observe the patterns of light and shadow on the ball. Relate this to the phases of the Moon.

35. When viewed from the North Pole, Earth spins counterclockwise, which is toward the east. This means that the stars appear to move in the opposite direction, which is toward the west. This is just like when you're sitting in a train that begins moving eastward. The only way you know that you're moving eastward is because things outside your window give the appearance of moving westward. Just as Earth spins counterclockwise, the Moon revolves around us counterclockwise, though not as fast as we spin. Look where the Moon is located one night at, say, 11:00. Look for the Moon the next night at the same time, and you'll see that it has moved eastward (a counterclockwise direction) from where it was on the previous night.

36. The crescent Moon always points toward the Sun. You can use this fact to estimate your latitude. Down by the equator (0° latitude), the setting crescent Moon lies flat on the horizon, while up close to the North Pole (90° latitude), the crescent Moon stands on its end. Deviations to this can arise because of Earth's 23° tilt and because the Moon's orbit lies 5° outside the ecliptic. Nonetheless, those who live in Alaska see a crescent Moon that is much more upright than those who live in Hawaii. With this in mind, the next time you see the crescent Moon close to the horizon, look carefully at its angle and try correlating that angle to your local latitude.

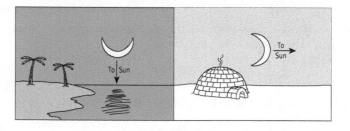

37. The planets of our solar system orbit in roughly the same plane, which is the plane of our solar system. We can identify the plane of our solar system in the night sky by noting the positions of the planets, which, from our point of view on Earth, appear in a roughly straight line relative to one another. This straight line, which is a cross-section of our solar system, always intersects with the Sun and often with the position of our Moon. On a clear evening after sunset, several planets can often be seen in the western sky forming a line that points directly toward the Sun. Upon finding this alignment, you are looking directly at the plane of our solar system. Check it out! How might this line look different if viewed from the North Pole versus the equator?

38. The dates of meteor showers are rather predictable as listed in Table 6.2. How intense the shower might be, however, is still somewhat of a guess. So keep your eye to the nighttime sky for these meteor showers. While doing

so, review in your mind the distinctions among meteoroids, meteors, meteorites, and comets. Also notable in our nighttime skies are the lunar eclipses, which can be seen by anyone who happens to be on the nighttime side of Earth during the eclipse (assuming skies are clear). Here are the dates for upcoming lunar eclipses viewable in North America.

Date of eclipse	Type
Apr. 15, 2014	Total
Oct. 8, 2014	Total
Sep. 28, 2015	Total
Jan. 21, 2019	Total

THINK AND COMPARE (ANALYSIS)

39. Rank these planets in order from longest to shortest year: (a) Mercury, (b) Venus, and (c) Earth.

40. Rank these planets in order of increasing number of moons: (a) Mars, (b) Venus, and (c) Earth.

41. Rank in order of increasing average density: (a) Jupiter, (b) Saturn, and (c) Earth.

42. Rank in order of increasing pressure at the center of each planet: (a) Jupiter, (b) Saturn, and (c) Earth.

43. Rank in order of decreasing number of people who have seen a: (a) solar eclipse, (b) lunar eclipse, and (c) new Moon.

44. Rank in order of increasing average distance from the Sun: (a) Kuiper belt objects, (b) asteroids, and (c) Oort cloud objects.

THINK AND SOLVE (MATHEMATICAL APPLICATION)

45. Knowing that the speed of light is 300,000 km/s, show that it takes about 8 min for sunlight to reach Earth.

46. How many days does sunlight take to travel the 50,000 AU from the Sun to the outer reaches of the Oort cloud?

47. The light-year is a standard unit of distance used by astronomers. It is the distance light travels in one Earth year. In units of light-years, what is the approximate diameter of our solar system, including the outer reaches of the Oort cloud? (Assume that 1 light-year equals 63,000 AU.)

48. The nearest star to our Sun is Alpha Centauri, which is about 4.4 light-years away. Assume that it too has an Oort cloud about 1.6 light-years in diameter. Show that there is enough space between us and it to fit about 1.75 solar systems.

49. If the Sun were the size of a beach ball, Earth would be the size of a green pea 110 m away. Show that the nearest star, Alpha Centauri (4.4 light-years away), would be about 30,000 km distant. (*Hint:* Find the distance to Alpha Centauri in units of AU.)

THINK AND EXPLAIN (SYNTHESIS)

50. According to nebular theory, what happens to a nebula as it contracts under the force of gravity?

51. What happens to the shape of a nebula as it contracts and spins faster?

52. A TV screen is normally light gray when not illuminated. How is the darkness of sunspots similar to the black parts of an image on a TV screen?

53. When a contracting ball of hot gas spins into a disk shape, it cools. Why?

54. If Earth didn't spin on its axis but still revolved around the Sun, how long would an Earth day be?

55. If Earth didn't spin on its axis but still revolved around the Sun, would the Sun set on the eastern or western horizon or not at all?

56. The greenhouse effect is very pronounced on Venus but doesn't exist on Mercury. Why?

57. What is the cause of winds on Mars (and also on almost every other planet)?

58. Why is there so little wind on the surface of Venus?

59. If Venus were somehow transported into the habitable zone, would conditions once again become favorable for life?

60. Mercury and Venus are never seen at night straight up toward the top of the sky. Why not?

61. What is the major difference between the terrestrial and jovian planets?

62. What does Jupiter have in common with the Sun that the terrestrial planets don't? What differentiates Jupiter from a star?

63. When it comes to celestial bodies, such as planets and stars, why doesn't a larger size necessarily mean a larger mass?

64. Why are the seasons on Uranus different from the seasons on any other planet?

Uranus

65. Earth rotates much faster than Venus. How does the giant impact theory of the Moon account for this fact?

66. Why are many craters evident on the surface of the Moon but not on the surface of Earth?

67. Why is there no atmosphere on the Moon? Defend your answer.

68. Is the fact that we see only one side of the Moon evidence that the Moon spins or that it doesn't spin? Defend your answer.

69. Photograph (a) shows the Moon partially lit by the Sun. Photograph (b) shows a Ping-Pong ball in sunlight. Compare the positions of the Sun in the sky when each photograph was taken. Do the photos support or refute the claim that they were taken on the same day? Defend your answer.

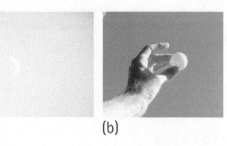

(a)   (b)

70. We always see the same face of the Moon because the rotation of the Moon on its axis matches the rate at which it revolves around Earth. Does it follow that an observer on the Moon always sees the same face of Earth?

71. If we never see the back side of the Moon, would an observer on the back side of the Moon ever see Earth?

72. In what alignment of the Sun, the Moon, and Earth does a solar eclipse occur?

73. In what alignment of the Sun, the Moon, and Earth does a lunar eclipse occur?

74. What does the Moon have in common with a compass needle?

75. If you were on the Moon and you looked up and saw a full Earth, would it be nighttime or daytime on the Moon?

76. If you were on the Moon and you looked up and saw a new Earth, would it be nighttime or daytime on the Moon?

77. Earth takes 365.25 days to revolve around the Sun. If Earth took this same amount of time to spin on its axis, what might we note about the Sun's position in the sky?

78. Do astronomers make stellar observations during the full Moon part of the month or during the new Moon part of the month? Does it make a difference?

79. Nearly everybody has witnessed a lunar eclipse, but relatively few people have seen a solar eclipse. Why?

80. Because of Earth's shadow, the partially eclipsed Moon looks like a cookie with a bite taken out of it. Explain with a sketch how the curvature of the bite indicates the size of the Earth relative to the size of the Moon. How does the tapering of the Sun's rays affect the curvature of the bite?

Use the following illustration for Exercises 81–84.

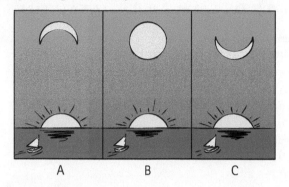

81. Which of the three orientations of the Moon at sunset is most correct?

82. Assuming the illustrations depict a sunset, within 24 hours of when this scene is depicted will the Moon appear to be farther from or closer to the Sun?

83. Is the sailboat sailing at a location closer to the North Pole or closer to the equator? How can you tell?

84. Where and how would the Moon be positioned if the scenes were close to the North Pole?

85. In what sense is Pluto a potential comet?

86. Smaller chunks of asteroids are sent hurling toward Earth much more frequently than larger chunks of asteroids. Why?

87. Why are meteorites so much more easily found in Antarctica than in other continents?

88. A meteor is visible only once, but a comet may be visible at regular intervals throughout its lifetime. Why?

89. What would be the consequence of a comet's tail sweeping across Earth?

90. Chances are about 50–50 that in any night sky there is at least one visible comet that has not been discovered. This keeps amateur astronomers busy looking night after night because the discoverer of a comet gets the honor of having it named for him or her. With this high probability of comets in the sky, why aren't more of them found?

THINK AND DISCUSS (EVALUATION)

91. Project what human civilization would be like if Earth had no Moon.

92. What are the chances that microbial life forms might one day be found elsewhere in our solar system? How much effort should we spend on searching for such life forms, and what precautions should we take upon such a discovery?

READINESS ASSURANCE TEST (RAT)

If you have a good handle on this chapter, if you really do, then you should be able to score 7 out of 10 on this RAT. If you score less than 7, you need to study further before moving on.

Choose the BEST answer to each of the following:

1. The Sun contains what percentage of the solar system's mass?
   (a) about 35%
   (b) 85%
   (c) the percentage varies over time
   (d) over 99%

2. The solar system is like an atom in that both
   (a) are governed principally through the electric force.
   (b) consist of a central body surrounded by objects moving in elliptical paths.
   (c) are composed of plasma.
   (d) are mainly empty space.

3. The nebular theory is based on the observation that the solar system
   (a) follows patterns indicating that it formed progressively from physical processes.
   (b) has a structure much like an atom.
   (c) is highly complex and appears to have been built by chaotic processes.
   (d) appears to be very old.

4. When a contracting hot ball of gas spins into a disk shape, it cools faster due to
   (a) increased radiation transfer.
   (b) increased surface area.
   (c) decreased insulation.
   (d) increased convection currents.
   (e) eddy currents.

5. Each second, the burning Sun's mass
   (a) increases.
   (b) remains unchanged.
   (c) decreases.

6. Compared to your weight on Earth, your weight on Jupiter would be about
   (a) 3000 times as much.
   (b) half as much.
   (c) 3 times as much.
   (d) 300 times as much.
   (e) 100 times as much.

7. When the Moon assumes its characteristic thin crescent shape, the position of the Sun is
   (a) almost directly in back of the Moon.
   (b) almost directly behind Earth, so that Earth is between the Sun and the Moon.
   (c) at right angles to the line between the Moon and Earth.

8. When the Sun passes between the Moon and Earth, we have
   (a) a lunar eclipse.
   (b) a solar eclipse.
   (c) met our end.

9. Asteroids orbit
   (a) the Moon.
   (b) Earth.
   (c) the Sun.
   (d) all of these
   (e) none of these

10. With each pass of a comet about the Sun, the comet's mass
   (a) remains virtually unchanged.
   (b) actually increases.
   (c) is appreciably reduced.

Answers to RAT

1. d, 2. d, 3. a, 4. b, 5. c, 6. c, 7. a, 8. c, 9. c, 10. c

CHAPTER 7
Rocks and Minerals

ALMOST ALL manufactured products contain minerals or substances derived from minerals. From the aluminum in cans to the graphite in pencils to the halite on your French fries, minerals are practically everywhere. What exactly is a mineral? Where do all the minerals we consume come from? Minerals join together to create rocks, which are the dominant material of Earth. Rocks, like minerals, are economically important. To name just a few examples, coal is a rock burned for fuel, and marble and granite are popular ornamental stones. Rocks provide key information to science, too. They tell the story of Earth's past, if you know how to read them. The properties of rock affect geologic processes such as erosion, flooding, and earthquakes. In what sense does rock recycle? As "rock hounds" know, rocks are fascinating once you learn their story.

7.1 What Is a Mineral?

LEARNING OBJECTIVE
State the characteristics of a mineral.

EXPLAIN THIS Why are diamond and graphite classified as two different minerals even though both are made of pure carbon?

In everyday language, a *mineral* is a part of your diet ("vitamins and minerals"). But in Earth science, a *mineral* is something else. A **mineral** is a material that has these five characteristics:

1. *A mineral is naturally occurring.* In other words, a mineral is formed by nature rather than by people in a laboratory. Silver is a mineral, but nylon is not.
2. *Minerals are inorganic.* Minerals aren't produced just by living things. Wood isn't a mineral because living things—trees—are the only producers of wood.
3. *Minerals have a crystal structure.* Atoms, ions, or molecules are arranged in regular, repeating patterns in minerals. Halite (table salt) has the crystal structure of a cube repeated over and over again (Figure 7.1). Most solids—minerals and nonminerals alike—have a crystal structure. Two important exceptions are glass and plastic, which are *amorphous solids*, solids in which the particles are random and disorderly.
4. *Minerals are solid.* The ice in a glacier is a mineral, but liquid water is not.
5. *Minerals have a specific chemical composition.* For example, the mineral corundum always has the same chemical formula: Al_2O_3. This is corundum's formula whether it is in pure white form or has impurities that give it a red color (ruby) or a blue color (sapphire).

To be considered a mineral, a substance must have all five characteristics. For instance, sugar is solid and has a crystal structure. However, sugar is not a mineral because it is the product of a plant—sugar cane or sugar beets.

Sometimes two minerals contain the same elements in the same ratio but their atoms are arranged differently. As a result, they have different crystal structures

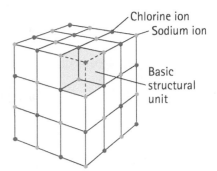

(a)

(b)

FIGURE 7.1
(a) Crystal structure of halite. (b) Grains of the mineral halite (table salt).

(a)

FIGURE 7.2
Fine "crystal" is not really crystal at all. Fine crystal is glass, an amorphous solid. In an amorphous solid, atoms are jumbled together in a random fashion. Gems, such as those in the lady's earrings, are true crystals—they have an orderly atomic structure.

(b)

FIGURE 7.3
(a) Stone Age stone tools. (b) Marble is taken from this modern quarry and used for buildings and sculpture.

FIGURE 7.4
Both graphite and diamond are pure carbon. (a) In diamond, each carbon atom is bonded to each of its neighbors. (b) In graphite, carbon atoms are bonded in two dimensions, forming sheets.

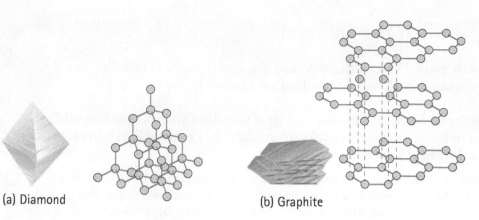

(a) Diamond

(b) Graphite

UNIFYING CONCEPT

● *The Atomic Theory of Matter*
Section 9.1

and different properties. Such minerals are called *polymorphs*. Diamond and graphite (the "lead" in pencils) are polymorphs. They are both pure carbon, but diamond and graphite are different minerals because their atoms are arranged differently. In diamond, the carbon atoms form tight, three-dimensional networks (Figure 7.4). This makes diamond very hard. But, in graphite, the carbon atoms form sheets that slip past one another easily. When you write with a pencil, sheets of graphite atoms pull apart, and this leaves a mark on paper.

CHECK YOURSELF
1. **The graphite in pencil "lead" is a mineral. Why isn't the paper you write on a mineral?**
2. **Gold atoms bond together to make a tiny cube. This tiny cube is repeated over and over to make crystals of gold big enough to see. Halite (table salt) also has a cubic crystal structure. If gold and halite have the same crystal structure, why aren't they classified as the same mineral?**

CHECK YOUR ANSWERS
1. Paper is not a mineral for three reasons: One, it has no specific chemical composition. Two, it has an organic source—trees. Three, paper is made by people; it does not exist naturally in the environment. Pencils are also made by people, but the graphite in them has a specific chemical composition (carbon) and is a naturally occurring inorganic substance.
2. Gold and halite have different chemical compositions.

LEARNING OBJECTIVE
Name seven properties of minerals that are useful in identifying them.

7.2 Mineral Properties

EXPLAIN THIS Why do some minerals break into cubes when you hit them with a hammer?

About 4000 minerals are known today. Minerals can be classified into different groups by their physical properties. Seven important physical mineral properties are crystal form, hardness, cleavage, luster, color, specific gravity, and streak. Some minerals also have the property of being radioactive. Others are fluorescent or magnetic or toxic. Most of Earth's minerals look like everyday rocks, but some have vibrant colors and amazing forms (Figure 7.5).

(a)   (b)   (c)   (d)   (e)   (f)

FIGURE 7.5
A few of the many minerals with a striking appearance. (a) Hematite has a grape-cluster shape. (b) Amethyst is the purple variety of quartz, which grows in hexagonal (six-sided) crystals with pointed ends. (c) Pyrite, or "fool's gold," typically forms cubic crystals marked with parallel lines called "striations." (d) Rosasite has fibrous, blue-green crystals. (e) Rhodochrosite (whose name means "rose-colored") has rhombohedral crystals. (f) Asbestos forms strong, heat-resistant fibers.

Crystal Form

Each of the mineral samples shown in Figure 7.5 has a characteristic *crystal form*, or external shape. A mineral's crystal form is determined by its microscopic crystal structure. Sometimes a mineral's outward crystal form is *the same* as its internal structure of atoms. Figure 7.2 shows the cubic crystal structure of halite, which is mirrored in halite's cubic crystal form. Look at some salt crystals with a hand lens and you can see this cubic crystal form.

You are lucky if you find well-formed crystals in nature because they are rare. Usually, lots of crystals grow together in cramped locations. As they grow, each tiny crystal competes with neighboring crystals for space. The crystals that develop are so small and intermixed with one another that the mineral's crystal form can't be observed without a microscope.

Hardness

A mineral's *hardness* is its resistance to scratching. A harder mineral can scratch a softer one, but not the other way around. Why are some minerals harder than others? Hardness depends on the strength of a mineral's chemical bonds—the stronger its bonds, the harder the mineral. The carbon atoms in diamond are tightly bound, so diamond is especially hard. Mohs scale of hardness (Table 7.1) rates the hardness of different minerals on a scale of 1 to 10. Diamond has a rating of 10.

A piece of quartz can scratch feldspar, but feldspar cannot scratch quartz.

TABLE 7.1	MOHS SCALE OF HARDNESS	
Mineral	**Hardness**	**Object of Similar Hardness**
Talc	1	
Gypsum	2.5	Fingernail
Calcite	3	Copper wire
Fluorite	4	
Apatite	5.5	
Feldspar	6	Window glass
Quartz	7	Steel file
Topaz	8	
Corundum	9	
Diamond	10	

CHECK YOURSELF

1. Can quartz scratch topaz? Can topaz scratch quartz? Defend your answers.
2. Your friend finds a ring that looks like a diamond. But it could be a cubic zirconium—a "fake diamond." Zirconium has hardness 9. Your friend tests the ring and finds that it will scratch glass. Is the ring a diamond?

CHECK YOUR ANSWERS

1. Quartz, with hardness 7, cannot scratch topaz, with hardness 8, because topaz is harder than quartz. Topaz can scratch quartz (and all other minerals with hardness less than 8).
2. You cannot tell because any mineral with hardness greater than 6 will scratch glass.

Cleavage and Fracture

Another property determined by a mineral's crystal structure and chemical bond strength is cleavage. *Cleavage* is the tendency of certain minerals to break along distinct planes of weakness, areas where the bonds holding the crystal together are weakest. Minerals that exhibit cleavage break along flat, even surfaces.

FIGURE 7.6
(a) Muscovite is a mineral of the mica group. It has the property of cleavage and easily breaks into flat sheets.
(b) Calcite has perfect cleavage in three directions. It breaks up into little cubes when you hit it with a hammer.

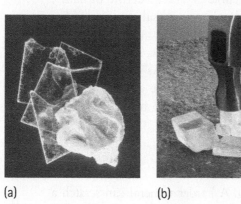

(a)   (b)

Minerals may display cleavage in one or more directions. For instance, mica displays cleavage in one direction. Mica's crystal structure is atoms arranged in stacks. If you hit a piece of mica with a hammer, the mica breaks into sheets (Figure 7.6). Other minerals have perfect cleavage in multiple directions, which allows them to be cut into neat blocks. Jewelers use the natural cleavage of diamonds, emeralds, and certain other minerals to cut them into beautiful gemstones.

A mineral that does not have cleavage breaks unevenly instead of along flat planes. We call this *fracture*. For instance, if you hit a piece of quartz with a hammer, it breaks along smooth, curved surfaces. This kind of fracture is called a *conchoidal* fracture (Figure 7.7).

Luster

The way a mineral reflects light is its *luster*. Geologists use a variety of terms to describe luster: Very shiny minerals have a "metallic" luster. Minerals that have a greasy or oily appearance have a "waxy" luster. Rough, dull minerals have an "earthy" luster. Other minerals have a "pearly" or "silky" luster.

FIGURE 7.7
This quartz sample does not exhibit cleavage. When it breaks, it develops a conchoidal fracture—a smooth, curved surface resembling a broken soda bottle.

Color

Sometimes a mineral's *color* can help you identify it—but only sometimes. This is because the same mineral can exist in several colors. Pure quartz is colorless, but quartz can also be purple, milky white, rose pink, yellow, or smoky brown if it contains impurities. Similarly, pure corundum is white. But if one out of every 5000 aluminum atoms is replaced with a chromium atom, we have the red variety of corundum prized as ruby (Figure 7.8).

Also, you can't use color to identify minerals because sometimes different minerals have the same color. Pyrite, or fool's gold, is gold in color, but so is the element gold. Is that mineral you found in the stream bed precious gold or merely pyrite? You must check other properties to be sure.

Specific Gravity

Specific gravity is the ratio of the weight of a mineral to the weight of water. The specific gravity of copper is 9, so copper is nine times heavier than water for a given volume.

Although color isn't a good property for identifying minerals, specific gravity is. The specific gravity of gold is 19, while fool's gold (pyrite) has a specific gravity of 5. You can tell which is which by how heavy each mineral feels in relation to its size. Note that specific gravity is a lot like density: Both tell you how heavy a material is for its volume. The difference between the two is that specific gravity has no units.

Streak

Streak is the color of a mineral in its powdered form. To find a mineral's streak, you rub it on a piece of unglazed porcelain called a *streak plate*. The mineral's streak is not always the same as the color of the mineral itself, but it is characteristic of the mineral. For example, hematite comes in a variety of colors, but it always has a reddish-brown streak.

Ruby

Sapphire

FIGURE 7.8
Rubies and sapphires are varieties of the mineral corundum that occur when chemical impurities are present. As these examples show, color alone is not a reliable indicator of a mineral's identity.

UNIFYING CONCEPT

● *Density*
   Section 2.3

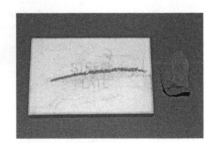

FIGURE 7.9
A mineral's streak is helpful in identifying it.

CHECK YOURSELF

1. Why is crystal form alone not sufficient for identifying a mineral?
2. You work in the stockroom of a museum. A mineral sample has lost its label. What properties are the best ones to use to identify this mineral?

CHECK YOUR ANSWERS

1. Different minerals can have the same crystal form. For example, both gold and halite have a cubic structure. Crystal form *and* chemical composition provide a better test.
2. Specific gravity, streak, and hardness are the best. Although each property cannot be used alone, when used together, they are reasonably accurate means of identification.

7.3 Types of Minerals

EXPLAIN THIS Why are silicates the most common minerals in Earth's crust?

ou learned in chemistry that there are 112 naturally occurring chemical elements. Most of these elements are rare. In fact, only eight elements make up 98% of Earth's entire mass! Just two chemical elements, silicon and oxygen, make up more than 75% of Earth's crust. It is no surprise, then,

LEARNING OBJECTIVE
Identify the major differences between silicate and nonsilicate minerals.

FIGURE 7.10
Although there are 112 naturally occurring elements, only a handful or so make up almost all of Earth's mass. More specifically, eight elements make up 98% of Earth's mass. Just two elements—silicon and oxygen—make up more than 75% of Earth's crust. This is why most minerals are silicates.

that most of Earth's minerals contain silicon and oxygen. Minerals that contain silicon and oxygen bonded together are called **silicates**. Minerals that do not contain silicon and oxygen bonded together are *nonsilicates*. Earth's 4000 or so minerals are divided into these two groups.

Silicates

Silicates, the large class of minerals that contains silicon and oxygen, is divided into two groups: *ferromagnesian* and *nonferromagnesian* silicates. Ferromagnesian silicates always contain iron or magnesium or both of these elements. (*Ferrum* is Latin for "iron," and *magnesian* refers to magnesium.) Ferromagnesian silicates tend to be dark, dense, and glassy and are often found in the oceanic crust. Olivine and hornblende are two examples of ferromagnesian silicates. Nonferromagnesian minerals are generally lighter in color and less dense, and they are extremely common in the continental crust. Feldspar is a nonferromagnesian silicate; feldspar minerals alone make up about half of Earth's crust!

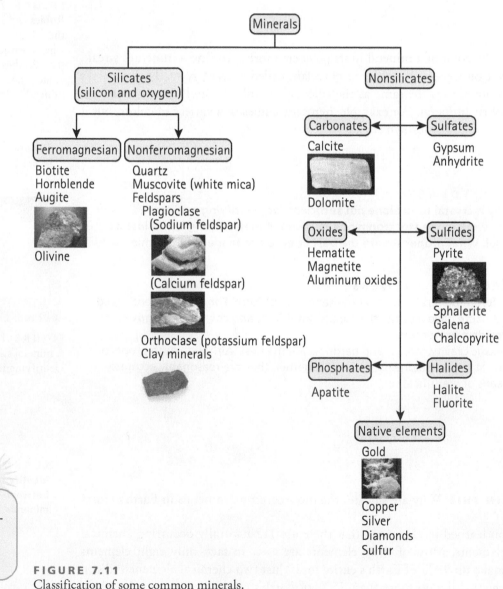

Gold is truly a precious mineral. All the gold that has ever been discovered would fit into a cube with sides equal to those of a baseball diamond!

FIGURE 7.11
Classification of some common minerals.

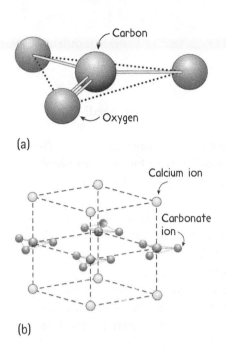

Carbon

Oxygen

(a)

Calcium ion

Carbonate ion

(b)

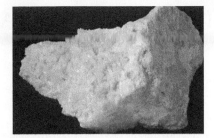

(c)

(d)

FIGURE 7.12
(a) The carbonate ion, CO_3^{2-}, has a triangular structure that features a central carbon atom bonded to three oxygen atoms. (b) Because carbonate minerals, such as calcite and dolomite, have a layered, sheetlike structure, they display the property of cleavage. (c) Dolomite rock (also called *dolostone*) is composed mainly of the mineral dolomite. (d) These cliffs along a stream in the Ozark Mountains of Missouri are made up of dolomite rock.

Nonsilicates

Nonsilicate minerals, including carbonates, sulfates, oxides, and native elements, do not contain silicon bonded to oxygen. Although they account for only about 8% of Earth's crust, they are quite important to nature's ecosystems as well as to civilization. The carbonates, for example, are used in cement. Oxide minerals are used in countless manufactured products such as medicines and airplane parts. The nonsilicate minerals also include the native elements, minerals made up of a single element. Some native elements are gold, silver, copper, carbon, and sulfur. It's easy to think of ways people use these elements—from jewelry to pencil leads!

UNIFYING CONCEPT

● *The Ecosystem*
Section 21.1

CHECK YOURSELF
1. **Which of these photos could show ferromagnesian rock?**
2. **Which photo shows nonferromagnesian rock?**
3. **Which photo shows silicate rock?**

(a)   (b)

CHECK YOUR ANSWERS
1. Photo (a) could show ferromagnesian rock because it is black.
2. Photo (b) shows nonferromagnesian rock.
3. Both photos show silicate rocks, as Figure 7.11 indicates.

LEARNING OBJECTIVE
Explain why the silicate tetrahedron gives rise to so many different
minerals.

 Integrated Science 23A
CHEMISTRY

The Silicate Tetrahedron

EXPLAIN THIS How are the atoms in a silicate tetrahedron arranged?

All of the silicates are made up of the same basic building block—the *silicate tetrahedron*. The silicate tetrahedron is an ion with four oxygen atoms joined to one silicon atom. It has the shape of a pyramid (Figure 7.13). This basic building block can occur by itself or link with others. As a result, there are many different kinds of silicates. Just as carbon is the basis for the vast array of organic molecules, the silicate tetrahedron is the basis for a vast array of silicate minerals.

Olivine has a structure consisting of a single tetrahedron repeated millions of times. In pyroxene, the tetrahedra are linked to form a single chain. Silicate tetrahedra are arranged in sheets in mica and in three-dimensional networks in feldspar. The silicate tetrahedron is a sturdy and versatile building block (Figure 7.14).

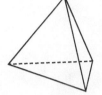

(a) Tetrahedron   (b) Silicate tetrahedron

FIGURE 7.13
(a) The tetrahedron is a geometric shape with four triangular sides.
(b) The silicate tetrahedron is an arrangement of four oxygen atoms with a silicon atom in the center.

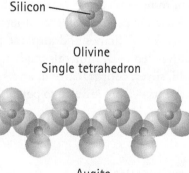

(a) Olivine
Single tetrahedron

(b) Augite
Single chain

FIGURE 7.14
(a) Olivine, an olive-green mineral common in Earth's mantle, is made up of a single tetrahedron. (b) Augite, a member of the pyroxene group of minerals that are found in volcanic lava, is built of single chains of silicate tetrahedra. (c) In feldspar, the crust's dominant mineral group, silicate tetrahedra join together in three-dimensional networks.

(c) Feldspar
Three-dimensional network

CHECK YOURSELF

1. The chemical formula for sapphire is Al_2O_3 (aluminum oxide). Do sapphire crystals contain silicate tetrahedra?
2. Why are there are more silicates in Earth's crust than other types of minerals?

CHECK YOUR ANSWERS

1. No. Silicate tetrahedra require silicon atoms. These are missing in sapphire, as you can tell by its chemical formula. Sapphire is a nonsilicate oxide.
2. Silicates are common because they are made of the very abundant elements silicon and oxygen and because these elements form a versatile building block—the silicon tetrahedron.

7.4   How Do Minerals Form?

LEARNING OBJECTIVE
Describe the four pathways by which most minerals form.

EXPLAIN THIS Why are diamonds unstable at Earth's surface?

You now know what minerals are and how they are classified. You also know something about mineral properties and their structures. But you still may wonder: Where do minerals come from, and how do they form? All minerals arise through *crystallization*, the growth of a solid whose atoms come together in a specific structure. There are four major processes by which minerals crystallize: cooling magma, hydrothermal solutions, precipitation, and pressure and temperature changes.

Cooling Magma

At Earth's surface, rocks and minerals are solid. But, if the temperature is high enough, they can melt to become liquids. As miners know, Earth's interior heats up quickly with depth. On average, the temperature inside Earth increases about 30°C for every kilometer below the ground. The **geothermal gradient**, shown in Figure 7.15, illustrates this change. Rocks and minerals thus exist as liquids in large quantity deep underground. This naturally occurring, molten rocky material is called *magma*.

Magma has a texture like thick oatmeal. Because silicates are the most abundant minerals, magmas are usually rich in silica (SiO_2). Magma contains water and gases and usually contains some solids as well as atoms and molecules in the liquid state. Because magma is hot and less dense than solid rock, it rises buoyantly toward Earth's cooler surface. As magma rises and cools, solid mineral crystals begin to form. Most minerals are formed in this way by cooling magma. Some of the common minerals that form from cooling magma are feldspar, quartz, mica, and magnetite.

Different minerals crystallize at different temperatures. So, as magma cools, it keeps generating different minerals in a series according to the minerals' melting points. Feldspar crystallizes out of a cooling magma before quartz because feldspar has a higher melting point than quartz (see Figure 7.15d). That is, feldspar changes from the liquid to the solid phase at a higher temperature than

FIGURE 7.15
Minerals form through four basic pathways. (a) Minerals form where seawater evaporates and solids are left behind. Example: gypsum. (b) Minerals form when crystals precipitate out of the hot water solutions formed by groundwater. Example: copper. (c) Minerals form where rock is altered by changes in pressure or temperature (metamorphosis). Example: feldspar (d) Minerals form where magma is cooling. Example: feldspar.

(a) Minerals form in areas once covered by salt water

(d) Minerals form where magma is cooling

(c) Minerals form where rock is undergoing metamorphosis

(b) Minerals form where crystals precipitate out of hot water solutions from groundwater

quartz does. Because quartz solidifies at a lower temperature, it forms later than feldspar after the magma has cooled even more. Because minerals crystallize out of magma in series, one particular type of magma can be the "parent" of many different minerals.

Hydrothermal Solutions

Sometimes minerals crystallize out of hydrothermal solutions rather than from magma. A hydrothermal solution is a mixture of very hot water (over 100°C) and dissolved substances. Such a solution forms when water stored underground (*groundwater*) seeps into deep cracks in rock. If magma resides nearby, it heats

FIGURE 7.16
The temperature inside Earth increases about 30°C for each kilometer of depth from the surface. This increase of temperature with depth is known as the *geothermal gradient.*

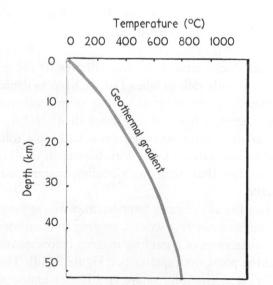

the groundwater, which enhances the water's ability to dissolve or react with the minerals in the surrounding rock. Dissolved metals and other substances crystallize out of the solution when it becomes saturated. Minerals often formed this way include gold, copper, sulfur, and pyrite.

Evaporation

Surface water contains many dissolved substances. When this water evaporates, minerals can form. Such *evaporite* minerals, including halite, are left behind when a sea, lagoon, or other body of surface water dries up. Minerals also can form when water changes temperature because this can cause elements to precipitate out of solution.

> With all natural resources, including minerals, we should practice the basic three Rs: Reduce how much you consume, reuse mineral products rather than throw them away, and recycle minerals when it's time to discard them.

Pressure and Temperature Changes

New minerals sometimes form inside rocks when the rock's environment changes—for example, when the temperature or pressure changes. You will learn more about this process, called *metamorphosis*, later in this chapter. Some minerals that form when rock undergoes metamorphosis are garnet, talc, and graphite.

Not every collection of atoms can make a mineral. A mineral will be *stable* only if its atoms hold together strongly enough. Temperature and pressure have a big effect on mineral stability. Diamonds illustrate this point. Diamonds form about 150 km underground, where high pressure pushes carbon atoms into tight networks. At Earth's surface, the pressure is much lower and a diamond is not really stable. The crystal structure of diamond eventually rearranges to become the mineral graphite. Fortunately, the conversion of diamond to graphite takes about a billion years, so diamonds are safe over the span of human lifetimes. It is only in this limited sense that we can say "diamonds are forever."

FIGURE 7.17
Diamonds aren't forever after all.

TECHNOLOGY

Synthetic Diamonds

In the laboratory, a sample of graphite can be sufficiently pressurized to turn it into a diamond. Until recently, achieving the required pressure was so costly that synthetic gem-quality diamonds were more expensive than mined diamonds. However, in 2004, two companies introduced synthetic gem-quality diamonds to the market. The synthetic diamonds cost roughly 30% less than mined diamonds. These new synthetic diamonds are visually and chemically identical to diamonds mined from Earth.

(a)   (b)

FIGURE 7.18
Which diamond is real? Which is synthetic? (Answer: The synthetic diamond is the one on the right.)

Mining

People use minerals in millions of ways. Just look around. Iron, copper, aluminum, and other metals are used to make cars, refrigerators, and CD players. Building materials, such as concrete, sheet rock, cement, and brick, are made from minerals. So are paint, plastics, films, drugs, explosives, money, lubricants, nuclear reactor cores, steel, food additives, and more.

In the United States, several billion tons of mineral resources are needed each year for people to go about their normal everyday activities. Each man, woman, and child in the United States uses thousands of kilograms of new mineral resources per year, and the average American home contains slightly more than a quarter million pounds (more than 113,000 kg) of minerals and metals (Figure 7.19).

Where do all these minerals come from? They are mined from Earth's crust. Mineral deposits that are large enough and pure enough to be mined for profit are called **ore**. Have you ever seen a mining site (Figure 7.20)? Surface mining removes layers of Earth to obtain minerals that are at or near Earth's surface. Strip mines, open-pit

FIGURE 7.20
The Kennecott Copper Mine in Utah is big enough to see from space. It is 1.2 km deep and 4 km wide. Billions of tons of rock have been removed from this mine in order to obtain copper and other minerals.

mines, and quarries are surface mines. Obtaining ores such as coal and diamonds can require digging deep holes into the ground. Underground mines typically consist of networks of tunnels that branch out for many miles. Once ore is removed from a mine, the ore is processed to extract the needed minerals.

The extraction of great amounts of ore can do environmental damage. Because the land is disrupted, ecosystems may be destroyed. Removal of vegetation can cause erosion and landslides. Also, fossil fuels are consumed on a grand scale to process the minerals. Pollutants, such as carbon dioxide and sulfur dioxide, and toxic waste, such as lead and chromium, are generated. Once the ore is obtained, it must be refined to release its load of minerals. We need minerals, but how can we mine for them responsibly?

Many mining operations reduce environmental damage through reclamation. Reclamation is the practice of returning land to the condition it was in before the mining was done.

Each U.S. citizen will use...

700 kg copper
53 kg gold
14,200 kg halite
260,000 kg coal
10,200 kg clays
2800 kg aluminum
15,900 kg iron ore
385 kg lead
385 kg zinc

in his or her lifetime.

FIGURE 7.19
Each U.S. citizen, on average, will use large amounts of minerals for food, clothing, and shelter as well as transportation, manufacturing, and recreational activities.

LEARNING OBJECTIVE
Distinguish between rocks and minerals.

7.5 What Is Rock?

EXPLAIN THIS How is a rock like a granola bar?

A **rock** is a solid, cohesive mixture of mineral crystals. The mineral crystals (grains) in rock are not necessarily all the same mineral; often many minerals are present, and sometimes glass as well. The minerals (and possibly glass) are held firmly together. Sand grains may be cemented or compacted together to make a rock, but if they are not consolidated, they are not a rock. The difference between minerals and rocks is that minerals are *chemical compounds*, whereas rocks are *physical mixtures*.

FIGURE 7.21
Rocks are solid mineral mixtures. This granite rock is a mixture of quartz, hornblende, and feldspar.

FIGURE 7.22
The three main classifications of rock. (a) Basalt and granite are igneous rocks. (b) Sandstone and limestone are igneous rocks. (c) Marble and slate are metamorphic rocks.

You can sometimes see the mineral crystals in a rock. Granite, the most common type of rock in the continental crust, is shown in Figure 7.21. It contains visible crystals of feldspar, quartz, and hornblende. But sometimes rock crystals are not so easily seen. Fine-grained rocks such as slate look smooth and even because they contain crystals that are too small to be seen with the naked eye.

Most surface rocks are covered with *soil* or what people call "dirt." Soil is a mixture of small bits of weathered rock, air, water, and *organic matter*—the decayed remains of plants, animals, and other organisms. But if you dig under the soil, you'll find rock. Wherever you dig, you're sure to find rock—some near Earth's surface and some deep down.

Rocks, like minerals, are as useful as they are abundant. People have been fashioning rock into useful tools since prehistoric times. Early humans didn't have many materials to choose from. Plastic, iron, steel, and such were not invented or discovered until modern times. The only materials available were trees, rocks, plants, minerals, and animal remains. Arrowheads made from obsidian could be sharpened enough to cut the skin of prey. Heavy granite rocks were used as blunt weapons. Large, flat sandstone rocks were used as grinding stones.

Another major use of rock is in building. The great cathedrals of Europe, the pyramids of Egypt, prehistoric stone temples, Mayan villages, ancient mosques, and even some entire ancient cities are built of rock. Modern buildings are often made of concrete, a material made from rock.

Rocks are classified into three major groups based on how they form (Figure 7.22). The three kinds of rocks are *igneous rocks*, *sedimentary rocks*, and *metamorphic rocks*.

FIGURE 7.23
People have been using rocks to make useful tools since the Stone Age.

7.6 Igneous Rock

EXPLAIN THIS What determines the size of the crystals in an igneous rock?

The word *igneous* means "fire" in Latin. **Igneous rocks** ("IG-nee-us") form by the crystallization and solidification of magma that is cooling. Igneous rocks consist of tightly interlocking crystals, which makes them strong—able to withstand strong forces. The igneous rock granite is a desirable material for kitchen countertops because of its strength as well as its beauty (Figure 7.24).

Igneous rocks vary in their mineral makeup and their texture. Mineral makeup is chemical composition, and texture refers to grain (crystal) size.

The mineral composition of an igneous rock reflects the chemical composition of the parent magma that generates the rock. Magmas around the world differ in composition according to the tectonic setting in which they form. The magmas generated at divergent plate boundaries and regions of oceanic crust are rich in the dark, iron- and magnesium-containing minerals as well as silica. When these magmas cool and crystallize, dark rocks including basalt and gabbro result (look ahead to Figure 7.28a). Magma generated in continental rock settings, on the other hand, has a higher silica content and less iron and magnesium. Light-colored rocks including granite and rhyolite solidify from high-silica magma.

Igneous rocks that form from magma cooling slowly underground are called **intrusive igneous rocks**. Intrusive igneous rocks are so named because the magma they derive from "intrudes" or pushes into the surrounding rock on its journey toward Earth's surface. And intrusive rocks are also sometimes called *plutonic* rocks, after Pluto, the Greek god of the underworld. Hence, underground igneous rock bodies are called *plutons*.

Plutons can be sheetlike or bulky depending on the rock they intrude into. *Dikes*, for example, are sheetlike igneous rock bodies that form when magma is injected into fractures cutting across rock layers (Figure 7.25a). A *batholith* is a large volume of plutonic rock that has been uplifted and exposed at Earth's surface after the overlying, softer rock has eroded away. Batholiths form the cores of many mountain systems. The Sierra Nevada mountain range is a gigantic batholith formed by the combined masses of many plutons (Figure 7.25b). It has a surface area of about 25,000 square miles!

FIGURE 7.24
Igneous rock, such as this granite, is strong because it consists of tightly interlocking crystals.

(a)   (b)

FIGURE 7.25
(a) This sheetlike igneous intrusion is a dike in the Swiss Alps. (b) The core of the Sierra Nevada mountain range is a giant batholith, or intrusive igneous body, revealed at Earth's surface due to erosion.

When magma rises all the way to Earth's surface without solidifying, it's called **lava**. Lava may erupt violently from a volcano, or it may ooze out of cracks in the seafloor. Either way, it cools quickly to form solid rock. The igneous rocks that form at Earth's surface are called **extrusive igneous rocks** (Figure 32.26), or *volcanic* rocks. Whereas intrusive igneous rocks generally have big crystals, extrusive igneous rocks have small crystals or no crystals at all.

FIGURE 7.26
When lava cools enough to solidify, it forms extrusive igneous rock.

Classifying Igneous Rocks

It's convenient to classify igneous rocks by their *texture*—the size of their crystals. There are four igneous textures:

1. *Coarse-grained*—crystals that are visible without a microscope
2. *Fine-grained*—microscopic crystals
3. *Glassy*—no crystals
4. *Porphyritic*—large crystals embedded in a matrix of smaller crystals

The size of a crystal in an igneous rock depends on how rapidly the parent magma cools. Slow cooling produces large crystals, and rapid cooling produces small crystals (Figure 7.27). Extremely rapid cooling produces glassy-textured rocks, such as obsidian, that have no crystals at all. Why is this so?

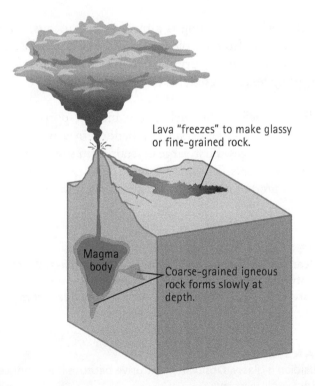

Lava "freezes" to make glassy or fine-grained rock.

Magma body

Coarse-grained igneous rock forms slowly at depth.

FIGURE 7.27
The texture of an igneous rock depends on how long it takes to cool. Coarse-grained igneous rocks have large crystals formed by slow cooling deep in Earth's interior. Fine-grained igneous rocks have small crystals and form closer to the surface.

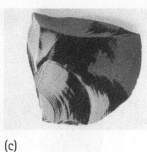

(a)   (b)   (c)   (d)

FIGURE 7.28
Igneous rocks displaying different textures: (a) gabbro, a coarse-grained rock; (b) rhyolite, showing a fine-grained texture; (c) an obsidian sample with a glassy texture; and (d) andesite porphyry—a porphyritic rock.

A mineral crystal grows by adding atoms to its outside surface. When crystals growing side by side become large enough for their edges to touch, crystal growth stops because there is no more room. The entire magma body is solidified as a patchwork of interlocking crystals.

When magma cools slowly—over thousands or millions of years—crystals have time to get quite large before they have to compete with their neighbors for available atoms or for space. Thus, when you see a coarse-grained rock, such as the granite or the gabbro ("GAB-row") shown in Figure 7.28a, with its big, chunky crystals, you know that it cooled slowly from magma over a long period of time.

Sometimes cooling can occur rapidly, over days, weeks, or months. When cooling is this fast, lots of tiny crystals form at the same time. Each crystal doesn't have time to grow very large before its neighbors crowd in on it. As a result, rapid cooling produces a fine-grained rock, such as the rhyolite ("RI-o-lite") shown in Figure 7.28b.

When lava cools into rock, the cooling is almost instantaneous. This can happen when drops of lava eject from a violent volcano. The atoms lose energy before they arrange themselves in *any* crystal structure—they just freeze in place. An abrasive or glassy texture results. Obsidian is an example, shown in Figure 7.28c.

Porphyritic ("por-fuh-RIT-ic") rocks, such as the andesite porphyry shown in Figure 7.28d, are rocks with large crystals embedded in a matrix of tiny ones. These rocks develop in stages. First, large crystals form slowly at depth as a column of magma rises and cools. Then, the magma cools quickly as it erupts at or near Earth's surface, producing the fine-grained crystal matrix.

CHECK YOURSELF
1. Obsidian is a volcanic glass that looks like manufactured glass. What is its texture? Is it intrusive or extrusive, and how do you know?
2. What is the texture of granite? How quickly does it crystallize from magma?

CHECK YOUR ANSWERS
1. The texture of obsidian is glassy. Obsidian is extrusive because it is produced by the nearly instant cooling of lava.
2. Granite has a coarse-grained structure, which indicates that it crystallizes slowly from magma over a period of thousands to millions of years.

7.7 Sedimentary Rock

LEARNING OBJECTIVE
Describe how sedimentary rocks form.

EXPLAIN THIS How can sedimentary rock be the most common type of rock at Earth's surface yet the least common type of rock in Earth's crust?

Sedimentary rock is rock formed by the accumulation of weathered material. When a rock lies at or near Earth's surface, it gets broken down or *weathered* from the action of water, wind, organisms, reactive chemicals, or ice. The weathered rock fragments may be large or small, or they may even be tiny dissolved particles. Such fragments of weathered rock are called **sediments**.

Sediments don't stay in one spot forever. They are picked up and moved by streams, wind, glaciers, or other means of transportation in the process called *erosion*. Erosion ultimately moves sediments downhill and toward the sea because of gravity. Erosion comes to an end when the sediments are dumped at a new location, or *deposited*.

Sediments mixed with organic matter make soil. But sediments that undergo the process of *lithification* (from the Greek *lithos*, meaning "stone") become sedimentary rock, which is more compact, dense, and cohesive than the original sediments. Lithification occurs when sediments are compacted, or compressed, by the weight of overlying layers. Or, the sediments may be held together by a natural cement that forms when mineral-rich water flows into empty spaces between sediments and evaporates. Sometimes cementation and compaction both occur.

Only about 5% of Earth's crust is composed of sedimentary rock. However, most of the rocks you come into contact with are sedimentary. They are spread out in a thin patchwork that covers about 75% of the continental crust. Sedimentary rock forms layers called **strata** that have been built up over thousands or millions of years. You may have noticed strata along cliffs or road cuts (Figure 7.29).

Sedimentary rocks sometimes contain **fossils**, the remains or traces of ancient life forms (Figure 7.30). Fossils are a record of the drama of life on Earth. Even without fossils, sedimentary rocks provide clues about Earth's geologic past—the positions of its continents, the rise and fall of sea level, and climate changes over time.

Sedimentary rocks are classified into two main groups. **Clastic rocks** (from the Greek word *klastos*, which means "broken up") are formed when bits, pieces, or particles of weathered rock hold together. **Chemical rock** results when minerals precipitate out of a solution and then stick together.

Clastic sedimentary rocks are usually classified on the basis of the average size of their particles (Figure 7.31). *Sandstone* is composed of sand-sized sediment particles. *Shale* is made of finer sediments that cannot be seen with the naked eye. *Conglomerate* is a coarse-grained rock made of rounded particles larger than 2 mm in diameter. *Breccia* ("BRE-chee-a"), another coarse-grained clastic sedimentary rock, is made of large, angular pieces of rock held together by natural mineral cement.

Chemical sedimentary rocks are made when crystals precipitate out of a solution. Minerals can precipitate when water evaporates or when certain chemical reactions occur. For example, a chemical sedimentary rock can originate when rainwater dissolves rock. Mineral-rich water flows toward the ocean. Minerals remain dissolved in ocean water until so much water evaporates that its concentration of minerals exceeds its solubility limit. Then mineral crystals precipitate out of the water and sink to the ocean floor. Eventually, enough mineral crystals collect, compact, and join together to form a rock.

FIGURE 7.29
The strata of this sedimentary rock formation are visible in this photo. This formation is in Dorset, England. These strata were deposited more than 100 million years ago in the Jurassic period—a time when dinosaurs roamed the land.

FIGURE 7.30
Hundreds of dinosaur fossils and skeletons have been found in the sandstone at Dinosaur Provincial Park in Canada. Sandstone is a common sedimentary rock.

If you have to guess what kind of rock is in your backyard, guess sedimentary rock. Sedimentary rocks cover most of the continental crust.

FIGURE 7.31
Sedimentary rocks. (a) Shale, the most abundant sedimentary rock, is composed of fine particles. (b) Sandstone is made of medium-sized particles, about the size of sand grains. (c) Conglomerate consists of a variety of large, rounded particles. (d) Breccia consists of large, angular pieces of rock held together by cement.

(a)

(b)

(c)

(d)

Sometimes biological processes are involved in making chemical sedimentary rocks. Consider limestone: Marine animals, including clams and corals, chemically extract calcium carbonate ($CaCO_3$) from ocean water to build their shells and skeletons. When these organisms die, their shells and skeletons break up and pile up on the ocean bottom. Over time they can become buried, compacted, and cemented to form limestone. *Coquina* is a biochemical limestone composed of shells and shell fragments. *Chalk* is a fine-grained limestone that is also formed from the shells of marine organisms. *Travertine*, on the other hand, is a limestone formed inorganically—for example, by the precipitation of calcium carbonate (also called calcite) from mineral springs (Figure 7.32).

(a)   Coquina   (b)   Chalk   (c)   Travertine

FIGURE 7.32
Coquina (a) and chalk (b) are two kinds of limestone. They are both chemical sedimentary rocks, formed from small marine animals, such as clams, that chemically extract calcium carbonate from seawater. Travertine is also limestone and a chemical sedimentary rock, although it is not derived from a biological source. The travertine specimen shown here (c) was formed when calcium carbonate precipitated out of a mineral spring in Turkey.

Integrated Science 23B
BIOLOGY, CHEMISTRY, AND PHYSICS

Coal

EXPLAIN THIS Why does coal contain energy-rich organic molecules?

During the 19th century, coal replaced wood as the fuel of choice. Although coal was dangerous to mine, bulky to handle, and dirty to burn, it became widely available and produced more heat per volume than wood. When liquid and gaseous fossil fuels became available later in the 19th century, they began to replace coal, especially for home use. Coal is still an important energy source, however. Currently, about 20% of all U.S. energy is supplied by coal. And coal-fired power plants account for more than half of the electricity generated in the United States. As oil and gas supplies decline, there is increasing interest in expanding the role of coal as a fuel. On the other hand, there is concern about the environmental effects of coal, including greenhouse gas (carbon dioxide) emissions, air pollution from ash and toxic metals, and sulfur emissions that contribute to water pollution and acid rain.

FIGURE 7.33
(a) Anthracite coal. (b) A coal seam in New Zealand.

(a)

(b)

COAL – A ROCK WE BURN FOR FUEL!

Coal is a black or brown combustible sedimentary rock (Figure 7.33). It occurs in rock strata called *coal seams* that are fairly common, particularly in the United States. It's estimated that more than 10 trillion tons of coal are stored in Earth's crust. The United States owns about 25% of the world's current reserves of this energy-rich rock.

Coal is derived from ancient land plants. Most coal was formed about 300 million years ago, when much of Earth was covered by steamy swamps. As the green plants died, their remains sank to the bottoms of the swamps. Plant material did not decay easily in the oxygen-poor swamp water. So the plant debris accumulated, layer upon layer, and the energy-rich molecules stored in the debris remained intact because they didn't react with oxygen. Eventually, the plant remains formed a dense, soggy, only partially decomposed organic material called *peat*.

Over geologic time, Earth's surface kept changing. Great rivers brought sand, clay, and other sediments to bury the peat. Sandstone and other sedimentary rock formed overlying strata, which heated and pressurized the buried peat even more. The spongy peat transformed into soft, brown coal (known as *lignite*) and then, with more time, heat, and pressure, into the harder coal *bituminous* (Figure 7.34). Bituminous that was squeezed and folded by tectonic forces during mountain building ultimately formed the highest-energy form of coal, *anthracite*. Lignite and bituminous are sedimentary rocks, but anthracite is a metamorphic rock.

Coal is a lot like petroleum. Both are fossil fuels. They contain hydrocarbons rich in chemical potential energy. Both coal and petroleum are nonrenewable resources that formed over millions of years when organisms died and were buried and then decayed in the absence of oxygen. Like all fossil fuels, coal and petroleum send carbon dioxide (a "greenhouse gas") into the atmosphere when burned, contributing to climate change. While petroleum is derived from ancient marine organisms, coal is the product of ancient land plants.

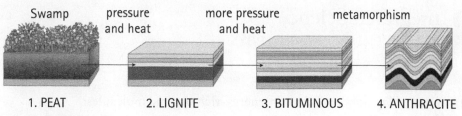

FIGURE 7.34

The formation of coal. (a) Peat forms from plant remains in a stagnant swamp. (b) The peat is buried by sediments and subjected to great heat and pressure over time. Lignite, a soft, brown, low-energy coal forms. (c) More time, burial, heat, and pressure lead to the formation of bituminous, a soft, black coal used for energy production. (d) Tectonic forces squeeze bituminous to anthracite, the hardest, highest-energy form of coal.

Coal is sometimes called "buried sunshine." The ancient land plants that coal comes from, like all plants, captured solar energy through photosynthesis to manufacture the organic molecules of their tissues. When coal is combusted—chemically reacted with oxygen—its large reserves of chemical potential energy are unlocked and can be transformed into other kinds of useful energy.

UNIFYING CONCEPT

● *The Law of Conservation of Energy*
Section 4.10

CHECK YOURSELF

Why is coal sometimes called "buried sunshine"?

CHECK YOUR ANSWER

The ultimate source of the chemical energy in coal is the Sun.

LEARNING OBJECTIVE

Identify how metamorphic rocks differ from sedimentary and igneous rocks.

7.8 Metamorphic Rock

EXPLAIN THIS How are garnets, reddish-black gems, derived from plain sandstone?

How is a rock altered when it is subducted and sinks to a deeper location with higher temperature or pressure than the environment in which it formed? Or when it is subjected to the high stresses and temperatures associated with mountain building? How is a rock altered when it is exposed to the hot, reactive chemical fluids associated with magma? Such changes in the physical and chemical conditions to which a rock is exposed can transform rock. New rock is made from old. The new rock is stable under the new conditions, while the preexisting rock was not.

The word *metamorphism* literally means "changed form." Rocks that change form deep in Earth's interior to become more stable under new conditions are called **metamorphic rocks**. Igneous, sedimentary, and metamorphic rocks can all undergo metamorphism. During metamorphism, a rock's texture, size, shape, density, or mineral makeup may be altered.

The process occurs at depths ranging from a few kilometers below the surface all the way to the crust–mantle boundary, where elevated heat, pressure, and chemical fluids exist. *Regional metamorphism* affects large areas of rock. Regional metamorphism occurs deep in Earth's crust, where temperature and pressure are high enough to form huge regions of metamorphic rock. Regional metamorphism is usually produced from the heating and stresses that occur during mountain building and plate tectonic movement. On the other hand, when hot magma rises to shallow regions of the crust and heats the surrounding cooler rocks there, those rocks may metamorphose. This type of metamorphosis affects smaller regions of rock and is called *contact metamorphism*.

Note that minerals do not melt when a rock metamorphoses. Minerals may change their identity through recrystallization, but this does not require melting. *Recrystallization* occurs when a mineral's crystal structure collapses under the influence of elevated temperature or heat, and its atoms migrate and recombine to form new minerals. Recrystallization also happens when intruding chemical fluids supply new atoms that react with the minerals in preexisting rock, so that new mineral crystals form. Recrystallization can occur many times, but, once minerals actually melt, metamorphism is over and igneous activity has begun.

Metamorphism varies in degree. When a rock's environment changes only slightly and the rock is altered in a minor way, the change is referred to as *low-grade metamorphism* (Figure 7.35). The metamorphosis of the sedimentary rock shale into the metamorphic rock slate is an example of this—the rock changes mainly in that it becomes more dense as its mineral grains are aligned more compactly. Low-grade metamorphism takes place at just slightly higher temperatures and pressures than those that lithify sediments. High-grade metamorphism takes place under extreme conditions and can obliterate all features of the parent rock. An interesting example is "shock metamorphism," which yields the mineral stishovite, a high-density, tetragonal form of silica. The process occurs at ultrahigh pressures but not necessarily at high temperatures. Where might you find such conditions? At the site of a meteor impact. The first crystals of stishovite were discovered at Meteor Crater in Arizona (Figure 7.36). Today, the presence of stishovite is taken as diagnostic evidence of a meteor impact at craters of unknown origin.

Many metamorphic rocks are foliated. **Foliated rocks** contain minerals that are aligned in a particular direction, forming parallel layers that look like pages in a book. Usually the minerals are oriented perpendicular to the direction of applied pressure. Foliated metamorphic rocks, such as gneiss ("nice"), shown in Figure 7.37, often display distinctive banding from light and dark minerals.

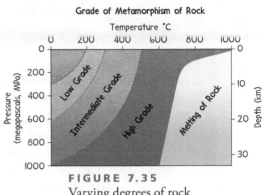

FIGURE 7.35
Varying degrees of rock metamorphism.

FIGURE 7.36
Meteor Crater in Arizona, the site of "shock metamorphism."

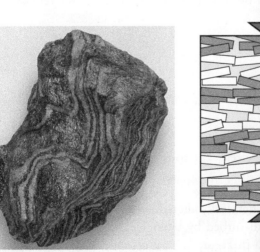

(a) Macroscopic view of gneiss   (b) Microscopic view of gneiss

FIGURE 7.37
(a) Foliated metamorphic rocks, such as the gneiss shown here, contain minerals aligned in a particular direction. (b) Usually they are aligned in a direction perpendicular to the applied force.

Increasing metamorphism

Increasing temperature and/or pressure

Shale

Slate

Schist

Gneiss

FIGURE 7.38
Shale, a sedimentary rock, recrystallizes to form gneiss in a series of metamorphic changes.

Metamorphic rocks that consist of just one non-platy mineral (except for impurities) are nonfoliated—that is, they don't exhibit layers. For example, limestone metamorphoses to marble, a nonfoliated metamorphic rock.

To summarize the metamorphosis of rock, consider an example—the transformation of shale to gneiss, which occurs through the series of metamorphic changes shown in Figure 7.38. If you start with clay and squeeze the water out of it at high pressure, you get the sedimentary rock shale. Compress shale by piling more rock and sediments on top or by the action of tectonic forces, and the shale metamorphoses into slate. Even higher temperatures and pressures can metamorphose slate into *schist*. Schist contains minerals, including beautiful reddish-black garnets, which form only under extremely high pressure and temperature. The garnet crystals were not in the original clay that created the shale, but as the rock was squeezed at higher and higher pressures, the garnet crystals began to grow at the expense of other minerals. Schist is not the end of the line for shale, however. With more pressure and temperature, schist metamorphoses into gneiss. Gneiss has a mineral structure that is completely different from that of the shale from which it began. The original atoms, those of the shale, are still there, but recrystallization has reformulated the original minerals and transformed the shale's visible texture. Yet even with gneiss the process of metamorphism is not over. If the temperature rises even higher, the gneiss begins to melt and becomes a partially melted rock called a *migmatite*.

You may wonder whether one rock can metamorphose into another and another indefinitely. It cannot. Once a rock melts completely, it becomes magma. And when the magma cools to form a rock, the new rock will, by definition, be an igneous rock.

CHECK YOURSELF
1. When can a rock no longer undergo metamorphosis?
2. Why does recrystallization occur in a rock?

CHECK YOUR ANSWERS
1. A rock cannot continue to undergo metamorphosis once it melts.
2. Recrystallization occurs because rock has been exposed to high temperatures or pressures or because it has been exposed to chemical fluids.

LEARNING OBJECTIVE
Draw the rock cycle.

7.9 The Rock Cycle

EXPLAIN THIS How does melting reset the rock cycle?

No rock escapes the forces of change. Rocks are broken, heated, compressed, stretched, bent, chemically altered, worn away, moved, melted, uplifted, and otherwise disturbed by biological, chemical, and physical agents. The **rock cycle**, shown in Figure 7.39, is a model that sums up the

MasteringPhysics®
TUTORIAL: The Rock Cycle

Melting

Magma/Lava

Crystallization

Metamorphic rock

Metamorphism

Igneous rock

Weathering, erosion, deposition

Sedimentary rock

Lithification

Sediment

FIGURE 7.39

The rock cycle shows the processes that can change rock from one kind into another over and over again. Rocks can take more than one pathway through the cycle. The arrows represent the processes of change. The boxes represent the materials that undergo change.

formation, breakdown, and re-formation of rock as a result of igneous, sedimentary, and metamorphic processes.

Rocks can follow many different pathways around the rock cycle. Sometimes igneous rock, for example, is subjected to heat and pressure far below Earth's surface and becomes metamorphic rock. Or, metamorphic or sedimentary rocks at Earth's surface may decompose to become sediment that undergoes compaction and becomes new sedimentary rock. There are many possible variations of the cycle. Cycles even occur within cycles. Whatever the route, Earth's crust is formed when molten rock rises from the depths of Earth, cools, and solidifies to form a crust that, over time, is reworked by shifting and erosion, and it can eventually be returned to the interior, where it may be completely melted and once again become magma.

Many of Earth's materials move in cycles. Just as rock undergoes cycles of change, water changes phase and moves from the ocean, to the atmosphere, to the land, and back to the ocean in the *hydrologic* cycle. Both carbon and nitrogen move through Earth, to the atmosphere, and through living things in *biogeochemical* cycles.

LEARNING OBJECTIVE
State the age of Earth, the age of the oldest fossil, the age of the earliest fossilized human footprints, and the time of the Cretaceous extinction, along with the rock evidence for each of these ages.

Integrated Science 23C
BIOLOGY AND ASTRONOMY

Earth's History Is Written in Its Rocks

EXPLAIN THIS How is "shocked quartz" in the rock record suggestive of an asteroid impact?

How old is Earth? Was your home state once under the sea? Was your city a dinosaur's breeding ground? Amazing facts about Earth are revealed if you know how to interpret the *rock record*—the geologic clues recorded in rocks.

Radiometric dating is a laboratory method that can be used to determine the age of rock in years. Such testing indicates that the oldest known *rock* on Earth is a 4-billion-year-old gneiss formation in Canada (Figure 7.40). The oldest known natural *object* of terrestrial origin is a zircon mineral crystal enclosed in a metamorphosed sandstone rock in Australia. Radiometric dating shows that this crystal is 4.3 billion years old. These ages, coupled with astronomical evidence, put the age of Earth at about 4.6 billion years. A difficult stretch of time to comprehend! If the 4.6-billion-year age of Earth were condensed into a single year, all of recorded human history would take place in the last minute of New Year's Eve.

Rock and mineral ages tell much about Earth's past—so do fossils. A fossil is any record of past life, such as bones, teeth, shells, impressions, and footprints. The earliest fossils known are stromatolites, large rocky structures built by *cyanobacteria* (blue-green algae) 3.5 billion years ago (Figure 7.41). The discovery of these fossils puts a lower limit on the beginning of life. Life must have existed on Earth *at least* 3.5 *billion* years ago. Another fossil find—this one only one thousandth the age of stromatolites at 3.6 *million* years old—displays the earliest known human footprints. From this fossil dig, scientists have inferred much about early hominids, even information about their social behavior (Figure 7.42).

FIGURE 7.40
Radiometric techniques have shown that the Acasta Gneiss complex in Canada is 4 billion years old and is Earth's oldest rock outcropping.

FIGURE 7.41
This artwork of Precambrian Earth shows meteorites crashing into Earth's volcanic surface. Cyanobacteria thrive in the water. Stromatolites—the rocky structures built by cyanobacteria—are evidence of cyanobacteria's presence.

(a)   (b)

FIGURE 7.42
(a) This 3.6-million-year-old volcanic rock features two sets of adult footprints and a third of a child. These are the oldest known human-type footprints. They belong to early humanlike creatures called *Australopithecus afarensis*. (b) Paleontologists have determined that *Australopithecus afarensis* had the upright gait of modern humans.

FIGURE 7.43
These layers of the Grand Canyon, called the *Redwall Limestone*, are built of the rocky remains of marine animals, which indicates that the Redwall Limestone was once covered by a shallow sea.

Knowledge of the environments in which different kinds of sedimentary rock form helps scientists understand different geologic settings. For example, much of the world's limestone is formed from the calcium carbonate–rich skeletons and shells of marine organisms. So the presence of limestone suggests that a location was once under the sea. Figure 7.43 shows a section of the Grand Canyon called the Redwall Limestone. The limestone there indicates that this part of the Grand Canyon was once covered by seawater.

A dramatic example of the stories written in rock is the *Cretaceous extinction*. The Cretaceous period occurred between 150 and 65 million years ago. It ended with a mass extinction that killed more than 60% of Earth's species over a period of about 2 million years. Famously, the dinosaurs were devastated.

What caused the Cretaceous extinction? Scientists agree that climate change was the key factor. Mild Mesozoic climates suddenly turned cool, and sunlight grew scarce. But what was the underlying cause of the sudden climate change? This is where the geologic detective work gets interesting. Geologists support the *impact hypothesis*—the idea that a large asteroid struck Earth at the end of the Cretaceous period and triggered the climate changes that wiped out species (Figure 7.44).

There are several lines of evidence recorded in the rock record that support the impact hypothesis. Consider this: There is a thin layer of clay in the rock record that contains high levels of iridium. Iridium is a rare element on Earth, but it can occur in high concentrations in asteroids. The position of the iridium layer in the rock record matches the time of the Cretaceous extinction.

FIGURE 7.44
According to the impact hypothesis, a large asteroid triggered climate changes that caused a mass extinction at the end of the Cretaceous period.

FIGURE 7.45
The Chicxulub crater on the Yucatan Peninsula of Mexico, soon after it formed. Did the impact that produced this crater end the reign of the dinosaurs?

Could the iridium have been placed in the rock record by an asteroid crashing into Earth and exploding over a large area? The timing is right; the iridium was deposited about 65 million years ago—the time of the great Cretaceous extinction. A large object almost certainly did hit Earth then. An impact crater dating to this time, called *Chicxulub*, has been found in Mexico (Figure 7.45). The crater is more than 180 kilometers across; to produce a crater that size, an asteroid must have been larger than 10 kilometers in diameter. Such an asteroid could have triggered a mass explosion that ignited wildfires that blocked the Sun. The rock record shows a layer of soot in North American rocks that dates to the time of the proposed impact. Besides the iridium and soot, we also find "shocked" quartz, spheres of melted rock near Chicxulub. The crater, the soot, the shocked quartz, and the iridium—all of these point to a massive asteroid impact in the late Cretaceous. As you can see, rock is many things—including a record of Earth's amazing history.

For instructor-assigned homework, go to www.masteringphysics.com (MP)

SUMMARY OF TERMS (KNOWLEDGE)

Chemical rocks Sedimentary rocks formed from minerals precipitated out of solution.

Clastic rocks Sedimentary rocks that are composed of pieces of preexisting rocks.

Extrusive igneous rock An igneous rock that forms at Earth's surface.

Foliated rocks Rocks that contain crystals arranged in parallel bands.

Fossils The remains or traces of ancient life forms.

Geothermal gradient The increase of temperature with depth in Earth's interior.

Igneous rock Rock that forms from magma that cools.

Intrusive igneous rock Igneous rock that forms from magma that cools underground.

Lava Magma that erupts at Earth's surface.

Metamorphic rock Rock that forms by the alteration of preexisting rock deep in Earth's interior due to the effects of temperature, pressure, or reactive chemicals.

Mineral A naturally occurring, solid, inorganic, crystal material with a specific chemical composition.

Ore Mineral deposits that are large enough and pure enough to be mined for profit.

Rock A solid, cohesive mixture of one or more kinds of mineral crystals.

Rock cycle A series of processes by which rock is formed, breaks down, and re-forms into different kinds of rock.

Sedimentary rock Rock that forms over time as bits and pieces of preexisting rock are consolidated through compaction and/or cementation.

Sediments Fragments of weathered rock or living organisms.

Silicates Minerals that contain silicon and oxygen and make up more than 75% of Earth's crust.

Strata Parallel layers of sedimentary rock.

READING CHECK (COMPREHENSION)

7.1 What Is a Mineral?

1. Diamond and graphite are minerals made of 100% carbon. Are diamond and graphite the same mineral or different minerals? Why?

2. Are plastic and nylon minerals?

3. Describe the microscopic structure of a mineral.

7.2 Mineral Properties

4. What is the chemical formula for rubies? Why are rubies red?

5. Identify six or more properties of minerals.

6. How does the hardness of a mineral relate to its chemical bonds?

7.3 Types of Minerals

7. How many minerals are known to exist? What are the two main groups into which minerals are classified?

8. Which is the largest group of minerals? What is the common feature of all minerals in this group?

9. Which are more common in Earth's crust and mantle—silicates or nonsilicates?

7.4 How Do Minerals Form?

10. List four ways that minerals can form.

11. A rock deep in Earth has a temperature higher than the melting point it has at Earth's surface. Why can this buried rock remain in the solid state even though its temperature is very high?

12. When can the rock described in Exercise 11 melt to become magma?

7.5 What Is Rock?

13. Earth's crust is made of rock, so why don't we see solid rock everywhere on the surface?

14. When can't we see the crystals in rocks?

7.6 Igneous Rock

15. What is the difference between extrusive and intrusive igneous rocks?

16. Why are most igneous rocks very hard?

7.7 Sedimentary Rock

17. Describe the process by which sedimentary rocks form.

18. Why are fossils found in sedimentary rocks rather than in metamorphic rocks?

7.8 Metamorphic Rock

19. Heat and pressure can make one rock change, or metamorphose, into another. Where do the heat and pressure that metamorphoses rock typically come from?

20. What kinds of rocks can undergo metamorphism?

7.9 The Rock Cycle

21. Are rocks permanent features of Earth? Explain.

22. How are all rocks related to one another?

THINK INTEGRATED SCIENCE

23A—The Silicate Tetrahedron

23. What do all of the most common minerals in Earth's crust share?

24. In what way is the silicate tetrahedron like a building block or a Lego?

23B—Coal

25. How is coal unlike other sedimentary rocks?

26. Describe the formation of coal.

27. What is coal made of?

23C—Earth's History Is Written in Its Rocks

28. How old is Earth? How old is the oldest rock formation? The oldest object of terrestrial origin?

29. What does the layer of iridium in the rock record tell about the demise of dinosaurs?

30. Fossils of ancient sea creatures have been found on modern mountains. Explain how this is possible.

THINK AND DO (HANDS-ON APPLICATION)

31. Look at some halite crystals under a magnifying glass or microscope and observe their shapes. They are not round or triangular but cubes. The salt factory has no machines designed to give salt these cubic shapes. The cubic shape occurs naturally and mirrors how the atoms of salt are organized—cubically.

32. Smash a few salt cubes and then look at them carefully again. What you'll see are smaller salt cubes. Explain why salt breaks into cubes in terms of the property of cleavage.

THINK AND SOLVE (MATHEMATICAL APPLICATION)

33. Concrete is made from sand, gravel, and cement (which is made from shale, limestone, and the minerals quartz, gypsum, iron, alumina, manganese, and clay). Every year, 4700 lb of concrete is produced for every person in the United States, so that our roads, homes, schools, businesses, factories, and so on can be built or maintained.

Calculate how much concrete is produced for your entire class in one calendar year. (Source: Mineral Information Institute, www.mii.org.)

34. (a) What is the average temperature of Earth's interior 20 km below the surface? (b) How much warmer is it 30 km below the surface compared to 10 km below?

THINK AND EXPLAIN (SYNTHESIS)

35. A geologist finds an igneous rock that has large crystals embedded in a matrix of smaller crystals. What is the texture of this rock? How did it form?

36. Why are the ferromagnesian silicates often dark, dense, and magnetic?

37. Why do rocks made from slowly cooling magma have large crystals? Give an example of this kind of rock.

38. How does the atomic structure of glass differ from the atomic structure of the mineral calcite?

39. The chemical formula for quartz is SiO_2. Coesite has the same chemical formula. Do coesite and quartz have the same physical properties? Why or why not?

40. There are many types of igneous rocks. Are there as many types of magma? Explain why or why not.

41. Identify a natural cycle other than the rock cycle.

42. What is the difference between a clastic and a chemical sedimentary rock?

43. An impression is a type of fossil that is made by an organism that is buried quickly, before it can decompose. Is this impression of a fish contained in an igneous, sedimentary, or metamorphic rock? Defend your answer.

44. What is more plentiful on Earth—the group of minerals known as feldspars or the group of minerals known as silicates?

45. A tectonic plate is subducted. Why will its rocks and minerals change?

46. Why do some high-quality drills have diamond tips?

47. Toothbrushes and toothpastes usually consist of mica (it provides sparkles), limestone (it rubs away plaque), and plastic (it forms the handle and bristles). Which of these ingredients is a mineral? Which is a rock? Which is neither rock nor mineral?

48. "Minerals in Earth's crust generally do not contain oxygen because oxygen is a gas at surface temperatures." Is this statement right or wrong? Defend your answer.

49. Why are intrusive igneous rocks coarse grained? Why are extrusive igneous rocks fine grained?

50. Which of the three classes of rocks is formed at low temperatures?

51. Would you expect to find a fossil in marble? Why or why not?

52. Why should mines be air-conditioned?

53. The chemical formula for quartz is SiO_2. What is the chemical formula of coesite, a polymorph of quartz?

54. Why are metamorphic rocks formed underground?

55. Sedimentary rocks usually form under water. Why is this so? (*Hint:* Remember the role of gravity.)

56. Cycles in nature, such as the rock cycle, consist of both materials and processes. What are the processes of change that take place in the rock cycle? What are the materials that are affected by these processes?

57. How is the magma that crystallizes to make rhyolite different from the parent magma of basalt?

58. How can one magma body produce many different kinds of igneous rocks? (*Hint:* Remember that magma contains many different minerals.)

59. Why are quartz and diamond so much harder than gold?

60. Name two properties of minerals that are based on the mineral's crystal structure.

61. One of your friends thinks that all mining should be stopped because it can damage the environment. Another friend thinks that mining shouldn't be subject to any laws that would protect the environment. Which friend do you agree with—or don't you agree with either of them? Explain your thinking.

62. Earth's mineral resources are plentiful, but once extracted and used, they do not renew in a human lifetime. What are some possible environmental problems associated with the extraction of minerals?

63. Is the following rock a sedimentary rock, igneous rock, or metamorphic rock? Why do you think so?

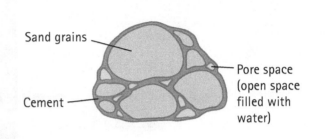

Sand grains

Cement

Pore space (open space filled with water)

READINESS ASSURANCE TEST (RAT)

If you have a good handle on this chapter, then you should be able to score 7 out of 10 on this RAT. If you score less than 7, you need to study further before moving on.

Choose the BEST answer to each of the following:

1. The silicates are the largest mineral group because silicon and oxygen are
   (a) the hardest elements on Earth's surface.
   (b) the two most abundant elements on Earth's surface.
   (c) found in the common mineral quartz.

2. What physical change in metamorphic rock signals the end of metamorphism?
   (a) freezing
   (b) melting
   (c) crystallization
   (d) evaporation

3. Wow! You find a rock that contains a fossil. The rock could be
   (a) diamond.
   (b) sandstone.
   (c) marble.
   (d) basalt.

4. Which of these does not belong in your mineral collection?
   (a) table salt
   (b) diamond
   (c) quartz
   (d) coal

5. Igneous rocks are the most common of the three types of rocks. Yet they are not often observed because they are typically buried under
   (a) metamorphic rocks.
   (b) sedimentary rocks.
   (c) minerals.

6. Large crystals are usually associated with
   (a) intrusive igneous rocks.
   (b) metamorphic rocks.
   (c) extrusive igneous rocks.
   (d) minerals.

7. During the early stages of Earth's development, when the entire planet was molten, there were no rocks. What kind of rocks must have been the first to form?
   (a) igneous rocks
   (b) sedimentary rocks
   (c) metamorphic rocks

8. Magma transfers heat to the surrounding rock as it rises toward Earth's surface. The rocks that absorb this heat may undergo
   (a) compaction.
   (b) regional metamorphism.
   (c) contact metamorphism.
   (d) cleavage.

9. Conglomerate is a sedimentary rock that consists of large, rounded pieces of other rocks embedded in mineral "cement." What type of sedimentary rock is conglomerate?
   (a) foliated
   (b) chemical
   (c) clastic
   (d) extrusive

10. An igneous rock can be transformed into a metamorphic rock by
    (a) weathering, erosion, deposition, then compaction to become a sedimentary rock, then heat and pressure.
    (b) being squeezed by great tectonic forces such as occur at a convergent plate boundary.
    (c) being heated by magma flowing nearby.
    (d) all of these

Answers to RAT

1. b, 2. b, 3. b, 4. d, 5. b, 6. a, 7. a, 8. b, 9. c, 10. d

CHAPTER 8

Plate Tectonics

MOST OF us are curious about the big ball we live on: planet Earth. We wonder, for example, how do mountains form? If you could dig a hole all the way to the center of Earth, what would you find there? If Earth's inner core is almost as hot as the Sun, why doesn't the planet melt? Is Earth's surface really a jigsaw puzzle of moving pieces? How do we know?

Earth science, the study of Earth's history, structure, and natural processes, answers such questions. It also addresses questions of great concern such as these: Can earthquakes, tsunamis, and volcanic eruptions be predicted? Are Earth's resources being consumed too quickly? Must we sacrifice modern conveniences to protect the environment? How is the climate changing? The Earth science chapters in this book will help you understand these and many other issues that affect the planet and your life.

We begin our study with plate tectonics, the theory that explains how Earth's surface reacts to the huge forces acting below.

8.1 Earth Science Is an Integrated Science

EXPLAIN THIS Jim wants to major in geology but he doesn't want to take physics. Why is this a problem?

Earth is a rocky sphere. Almost three-quarters of it is covered by water. A thin *atmosphere* (or layer of gases) surrounds it. Earth orbits the Sun yearly, spins on its axis daily, and teems with life. Earth science is an integrated science: To understand our Earth, it is necessary to understand processes that are described in physics, chemistry, biology, and astronomy. That's because our home planet is a complex system of living and nonliving parts and processes.

Geology is the broadest Earth science discipline. It is concerned with the composition and structure of Earth. *Meteorology* is the study of weather. *Petrology* is the study of rocks, while *mineralogy* is the science of the minerals within those rocks. *Paleontology* is the study of Earth's early history, including the dinosaurs and other creatures whose fossilized remains fascinate us today. *Hydrology* investigates the flow of Earth's waters, while *oceanography* focuses on the oceans. *Volcanology* is the study of volcanoes. There are many other branches of Earth science too. Cross-disciplinary geosciences include geophysics and environmental science.

Earth science is so integrated that even the social sciences are related to it. Why? People have a major impact on the planet. In fact, we have become a geologic force. Our ideas, choices, and actions affect Earth in a big way!

FIGURE 8.1
Earth scientists at work.

LEARNING OBJECTIVE
Describe the basic chemical composition of each of Earth's compositional layers: crust, mantle, and core.

Earth's crust makes up only 0.3% of the planet's entire volume, about the thickness of an apple peel compared to an apple.

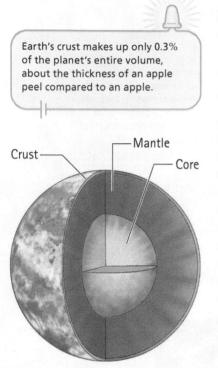

Crust — — Mantle

— Core

FIGURE 8.2
Earth has three layers that differ in their composition.

8.2 Earth's Compositional Layers

EXPLAIN THIS Why is Earth classified as one of the solar system's three "rocky" planets?

If you sliced Earth open and analyzed its chemical composition, you would find that it is layered like a hard-boiled egg. We recognize three main layers in an egg: the shell, egg white, and yolk. Similarly, Earth has three main layers: the crust, mantle, and core (Figure 8.2). Each of these layers consists of different materials.

The Crust

The **crust** is Earth's surface layer. Like an eggshell, it is thin and brittle and can crack. The crust is composed mainly of rocks that contain minerals rich in silicon and oxygen. You might be surprised to learn that the most common element in the crust is actually oxygen. So, you see, oxygen not only fills the air but it is a major ingredient of solid Earth, too!

Earth's crust has two parts: *continental crust*, which makes up the landmasses, and *oceanic crust*, which underlies the oceans. The oceanic crust is made of mostly dense, dark gray or black, fine-grained rock called *basalt*. Continental crust is mostly lighter, less dense, *granitic* rock. Both the oceanic crust and the continental crust are composed mainly of silicon and oxygen with smaller amounts of other elements. The basaltic rock of the ocean floor contains a higher proportion of the dark minerals iron and magnesium than granitic rock. This accounts for basalt's striking dark color (Figure 8.3).

The oceanic crust is only 7 km thick on average, a distance you could walk in about an hour. Continental crust is thicker—on average, it's about 40 km from the top to the bottom.

As Figure 8.4 shows, mountains are like tips of icebergs. They are mostly buried beneath the surface. The mountaintops you see above ground are supported by deep "roots"—huge masses of continental crust that reach far into the mantle. When the tops of mountains are worn away by erosion, the roots move upward, poke above Earth's surface, and keep rising as the mountain loses mass at the

(a) (b) (c)

FIGURE 8.3
(a) Basalt is a fine-grained, dark rock rich in silicon, oxygen, iron, and magnesium. The oceanic crust is composed almost entirely of basaltic rock. (b) The continental crust is composed of chiefly light-colored, low-density granitic rock. Half Dome in Yosemite, shown here, is a classic example of the granitic rock of the continental crust. (c) Oceanic rock is found on land as well as under the sea. This basalt formed on the seafloor but was uplifted to a high altitude by tectonic forces.

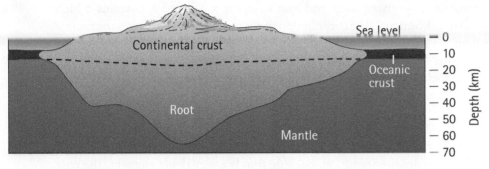

FIGURE 8.4
Mountains have "roots," blocks of continental crust that support them underground. The mountains we see are like the tips of icebergs.

top. So, as mountains wear down, they are continually replenished from below. The reason this happens is that the crust "floats" or buoys up and down in the mantle like a boat in the ocean. (Like all floating objects, the crust floats at the level where the buoyant force pushing it up equals the force of gravity pushing it down. Read more about this in Appendix E, the Physics of Fluids.) Just as a cargo ship rises higher in the water when it is unloaded, a mountain rises higher in the mantle when it "unloads" mass by erosion (Figure 8.5).

The vertical positioning of Earth's crust due to its flotation in the mantle is called *isostasy*. Isostasy explains why mountain roots rise up (and therefore why mountains take so long to wear away—they have reserve mass stored underground). Isostasy is also the reason that the oceanic crust sits lower in the mantle than the continental crust: The oceanic crust is made of denser rock, so, like the loaded cargo ship versus the empty one, the oceanic crust sinks deeper.

Now you know that Earth's crust moves up and down due to isostasy. But the crust also moves in far more complicated ways. Over geologic time, the entire crust churns, wrinkles, stretches, mixes up, and circulates. It's true that oceanic crust is mainly basaltic rock and continental crust is mainly granitic. Still, rocks of each type are intermixed throughout the crust. You can find ancient sea creatures embedded in black basaltic rock high in the mountains because, although these rocks formed on the seafloor, they were uplifted by great tectonic forces you will soon learn more about. Likewise, continental rock can be found on the seafloor among the basaltic rock because eroded continental sediments from the land eventually wash to the sea. The crust is a complex assemblage of rocks mixed over time like a very big pot of stew.

The Mantle

Hidden beneath Earth's crust is the **mantle**, a thick layer of hot rock. Geologists know much less about the mantle than they know about the crust. We cannot see into the mantle because light does not travel through rock. Nor can we drill into the mantle because rock is so hard that drilling equipment breaks before it reaches the bottom of the crust. Scientists would like to drill all the way to the mantle someday because most of Earth—82% of its mass and 65% of its volume—*is* mantle.

The mantle's thickness is 2900 km from the bottom of the crust to the top of the core. Geologists have sampled molten (melted) rock that travels through volcanic vents in the ocean floor. Chemical analysis of this rock shows that the mantle consists mostly of rock rich in silicon and oxygen, like the crust. But mantle rock has

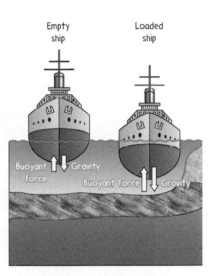

FIGURE 8.5
Isostasy: the vertical position of the crust is stable when gravity equals the buoyant force. Denser oceanic crust sits lower in the mantle than continental rock, just as the loaded ship sits lower in the water than the unloaded ship. Note that this principle of flotation governs the position of the crust in the mantle even though the mantle is solid. The reason is that the mantle actually flows very slowly over geologic time, as if it were a fluid.

UNIFYING CONCEPT

● *Density*
Section 2.3

● *The Gravitational Force*
Section 5.3

MasteringPhysics®
TUTORIAL: The Earth's Mantle

UNIFYING CONCEPT
● *Density*
Section 2.3

proportionately more magnesium and iron than the crust, and it contains a high proportion of calcium too. The contribution of the denser elements makes the mantle denser than the crust. The mantle's density is further increased by the weight of the overlying crust. The crust's weight bears down on the mantle, compressing the spaces between the rocks and also squeezing the rocks' molecular structures.

The Core

At the center of Earth lies its **core**. The core is a huge ball of hot metal, mostly iron with a lesser amount of nickel. Because iron is a very dense element, the core is much more dense than the mantle and the crust. The core has a radius of about 3500 km—approximately the distance from San Francisco to New York. Because we cannot observe the core, our knowledge of it is limited. What we do know about the core comes mainly from *seismology*, the study of earthquake waves.

CHECK YOURSELF
How is the Earth's crust like a ship?

CHECK YOUR ANSWERS
The crust floats on the mantle like a ship floats on the water. The crust's vertical position, as well as the ship's, is determined by its density.

LEARNING OBJECTIVE
Describe the process that divided Earth into layers of different density.

Integrated Science 22A
PHYSICS AND CHEMISTRY

Earth Developed Layers When It Was Young, Hot, and Molten

EXPLAIN THIS Why does drilling equipment break before it reaches the mantle?

The density of Earth's crust, mantle, and core increases in concentric layers moving from the surface to the center. What's the reason for these density layers?

Earth, like the Moon and inner planets, is mostly rock. And, rock is composed of what all matter in the universe is made of—chemical elements. There are 112 naturally occurring elements, as you know from chemistry. Most chemical elements are rare on Earth. In fact, only eight elements make up about 98% of Earth's entire mass (Figure 8.6). All of the other elements combined make up the remaining 2% of Earth's mass.

Earth's elements are not distributed evenly. The heavier ones

FIGURE 8.6
Only eight of the chemical elements are found in abundance on Earth.

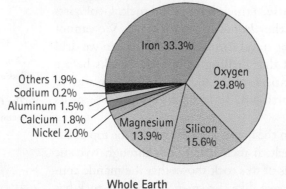

Iron 33.3%
Oxygen 29.8%
Others 1.9%
Sodium 0.2%
Aluminum 1.5%
Calcium 1.8%
Nickel 2.0%
Magnesium 13.9%
Silicon 15.6%
Whole Earth

are concentrated near the center of the planet, while the lighter elements are more abundant near the surface. The explanation for this has to do with Earth's early history. Earth formed 4.6 billion years ago from debris that was orbiting the newly forming Sun. Some of the debris collided and stuck together or "accreted" into a growing rocky mass, forming a rudimentary Earth. Earth grew as its gravity attracted more and more debris to it. Each time material from space collided with and stuck to Earth, the kinetic energy of the impacting bodies was transformed into heat, which warmed the developing planet. Earth was so hot, in fact, that it was *molten*—melted and able to flow. Under the influence of gravity, dense, iron-rich material sank to Earth's center to become the core. Less dense, silicon- and oxygen-rich material rose toward the surface by *differentiation*. **Differentiation** is the process by which gravity separates fluids according to density. (A mixture of oil and water, for example, undergoes differentiation when the denser water sinks to the bottom and the oil rises to the top.)

Eventually, the frequency of impacts slowed and Earth cooled. Lighter materials near Earth's surface solidified to form minerals that clustered together to make rocks. Figure 8.7 shows the current composition of Earth's crust. Note that almost half (46.6%) of the crust is oxygen (O), and a little more than a fourth (27.7%) of it is silicon (Si), so together these two lightweight elements make up about three-quarters of Earth's solid surface.

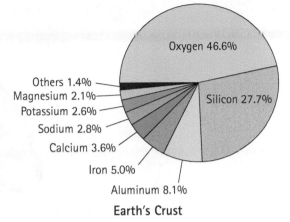

Earth's Crust

FIGURE 8.7
Percentages of the elements in Earth's crust by mass. Oxygen and silicon make up about 75% of Earth's crust.

UNIFYING CONCEPT

● *Density*
Section 2.3

● *The Gravitational Force*
Section 5.3

CHECK YOURSELF
Why was the early bombardment of Earth by space debris important to differentiation?

CHECK YOUR ANSWER
The kinetic energy of the space debris colliding with Earth was transformed into heat energy. The heat melted Earth's rock so it was molten and could flow. If the rock had been solid, it couldn't have settled into distinct layers.

8.3   Earth's Structural Layers

EXPLAIN THIS Why do geologists often speak of Earth's structural layers rather than the compositional layers?

LEARNING OBJECTIVE
Name and describe Earth's five functional layers.

To analyze Earth's interior, we can go beyond the three-layer, hard-boiled egg model. Geologists also divide Earth into five functional layers based on their physical properties. Physical properties include, for example, temperature, pressure, strength, and ability to flow. In terms of physical properties, Earth's five layers are the *lithosphere, asthenosphere, lower mantle, outer core,* and *inner core* (Figure 8.8).

The Lithosphere

The "rock sphere" we call the **lithosphere** ("LITH-uh-sphere") is a shell of cool, rigid rock. The lithosphere includes the crust and some of the upper portion of

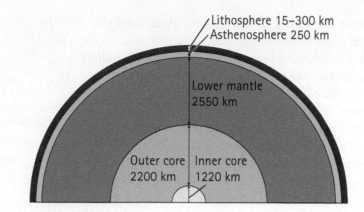

Lithosphere 15–300 km
Asthenosphere 250 km

Lower mantle
2550 km

Outer core
2200 km

Inner core
1220 km

FIGURE 8.8
When we look at Earth in terms of physical properties, we see that it has a five-layered structure: the lithosphere, asthenosphere, lower mantle, outer core, and inner core.

> Temperature and pressure both increase with depth in Earth's interior. This, along with Earth's varying composition, produces five layers with different physical properties.

Earth's mantle. On average the lithosphere is about 100 km thick. It is thickest below the continents and thinnest below the oceans. The lithosphere is not continuous like Earth's other layers. Instead, it is broken up into a patchwork of interlocking pieces. Pieces of lithosphere are called *tectonic plates*.

The Asthenosphere

The **asthenosphere** ("as-THEN-uh-sphere") lies under the lithosphere. It is made of mantle rock. The rock in the asthenosphere is soft and flows slowly like taffy or Silly Putty. We say it is "plastic"—that is, it is a solid that can flow slowly over immense spans of geologic time. Pieces of lithosphere are

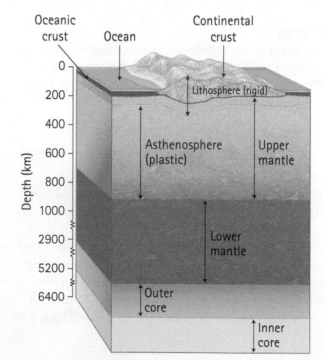

FIGURE 8.9
This diagram shows the relationship of the crust and mantle to the lithosphere and asthenosphere.

carried along on the flowing asthenosphere like rafts on a slowly flowing ocean.

When we say that the asthenosphere moves slowly, we mean *very* slowly. The hour hand on a clock moves about 10,000 times faster than the "flowing" asthenosphere. This layer flows so slowly that it would look like solid rock if you could see it.

The Lower Mantle

The **lower mantle** sits between the asthenosphere and the outer core. It consists of strong, rigid mantle rock. Despite its extreme heat, the lower mantle is not nearly as plastic as the asthenosphere.

The Outer Core

The **outer core** is a shell of hot, liquid metal—mostly iron with some nickel. The outer core lies beneath the mantle and above the inner core. Since the outer core is liquid, it spins as Earth rotates. The outer core also swishes and flows because its enormous heat stirs up convection currents within it.

The outer core creates Earth's magnetic field. Do you remember from physics that moving charged particles make up an electric current and that an electric current always produces a magnetic field? The iron and nickel in the outer core supply charged particles, and the Earth's rotation and convection supply motion. The result is an immense magnetic field stretching thousands of kilometers into space. This "geomagnetic" field is essential to life because it shields Earth from the *solar wind*— the stream of harmful high-energy particles emanating from the Sun.

The Inner Core

The **inner core** is a solid sphere of hot metal. It is mostly iron, like the outer core. Its temperature is estimated to reach a maximum of over 7000°C. This is about as hot as the surface of the Sun!

With such a high temperature, how does the inner core remain solid? The answer is that intense pressure from the weight of the overlying rock keeps the inner core from melting. Pressure in the inner core packs the atoms so tightly that they cannot flow as they do in a liquid state.

FIGURE 8.10
This computer simulation shows the magnetic field generated by the motion of Earth's fluid outer core. Magnetic field lines are blue where the field is directed inward and yellow where it is directed outward. You can see that the field beyond the mantle– core boundary has a smooth overall structure, while the field at the core is highly complicated.

UNIFYING CONCEPT

● *Convection*
  Section 6.9

LEARNING OBJECTIVE
Describe P-waves and S-waves and explain what each reveals about Earth's internal structure.

Integrated Science 22B
PHYSICS

Using Seismology to Explore Earth's Interior

EXPLAIN THIS Why do S-waves stop at the mantle–core boundary?

No one can observe Earth's internal structure. So, how do geologists know what's underground? Earthquakes are the key. An **earthquake** is the shaking or trembling of the ground that happens when big sections of rock underground shift or break. Earthquakes release vast amounts of energy.

Science knew very little about Earth's interior until very recently. In fact, Ford was manufacturing automobiles and there was a baseball World Series before scientists realized Earth has a core!

FIGURE 8.11
Block diagrams show the effects of seismic waves. The yellow portion of the left side of each diagram represents the undisturbed area. (a) Primary body waves alternately compress and expand Earth's crust, as shown by the different spacing between the vertical lines, similar to the action of a spring. (b) Secondary body waves cause the crust to oscillate up and down and side to side. (c) Love surface waves whip back and forth in a horizontal motion. (d) Rayleigh surface waves operate much like secondary body waves, but they affect only the surface of the Earth.

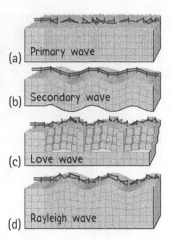

(a) Primary wave

(b) Secondary wave

(c) Love wave

(d) Rayleigh wave

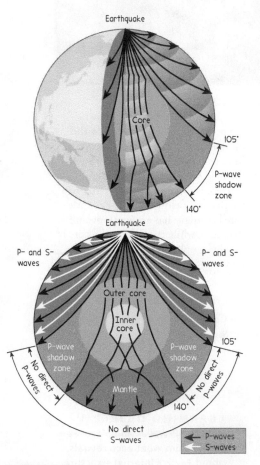

FIGURE 8.12
Cutaway and cross-sectional diagrams showing the change in wave paths at the major internal boundaries and the P-wave and S-wave shadows. The P-wave shadow between 105° and 140° from an earthquake is caused by the refraction of waves at the core–mantle boundary. The S-wave shadow is even more extensive. Any location more than 105° from an earthquake does not receive S-waves because the liquid outer core does not transmit them.

The energy radiates outward from the disturbance in the form of *seismic waves*. Seismic waves are mechanical waves, like sound waves, that travel through Earth. The study of seismic waves is called **seismology**, and seismology has provided most of what we know about Earth's interior.

Like any kind of wave, seismic waves may reflect or refract when they move from one material to another. Exactly how different kinds of seismic waves reflect and refract, as well as the changes in their speed and wavelength, reveals much about the medium the waves are traveling through.

Seismic waves come in two main varieties: *body waves*, which travel through Earth's interior, and *surface waves*, which travel on the surface (Figure 8.11). *Surface waves*, in turn, are divided into two types: *Rayleigh waves* and *Love waves* (each named after its discoverer). Rayleigh waves roll over and over in a tumbling motion similar to ocean waves. Love waves move in a snakelike, side-to-side transverse motion. Since Love waves shake things from side to side, they are particularly damaging to tall buildings. (Love waves are *not* loved by people who work in skyscrapers!) But it's the body waves, rather than the surface waves, that reveal Earth's inner structure because they travel deep inside Earth.

Body waves are classified as *primary waves* (P-waves) or *secondary waves* (S-waves). Primary waves are longitudinal waves; they compress and expand the material through which they move. P-waves are the fastest seismic waves, moving at speeds between 1.5 and 8 km per second through any type of material—solid rock, magma, water, and air. S-waves, on the other hand, are transverse waves; they vibrate the particles of their medium up and down and side to side, and they are slower than P-waves. Significantly, S-waves can travel through only solid materials, not liquids.

Near the turn of the 20th century, Irish geologist Richard Oldham was examining records of a massive earthquake in India when he discovered that its transverse S-waves traveled some distance through Earth and then stopped. He also observed that the longitudinal P-waves traveled to the same depth that the S-waves did but the P-waves then refracted and continued on at a lower speed. Since S-waves can't travel through liquids but P-waves can, though at a reduced speed, Oldham inferred that the earthquake waves had hit an internal boundary—a place where the solid Earth becomes liquid. In other words, he discovered that Earth has a distinct liquid center. The year was 1906.

Three years later, seismologist Andrija Mohorovičić ("mo-huh-RO-vih-chich") analyzed seismic readings from an earthquake near his town of Zagreb, Croatia. He detected a sharp increase in the speed of seismic waves at another boundary, one that lay shallower within the Earth. Mohorovičić realized that the wave speed increased because the wave was passing from a low-density solid to a high-density solid. Thus, Mohorovičić discovered that Earth is composed of a light, thin, outer crust that sits upon a layer of denser material, the mantle. The dividing line between Earth's crust and mantle has been called the *Mohorovičić discontinuity*, or "Moho," ever since.

In 1913, Beno Gutenberg reinforced Oldham's earlier findings by showing that the mantle–core boundary is very distinct and is located at a depth of 2900 km. He observed that, when P-waves reach this depth, they are refracted so completely that the boundary actually casts a P-wave shadow over part of Earth (Figure 8.12). The shadow is a region where no waves are detected. Furthermore, the sharp boundary between the mantle and core casts an S-wave shadow that is even more extensive than the P-wave shadow. And, since S-waves are transverse and unable to pass through liquids, Gutenberg's work reinforced earlier findings that the core, or part of it, must be liquid. Taken together, the discoveries of Oldham, Mohorovičić, and Gutenberg established the three-layer, hard-boiled egg model of Earth.

This simple picture of Earth's structure was refined in 1936 by Ingre Lehmen, a Danish seismologist. Her research showed that P-waves refract not only at the core–mantle boundary but again at a certain depth within the core, where they gain speed. This suggested that the core actually has two parts: a liquid outer core and a solid inner core. Thus, Lehman's work helped to show that Earth is indeed layered—but layers exist according to physical properties as well as by composition.

> Here's a tip for remembering body waves: P-waves are "push-pull waves" and S-waves are "side-to-side waves."

UNIFYING CONCEPT

● *Waves*
  Section 8.1

● *The Scientific Method*
  Section 1.3

CHECK YOURSELF
1. **What don't S-waves pass through Earth?**
2. **What is the Moho? How was it discovered?**

CHECK YOUR ANSWERS
1. S-waves can't travel through liquids, so they are interrupted by the liquid outer core.
2. The Moho is the boundary between Earth's mantle and crust. The Moho was detected by Mohorovičić, who observed an increase in the speed of P-waves across it.

8.4 Continental Drift—An Idea Before Its Time

LEARNING OBJECTIVE
Cite Wegener's evidence of continental drift.

EXPLAIN THIS Describe how scientists of the early 20th century viewed Wegener's ideas on continental drift. Why did they react this way?

If you've ever wondered what you would encounter if you dug a hole to the center of the Earth, now you know—thanks to seismology. But we live at Earth's surface, not underground. What's most crucial for us to understand is what's happening at Earth's surface and why it happens. Today we know that surface geology is largely determined by processes deep inside the Earth. For example, the continents are shaped and located as they are because the lithosphere floats in the asthenosphere. However, it took science many decades to figure out the connection between surface geology and Earth's internal structure.

Have you ever noticed on a world map that Africa and South America fit together like pieces of a giant jigsaw puzzle (Figure 8.13)? The first person to provide a detailed explanation of this was German scientist Alfred Wegener. Wegener's hypothesis, called **continental drift**, states that the world's continents

■ Continental shelf
□ Continent

FIGURE 8.13
The jigsaw puzzle fit of the continents suggests that they were once joined. The fit along the continental shelves is even better than the fit of the continents themselves.

FIGURE 8.14
German naturalist Alfred Wegener (1880–1930). As a young man, Wegener yearned to explore Greenland. While training for this adventure, he established a record for the longest balloon flight (52 hours). Wegener's next passion was for astronomy, and he earned a doctoral degree in the subject. Later, he became a university professor of meteorology and geophysics. He proposed the hypothesis of continental drift, which led to the discipline of plate tectonics—a productive life indeed. In 1930, Wegener died while crossing an ice sheet on an expedition to Greenland.

move slowly over Earth's surface. Wegener hypothesized that the individual continents of today's world were once joined as a single, giant landmass. Wegener named this supercontinent *Pangaea* ("pan-GEE-uh"), which is Greek for "universal land."

Wegener supported his hypothesis of continental drift with impressive biological evidence. For example, fossils of the same species of *Glossopteris* plant, shown in Figure 8.15, were found in places that are separated today by large oceans—India, Australia, South America, Africa, and Antarctica. Seeds from these plants were too heavy to have been blown from continent to continent. Also, fossils of *Mesosaurus*, a reptile, appeared in both Africa and South America. That creature couldn't swim and could not have evolved in exactly the same way in these widely separated regions. So, why do we find fossil evidence of this plant and this reptile in these separate places?

To explain the matching of *Glossopteris* and other plant and animal fossils, geologists of Wegener's time proposed that prehistoric land bridges once connected the continents. Yet there was no physical evidence that such land bridges ever existed. Continental drift, on the other hand, was supported by evidence, *and* it provided a neat explanation of matching fossils. The continents had once been a single landmass, with a single community of animals and plants. When the continents later split along the present-day Mid-Atlantic Ocean, representatives of these species were divided among the new continents.

Wegener also used rock matching as evidence to support his hypothesis of continental drift. For example, diamond-bearing rock formations occur where Africa and South America would meet if the Atlantic Ocean did not separate them. And, in some places, mountain chains separated by oceans have patterns of folds that would be continuous if the mountains were brought together (Figure 8.16).

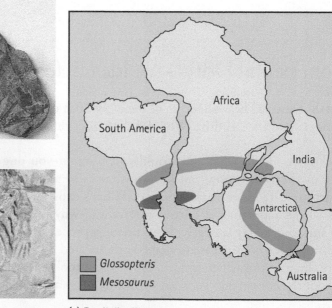

(a) *Glossopteris*

(b) *Mesosaurus*

(c) Fossil distribution

FIGURE 8.15
(a) This rock contains a fossil of a *Glossopteris* fern, an ancient seed plant. Can you see its long leaves? (b) This is a fossilized reptile called *Mesosaurus*. (c) These species couldn't cross the oceans. Why, then, were *Mesosaurus* and *Glossopteris* fossils distributed as shown here?

Besides the matching of fossils and rock, ancient climate evidence supported Wegener's hypothesis. For example, continental drift explained the puzzling evidence of ancient ice sheets on regions now located near the equator. How did these ice sheets form on land that is in such a warm location today? Continental drift provides an explanation: When the ice sheets formed on these landmasses, the landmasses were located near the South Pole.

Despite the evidence, Wegener's hypothesis was dismissed in scientific circles. No one, including Wegener, could provide a mechanism for continental drift. How could massive continents of solid rock "drift" across Earth's surface? What force could be strong enough? These questions put acceptance of continental drift on hold for decades.

CHECK YOURSELF

1. **What evidence might lead someone with no scientific knowledge to suspect that the continents were once connected?**
2. **Scientists of Wegener's day rejected his hypothesis of continental drift because they couldn't imagine how the continents could be made to move across the oceans. What didn't they know about the mantle?**

CHECK YOUR ANSWERS

1. The most obvious evidence is the matching of the edges of the African and South American continents, which can be seen on any world map or globe.
2. They did not know that the mantle has a plastic layer, the asthenosphere, over which "floating" continents can slide.

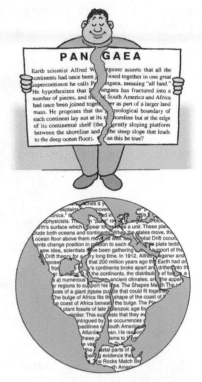

FIGURE 8.16
Wegener likened the fossil and rock matches to finding two pieces of torn newspaper with matching contours and lines of type. If the edges and the lines of type fit together, he said, the two pieces of newspaper must have originally been one.

8.5 Seafloor Spreading—A Mechanism for Continental Drift

EXPLAIN THIS Why is Earth's continental crust much older than its oceanic crust?

In the 1950s, many decades after Alfred Wegener proposed his hypothesis of continental drift, scientists used sonar technology to map the seafloor for the first time. They discovered that the ocean bottom is not flat, as had been presumed, but has deep canyons and trenches. It has many curious, flat-topped, underwater volcanoes.

An amazing discovery was the Mid-Atlantic Ridge, the longest and tallest mountain range in the world (Figure 8.17). The Mid-Atlantic Ridge is 19,312 km long. It winds through the center of the Atlantic Ocean basin parallel to the North American, South American, European, and African coastlines. Its highest peaks poke above sea level to form islands, including Iceland. In the center of the ridge and all along its length, there is a valley or *rift*. Continued investigation uncovered other midocean mountain ranges. Rocks of these midocean peaks were found to be the youngest rocks of the seafloor. We now know that an entire global system of underwater mountains called the **midocean ridge** winds all around Earth like the seam on a baseball.

LEARNING OBJECTIVE
Explain how new lithosphere is created and old lithosphere is destroyed through the process of seafloor spreading.

UNIFYING CONCEPT
● *The Scientific Method*
Section 1.3

Earth's longest and tallest mountains are under water!

FIGURE 8.17
Seafloor maps show that the ocean floor is not flat and calm. It is a dynamic place, crisscrossed with canyons, trenches, and mountain chains.

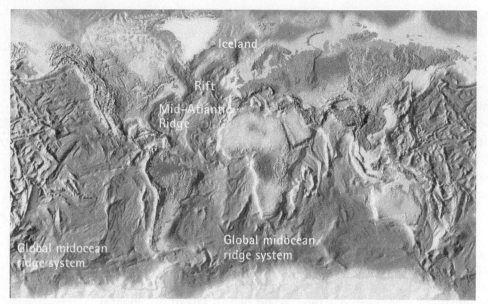

FIGURE 8.18
The Mid-Atlantic Ridge runs down the center of the Atlantic Ocean floor. Its highest peaks poke above sea level, creating islands such as Iceland, shown here. You can see Iceland's rift valley in this photo.

UNIFYING CONCEPT

● *The Gravitational Force*
  Section 5.3

Scientists also discovered ocean trenches, the deepest places on Earth. **Ocean trenches** are long, deep, steep troughs in the seafloor. Ocean trenches are found near continents, particularly around the edges of the Pacific Ocean. Also found at the ocean bottom were volcanic eruptions and zones of high-temperature water around underwater mountains. What kind of geologic activity could explain the seafloor's striking features?

American geologist Harry Hess answered this question with his theory of seafloor spreading. **Seafloor spreading** is the process by which new lithosphere is created at midocean ridges. Seafloor spreading works like a conveyor belt (Figure 8.19). Along the rift in a midocean ridge, slabs of lithosphere are slowly moving apart—too slowly for us to notice the movement. **Magma**, warm liquid rock from Earth's interior, wells up from the mantle and seeps out of the cracking rift, forming new lithosphere. Meanwhile, older lithosphere is pushed away from the rift zone. Gravity eventually pulls old oceanic lithosphere into the

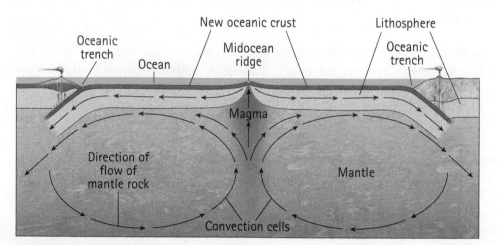

FIGURE 8.19
In conveyor-belt fashion, new lithosphere is formed at the rift zone of a midocean ridge while old lithosphere is recycled back into the mantle. As a result, the ocean floor is renewed about every 200 million years.

mantle at a deep ocean trench. The sinking of lithosphere into the mantle is called **subduction**. The subducted lithosphere is heated by the hot mantle and eventually partially melts into it. So, in general, while seafloor spreading creates new lithosphere at the spreading center of a rift zone, old lithosphere is destroyed at an ocean trench in a subduction zone.

Earth has remained about the same size since it formed 4.6 billion years ago. This means that the lithosphere is being destroyed as fast as it is created. Can you see that the rate of seafloor spreading must be about equal to the rate of subduction?

CHECK YOURSELF

1. Is the seafloor recycled? How?
2. If the seafloor is spreading and the continents are moving, why don't people notice it?

CHECK YOUR ANSWERS

1. New lithosphere is created where magma wells up at a spreading center, and it is destroyed where it sinks back into the mantle at a subduction zone. Once lithosphere melts into the mantle, it can eventually well up as magma to become seafloor again. In this way, the seafloor is recycled.
2. The motion occurs so slowly in comparison with human lifetimes that it is not perceived.

Integrated Science 22C
PHYSICS, CHEMISTRY, AND ASTRONOMY

Magnetic Stripes Are Evidence of Seafloor Spreading

EXPLAIN THIS The seafloor is covered with tiny compasses. Explain.

LEARNING OBJECTIVE
Describe what magnetic stripes are, and explain how they indicate that seafloor spreading has occurred.

Seafloor spreading provides a simple mechanism for plate motion. What's the evidence for this appealing picture?

Some of the earliest evidence for seafloor spreading came from *magnetic stripes*. Earth is a huge magnet with north and south magnetic poles. Once in a great while, Earth's magnetic poles flip—the north and south poles exchange positions. This is called a *magnetic reversal*. In a magnetic reversal, the polarity of the magnetic field (positions of the north and south poles) reverses. Earth's magnetic field has had the same polarity for the past 700,000 years, but evidence shows that it's due for a reversal. There have been more than 300 magnetic reversals during the past 200 million years.

The new rock that forms at midocean ridges contains small crystals of the mineral magnetite. Magnetite crystals are magnetic. Like tiny compass needles, magnetite crystals align with the field set up by Earth's magnetic poles. When the new rock cools and solidifies, the magnetite crystals freeze in place. Thus, the alignment of the crystals becomes "locked in" when magma solidifies as oceanic crust. Rocks of the seafloor therefore hold a record of the polarity of Earth's magnetic field at the time that they solidify.

Paleo means old or ancient. As a prefix, paleo is used to describe things that occurred in the past. For example, *paleoclimate* refers to ancient climates. *Paleomagnetism* is the study of ancient magnetic data, such as the history of Earth's magnetic reversals.

Direct Measurement of Continental Drift

Today, continental drift is not just deduced from evidence—it can be directly measured. The *Very Long Baseline Interferometry System* (VLBI), for example, was the first system to directly measure the relative motion of Earth's tectonic plates and continents. The VLBI used radio telescopes to detect and record radio signals emitted from quasars. Quasars are so far from Earth (billions of light-years away) that they are virtually pointlike. Their radio emissions, therefore, can be used like a surveyor's beam from a stationary source. The same signal from a quasar arrives at slightly different times at different measuring sites. So, when the VLBI tracked changes in the arrival times of radio signals over a period of years, it showed the rate of movement of the sites relative to each other.

The Global Positioning System (GPS) is currently used to measure the relative motion of different points on Earth. Because GPS results agree with the VLBI results, they provide a cross-check. The GPS system consists of 20 or so satellites that orbit Earth at an altitude of 20,000 km. These satellites transmit signals back to Earth continuously. Scientists at ground stations around the world use the signals to pinpoint their positions in terms of latitude, longitude,

GPS satellites are used to measure continental drift directly.

and altitude. Scientists repeatedly measure locations of ground stations, monitor changes in their relative positions, and thus track continental movement.

The different measurements of continental drift agree with one another and with theoretical predictions. For example, results show that Hawaii is moving in a northwesterly direction toward Japan at a rate of 8.3 cm per year. Maryland is moving away from England at a rate of 1.7 cm per year.

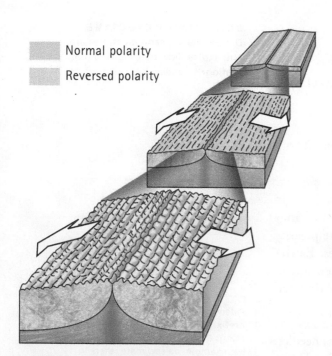

Normal polarity

Reversed polarity

FIGURE 8.20

The symmetrical pattern of magnetic stripes on both sides of the spreading center shows that seafloor forms on both sides of a midocean ridge at about the same time.

Scientists surveying the seafloor in the 1950s noticed odd patterns in its magnetic character. They found magnetic "stripes," or bands of oppositely directed magnetic rock, on both sides of midocean ridges. One stripe had "normal" (present-day) polarity, while the band next to it had opposite or "reversed" polarity (Figure 8.20). Initially, scientists thought the alternating bands of normally and reversely magnetized rocks were so incredible that their measurements must be wrong. But other studies consistently found the same pattern. Then, in the 1960s, when the seafloor was revealed to be geologically active, scientists could see that magnetic stripes can be explained as a result of seafloor spreading. Matching magnetic stripes, symmetrically arranged on either side of an ocean ridge, strongly suggest that the seafloor spreads outward from a central rift.

The ages of the seafloor basalts reinforce the picture. Radiometric dating reveals that the rocks of the seafloor are youngest close to the ocean ridges and they become progressively older moving away from the ridges. Like the magnetic stripes, the age pattern in oceanic crust is symmetrical across a ridge. It thus appears that, as seafloor spreading progresses, previously formed rocks continually spread apart and move away from the ridge while fresh molten rock rises from the asthenosphere to form new lithosphere at the ridge.

CHECK YOURSELF

1. Why doesn't the polarity of magnetite crystals reverse when Earth's magnetic field reverses?
2. Why is the pattern of magnetic stripes the same on both sides of a midocean ridge?
3. If there were a magnetic pole reversal tomorrow, in which direction would a compass needle point?

CHECK YOUR ANSWERS

1. Magnetite crystals can align with Earth's magnetic field only when they are free to turn. They are free to turn when they are in liquid rock, but frozen in place when the rock cools to become solid.
2. The stripes are symmetrical because they consist of bands of rock laid down at the same time.
3. A compass needle would point south.

8.6   The Theory of Plate Tectonics

EXPLAIN THIS Why was the history of planet Earth largely a mystery before the 1960s?

LEARNING OBJECTIVE
Summarize the theory of plate tectonics in one or two sentences.

Plate tectonics is the far-reaching theory that explains the large-scale forces that act inside the Earth to shape its surface. It is founded on Wegener's hypothesis of continental drift but further refined and expanded by evidence gathered from the ocean floor in the 1950s and 1960s. When it was completed, the theory of plate tectonics was able to do for geology what the theory of evolution did for biology. As geology writer John McPhee once said, "The whole world suddenly makes sense."

Plate tectonics states that Earth's rigid outer shell, the lithosphere, is divided into a dozen or so large pieces plus a number of smaller ones (Figure 8.21). Each piece of lithosphere is called a **tectonic plate** or, simply, a *plate*. Plates are up to 100 km thick. Being slabs of lithosphere, tectonic plates consist of the uppermost mantle plus the crust. The plates ride atop the plastic asthenosphere below. Some

UNIFYING CONCEPT

● *The Scientific Method*
Section 1.3

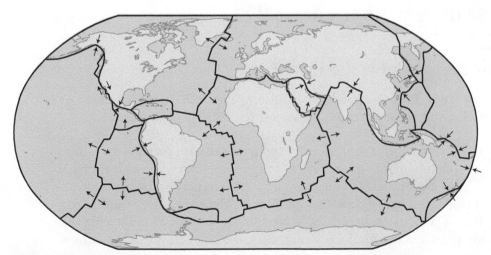

FIGURE 8.21
The lithosphere is broken into pieces called *tectonic plates*. There are a dozen or so major plates plus a number of smaller ones.

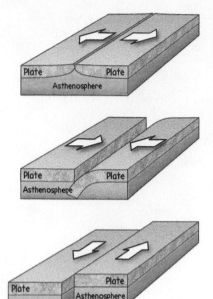

FIGURE 8.22
Plates interact at their boundaries, which results in intense geologic activity in those areas.

plates are large; others are small. Some are relatively immobile, while others are more active. Note that it is the plates that shuffle about Earth's surface. The continents move only because they are embedded in the plates. So, we can see that Wegener's hypothesis was a bit incomplete because whole plates are drifting—not merely the continents.

The continents don't have the same boundaries as the plates. The North American Plate, for example, is much larger than the North American continent. The western side of the North American Plate approximately traces the continent's West Coast, but the plate extends eastward halfway across the Atlantic Ocean to the Mid-Atlantic Ridge.

Earth's plates move in different directions at different speeds, ranging from 2 cm per year to about 15 cm per year. Plates that carry continents, such as the North American Plate, are slow movers, while oceanic plates, such as the Pacific Plate, tend to move much faster. This is because the continents act like heavy barges, with subsurface material—"roots"—extending farther down into the mantle than oceanic plates. Just as a barge dragging its bottom along a rocky river bed encounters resistance, so do continental plates when they drag their extended bottoms through the asthenosphere.

Plates pull apart, crash, merge, and separate from one another over geologic time. Because of all these interactions between plates, the edges of plates, *plate boundaries*, are regions of intense geologic activity (Figure 8.22). While interiors of plates are relatively quiet, most earthquakes, volcanic eruptions, and mountain building occur where plates meet.

CHECK YOURSELF
How does the theory of plate tectonics differ from the hypothesis of continental drift?

CHECK YOUR ANSWER
Plate tectonics states that plates, not just continents, move. Also, because the theory of plate tectonics includes seafloor spreading, it provides a way for continents to move—a *mechanism.*

LEARNING OBJECTIVE
Describe the role of mantle convection and the role of gravity in tectonic plate motion.

 Integrated Science 22D
PHYSICS

What Forces Drive the Plates?

EXPLAIN THIS Rock is a good heat insulator. Why is this important for plate motion still occurring today, billions of years after Earth's formation?

What forces are strong enough to push the seafloor apart and move huge chunks of lithosphere? There are two important factors: (1) the force of gravity and (2) the escape of Earth's internal heat by convection.
Earth contains a tremendous amount of heat. There are three main sources of this heat: The first is radioactivity. When unstable isotopes of the mantle and core undergo radioactive decay, they emit vast amounts of energy in the form of

electromagnetic radiation and the kinetic energy of accelerated particles. When this energy is absorbed by rock, some of it is converted into heat, warming the rock. Second, heat remains stored in the Earth from the "Great Bombardment," the time in Earth's early history when chunks of space debris frequently crashed into Earth. The kinetic energy of the colliding particles was transformed into heat energy by friction when the particles crashed into the rock. The third source of Earth's heat also relates to Earth's early history. As denser material sank toward Earth's center through the process of differentiation, the gravitational potential energy of dense, sinking material was converted to kinetic energy then ultimately to heat.

As we know from the second law of thermodynamics, heat always flows from warmer to cooler places. This is why heat moves from Earth's interior to its surface. Heat flows from Earth's interior to its surface mostly through the process of convection. The convection cells in Earth are like the convection cells in a pot of boiling water (Figure 8.23). Hot material rises in the mantle and then moves horizontally while it slowly cools. The asthenosphere carries lithosphere with it, piggyback style. Cooled material sinks at subduction zones back into deeper parts of the mantle. The convection cells in the mantle that carry heat away from Earth's interior are the major driving force of plate tectonics.

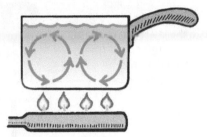

FIGURE 8.23
Convection cells in a pot of water.

UNIFYING CONCEPT

● *The Second Law of Thermodynamics*
  Section 6.5

● *Convection*
  Section 6.9

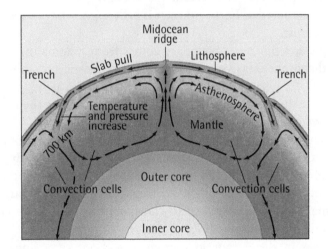

FIGURE 8.24
Simplified view of convection cells within the mantle.

UNIFYING CONCEPT

● *The Gravitational Force*
  Section 5.3

● *Density*
  Section 2.3

Gravity plays a role too. As the lithosphere moves away from spreading centers, it cools and becomes more dense. When the cool edge of the plate is dense enough to sink into the asthenosphere, it pulls the rest of the plate along with it. This process is called *slab pull*, and it contributes to the motion of tectonic plates.

Recent evidence is refining our understanding of mantle convection. Many scientists think convecting rock may be more like the irregular blobs in a lava lamp than the more regular circulating currents in a pot of boiling water.

CHECK YOURSELF
1. Why does the asthenosphere flow?
2. What role does gravity play in plate motion?

CHECK YOUR ANSWERS
1. Convection is the reason the asthenosphere flows. The asthenosphere is at the top of a convection cell that carries heat away from Earth's interior to its surface.
2. Gravity pulls the dense, cold edge of older lithosphere into the asthenosphere. This pulls the rest of the plate as well.

LEARNING OBJECTIVE
Summarize the characteristics of diverging, converging, and transform plate boundaries.

8.7 Plate Boundaries

EXPLAIN THIS Why should you live on a plate boundary if you want to experience earthquakes and other kinds of intense geologic activity?

Tectonic plates meet at *plate boundaries*. Because the plates interact with one another at their boundaries, a great deal of geologic activity occurs there. Mountain building, volcanoes, and earthquakes are much more common at plate boundaries than inside the plates. There are three types of tectonic plate boundaries:

- *Divergent boundaries*, where plates move away from each other
- *Convergent boundaries*, where plates move toward each other
- *Transform boundaries*, where plates slide past each other

Divergent Boundaries

Neighboring plates move away from one another along border zones called **divergent boundaries**. The plates are literally pulled apart at divergent boundaries as tensional forces tug them in opposite directions. As the plates separate, magma wells up from below and erupts into the widening gap between the plates. (Magma that has erupted at Earth's surface is called *lava*.) Lava cools and solidifies to make new crust.

The lava that erupts at a divergent boundary comes from magma in the asthenosphere. The asthenosphere, as you know, consists of plastic but still solid rock. However, when plates separate, the overlying weight on the asthenosphere decreases, so the pressure there is reduced. Rock in the asthenosphere then melts (partially) to become magma.

Lava can seep through fissures in Earth's surface or it can erupt through a central vent, which makes a volcano. (A fissure is simply a crack extending far into the planet through which magma can travel.) We are better acquainted with eruptions from volcanoes because they are exciting and dangerous, but the outpourings of magma from fissures are actually far more common—the rift at a midocean ridge is a fissure, for example.

Divergent boundaries in the ocean floor produce seafloor spreading. The Mid-Atlantic Ridge is a divergent boundary, dividing the North American Plate and the Eurasian Plate in the North Atlantic and the South American Plate and the African Plate in the South Atlantic. The rate of spreading at the Mid-Atlantic Ridge ranges between 1 cm and 6 cm per year. However slow this spreading may seem, over geologic time, the effect is tremendous. During the past 140 million years, seafloor spreading has transformed a tiny waterway through Africa, Europe, and the Americas into the vast Atlantic Ocean of today.

Divergent boundaries aren't only on the seafloor. They can also be in the middle of a continent, and then the continent tears apart. The East African Rift Zone is an example. If spreading continues there, the rift valley will lengthen and deepen and eventually extend out to the edge of the present-day African continent. The African continent will separate, and the rift will become a narrow sea as the Indian Ocean floods the area. The easternmost corner of Africa will then be a large island.

Convergent Boundaries

Earth has remained more or less its present size since it formed about 4.6 billion years ago. This means that lithosphere must be getting destroyed about as fast

MATH CONNECTION

Calculate the Age of the Atlantic Ocean

It's easy to calculate the age of the Atlantic Ocean if you can reasonably estimate the rate of seafloor spreading and the present width of the ocean. The Atlantic Ocean is currently about 7000 km or 7×10^8 cm wide. We assume that the average rate at which the plates diverge in the Atlantic Ocean is 5 cm per year, and we make the assumption that this rate has been constant over geologic time. We then apply the familiar equation that relates speed, time, and distance:

$$\text{Time} = \frac{\text{distance}}{\text{speed}}$$

$$= \frac{7 \times 10^8 \text{ cm}}{5 \text{ cm/year}}$$

$$= 1.4 \times 10^8 \text{ years}$$

$$= 140 \text{ million years}$$

Problem The Red Sea is presently a narrow body of water located over a divergent plate boundary. Based on current studies of the rate of seafloor spreading, the Red Sea will be as wide as the Atlantic Ocean in 200 million years. In order for this to be true, how fast is the seafloor spreading away at this divergent boundary?

Solution If we take the current width of the Red Sea as negligible, the seafloor will widen by a distance of 7×10^8 cm in 200 million years. The speed at which the seafloor spreads is then:

$$\text{Speed} = \frac{\text{distance}}{\text{time}}$$

$$= \frac{7 \times 10^8 \text{ cm}}{2 \times 10^8 \text{ cm}}$$

$$= 3.5 \text{ cm/yr}$$

as it is created. The destruction of Earth's lithosphere takes place at **convergent boundaries**. Here, plates come together in slow-motion collisions. Usually, one plate *subducts*, or descends, below another. The area around a subducting plate is called a **subduction zone**.

Plates converge in three different ways, depending on the kind of lithosphere that is involved. The three kinds of convergent plate boundaries are:

• Oceanic–oceanic convergence
• Oceanic–continental convergence
• Continental–continental convergence

In *oceanic–oceanic convergence*, both of the colliding plates are capped with oceanic crust. When these plates meet, the older (and therefore cooler and denser) plate bends and slides beneath the younger, less-dense plate. This creates a deep *ocean trench*, a long depression in the seafloor found in a subduction zone. Ocean trenches run parallel to the edges of convergent boundaries. They can be thousands of kilometers long, from 8 to 12 kilometers deep, and about 100 kilometers wide. Trenches are the deepest places on Earth, inhabited by strange organisms called *extremophiles* that can survive at extreme high pressure, low temperature, and no light.

Figure 8.25 shows that mantle rock in the subduction zone partially melts to form magma. It buoyantly rises and erupts at the surface as lava. Over millions of years, the erupted lava and volcanic debris accumulate on the ocean floor until they grow tall enough to poke above sea level and form a volcanic island.

Volcanoes of this kind are grouped together in *island arcs* that parallel the trenches, such as the Aleutian Islands off the Alaskan Peninsula. Strong to moderate earthquakes are common along such boundaries as the descending plate sticks and slips by the overriding plate.

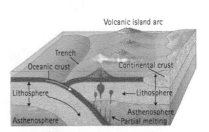

FIGURE 8.25

Oceanic–oceanic convergence occurs when plates that do not carry continental crust at their leading boundaries meet. A trench forms in the subduction zone, and an island arc of volcanoes grows from magma that is generated in the collision.

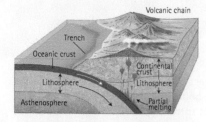

FIGURE 8.26
Oceanic–continental convergence occurs when a plate with oceanic crust at its leading edge is subducted beneath a plate with continental crust along its leading edge. A deep ocean trench and a coastal mountain range form as a result.

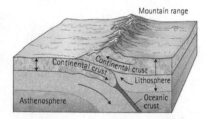

FIGURE 8.27
Continental–continental convergence occurs when continental crust caps the leading edge of each colliding plate. Mountains form where crust wrinkles and pushes upward.

A second kind of plate collision is *oceanic–continental convergence* (Figure 8.26). In this case, a plate capped with continental crust on its leading edge slowly collides with a plate capped by oceanic crust. Being denser, the basaltic oceanic plate subducts beneath the less dense, granitic continental plate. A deep ocean trench forms offshore where the converging plates meet. As mantle rock partially melts, magma forms in the subduction zone and rises up and erupts at the surface as lava. Lava erupts, cools, and accumulates many times. Eventually, a volcanic mountain chain may develop.

But, why does rock partially melt in the subduction zone to form magma? It's not because the subducting plate is hot. Subducting lithosphere, remember, is cool and dense—it's relatively cold rock that sinks down into the asthenosphere. When a descending plate reaches a depth of 100–150 km, the heat and pressure of the surrounding environment drive water trapped in the subducting plate into the overlying mantle. The water acts like salt on ice or like flux at a foundry—it lowers the freezing point of the mantle rock. So, with the injection of water, the overlying mantle partially melts without changing temperature. Magma is generated and buoyantly rises. Often, it pools beneath the continental crust, where it may partially melt some of the neighboring crustal rocks. Eventually, this molten rock migrates to the surface, where it erupts—either calmly or explosively. The residents of the Pacific Northwest should appreciate this process because it has created the beautiful mountains of the Cascade Range.

Finally, when plates that are converging head-on have continental crust along their leading edges, they display *continental–continental convergence* (Figure 8.27). In this case, the blocks of colliding crust consist of the same type of buoyant granitic rock. Because the blocks of rock have the same density, neither sinks below the other when they collide—there is no subduction. Instead, the continents push one another upward, like crumpled cloth, and towering, jagged mountain chains result. For example, the Himalayas are the highest mountains in the world, rising to a majestic 8854 m (5.5 mi) above sea level. The Himalayas formed when the subcontinent of India rammed into Asia about 50 million years ago. By welding together along the plate boundary, India and Asia merged as one. The Himalayas are still growing at a rate of about 1 cm per year as the Eurasian and Indian plates continue to converge (Figure 8.28).

FIGURE 8.28
The continent-to-continent collision of India with Asia produced—and is still producing—the Himalayas.

Transform Boundaries

A **transform boundary** is a region where two tectonic plates meet, but rather than converging or separating, they slide past each other. Lithosphere is neither created nor consumed at these boundaries, since plates simply rub along each other as they move in opposite directions.

Transform boundaries are very large *faults*. A fault is any crack that divides two blocks of rock that have moved relative to each other. Faults can be much smaller than transform boundaries; networks of them often form near plate boundaries and branch into the interiors of plates.

Usually, transform boundaries join two segments of a midocean ridge. For example, the Mid-Atlantic Ridge is broken up into segments, which are connected by transform faults (Figure 8.29). These faults "transform" (or transfer) the motion from one ridge segment to another. As the figure shows, lithosphere at one ridge moves in a direction opposite that of the lithosphere of another ridge. In this way, slippage along the transform boundaries allows the tectonic plates to move.

As the rocky plates at a transform boundary grind past each other, their motion is usually steady and slow. But, in some locations friction is so great that entire sections of rock become stuck against each other. Plate motion continues, and the blocks of "stuck" rock become compressed or stretched. (Recall from earlier in this chapter that, even though rock *seems* brittle, it is not. It is capable of compressing as well as stretching and storing energy like a spring.) When the compressional or tensional forces pushing or pulling the rock exceed friction, the stressed rock suddenly breaks loose and slips, releasing its stored energy in a sudden jerk. This sticking and slipping of blocks of rock causes earthquakes.

Although most transform faults are located within the ocean basins, a few are found on continental plates. One continental transform fault that gets a lot of attention is the San Andreas Fault, which is shown in the drawing and photo in Figure 8.30. The San Andreas Fault is the thickest thread in a tangle of faults that collectively accommodate the motion between the North American Plate and the Pacific Plate in California.

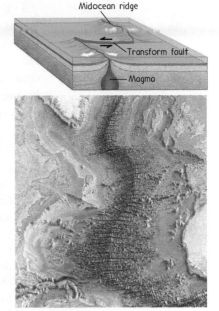

FIGURE 8.29
Most transform boundaries offset segments of a midocean ridge as shown, allowing plates to move laterally along Earth's surface. The plates stick and slip as they move along the boundary, causing earthquakes.

UNIFYING CONCEPT

● *Friction*
Section 2.8

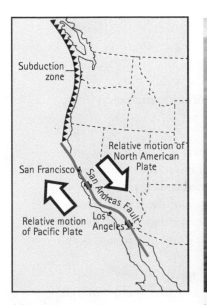

FIGURE 8.30
(a) The San Andreas Fault is a transform-fault plate boundary infamous for its earthquakes. The slice of California moving northwesterly lies on the Pacific Plate, while the rest of California sits on the North American Plate. (b) In this photo of the San Andreas Fault, notice the long valley created by many years of rock grinding along the fault.

(a)   (b)

The slice of California to the west of the fault is slowly moving northwest, while the rest of California is moving southeast. Contrary to popular opinion, you can see from the directions of the plates that Los Angeles is not going to split off and fall into the ocean. Instead, it will steadily advance northwesterly toward San Francisco while San Francisco moves in the opposite direction. In about 16 million years, the two cities will be side by side. In the meantime, California residents can expect plenty of earthquakes.

CHECK YOURSELF

1. The African Plate is slowly moving northward toward the Eurasian Plate. Both plates have continental crust along the edges where they would meet. What is likely to happen if these plates collide with each other?
2. What types of plate boundary involve subduction? Which do not involve subduction?
3. Do volcanic island arcs and coastal mountain ranges form at spreading centers?
4. In one sentence, distinguish among the three major kinds of plate boundaries.

CHECK YOUR ANSWERS

1. A mountain range may form along their continental–continental convergent boundary.
2. Plate boundaries that involve subduction are oceanic–continental and oceanic–oceanic convergent boundaries. The other kinds of boundaries do not involve subduction; these are transform boundaries, divergent boundaries, and continental–continental convergent boundaries.
3. No. Volcanic island arcs and coastal mountain ranges are associated with convergent plate boundaries.
4. Tectonic plates move apart at divergent boundaries, come together at convergent boundaries, and slide past one another at transform boundaries.

LEARNING OBJECTIVE
Describe the conditions in ocean trenches that make life difficult.

Integrated Science 22E
BIOLOGY

Life in the Trenches

EXPLAIN THIS How can food chains develop in an ocean trench even though the lack of light means that no plants are present?

When lithosphere is destroyed, it sinks and bends at a subduction zone. The bending plate creates a deep, dark depression in the ocean floor—an ocean trench. Ocean trenches, as you learned earlier, are the deepest places on Earth. The Mariana Trench is the deepest trench of them all. It reaches 11,000 m (7 mi) below sea level. If the world's tallest surface mountain, Mt. Everest, were sunk to the bottom of the Mariana Trench, there would still be a mile of ocean above it!

Conditions in the trenches are extreme. Water is nearly frozen. Pressure reaches more than 1000 atmospheres (about 16,000 lb per square inch). Sunlight is totally absent in the pitch-black depths.

Yet life thrives in the trenches. The trenches are inhabited by strange organisms called *extremophiles*. Trench extremophiles can survive at extreme high pressure, low temperature, and no light. Trench extremophiles include species of worms, shrimp, fish, crabs, and microbes. The world's deepest-dwelling fish, *Abyssobrotula galatheae*, was found in the Puerto Rican Trench at a depth of 8372 m (more than 5 mi). The adaptations of trench extremophiles are not well understood.

Some ocean trenches contain *hydrothermal vents*. Hydrothermal vents are cracks in the oceanic crust. Most often they are found in the newly formed oceanic crust in active rift zones. However, some hydrothermal vents occur where tectonic plates grind past one another in an ocean trench. Heat and chemicals such as hydrogen sulfide are released from Earth's interior at these vents. Pressure-adapted bacteria consume these chemicals and convert the chemical energy stored in them into the energy they need for life. These chemical-consuming bacteria also produce oxygen as a waste product. The process is called *chemosynthesis*. Other organisms eat the bacteria, and still other organisms eat the bacteria-eaters. And so a food chain develops in a hydrothermal vent despite the lack of light for photosynthesis (Figure 8.32).

FIGURE 8.31
The black anglerfish has a huge jaw and teeth that make it an effective predator. This fish needs to be an effective predator because food is so scarce in ocean trenches, where it lives. This fish also has a glowing or bioluminescent "lure" attached to its head to attract prey. Microbes that glow in the dark produce the light for the lure.

FIGURE 8.32
A hydrothermal vent community.

UNIFYING CONCEPT

● *The Ecosystem*
Section 21.1

CHECK YOURSELF
1. What are the physical conditions in the trenches that make life difficult there?
2. Where does the heat that escapes from hydrothermal vents come from?

CHECK YOUR ANSWERS
1. Lack of light, extreme cold, and extremely high pressure.
2. The heat comes from Earth's interior—more specifically, from the asthenosphere.

For instructor-assigned homework, go to www.masteringphysics.com MP

SUMMARY OF TERMS (KNOWLEDGE)

Asthenosphere One of Earth's structural layers—a layer of weak, warm rock that flows slowly over geologic time.

Continental drift The hypothesis that the world's continents move slowly over Earth's surface.

Convergent boundaries Places where tectonic plates come together.

Core Earth's innermost layer, which is mostly iron and includes the inner core and outer core.

Crust Earth's surface layer, consisting of oceanic and continental crust.

Differentiation The process by which Earth formed layers according to density.

Divergent boundaries Places where tectonic plates pull apart.

Earth science The study of the history, structure, and natural processes of planet Earth.

Earthquake The shaking of the ground that results when rock under Earth's surface moves or breaks.

Geology The Earth science that is concerned with the composition and structure of Earth.

Inner core One of Earth's structural layers—a solid sphere of hot metal, mostly iron, at the center of Earth.

Lithosphere Earth's outermost structural layer, consisting of cool, rigid rock.

Lower mantle One of Earth's structural layers—the lowest portion of the mantle, a zone of strong, rigid rock.

Magma Molten rock in Earth's interior.

Mantle The thick layer of dense, hot rock between Earth's crust and core.

Midocean ridge A global system of underwater mountains created by seafloor spreading.

Ocean trenches Long, deep, steep troughs in the seafloor where an oceanic plate sinks beneath an overlying plate.

Outer core One of Earth's structural layers—a shell of hot, liquid metal beneath the mantle and above the inner core.

Plate tectonics The theory that Earth's lithosphere is divided into large plates that move slowly around the globe.

Seafloor spreading The process by which new lithosphere is created at midocean ridges as older lithosphere moves away.

Seismology The study of seismic waves, waves that travel through Earth as a result of an earthquake or other disturbance.

Subduction The sinking of oceanic lithosphere into the mantle.

Subduction zone The region where an oceanic plate sinks into the asthenosphere at a convergent plate boundary.

Tectonic plates Separate pieces of lithosphere that move on top of the asthenosphere.

Transform boundaries Places where tectonic plates slide along beside one another as they move.

READING CHECK (COMPREHENSION)

8.1 Earth Science Is an Integrated Science

1. Name three or more branches of Earth science, and describe the focus of each.

2. Why is Earth science an integrated science?

8.2 Earth's Compositional Layers

3. In what way is Earth like a hard-boiled egg?

4. What kind of rock is most common in the oceanic crust? In the continental crust?

8.3 Earth's Structural Layers

5. Name and describe Earth's five structural layers.

6. Does the asthenosphere have the same composition throughout? What *is* uniform throughout the asthenosphere?

7. What are the large, interlocking pieces of lithosphere called?

8.4 Continental Drift—An Idea Before Its Time

8. Describe the fossil evidence that supported Wegener's hypothesis of continental drift.

9. Why was the hypothesis of continental drift dismissed by scientists for decades?

10. Describe evidence from the rock record that supports continental drift.

8.5 Seafloor Spreading—A Mechanism for Continental Drift

11. Where is lithosphere created? Where is it destroyed?

12. How does seafloor spreading relate to continental drift?

13. Earth has remained about the same size since it formed 4.6 billion years ago. What does this suggest about the rate of seafloor spreading compared to the rate of subduction?

8.6 The Theory of Plate Tectonics

14. In what way is the theory of plate tectonics like the theory of evolution, Newton's laws, and the periodic table?

15. Describe how tectonic plates move in terms of speed and direction.

16. How does plate tectonics differ from continental drift?

8.7 Plate Boundaries

17. Which is a more geologically stable place to live—along a plate boundary or in the interior of a plate? Explain.

18. Describe the three major kinds of plate boundaries.

19. How do plates interact when they collide? There are three possible ways; describe them all.

20. What type of plate boundary is the San Andreas Fault?

THINK INTEGRATED SCIENCE

22A—Earth Developed Layers When It Was Young, Hot, and Molten

21. What elements make up 98% of the Earth by weight?

22. In what way is Earth like a jar of water and oil left standing?

23. What two elements constitute about three-fourths of Earth's solid surface?

22B—Using Seismology to Explore Earth's Interior

24. Cite the seismic evidence that Earth has a liquid outer core.

25. What did studies of P-wave and S-wave shadows reveal about Earth's interior?

26. What is the difference between body waves and surface waves? Which of these seismic waves reveals key information about Earth's internal structure?

22C—Magnetic Stripes Are Evidence of Seafloor Spreading

27. What is a magnetic reversal, and how are magnetic reversals recorded in rock?

28. Where is the oldest rock—near a spreading center or far away from it? Explain your thinking.

29. How do magnetic stripes provide evidence of seafloor spreading?

22D—What Forces Drive the Plates?

30. In what way does the second law of thermodynamics relate to plate tectonics?

31. What are the two main factors in the movement of tectonic plates?

32. In what way is the asthenosphere like a pot of boiling water?

22E—Life in the Trenches

33. Photosynthesis cannot occur in a hydrothermal vent because there is no light there. How, then, can the microbes that serve as the lowest level of a food chain in a hydrothermal vent obtain the energy they need for life?

34. Where do most hydrothermal vents occur? Can they occur in other places as well? Explain.

35. Do all trench-dwelling organisms live in hydrothermal vent communities? Explain.

THINK AND DO (HANDS-ON APPLICATION)

36. Simulate motion along a transform fault with your hands. Press your palms together and move your hands in opposite directions, as shown in the figure. Notice that friction keeps them "locked" together until opposing forces no longer balance, friction no longer holds, and your palms slip suddenly past each other. This nicely models the sticking and slipping that occur along a transform fault.

THINK AND SOLVE (MATHEMATICAL APPLICATION)

37. A sample of basalt has a mass of 5.6 g and a volume of 2 cm³. Show that the density of basalt is 2.8 g/cm³.

38. The San Andreas Fault separates the northwest-moving Pacific Plate, on which Los Angeles sits, from the North American Plate, on which San Francisco sits. If the plates slide past each other at the rate of 3.5 cm per year, show that the two cities will be neighbors in about 17 million years. (The distance from San Francisco to Los Angeles is 600 km.)

39. Suppose that a fence is built across the San Andreas Fault in 2013. Show that the fence will separate and the two sections of the broken fence will be 70 cm apart in 2033. Assume that the average rate of movement along the plate boundary is 3.5 cm (about 1½ in) per year.

40. The Nazca and Pacific Plates are spreading relatively fast—at the rate of 14.2 cm (5.6 in) per year. The East Pacific Rise is a midocean ridge system that divides these plates. If the central segment of the rise is 200 km wide, show that it is about 700,000 years old.

THINK AND EXPLAIN (SYNTHESIS)

41. Is Earth's inner core solid and the outer core liquid because the inner core is cooler than the outer core? Explain your answer.

42. How is magma generated at divergent plate boundaries?

43. What would happen if new lithosphere were created faster than it is destroyed?

44. Why do mountains rise in the mantle as they erode? What principle of Earth science explains this process?

45. What kinds of plate boundaries feature subduction zones?

46. Why are earthquakes common in subduction zones?

47. Briefly describe how an island arc forms.

48. Why are there expressions such as "solid earth" and "old as the hills," which suggest that Earth is unchanging?

49. How did seismic waves contribute to the discovery of Earth's deep internal layers?

50. Copy the diagram (which is not to scale) of Earth's interior. Add these labels: inner core, outer core, mantle, oceanic crust, continental crust, ocean.

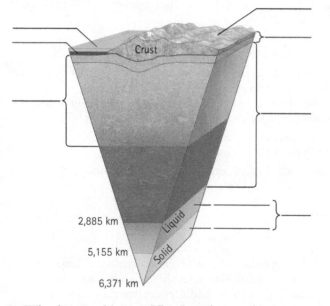

2,885 km
5,155 km
6,371 km

51. Why does Earth's crust "float" on the mantle?

52. Why are volcanic mountain ranges often found along oceanic–continental convergent boundaries?

53. What is the evidence that tectonic plates move?

54. Why are most earthquakes generated near plate boundaries?

55. The magnetic stripes that were laid down on the Pacific Ocean seafloor are wider than the magnetic stripes laid down over the same time period on the Atlantic Ocean seafloor. What does this tell you about the rate of seafloor spreading of the Pacific Ocean compared with that of the Atlantic Ocean?

56. How is Earth's lithosphere like a jigsaw puzzle? How is it NOT like a jigsaw puzzle?

57. Earth's surface is largely covered by volcanic rock or rock that is derived from volcanic rock. Use what you know about plate tectonics to explain why this is true.

58. Could Los Angeles fall into the ocean, as is popularly thought? Why or why not?

59. Is plate tectonics a theory based on integrated science? Why or why not?

60. The graph shows how the seafloor of the Atlantic Ocean varies with depth. Why was this picture surprising to scientists before Harry Hess? How does this graph support the hypothesis of continental drift?

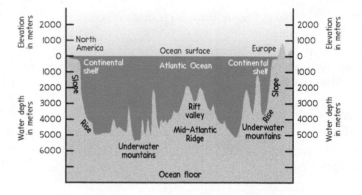

61. Evidence of ancient ice sheets has been found in areas near the equator. Give two possible explanations for this.

62. What is meant by magnetic pole reversals? What useful information do they provide about Earth's history?

63. What is a likely cause of Earth's magnetic field?

64. What would happen if new crust were created faster than it is destroyed?

65. Write a letter to your grandmother or grandfather with a one-paragraph summary of plate tectonics. (Plate tectonics was not an accepted theory until the 1960s, so people born much earlier than that missed out on this important theory in their education!)

THINK AND DISCUSS (EVALUATION)

66. Earth's Moon has a lithosphere that is continuous, not divided into continental and oceanic lithosphere as on Earth. Would you expect that there would be plate tectonic activity on the Moon similar to Earth? Why or why not?

67. The 1993 adventure film *The Core* is based on the premise that Earth's core has stopped spinning. Earth's

magnetic field is therefore disrupted and humanity is in peril. Six scientists journey to the center of Earth to set off a nuclear device to set the outer core spinning again. Discuss the scientific flaws with this basic story line.

68. Play a game of "fortunately/unfortunately." First, finish the sentence: "Fortunately, because of plate tectonics . . . ." Then

have a partner finish a different sentence: "Unfortunately, because of plate tectonics . . . ." Go back and forth with your partner until you have a list of ways in which plate tectonics helps people and ways in which it makes life challenging.

69. What is the principal difference between the theory of plate tectonics and the continental drift hypothesis?

70. What law of physics relates heat flow to plate tectonics? Discuss how this law underlies plate tectonics and other everyday processes.

71. Are continents a permanent feature of our planet? Discuss why or why not.

72. Discuss the role of heat and the role of gravity in the motion of tectonic plates.

73. Where does the heat in Earth's interior come from?

74. How would GPS technology have been helpful to Alfred Wegener?

75. When the problem of disposing of radioactive waste first arose, some scientists suggested dumping it into subduction zones. What are two possible challenges with this method of disposal?

READINESS ASSURANCE TEST (RAT)

Choose the BEST answer to each of the following questions.

1. The lithosphere includes the crust and the top part of the
   (a) asthenosphere.
   (b) mantle.
   (c) core.
   (d) lower mantle.

2. The layer of Earth made up of soft rock that flows slowly over time is the
   (a) lithosphere.
   (b) lower mantle.
   (c) hydrosphere.
   (d) asthenosphere.

3. What type of plate boundary lies between two plates that are moving away from each other?
   (a) convergent boundary
   (b) divergent boundary
   (c) transform boundary
   (d) continental–continental convergent boundary

4. A long, deep, steep depression in the seafloor where subduction occurs is a(n)
   (a) midocean ridge.
   (b) rift zone.
   (c) ocean trench.
   (d) hydrothermal vent.

5. Is Earth's inner core a solid, liquid, or gas? Why?
   (a) a solid, because high pressure keeps it from melting
   (b) a liquid, because the temperature of the core is higher than the melting point of iron
   (c) a gas, because the inner core is nearly as hot as the surface of the Sun

6. Why is the outer core the source of Earth's magnetic field?
   (a) Moving liquid iron particles there form an electric current, and an electric current always produces a magnetic field.
   (b) It has north and south magnetic poles that reverse over time.
   (c) It contains iron, a magnetic material.

7. Why doesn't the heat in Earth's core melt Earth?
   (a) Heat tends not to move from place to place.
   (b) The core is a solid.
   (c) Heat escapes slowly to the surface because rock is a poor conductor.
   (d) Actually, Earth's core is not very hot.

8. Why is the inner core Earth's most dense region?
   (a) The inner core is made of mostly iron, which is very dense.
   (b) Dense material sank toward Earth's center when Earth was molten.
   (c) Pressure packs the atoms in the inner core tightly together.
   (d) all of these

9. Fossils such as *Glossopteris* and *Mesosaurus* have been found in widely separated continents because
   (a) *Mesosaurus* was a good swimmer and *Glossopteris* had lightweight seeds.
   (b) land bridges once connected all the continents.
   (c) all the continents were once joined in a supercontinent called Pangaea.
   (d) Alfred Wegener played a hoax on the scientific community.

10. Plate tectonics explains
   (a) how seafloor spreading and subduction account for the movement of tectonic plates.
   (b) why the continents move.
   (c) why plate boundaries are such active geologic regions.
   (d) all of these

Answers to RAT

1. b, 2. d, 3. b, 4. c, 5. a, 6. a, 7. c, 8. d, 9. c, 10. d

CHAPTER 9

Earth's Surface—Land and Water

I MAGINE VIEWING Earth from a satellite and surveying its entire surface. The first thing you'd notice is that most of Earth—71%—is covered by ocean. The remaining 29% is taken up by seven continental landmasses. You'd see thousands of volcanoes on Earth's surface and notice that most of them are dotted along the rim of the Pacific Ocean. Earth's crust, in some places, is wrinkled by tight folds; in other places, it's etched by cracks and faults. Jagged peaks form mountain chains, many of which are located near coastlines. From your satellite view, you'd notice many other kinds of surface features, such as smoldering craters, snaking rivers, stark white glaciers, and fan-shaped deltas where rivers meet the sea. Looking at Earth as a whole, you'd see that its surface is quite varied—as if it had been broken and bent, twisted and pulled, built up and worn down. And, of course, over geologic time, it has! It's not so easy to board a satellite to survey Earth, but in this chapter you will nonetheless take a world tour of Earth's vast and varied surface.

9.1   A Survey of Earth

LEARNING OBJECTIVE
Describe Earth's major landforms.

EXPLAIN THIS If a sailor put a message in a bottle in the Atlantic Ocean, someone sailing on the Pacific Ocean might one day receive it. Explain how it's possible for an object to move from one ocean to another.

Almost three-quarters of Earth is covered by ocean. The land surface consists of scattered islands and seven large continents: Africa, Antarctica, Asia, Australia, Europe, North America, and South America. Earth's *topography*, or the shape of its surface, ranges from flat to bumpy to wrinkled. The most prominent topographic features of the continents are the linear mountain belts—for example, the Alpine-Himalayan Belt. The continents also feature expansive flat areas called *plains*, which are typically found at low elevations (Figure 9.1), and *plateaus*, which are uplifted flat areas composed of horizontal rock layers. On average, the continents lie 840 meters above sea level. Earth's continental elevation varies between the extremes of its highest point, Mt. Everest (8848 m, or 29,028 ft, above sea level), and its lowest point, on the shores of the Dead Sea (400 m, or 1312 ft, below sea level).

FIGURE 9.1
Plains in Kenya's Masai Mara National Reserve.

The three major oceans on Earth are the Pacific Ocean (Earth's largest, deepest, and oldest); the Atlantic Ocean (Earth's coldest and saltiest); and the Indian Ocean (the smallest). However, these oceans are connected, so, in truth, there is only one vast global ocean. Beneath the oceans, paralleling some coastlines, there are long, narrow ocean trenches. These are Earth's deepest places. The lowest point on Earth is in the Mariana Trench, with a depth of 11,033 m (36,198 ft)—that's deeper than any surface mountain is tall. Also under the ocean lies the global midocean ridge system, a continuous mountain belt 65,000 km (40,000 mi) long. Between the ocean trenches and ridges are deep undersea plains.

FIGURE 9.2
The Matterhorn in Switzerland. This mountain is named for its characteristic "horn" feature, which was produced by the action of massive glaciers.

About 10% of the world's land surface is covered by glaciers or other massive bodies of ice. One vast glacier nearly covers the entire continent of Antarctica.

Earth has a great diversity of *landforms* or surface features in addition to the plains, plateaus, trenches, and mountains (Figure 9.2). Some of these features—faults and folds, for example—were created largely through tectonic processes. Other landforms, such as valleys, canyons, deltas, and dunes, result mainly from the action of water, wind, gravity, and ice as they wear down and redistribute rock.

Also, much of Earth's present surface has been shaped not by nature but by people. In highly populated cities, more than 90% of the ground may be covered by paved streets, buildings, parking lots, and other human-made structures and materials. So, we see that humans are a major geologic force that is shaping Earth's surface in dramatic ways.

FIGURE 9.3
In modern times, people have changed much of Earth's surface. Industrialization, technology, agriculture, and the large human population all have major impacts.

TECHNOLOGY

Remote Sensing

Today, *remote sensing* is the primary tool used for mapping landforms and observing rapid or slow changes on Earth's surface. Remote sensing involves imaging Earth's surface with satellite-based cameras, radio receivers, scanners, thermal sensors, and other instruments. Such tools are used to create digital images, maps, and graphs of Earth's surface features. Most often, remote-sensing devices gather data in the form of electromagnetic waves—visible light, infrared radiation, microwaves, and so on.

There are many remote-sensing applications. Satellite images are used for mapmaking and surveying, to detect temperature variations on Earth's surface, and to track weather changes. Satellite images provide clues that point to subsurface deposits of mineral ores, oil, gas, and groundwater, and they help scientists and others to manage the land, the ocean, and the atmosphere.

Satellite pictures also allow us to compare landscapes before and after such natural events as floods, earthquakes, and fires, and to assess the damage done. In 2005, satellite images helped rescuers, homeowners, and the public identify the damage to New Orleans and the Gulf Coast after Hurricane Katrina. Satellite images, posted to the National Oceanographic and Atmospheric Administration (NOAA) Web site, were the first images of the devastated Gulf Coast that were made available to the public.

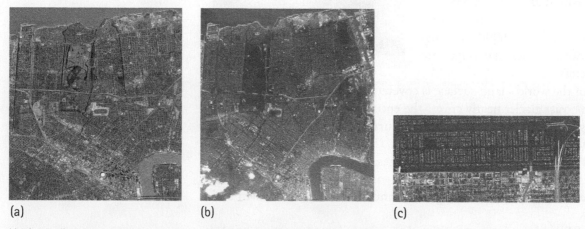

(a) This satellite image shows New Orleans, Louisiana, on March 9, 2004. At the time, New Orleans was a city with 1.3 million people and extensively developed buildings and roads. Because New Orleans lies below sea level, a system of levees was built to prevent flooding by surrounding waters. (b) New Orleans after Hurricane Katrina struck on August 31, 2005. The storm surge and rains led to the breaching of levees. Flooding, as shown here, occurred in more than 80% of the city. (c) An enlarged view of a portion of part (b), showing submerged roads and buildings.

9.2   Crustal Deformation—Folds and Faults

LEARNING OBJECTIVE
Identify the three types of stress that act on Earth's crust, and describe their effects.

EXPLAIN THIS Why does rock tend to break at Earth's surface but to bend below the surface?

Earth's surface is divided into a dozen or so massive patches of rock called tectonic plates. The movement of tectonic plates produces great **stresses**, or forces on Earth's rock. There are three types of stress:

1. *Compression* is the pushing together of masses of rock. Converging plates experience compressive stress.
2. *Tension* is the pulling apart of rock. Diverging plates undergo tensional stress.
3. *Shear stress* is produced when plates slide past one another.

A rock can respond in one of three ways to these applied stresses. It can *fracture* or break, as we commonly observe at Earth's surface. (What happens when you hit a rock with a hammer, for instance?) But rock responds to stresses in less familiar ways as well. It can *deform elastically*, in which case it bounces back to its initial size and shape when the applied stress is removed. Or, if the stress exceeds a level of stress called the "elastic limit" of the rock, the rock *deforms plastically*. The stressed rock permanently loses its original form—like Silly Putty™. Which of these three responses actually occurs depends on the nature of the rock, its temperature, the rate at which the stress is applied, and the confining pressure on the rock.

Colder surface rock is more brittle than warmer subsurface rock, which can slowly bend and flow. So, surface rocks typically fracture when their elastic limit is exceeded, but rock buried deep inside Earth often deforms plastically to produce folds.

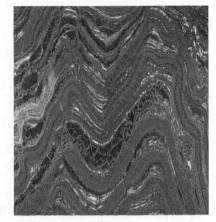

FIGURE 9.4
This banded iron formation (BIF) is a rock formed from layers of the iron oxide mineral hematite (red), tiger's eye, and jasper. At more than 3 billion years old, BIFs are among the oldest rocks on Earth. Deep burial of the rock and subsequent tectonic compression folded it. This sample is only about 2 cm across, so the folds in the rock are quite small.

Folds

Folds are bends in layered rock. Folds vary in size from tight, or even microscopic, folds in metamorphic rock (Figure 9.4) to broad undulations, such as those in folded sedimentary rock (Figure 9.5).

Folds in rock result from compressive forces. They are like the wrinkles you might find in a rug when you push on one end. Imagine the enormous forces required to wrinkle rock! Usually the force comes from the collision of tectonic plates, but sometimes other factors produce this compression, such as the movement of magma.

Folds typically form series of arches and troughs. Arch-shaped folds, as shown in Figure 9.6, are called *anticlines*. *Synclines* are trough-shaped folds. The rocks at the center of a syncline are the youngest; that is, as you move horizontally away from the syncline's center, the rocks get older and older. In an anticline, the opposite is true: The rocks nearest the center of the fold are the oldest.

FIGURE 9.5
Folded strata are revealed in a roadside cliff along the San Andreas Fault in California. The North American Plate and the Pacific Plate are on opposite sides of the fault. The plates rub against each other as they move in opposite directions. This motion compresses and warps the rock at the plate boundary into folds.

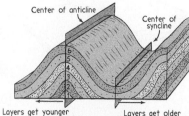

Center of anticline
Center of syncline
Layers get younger
Layers get older

FIGURE 9.6
Anticline and syncline folds. Layer 1 is the oldest rock and layer 6 is the youngest. In a syncline, the youngest rock layers are near the center of the fold. In an anticline, the oldest rock is nearest the center.

CHECK YOURSELF

1. **Have you ever tossed a rock and seen it bend rather than break? What is your explanation for this?**

2. **When we can see a cross-section of Earth's surface—for example, at a road cut—layers of sedimentary rock sometimes look wavy. Why?**

CHECK YOUR ANSWERS

1. Not likely. Rock is brittle at Earth's surface because the temperature and pressure are low there, compared with the temperature and pressure in Earth's interior, where rock *can* bend.

2. The cross-section in such rock reveals synclines and anticlines—folds formed by compressive stress, most often related to the collision of tectonic plates.

Faults

A fracture is a crack in rock; a **fault** is a fracture where the rocks on either side have moved relative to each other. Movement along faults can occur rapidly in the form of a big earthquake, but such movement usually happens so gradually that we don't notice it.

Faults mostly exist at plate boundaries where extreme tectonic stresses crack the crust, but faults can occur in the middle of a plate too. Faults vary in length from a few centimeters to hundreds of kilometers. The amount of displacement along faults also varies greatly, again in a range from centimeters to many kilometers. Faults are typically found in networks, rather than as single cracks, and at shallow depths, usually in the top 10–15 km of Earth's crust.

Faults are classified on the basis of the direction of displacement. There are three basic kinds: dip-slip faults, strike-slip faults, and oblique faults. To discuss these faults, it's useful to employ terminology coined by miners. Note the fault in Figure 9.7 (the slanted line in the top drawing). Imagine that you could pull the block diagram apart at the fault, as shown in the lower drawing. The half containing the fault surface where someone could stand is called the *footwall block*. The fault surface on the other block is also inclined, but in such a way as to make standing impossible; this is the *hanging-wall block*. (Miners could hang a lamp on a hanging wall and stand on a footwall.)

In a *dip-slip fault*, the hanging wall and footwall move vertically along the fault plane, as shown in Figures 9.8 and 9.9. Dip-slip faults are further classified as *normal faults* and *reverse faults*. In a reverse fault, the hanging wall moves up relative to the footwall. This fault motion, caused by compressional forces, is shown in Figure 9.8. In a normal fault, the hanging wall moves down relative to the footwall. (The name arises because it seems "normal" for the overhanging wall to slide down a sloping fault plane, since we are so accustomed to the effects of gravity.) The motion along a normal fault is due to tensional forces and is shown in Figure 9.9.

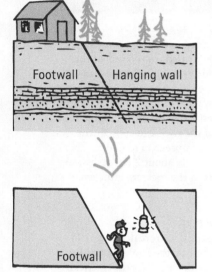

FIGURE 9.7
The terms *footwall* and *hanging wall* were commonly used by miners because a miner could hang a lamp on a hanging wall and stand on a footwall.

FIGURE 9.8
Reverse faulting occurs when compression pushes the hanging wall and footwall together and the rocks in the hanging wall are pushed upward relative to the rocks in the footwall. (a) A reverse fault before erosion. (b) A reverse fault after erosion.

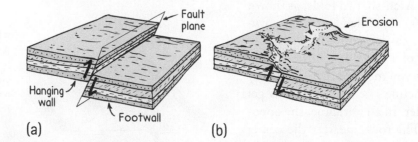

(a) (b)

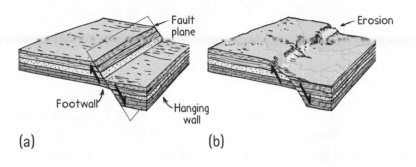

FIGURE 9.9
Normal faulting occurs when tension pulls the hanging wall and footwall apart and the rocks in the hanging wall drop down relative to the rocks in the footwall. (a) A normal fault before erosion. (b) A normal fault after erosion.

Strike-slip faults are characterized by horizontal motion (Figure 9.10). The world's most famous strike-slip fault, the San Andreas Fault, occurs at a transform-fault plate boundary that runs through California. Sticking and slipping of rock blocks along the San Andreas Fault (really a zone of networked faults) is responsible for many of the earthquakes California is noted for, including the great earthquake of 1906, which nearly destroyed San Francisco.

In an *oblique fault*, the blocks of rock have a combined motion. They move horizontally, as in a strike-slip fault, and vertically, as in a dip-slip fault. Oblique faulting occurs where there is a combination of tensional and compressional or shear forces.*

Networks of faults can be quite complex, and they can be used to read the history of tectonic events recorded in rock. For example, reverse faults correspond to compression. So if you find reverse faulting, your location could be a past or present convergent plate boundary. Normal faulting represents tension in rock. So if normal faults are present, you may be at a diverging plate boundary, a place where tectonic plates pull apart. Faults also have great economic importance because they can control the movement of groundwater and the distribution of minerals and fossil fuels. So faults are important for many reasons, not just because they are the locations of most earthquakes.

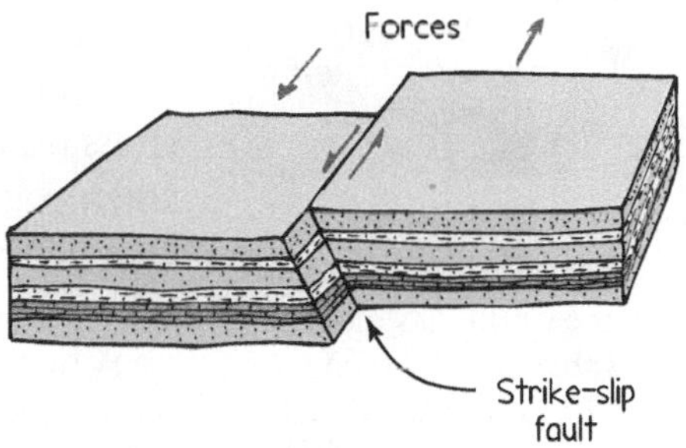

FIGURE 9.10
Blocks of rock rub and move past one another at a strike-slip fault.

CHECK YOURSELF
1. You are walking across a desert landscape and note that the ground is cracked and dry. Should you conclude that the cracks you see are faults? Why or why not?
2. Why should a home builder be interested in the geologic study of faults?
3. What action occurs at a normal fault? Why is a normal fault so named?

CHECK YOUR ANSWERS
1. No, faults are not simply cracks in Earth's surface. Faults are deep cracks along which sections of rock shift relative to one another. Actually, most faults cannot be seen at Earth's surface.
2. Since earthquake safety is a consideration in building design, home builders should be knowledgeable about earthquakes and therefore faults.
3. The hanging wall moves down relative to the footwall. This is a "normal" motion because it is the direction objects fall under the influence of gravity.

*Shear forces occur when one block of rock pushes on another block with a force that is at an angle to, rather than perpendicular to, the fault plane.

LEARNING OBJECTIVE
State the four major types of mountains, and explain how they form.

9.3 Mountains

EXPLAIN THIS Explain how compression produces some mountains but tension produces other mountains.

Mountains are surely some of Earth's most magnificent features (Figure 9.11). *Mountains* are defined as thick sections of crust that are elevated with respect to the surrounding crust. No two mountains are alike, but we can identify four basic types, which are classified according to their structural features: (1) folded mountains, (2) upwarped mountains, (3) fault-block mountains, and (4) volcanic mountains.

Folded Mountains

Folded mountains are the most common type of mountain. They form over millions of years as tectonic plates collide. Tectonic collisions put compressive stress on rock so that it crumples to make folds. This is just like what happens when you push on a piece of paper or a rug from the edges and it wrinkles, except that the folds in rock are enormous. The world's tallest mountain ranges are folded mountains.

When you see large regions of folded mountains in the interiors of continents, you know that tectonic plates have collided there in the past. The Canadian Rockies are folded mountains resulting from recent plate convergence. The Himalayas are folded mountains too. They are still converging and growing as the Indian Plate keeps ramming into the Eurasian Plate. The Appalachian Mountains in the eastern United States were formed by a very ancient tectonic convergence 300 million years ago. They were once several kilometers taller than they are today, but erosion has worn them down.

The normal thickness of continental crust is about 35 km (22 miles). When a new folded mountain range forms, that thickness can be doubled. The Himalayas are about 80 km (50 miles) thick from the bottom of the crust to the summit of the highest mountains.

Upwarped Mountains

The Black Hills of South Dakota and the Adirondack Mountains of New York are **upwarped mountains**. Upwarped mountains have domelike shapes. Like folded mountains, they are produced by the compression of rock. However, upwarped mountains are usually single anticlines that form when Earth's crust heaves upward as a great amount of magma pushes its way up underneath. As Figure 9.12 shows, upwarped mountains are made up of older igneous and metamorphic bedrock that was once flat and overlain with sediment, but then was upwarped (pushed upward). As these regions were lifted, erosion removed the

FIGURE 9.11
The Himalayas, the highest mountain range in the world, has more than 30 peaks that are more than 7600 m high. The Himalayas are folded mountains formed by colliding continental tectonic plates. They are located on the borders of Pakistan, India, Nepal, and Tibet.

FIGURE 9.12
The Black Hills of South Dakota feature this large dome, an upwarped mountain. Sedimentary rock has eroded from the top, leaving an exposed dome of igneous and metamorphic rock.

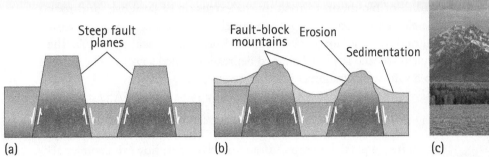

FIGURE 9.13

(a) Fault-block mountains are formed by blocks of rock that are uplifted along steep fault planes. (b) Erosion and deposition round out the fault planes that bound the mountains. (c) The Teton Range of Wyoming rises sharply above the surrounding land. This is a characteristic shared by fault-block mountains in general.

easily weathered sedimentary surface rock. Domes of durable igneous and metamorphic rock were left behind.

Fault-Block Mountains

Mountain-size folds and domes result from compression, but tensional stress can produce mountains too. Mountains that form from tension and that have at least one side bounded by a normal fault are called **fault-block mountains**. Fault-block mountains occur when there has been broad uplifting over a large area. The uplifting stretches and elongates the crust so that it breaks along fault lines. Huge blocks of crust are sometimes thrust upward along steep fault planes while other sections of rock drop down, as Figure 9.13 shows. Blocks of rock end up stacked against one another like a series of toy block towers. Fault-block mountains rise steeply above the surrounding landscape. The western United States features many fault-block mountains, including the Teton Range in Wyoming and the Sierra Nevada in California.

CHECK YOURSELF

1. Suppose huge blocks of crust drop down along normal faults. Between them, a block is left standing and over time it is uplifted to great heights. What kind of mountain is this?

2. The Sierra Nevada Range of California features fault-block mountains. Were these mountains produced by compressive or tensional forces?

3. A section of crust is compressed as it is pushed upward by forces acting on it from below. If the rock bends and arches upward to form a dome in response to this stress, what type of mountain will result? What kind of mountain will result if the rock breaks and moves upward along fault lines?

CHECK YOUR ANSWERS

1. A fault-block mountain

2. Tensional forces

3. An upwarped mountain; a fault-block mountain

Volcanoes

A **volcano** is a hill or mountain formed by the extrusion of lava, ash, and rock fragments. The ejected materials erupt through the volcano's central vent, flow downhill, cool, and accumulate to give this landform its conical shape. At the summit of a typical volcano is a bowl-shaped depression called a *crater*. The crater is connected to a subsurface magma chamber by a pipelike vent.

Some volcanoes have unusually large craters. A crater that exceeds 1 kilometer in diameter is called a *caldera*. In most cases, calderas form when the summit of a volcano collapses into a partially emptied magma chamber; however, some calderas have been formed by explosive eruptions in which the top of the volcano was blown out, as shown in Figure 9.14. Yellowstone National Park is actually one huge caldera, about 40 miles in diameter!

There are three kinds of volcanoes, based on the types of material that erupt from them (Figure 9.15). Volcanoes that are built up from a steady supply of fluid basaltic lava are called *shield volcanoes*. Basaltic lava has a low viscosity—in other words, it flows easily. Shield volcanoes are shaped like a warrior's shield because the easily flowing lava that erupts from them pours out in all directions to form thin, gently sloping sheets.

Cinder cones are volcanoes that are very steep but rarely rise higher than 300 meters above ground level. Cinder cones are built from various ejected materials, including ash, cinders, glass and lava fragments, and rocks that erupt explosively from a single vent and pile up at a steep angle.

A *composite cone*, also known as a *stratovolcano*, is a volcano with a high, steep-sided summit and gently sloping flanks built of alternating layers of lava, ash, and mud. Mount St. Helens in Washington is an example of an active composite cone. In 1980, it erupted violently, disrupting the lives of thousands of people and transforming more than 200 square miles of lush forest into a burned, gray landscape.

Most volcanoes form near divergent or convergent plate boundaries. To see this, look at Figure 9.16, which shows a string of volcanoes in the *Ring of Fire*. The Ring of Fire encircles much of the Pacific Ocean. This is where 75% of the world's volcanoes are located. About 600 of these volcanoes are active. Tectonic plates meet at convergent boundaries all along the Ring of Fire.

Some volcanoes are not produced at the margins of tectonic plates but are instead created by hot spots. A **hot spot** is a stationary, exceptionally hot region deep in Earth's interior, usually originating at the mantle–core boundary. Mantle rock overlying a hot spot softens and is moved slowly upward by convection. Rising columns of hot, softened rock, called *mantle plumes*, make their way to the surface. This warmed rock melts under reduced pressure as it moves closer to the surface by convection, and then it erupts.

Most hot spots are located under the seafloor. Lava that erupts from a hot spot gradually builds a **seamount**, an undersea volcanic peak. Over geologic time, lava from countless eruptions enlarges a seamount. Ultimately, if the seamount gets

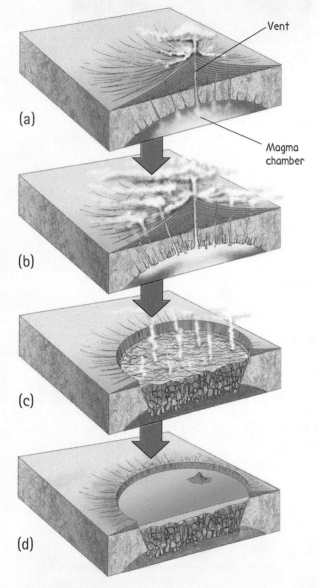

FIGURE 9.14

(a) Magma rising from a magma chamber into the vent of a volcano. (b) The formation of a caldera can involve a massive volcanic eruption, as shown here. (c) Material exploding from the volcano creates a much larger crater than the original volcanic vent. The magma chamber beneath the caldera eventually solidifies and, without a supply of magma, the volcano becomes dormant or extinct. (d) Rain and groundwater may eventually fill the caldera to form a lake.

Labels in figure: Vent, Magma chamber, (a), (b), (c), (d)

(a)

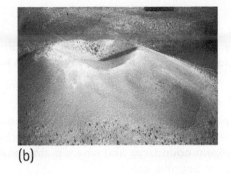
(b)

(c)

FIGURE 9.15
The three types of volcanoes. (a) Shield volcanoes, such as Mauna Loa, have broad, gentle slopes. (b) Cinder cones, such as Sunset Crater in Arizona, generally have smooth, steep sides and bowl-shaped summit craters. (c) Composite cones (also called *stratovolcanos*) such as Mount St. Helens (*foreground*) and Mount Rainier (*background*) are steep like cinder cones, but they are usually bigger because the mixture of lava and ash they erupt helps to hold them together. Note the volcanic ash on the southern flank of Mount St. Helens.

big enough, it will poke above the ocean as a volcanic island. Plates move, so that eventually a volcanic island loses its position over a hot spot. Because of this, the volcano will eventually lose its source of magma and become extinct. Over time, a new volcanic island can grow over the hot spot, and, if it does, a series of mountainous volcanic islands develops. This is how the Hawaiian Islands were created.

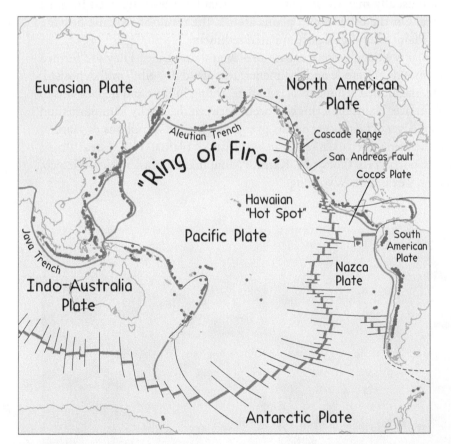

Yellowstone National Park is the remnant of an ancient volcano that violently erupted about 600,000 years ago. It released 1000 cubic kilometers of material, enough to cover half of North America in up to 2 m (6 ft) of debris. Most of the hot springs, bubbling mud pots, steaming pools, and spouting geysers that the Yellowstone area is famous for lie within the caldera.

FIGURE 9.16
The Ring of Fire is the location of more than 75% of the world's volcanoes. Volcanoes are represented by red dots. Ocean trenches are shown as blue lines. Transform plate boundaries are designated by crosshatching. The plate boundaries along the Ring of Fire are convergent boundaries (not shown) along which subduction occurs.

CHECK YOURSELF
1. **Where are most of the world's volcanoes formed?**
2. **Why does a series of islands develop over a hot spot?**

CHECK YOUR ANSWERS
1. Most volcanoes are formed near plate boundaries. Volcanoes form where one plate subducts beneath another, triggering magma generation (convergent boundary), and where plates move away from one another (divergent boundaries).
2. The motion of the plates carries crust over a hot spot so that, over time, a chain of volcanoes may develop there.

LEARNING OBJECTIVE
Differentiate between plains and plateaus.

9.4 Plains and Plateaus

EXPLAIN THIS Why are plains located at the bases of mountain ranges?

Unlike mountains, plains and plateaus are flat. *Plains* are broad, flat areas that don't rise far above sea level. *Plateaus*, on the other hand, are flat areas uplifted more than 600 m above sea level (Figure 9.17).

Plateaus are usually massive sections of rock that have been uplifted by great tectonic forces. On the other hand, plains are not the result of tectonic heaving and shoving. Plains are built of accumulated sediment.

Typically, plains extend from the base of a mountain range. They are formed as the nearby mountains erode and sediments are washed downhill and deposited. Little by little, the eroded sediments accumulate, filling in dips and depressions to create a level surface. Plains built this way occur between the Rocky Mountains and the Mississippi River. The process occurs over geologic time—millions of years.

Much of the midwestern United States consists of plains. The "Great Plains states" include portions of Colorado, Kansas, Montana, Nebraska, New Mexico, North Dakota, Texas, and Wyoming.

FIGURE 9.17
Flat landforms: plains and plateaus. (a) Buffalo Gap National Grassland in South Dakota is a low, flat landform—a plain. (b) The Colorado Plateau covers a huge uplifted area in four states: Utah, New Mexico, Arizona, and Colorado. The Colorado River cuts the Colorado Plateau, forming the Grand Canyon in Arizona.

(a)

(b)

9.5 | Earth's Waters

LEARNING OBJECTIVE
Describe how Earth's waters move in the water cycle.

EXPLAIN THIS   Why is most of Earth's fresh water unavailable for drinking?

Water is vital to life, as we know. Water seems plentiful—most of Earth's surface is covered by it. However, consider the data in Figure 9.18. Almost all of Earth's water is salt water in the ocean. Less than 3% of Earth's water is fresh. Most fresh water is solid ice and snow in the mountains and in polar regions. The remainder of Earth's fresh water is groundwater; surface water in rivers, streams, and lakes; and water in the atmosphere and biosphere.

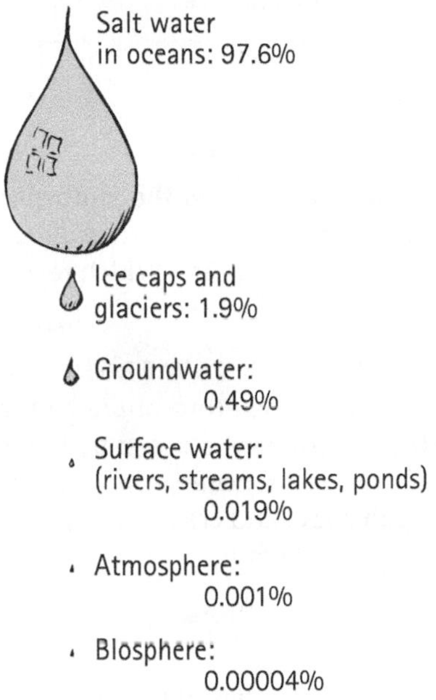

Water on Earth is constantly circulating, moving among the ocean, atmosphere, surface, and underground in a cycle, as shown in Figure 9.19. This cycle is called the **hydrologic cycle** or simply the *water cycle*. As water flows it also changes phase, evaporating and condensing in different parts of the cycle. The Sun gives water the energy it needs to evaporate. Gravity supplies the force that pulls water back to Earth's surface as *precipitation* (rain, snow, sleet, or hail). Gravity's constant pull moves water across Earth's surface downhill toward the oceans.

Each of the places where water is stored as it moves through the water cycle is called a **reservoir**. Glaciers, the oceans, the atmosphere, cracks and pores in underground rock—and even the human body and other parts of the biosphere—are all reservoirs for Earth's total water supply. Water stays in different reservoirs for different lengths of time. An average water molecule will spend nine days in the atmosphere before falling as precipitation, but 3200 years in the ocean before leaving as evaporation. The average amount of time that a water molecule spends in each reservoir is called its **residence time**. Table 9.1 shows the residence times for a number of different reservoirs.

Salt water
in oceans: 97.6%

Ice caps and
glaciers: 1.9%

Groundwater:
0.49%

Surface water:
(rivers, streams, lakes, ponds)
0.019%

Atmosphere:
0.001%

Biosphere:
0.00004%

FIGURE 9.18
Distribution of Earth's water. How much of Earth's water is available for drinking?

UNIFYING CONCEPT
● *The Gravitational Force*
Section 5.3

MasteringPhysics®
ACTIVITY: The Hydrologic Cycle

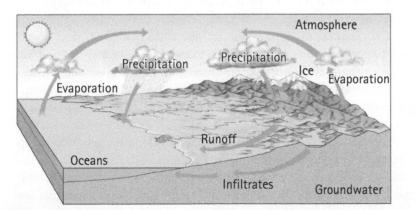

FIGURE 9.19
The major processes and reservoirs of the hydrologic cycle.

TABLE 9.1	RESIDENCE TIME OF WATER IN VARIOUS RESERVOIRS
Oceans	3200 years
Glaciers	20 to 100 years
Shallow groundwater	100 to 200 years
Deep groundwater	10,000 years
Lakes	50 to 100 years
Rivers	2 to 6 months
Atmosphere	9 days

CHECK YOURSELF

1. How does water enter the atmosphere? How does water enter the ocean?
2. Once an average water molecule enters a certain reservoir, it will remain there for 10,000 years. Which reservoir is this?

CHECK YOUR ANSWERS

1. Water enters the atmosphere by evaporating from the ocean or land surface. It enters the ocean by flowing across the surface, or by falling directly into the ocean, or by soaking into the ground and then flowing through rocks and cracks to the ocean.
2. Deep groundwater

There are many cycles in nature, including the rock cycle, the water cycle, and biogeochemical cycles. In any natural cycle, materials flow from one reservoir to another over and over again. Nature recycles!

LEARNING OBJECTIVE
Identify the regions of the ocean floor.

9.6 The Ocean

EXPLAIN THIS Why are the abyssal plains the flattest places on Earth?

The United States Geological Survey (USGS) estimates that there are 315 billion cubic miles of water in the ocean. What does Earth's surface look like under all this water? Oceanographers describe three main topographical units of the ocean floor: continental margins, deep-ocean basins, and midocean ridges.

A **continental margin** is a transition zone between dry land and the deep ocean bottom. Continental margins make up about 28% of the total ocean floor. There are two main kinds of continental margins: *passive margins* and *active margins*. Passive margins are located far away from active plate boundaries. They are geologically peaceful places with few earthquakes and little volcanism. Passive margins are wide and gently sloping. They consist of a *continental shelf*, *continental slope*, and *continental rise*. The shelf portion is nearly level continental crust that has been flooded by the sea. The continental slope is a relatively steep and narrow boundary between continental and oceanic crust. And the continental rise is a mound of accumulated sediment that eroded from the continental slope and is piled up at the foot of the slope (Figure 9.20a). Passive margins are found along the Atlantic Coast. Have you ever visited beaches on the East Coast of the United States? In many places, the continental shelf is wide and nearly flat, allowing plenty of space for swimming and boating near the shore.

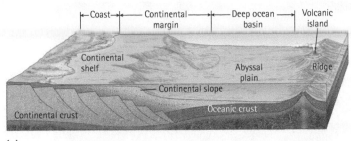

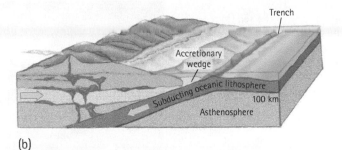

FIGURE 9.20

The continental margin is the transition zone between the coast and the ocean basin. The vertical drops are less steep in reality than shown here. (a) A passive margin is a place of geologic stability. (b) An active continental margin is associated with tectonic activity.

On the other hand, the West Coast lies along an active margin. An active margin is a place where the edge of a continent coincides with a tectonic plate boundary. Sections of the West Coast's active margin are involved in subduction or transform faulting. Active margins are common all along the Pacific Rim. The continental slope at an active margin can be the same feature as the landward wall of an ocean trench, as Figure 9.20b shows. Note that the active margin features an accumulation of sediment called an *accretionary wedge*. This is a mass of continental crust that is donated to the overlying plate by the descending plate. During subduction, sediments scrape off the descending plate. They crunch together and attach to the overriding plate as the accretionary wedge. Active margins are steeper, narrower, and more active than passive margins (Figure 9.20b).

The **ocean basin** is the deep depression in the lithosphere situated between continental margins and the midocean ridge. The ocean basin covers about 30% of Earth's surface. This is about the same area as all of Earth's exposed land. The ocean basin ranges between 3 and 5 km deep. It is composed of oceanic crust—dense, dark rock which is rich in basalt. The ocean basin contains abyssal plains, seamounts, and ocean trenches.

The **abyssal plains** are the flattest places on Earth because thick accumulations of sediment bury the uneven and rocky oceanic crust there. There is less than a 1-ft vertical change for every 1000 square feet of area in the abyssal plains—they are literally flatter than a pancake.

What would you find if you could deep dive below the ocean surface to visit the abyssal plains? The ocean changes with depth. The deeper you go, the less light there is. Sunlight can penetrate to only about 200 m, so the deep ocean is black. Temperature decreases with depth also. While the top 100–500 m of the ocean mixes and stays at about 25°C on average, the bottom of the ocean is dense and near freezing. Pressure increases with depth in the ocean. If you were to dive to the abyssal plains, which average about 4000 m below sea level, the force pressing in on you would be hundreds of times what atmospheric pressure is and you would immediately implode. Amazingly, abyssal organisms are adapted to this enormous pressure, total darkness, extreme cold, and scarcity of food. Most abyssal organisms eat dead organic matter that "snows" down on them from higher levels of the ocean.

Scattered about the ocean floor—particularly in the Pacific Basin—are the seamounts. As mentioned in Section 24.3, seamounts are isolated undersea volcanoes. They are steep-sided and tall; some tower thousands of meters above the abyssal plains.

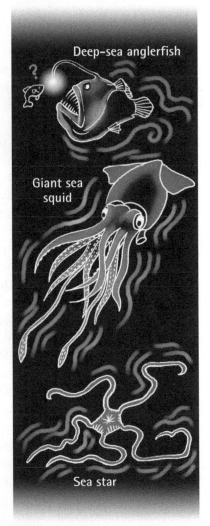

FIGURE 9.21

There are almost no light, little food, and extremely high pressure (5880–8820 pounds per square inch) in the abyssal plains. Nevertheless, life exists there. Residents of the abyssal plains include the giant sea squid, the largest of all invertebrates. It's more than 150 feet long and weighs more than a ton. Vicious anglerfish use light lures to attract their prey. Sea stars have luminescence on their arms that can be left behind to trick predators.

FIGURE 9.22
The topography of the sea floor. Note the midocean ridge, shown in darker blue. The Mid-Atlantic ridge is a section of the midocean ridge that marks a diverging plate boundary in the Atlantic basin.

UNIFYING CONCEPT

● *Friction*
Section 2.8

Ocean trenches are deep furrows in the seafloor adjacent to active continental margins as discussed above. These are some of the sea's most hidden but fascinating places. Ocean trenches are the deepest places in the oceans, sometimes exceeding 10,000 m (more than 6 miles) in depth. That's much deeper than the height of most of Earth's surface mountains. Trenches are where the edge of one tectonic plate disappears as it slips under another plate and dives down into the mantle. The down-going plate bends as it slips under the trench, but it gets stuck along the way because of friction. When the force on the down-going plate exceeds the friction holding it in place, it slips, causing an earthquake. The friction caused by the motion of the down-going plate also creates heat, which contributes to the production of magma and the eventual formation of volcanoes.

The *midocean ridge* rises up from the ocean basin, typically demarcating seafloor spreading at a divergent plate boundary. It is a continuous chain of mountains that runs all around the globe like the seam on a baseball. It is about 65,000 m long, covering 21% of Earth's surface. Unlike surface mountains built of continental rock, the midocean ridge system is composed of dark, young basaltic rocks that erupted as magma, cooled, and were uplifted. This is Earth's longest topographic feature and very tall, rising 1000–3000 m above the surrounding plains. The term "ridge" is somewhat misleading, however, because the midocean ridge system is actually hundreds of meters wide. Broad rift valleys exist along the ridge crest in many locations.

The Mid-Atlantic Ridge is a portion of the midocean ridge that has been extensively studied because it sits in the middle of the Atlantic Ocean. The Mid-Atlantic Ridge stands between 2500 and 3000 m above the ocean floor but is still 2000–3000 m below sea level.

LEARNING OBJECTIVE
Describe where the salts in the ocean come from.

 Integrated Science 24A
CHEMISTRY AND BIOLOGY

The Composition of Ocean Water

EXPLAIN THIS Why is the salinity of ocean water so constant?

eople lost at sea can die of thirst even though they are surrounded by miles of water. Why? Ocean water is too salty to drink. Most of this salt is sodium chloride, the salt you safely sprinkle on your popcorn. Nevertheless,

TABLE 9.2	ABUNDANT SALTS OF THE SEA
Salt of Seawater	Weight per 1000 g
Sodium chloride (NaCl)	23.48 g
Magnesium chloride (MgCl$_2$)	4.98 g
Sodium sulfate (Na$_2$SO$_4$)	3.92 g
Calcium chloride (CaCl$_2$)	1.10 g
Sodium fluoride (NaF)	0.66 g
Total	34.8 g

if you were to drink ocean water, you could die of dehydration because your cells would pump water out of themselves, trying to dilute the excess salt in your bloodstream and becoming dehydrated as a result.

The salt in the ocean comes from minerals in Earth's crust that have been weathered and eroded for billions of years. Rivers and streams have carried dissolved elements and salts from the crust to the ocean, and they have been deposited there. Water, "the universal solvent," has a strong ability to dissolve salts, so salts exist as ions in the sea.

Salinity is defined as the proportion of dissolved salts to pure water. Seawater contains about 35 g of dissolved salts for every 1000 g of solution or 35 parts per thousand. Thus the salinity of seawater is about 35 g per 1 kg of seawater, which is represented as 35‰. How salty is seawater in everyday terms? One cubic foot of seawater contains 2.2 lb of salts.

It is a remarkable fact that the composition of seawater has remained virtually constant over millions of years—perhaps even a billion years. After all, there is a great deal of activity in the oceans. Salts and other compounds are continuously added to seawater by eroded continental rock, volcanic vents, dead marine organisms, and other sources.

To keep the composition of seawater constant, salts and other compounds must be removed from the sea as fast as they are deposited. Much salt is removed from seawater by chemical precipitation. Also, precipitates and other materials are taken into the mantle by subduction. Marine life has a strong influence on the composition of seawater by removing salts, dissolved gases, and other solutes. Multitudes of tiny *foraminifera* (marine protozoans) and various *crustaceans* (such as crabs and shrimp) remove calcium salts to build their bodies. Diatoms, which are microscopic marine algae, draw heavily on the ocean's dissolved silica to form their shells. Some animals concentrate elements that are present in seawater in minute, almost undetectable amounts. Lobsters extract copper and cobalt while certain seaweeds concentrate iodine. Vanadium is another rare element in seawater that serves a biological purpose. Sea cucumbers are blob-like animals that thrive in herds on the sea floor. They take vanadium from seawater and use it to make a blood pigment. Just as iron makes human blood red, vanadium makes sea cucumber blood yellow!

> Water drains from Earth's surface and carries much of its material to the ocean. Besides salts, ocean waters hold decomposed biological material, dissolved gases, and waste from human activities. Ocean water has been called a weak solution of almost everything!

> The Dead Sea—which is actually a lake—is about 35% salt, or 10 times as salty as the ocean. Why so salty? The Dead Sea is the lowest location on land, so water that runs into it has no outlet; the water stays there until it evaporates, leaving behind a salty mineral residue. We call it the Dead Sea because nothing can live in this extremely *hypersaline* lake.

FIGURE 9.23
A sea cucumber, one of the many organisms that removes substances from ocean water to maintain the ocean's salinity over time.

CHECK YOURSELF
1. **How could calcium salts taken into the mantle in a subduction zone ever become part of a crab's shell?**
2. **How many grams of salt are in 2 kg of seawater?**

CHECK YOUR ANSWERS

1. Crust that is pulled into the mantle through subduction may melt to form magma, and then flow back toward Earth's surface and one day erupt, forming a surface or underwater volcano. If the lava's minerals dissolve in the seawater, the crab could incorporate them in its shell.
2. Every 1000 g of water contains 35 g of salt. So 2000 g of water, or 2 kg, contains 70 g of salt.

LEARNING OBJECTIVE
Draw a diagram that shows Earth's freshwater reservoirs.

9.7 Fresh Water

EXPLAIN THIS Trace the route a water drop could take after it infiltrates the soil and then eventually emerges in a spring.

Fresh water is water that has a low concentration of minerals and salts. It's the water we and other animals drink and the water that most plants need, but less than 3% of Earth's water is fresh water. Most fresh water is frozen in ice sheets and glaciers, so it's not available for human use (Table 9.3). The largest supply of fresh water for human use is groundwater, which is water that has soaked underground. Surface water—liquid water in lakes, ponds, rivers, streams, springs, and puddles—is far less plentiful than groundwater, but it has a huge impact on life and surface geology. Rivers and streams, for example, contain only one one-thousandth of one percent (0.001%) of Earth's total water at any given time. Yet running water moves through them quickly, so rivers and streams play a major role in moving rock and sculpting Earth's surface. The ultimate source of Earth's fresh water is precipitation.

Surface Water

When rain falls on land, most of it goes back up into the atmosphere through evaporation. Most of what doesn't evaporate soaks into the ground. This absorption of water by the ground is called **infiltration**. Whatever water the ground can't absorb becomes **runoff**, water that moves over Earth's surface. The proportion of rainfall that becomes runoff depends on the type of soil and on how wet or dry it is, as well as the steepness of the slope, the presence of plant life, and

FIGURE 9.24
Ponds like this one form when water collects in depressions in Earth's surface. Less than 1% of Earth's total water supply is fresh liquid water available to animals for drinking.

TABLE 9.3	DISTRIBUTION OF EARTH'S FRESH WATER	
Parts of the Hydrosphere	Volume of Fresh Water (km³)	Percentage of Total Volume of Fresh Water
Ice sheets and glaciers	24,000,000	84.945
Groundwater	4,000,000	14.158
Lakes and reservoirs	155,000	0.549
Soil moisture	83,000	0.294
Water vapor in the atmosphere	14,000	0.049
River water	1,200	0.004
Total	28,253,200	100.0

(a) (b) (c)

FIGURE 9.25
A variety of streams. Streams merge to form bigger streams, and bigger streams merge to form rivers. Streams ultimately discharge their water to the sea.

the rate at which the rain falls—whether it's a sudden downpour or a sustained, gentle rain.

During and after a rainstorm, runoff collects in sheets that move downhill and merge to form *streams*. A stream is any body of flowing surface water, from the tiniest woodland creek to the mightiest river (a river is just a large stream). As streams move downhill, they merge with other streams. In this process, some streams can become quite large: Witness the Mississippi River in the United States and the Amazon River in South America. Whatever the size, most streams eventually discharge into the sea.

The area of land that drains into a stream is called the stream's *drainage basin* or **watershed**. Watersheds can be large or small, and every stream, tributary, and river has one. Large rivers that gather many streams also claim the streams' watersheds. In other words, the watershed of a large river is a patchwork of the many smaller watersheds that service the smaller streams.

Watersheds are separated from one another by **divides**, lines that trace the highest ground between streams. Under most circumstances, the separation is complete— rain that falls on one side of a divide cannot flow into an adjacent basin. A divide can be hundreds of kilometers long if it separates two large watersheds, or it can be only a short mountain ridge separating two small gullies. The Continental Divide, a continuous line running north to south down the length of North America, separates the Pacific basin on the west from the Atlantic basin on the east. Water to the west of the Continental Divide eventually flows to the Pacific Ocean, and water to the east of it flows to the Atlantic Ocean (Figure 9.26).

Surface runoff pauses on its way to the sea when it flows into a lake. A lake is formed by surface and subsurface waters flowing into a depression in Earth's surface. For a lake with a stable water level, evaporation plus drainage out of the lake balances the water flowing into it.

Why do you see a lot of runoff on city streets? Pavement reduces the ground's ability to soak up water.

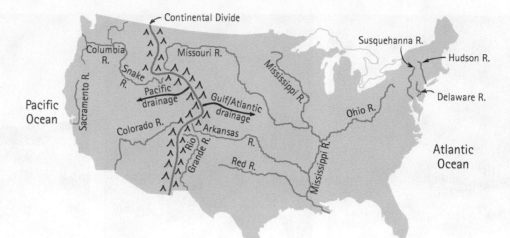

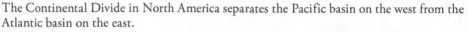

FIGURE 9.26
The Continental Divide in North America separates the Pacific basin on the west from the Atlantic basin on the east.

Groundwater

Rain and snowmelt absorbed by the ground may be retained by the soil. Some of this soil moisture is taken in by plants, and some of that water is transpired into the atmosphere. Water that isn't captured by soil percolates downward, moving between rocks and sediments and into the narrow joints, faults, and fractures in rock. Percolating water continues to move lower until it reaches the *saturation zone*. In the saturation zone, all the open spaces between sediments and rocks—and even the spaces between mineral grains *inside* rocks—are filled with water. Water that resides in the saturation zone is called **groundwater**. Groundwater continues to flow both downward and laterally in the saturation zone, eventually finding a stream or other outlet, often at the land surface (Figure 9.27).

Groundwater supplies streams, lakes, swamps, springs, and other surface waters. Most surface water is not obtained directly from runoff; instead, it flows into surface reservoirs from underground. During dry periods, when rain does not fall, it is groundwater that feeds surface waters. So, groundwater can provide needed water to the surface in time of drought.

Wells pump groundwater to the surface, where it is used for drinking, agriculture, and industry. In some regions, however, overuse of this resource has led to environmental problems, including land subsidence (lowering of the land surface), groundwater contamination, and streamflow depletion.

The upper boundary of the saturated zone is the **water table**. The level of the water table beneath Earth's surface varies with precipitation and climate. The water table is not flat like a kitchen table; rather, it tends to rise and fall with surface topography, as shown in Figure 9.27. Where the water table intersects the surface of the land, we find marshes, swamps, and springs. At lakes and perennial streams (streams that run all year), the water table is above the land surface.

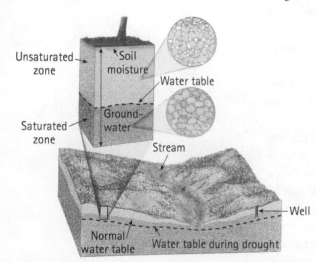

FIGURE 9.27
The unsaturated zone lies above the saturated zone. Groundwater resides in the saturated zone. The water table is the boundary between the two zones.

SCIENCE AND SOCIETY

Whose Water Is It?

If you have ever stood on the shore of one of the Great Lakes, or experienced the power of a waterfall, or been caught in a major downpour, it may seem to you that Earth's supply of fresh water is inexhaustible. From the perspective of one resident of the United States, water may be quite abundant. The world population, however, has grown to more than 7 billion people. If we were to spread ourselves evenly over all the habitable land, there would be more than 50 of us in every square kilometer. Thus it should come as no surprise that, collectively, we have a big impact on Earth's limited resources, including fresh water.

We are reminded that fresh water is a limited resource in the United States when farmers fight for the privilege to irrigate, or when our water utility bills rise, or when the water supply of downstream municipalities is endangered

as upstream municipalities release sewage into the water. Globally, there are many nations in which the primary supply of fresh water is rivers that originate in some other nation. As the upstream nation diverts fresh water for its own expanding population, political tensions rise. Over the next decade, for example, it is projected that agricultural development in Ethiopia and Sudan will reduce the flow of the Nile River into Egypt by 15%. Similarly, Turkey is currently expanding its damming and irrigation projects along the headwaters of the Euphrates River. Once fully implemented, these projects could result in a 40% reduction of the river's flow into Syria and an 80% reduction of the river's flow into Iraq. It is not surprising that the issue of water is a major source of political tension among these nations.

You may have noticed that, during a rainstorm, sandy ground soaks up rain like a sponge. Sandy soils soak up water very easily; other soils, such as clay soils, do not. Rocky surfaces with little or no soil are the poorest absorbers of water. The amount of groundwater that a material can store depends on its porosity. **Porosity** is the percentage of the total volume of rock or sediment that consists of *pore spaces* (open spaces). Pore spaces are usually found between sediments, but fractures in rock, spaces between mineral grains within a rock, and pockets formed in soluble rock also contribute to porosity.

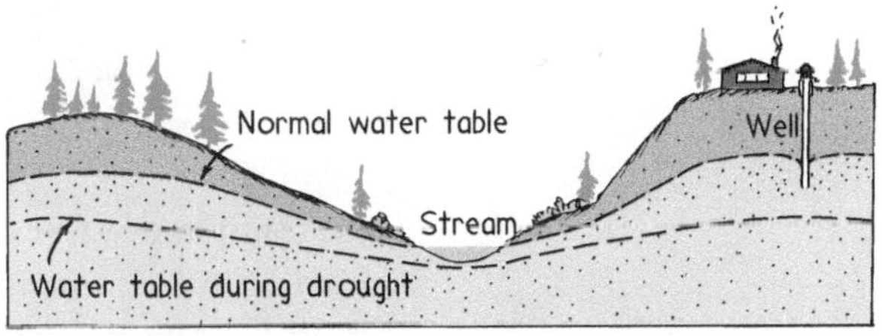

Rock or sediment may be very porous, but if the pore spaces are small and not interconnected, groundwater cannot freely move through it. **Permeability** is the ease with which fluids flow through the pore spaces in a rock or between rocks or sediments. Sand and gravel are highly permeable because they are composed of rounded particles that do not fit together tightly. Their pore spaces are large and connected, so water can flow easily from one pore space to the next. On the other hand, if the pore spaces are too small or poorly connected, water cannot flow through them at all. Clay sediments, for example, are composed of flat particles that fit tightly together. This is why clay, which can be quite porous, is practically impermeable (Figure 9.29).

An **aquifer** is a zone of water-bearing rock through which groundwater can flow. Aquifers generally have high porosity and high permeability. These reservoirs, which underlie the land surface in many places, contain an enormous amount of groundwater. They are important because wells can be drilled

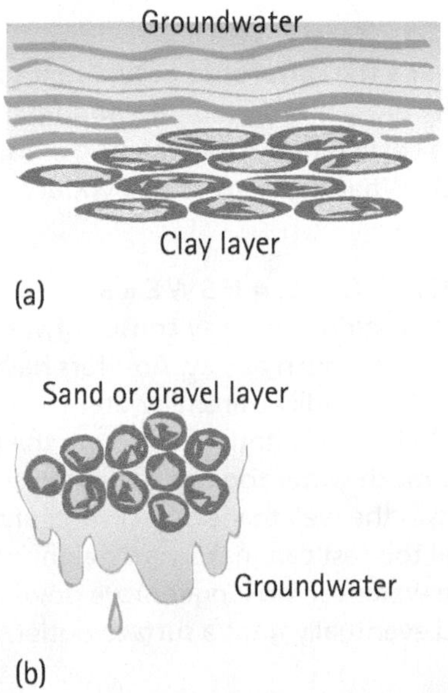

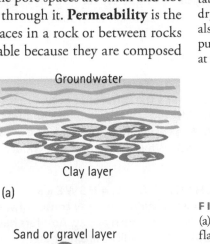

Groundwater

Clay layer

(a)

Sand or gravel layer

Groundwater

(b)

FIGURE 9.28
The water table roughly parallels the surface of the ground. If a well is drilled, the water level is at the water table. In times of drought, the water table falls, reducing streamflow and drying up wells. The water table also falls if the rate at which water is pumped out of a well exceeds the rate at which groundwater is replaced.

FIGURE 9.29
(a) The sediment particles in clay are flat and tightly packed, so the pore spaces are poorly connected. Clay is therefore not permeable. (b) The sediment particles in sand and gravel are relatively uniform in size and shape and they have large, well-connected pore spaces, so water can flow freely through sand and gravel. These are permeable materials.

FIGURE 9.30
The Ogallala Aquifer is the biggest
aquifer in the United States.

into them and water can be removed. More than half of the land surface in the
United States is underlain by aquifers. The vast Ogallala Aquifer stretches from
South Dakota to Texas and from Colorado to Kansas (Figure 9.30).

Groundwater accumulates as precipitation percolates down from the surface.
However, the process of restoring lost groundwater, called *recharging*, is slow.
An aquifer constantly gains water from its recharge zone (the area of land from
which the groundwater originates), but only a small amount of water reaches it
each year. Completely recharging a depleted aquifer may take thousands or even
millions of years. Thus, groundwater is considered a nonrenewable resource.

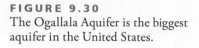

Groundwater, the largest supply
of fresh water available for human
use, has great economic importance. In the United States, more
than 40% of the water used for
everything except hydroelectric
power production and power-
plant cooling is groundwater.

Want to see the water table?
Most ponds and lakes are simply
places where the land surface is
below the water table. Swamps
and marshes are places where
the water table is level with the
ground surface.

CHECK YOURSELF
1. **What's the difference between a saturation zone and an aquifer?**
2. **Why are wells drilled into aquifers? Can a well run dry?**
3. **At a certain depth, percolating subsurface water encounters impermeable
   rock. What happens to this water?**

CHECK YOUR ANSWERS
1. A saturation zone may consist of water-bearing but impermeable rock or
   sediments, such as clay. Aquifers have high porosity *and* high permeability.
2. Aquifers readily transmit water to wells. Withdrawn water is replaced eventually by precipitation, although the process can be very slow. Pumping out
   too much water too fast depletes the water in the aquifer. Eventually, this
   causes the well to yield less water and even to run dry. Pumping your own
   well too fast can make your neighbor's well run dry, too.
3. The water can no longer move downward, so it moves laterally—sideways—
   and eventually finds a surface outlet.

9.8 Glaciers

EXPLAIN THIS What glacier contains more than half of Earth's fresh water?

LEARNING OBJECTIVE
Distinguish between alpine and
continental glaciers.

Near the poles and high in the mountains, there are places so cold that snow rarely melts. Instead, it piles up year after year. The weight of overlying snow crushes buried snow into ice crystals. A giant mass of ice the size of football fields or even a continent is produced. This is a **glacier**. There are two basic types of glaciers, as Figure 9.31 shows. *Alpine glaciers* form in the valleys of mountainous areas. *Continental glaciers*, which are also called *ice sheets*, are huge sheets of thick ice that cover a vast area such as a continent or an island. A single continental glacier called the Antarctic Ice Sheet almost covers the continent of Antarctica. It is so thick that it covers nearly everything except mountaintops. The Antarctic Ice Sheet contains about 90% of the glacial ice on the planet, or about 61% of Earth's fresh water.

(a)

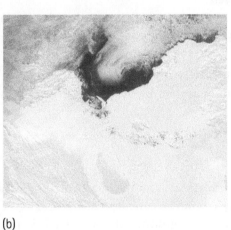

(b)

FIGURE 9.31
(a) An alpine glacier in the French Alps known as Glacier des Bossons. (b) As you can see in this satellite image, Antarctica is almost completely covered by a continental glacier called the Antarctic Ice Sheet.

Glaciers are sometimes called "rivers of ice" because they slowly glide across the land. High pressure at the base of the glacier can melt the ice there so that the glacier moves along a layer of liquid water. Gravity acts on a glacier too, constantly pulling it downhill. Alpine glaciers move much faster than continental glaciers because they are located on sloping land. As glaciers move, they carve the landscape like a giant bulldozer.

Integrated Science 24B
PHYSICS, CHEMISTRY, AND BIOLOGY

Water Pollution

LEARNING OBJECTIVE
Distinguish between point pollution and nonpoint pollution.

EXPLAIN THIS Describe the effects of large-scale industrialization and human population growth on water quality.

Water pollution is chemical, physical, or biological material introduced into water that harms organisms that depend on the water. The two biggest causes of water pollution are industrialization—the growth of large-scale factories and farms—and the human population explosion. Because

TABLE 9.4	COMMON KINDS OF WATER POLLUTANTS

Organic Chemicals
Fertilizers; pesticides; detergents; plastics; petroleum products, including gasoline and oil

Inorganic Chemicals
Metals; acids; salts

Toxic Chemicals
Chemicals that are poisonous to living things, including heavy metals such as arsenic and mercury; many industrial chemicals; some household chemicals, such as paint thinner and motor oil

Physical Pollutants
Heat; suspended particles, such as soil; litter, including fishing nets and plastic objects such as six-pack rings

Pathogens
Organisms that cause disease, such as bacteria and viruses; pathogens in untreated sewage and animal feces that are washed into the water

Organic Matter
Remains of organisms, including carcasses, feces, and plant material

UNIFYING CONCEPT

● *The Ecosystem*
Section 21.1

of industrialization and the exponential growth of the human population, waste that people produce can't be disposed of as quickly as it is made. The waste ends up in the ocean, groundwater, rivers, lakes, and streams.

Table 9.4 lists various kinds of water pollutants. Notice that some pollutants are disease-causing organisms, called *pathogens*, found in animal (including human) feces. Chemical water pollutants include toxic chemicals—poisons— and other chemicals that alter the chemistry of an ecosystem. One physical pollutant is heat. Are you surprised to see heat on the list? Some factories heat water and then discharge it into streams when they are finished with it. When the temperature of a stream rises, the amount of dissolved oxygen in it decreases. (Do you remember from chemistry that the solubility of oxygen decreases with temperature?) Fish and other aquatic organisms die when there is not enough dissolved oxygen for them to breathe.

The source of water pollution may be a particular factory that discharges excess heat or toxic chemicals. Or it may be an oil tanker that spills oil into the ocean, or a gas station that leaks chemicals into the groundwater. These are examples of *point pollution*—pollution due to a specific source. Point pollution is relatively easy to identify and therefore relatively easy to control.

Nonpoint pollution does not come from a single source. Nonpoint pollution comes from practically everywhere—homes, farms, freeways, city streets, and even acid rain. Nonpoint pollution is difficult to regulate and control because it comes from so many sources and because people may not see the connection between their activities and the polluted water. Therefore public awareness of nonpoint pollution is an important part of controlling water pollution. Table 9.5 shows some sources of point and nonpoint pollution.

TABLE 9.5   SOURCES OF WATER POLLUTION

Point Pollution
- Wastewater treatment plants
- Landfills
- Underground storage tanks, including gasoline tanks
- Septic tank systems

Nonpoint Pollution
- Salt applied to roadways
- Runoff from suburban and urban streets (contains litter, dog waste, oil, gasoline, etc.)
- Fertilizer
- Pesticides

CHECK YOURSELF

1. **How is studying integrated science helpful for understanding water pollution?**
2. **Why is public education important for controlling the problem of water pollution?**
3. **How can you help reduce point pollution? Nonpoint pollution?**

CHECK YOUR ANSWERS

1. Pollutants include biological, chemical, and physical agents.
2. People need to understand how certain activities cause pollution in order to develop ways of reducing pollution.
3. Your answer will depend on your particular circumstances. You can reduce the pollution that landfills create by being sure that you don't put any toxic chemicals, such as paint thinner, into the trash. Recycle electronics, glass, paper, and metals such as aluminum. To reduce nonpoint pollution, never litter and don't wash household chemicals down sewer drains. Tell a friend about the problem.

For instructor-assigned homework, go to www.masteringphysics.com (MP)

SUMMARY OF TERMS (KNOWLEDGE)

Abyssal plains The flat regions of the ocean basin.

Aquifer A zone of water-bearing rock through which groundwater can flow.

Continental margin The transition zone between dry land and the deep ocean bottom.

Divide An imaginary line that is the highest ground separating two drainage basins.

Fault A fracture through a rock along which sections of the rock have moved.

Fault-block mountain A mountain that forms from tension and that has at least one side bounded by a normal fault.

Fold A layer or layers of bent (plastically deformed) rock.

Folded mountain A mountain that features extensive folding of rock layers.

Glacier A mass of dense ice that forms when snow on land is subjected to pressure from overlying snow, so that it is compacted and recrystallized.

Groundwater The water that resides in a saturation zone.

Hot spot A stationary, hot region deep in Earth's interior, usually originating near the mantle–core boundary.

Hydrologic cycle The cycle of evaporation and precipitation that controls the distribution of Earth's water.

Infiltration Absorption of water by the ground.

Ocean basin The deep portion of the sea floor between continental margins and the midocean ridge.

Permeability The ease with which fluids flow through the pore spaces in sediments and rocks.

Porosity The percentage of the volume of a rock or sediment that consists of open space.

Reservoir Each of the places where water is stored as it moves through the water cycle.

Residence time The length of time water exists in a reservoir.

Runoff Precipitation not absorbed by the ground that moves over Earth's surface.

Seamount An undersea volcanic peak.

Stress A force applied to rock.

Upwarped mountain A dome-shaped mountain produced by a broad arching of Earth's crust.

Volcano A hill or mountain formed by the extrusion of lava, ash, and rock fragments.

Watershed The area of land that drains into a stream.

Water table The upper boundary of the saturated zone.

READING CHECK (COMPREHENSION)

9.1 A Survey of Earth

1. What percentage of the Earth is covered with ocean?
2. What is Earth's highest point? How high is it? What is Earth's lowest point? How deep is it?

9.2 Crustal Deformation—Folds and Faults

3. (a) Identify and describe the three types of stress a rock may experience. (b) Describe the three ways in which rock can respond to applied stress.
4. Why does folding occur deep below Earth's surface?
5. Name three kinds of faults and distinguish among them.
6. Why are faults worth knowing about?

9.3 Mountains

7. (a) Name four types of mountains, classified by common structural features. (b) Give an example of each of the four types of mountains.
8. How do hot spots produce mountains?
9. Where are most of the volcanoes on Earth located?
10. What are the three different types of volcanoes?

9.4 Plains and Plateaus

11. What is the difference between a plain and a plateau?
12. Why do plains usually extend out from the base of a mountain?

9.5 Earth's Waters

13. (a) Where is most of Earth's water? What percentage of it resides there? (b) Where is most of Earth's fresh water?

14. (a) Describe the hydrologic cycle. (b) What part of the hydrologic cycle has particular relevance to the shaping of Earth's landforms?

9.6 The Ocean

15. (a) Describe the three parts of a passive continental margin. (b) Describe the parts of an active continental margin.
16. Describe the overall topography of the ocean floor.

9.7 Fresh Water

17. Approximately what percentage of Earth's fresh water is frozen in ice caps and glaciers? About what percentage is in groundwater? About what percentage is in streams and lakes?
18. What happens to rainwater when it falls to Earth?
19. Do you live in a watershed? Defend your answer.
20. Where are all the pore spaces in rocks and sediments filled with water?
21. In what way is the water table different from a table?
22. What is the water that resides in the saturation zone called?
23. Besides runoff from precipitation, what is the source of Earth's fresh water? Explain.

9.8 Glaciers

24. Why are glaciers called "rivers of ice"?
25. What percentage of the world's glacial ice is included in the Antarctic Ice Sheet?

THINK INTEGRATED SCIENCE

24A—The Composition of Ocean Water

26. Why do we infer that salts must be removed from seawater about as fast as they are deposited?
27. The salinity of seawater is almost constant over time. Provide an explanation.

28. If you drink too much ocean water you will die of dehydration. Explain how this is so.
29. Where does the salt in ocean water come from?

24B—Water Pollution

30. What is the difference between point and nonpoint pollution? Which is easier to control? Why?

31. Name one biological water pollutant, one physical water pollutant, and one chemical water pollutant.

32. There is a saying: "The solution to pollution is dilution." Do you think this is a good general rule? What might be some limitations of this approach to controlling water pollution?

THINK AND DO (HANDS-ON APPLICATION)

33. Compare the permeability and porosity of several soil samples. To do so, collect several samples of soil taken from various locations and put them in different containers. Look at each one, and predict through which sample the water will move the fastest. Slowly add 100 mL of water to each sample until it can hold no more. Note the time it takes for the water to reach the bottom of the container. Which sample had the greatest porosity? Which had the greatest permeability?

THINK AND SOLVE (MATHEMATICAL APPLICATION)

34. The volume of solids in a sediment sample is 975 cm³, and the volume of open space is 325 cm³. What is the porosity of the sediment? Describe what the result of your calculation means in physical terms.

35. Show that liquid fresh water makes up about 0.50% of the water on Earth based on the data in Figure 9.18.

THINK AND EXPLAIN (SYNTHESIS)

36. A factory emits steam into the air. How could those same water molecules eventually reside in the ocean? In a river? In groundwater? In a bear's body?

37. Some people "fold" under stress. Others "crack up." How is this like what happens to rock?

38. Where would you expect to see more runoff—along a city street or in a prairie meadow? Why?

39. Most glacial ice is stored in polar regions. Why, then, would a severe melting of glacial ice cause the sea level to rise off the coasts of countries located near the equator?

40. What immediately happens to rainwater when it falls to Earth? What eventually happens to it?

41. List five major landforms in the United States, and describe them in as much geologic detail as you can.

42. Why must aquifers consist of material that has both high permeability and high porosity?

43. What are the two different kinds of continental margins? How do they differ?

44. The soil under Samantha's home is rich in clay. The ground therefore has high porosity but low permeability. Would Samantha be able to build a good well in her backyard? Why or why not?

45. Your friend says that groundwater is a nonrenewable resource. Do you agree?

46. Rain falls on land. Then what happens to it?

47. Why does the area of the continental shelf change over geologic time? (Hint: Is sea level constant?)

48. If surface reservoirs such as lakes and streams suddenly dried up, would people have another source of drinking water? Explain.

49. What is the relationship between the level of the water table and the depth to which a well must be drilled?

50. Which surface features record tectonic compression acting on rock? Which features show tectonic tension?

51. The removal of groundwater can cause subsidence. If the removal of groundwater is stopped, will the land likely rise again to its original level? Defend your answer.

52. Is groundwater stored in underground rivers? What's your reasoning?

53. If you look at a map of any part of the world, you'll see that older cities are located either next to rivers or where rivers existed at the time the cities were built. Explain.

54. The oceans consist of salt water. Yet evaporation of ocean water makes clouds, and clouds make rain, which is fresh water. Why is there no salt in rain?

55. The Amazon River Basin is a giant watershed with an area of about 6 million square kilometers. What does runoff in the Amazon River Basin flow toward?

56. Relate the saying "What goes up, must come down" to the water cycle.

57. Why does kelp, a type of photosynthesizing seaweed, thrive in coastal waters but not in the vicinity of abyssal plains?

58. How is rock underground like a sponge?

59. Is the infiltration of water greatest on steep, rocky slopes or on gentle, sandy slopes? Defend your answer.

60. If the water table at location X is lower than the water table at location Y, does groundwater flow from X to Y or from Y to X?

61. (a) Refer to the data in Table 9.1. Compare how long a given water molecule remains in each of the following reservoirs, and rank the reservoirs in order from longest to shortest residence time: Atlantic Ocean, Lake Tahoe, the air over Miami, groundwater at the bottom of an aquifer. (b) Describe the process by which a water drop exits each one of these reservoirs.

62. Look at Table 9.4. What is easier to control—toxic chemicals leaching out of landfills or toxic chemicals in surface runoff? Defend your answer.

READINESS ASSURANCE TEST (RAT)

If you have a good handle on this chapter, then you should be able to score 7 out of 10 on this RAT. If you score less than 7, you need to study further before moving on.

Choose the BEST answer to each of the following:

1. Snow becomes glacial ice when it is subjected to
   (a) decreasing temperature.
   (b) pressure.
   (c) rain.
   (d) plastic deformation.

2. When a rock deforms plastically, it
   (a) fractures.
   (b) changes its size or shape temporarily.
   (c) changes its size or shape permanently.
   (d) changes its mineral composition.

3. Why are faults important?
   (a) They are the usual locations of earthquakes.
   (b) They control the movement of groundwater.
   (c) They control the subsurface accumulations of fossil fuels.
   (d) all of these

4. Approximately what percentage of Earth's liquid water is fresh water?
   (a) 3%
   (b) 25%
   (c) 0.50%
   (d) 75%

5. Which process in the water cycle requires enormous energy input from the Sun?
   (a) precipitation
   (b) evaporation
   (c) condensation
   (d) percolation

6. The ocean basin
   (a) is covered by undersea mountains.
   (b) is mostly flat but features mountains and trenches.
   (c) has not been mapped sufficiently to be understood.
   (d) is an area of low pressure.

7. The Ogallala Aquifer
   (a) underlies several states.
   (b) is being pumped at a high rate.
   (c) is a source of fresh water.
   (d) all of these

8. The salinity of seawater has remained about the same for millions of years—perhaps even a billion years. Why?
   (a) Salts stopped forming in the ocean long ago.
   (b) Salts are included in the molecular formula of seawater.
   (c) Salts are removed from seawater about as fast as they are deposited.
   (d) Actually, there is more salt in the ocean today because salts are continuously washed into the sea.

9. Underground water in the saturation zone is called
   (a) groundwater.
   (b) soil moisture.
   (c) the water table.
   (d) an artesian system.

10. Fault-block mountains
    (a) arise from the stretching of Earth's crust.
    (b) are formed by the convergence of tectonic plates.
    (c) originate over hot spots.
    (d) are produced by upwelling magma.

Answers to RAT

1. b, 2. c, 3. d, 4. c, 5. b, 6. b, 7. d, 8. c, 9. a, 10. a

10

CHAPTER 10

Weather

EARTH IS the "Goldilocks planet"— of all the planets in the solar system, Earth is neither too hot nor too cold for life. It's just right. Why? How does the movement of Earth's atmosphere—that big sea of air in which we live (visible in the photo above)—make the weather change? How do other factors, such as ocean currents, the angle of the Sun's rays, the greenhouse gases, and the distribution of land and water, contribute to weather?

Weather has a direct effect on health and comfort. It influences daily choices, from what to wear to what to eat. Large-scale and long-term weather patterns—known as *climate*—affect everything around us too, from the shape of Earth's rivers and mountains to the life cycles of penguins and mosquitos. Read on to find out about meteorology, the science of weather, and climatology, the study of climate.

UNIFYING CONCEPT

● *The Scientific Method*
Section 1.3

10.1 The Atmosphere

EXPLAIN THIS State the reasons Earth's atmosphere is essential to life.

In science, a system is a set of interacting parts enclosed in a defined boundary. Within the Earth system, there are four interdependent parts or "spheres." These spheres include the atmosphere, lithosphere, hydrosphere, and biosphere. Earth's **atmosphere** is a thin envelope of gases, tiny solid particles, and liquid droplets that surrounds the solid planet. The hydrosphere is the sum of all the water at or near Earth's surface, the lithosphere is the outer shell consisting of the crust and mantle, and the biosphere is the portion of the planet that contains life. Earth's subsystems, or spheres, are not really separate. They interact in almost infinite ways. For example, the atmosphere weathers the lithosphere. And the biosphere affects the atmosphere when photosynthesizing organisms take carbon dioxide out of the air and add oxygen to it.

Even though Earth is a complex system of interacting parts that constantly changes in ways too complicated to completely track, science is good at detecting patterns and making predictions by breaking the system down into separate parts and cause-and-effect relations. To understand the extremely complex topics of weather and climate, we focus on the atmosphere. We look at how it is structured and what makes it change. **Weather** is defined as the state of the atmosphere at a particular time and place. Weather is made up of six elements of the atmosphere: atmospheric pressure, temperature, wind, precipitation, cloudiness, and

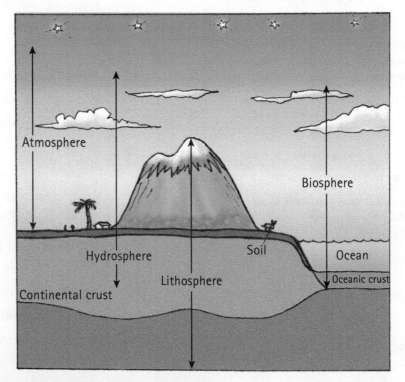

FIGURE 10.1
Earth is a system composed of subsystems or "spheres." Earth's environmental spheres are: the atmosphere, hydrosphere, lithosphere, and biosphere. When we study weather, we focus mainly on the atmosphere.

FIGURE 10.2
Changes in the atmosphere produce changes in the weather. On the left, the atmosphere is wet, cold, windy, and cloudy. On the right, the atmosphere is warm, clear, still, and dry.

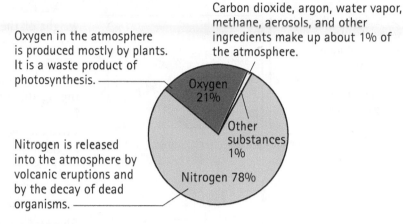

Oxygen in the atmosphere is produced mostly by plants. It is a waste product of photosynthesis.

Carbon dioxide, argon, water vapor, methane, aerosols, and other ingredients make up about 1% of the atmosphere.

Oxygen 21%

Other substances 1%

Nitrogen 78%

Nitrogen is released into the atmosphere by volcanic eruptions and by the decay of dead organisms.

FIGURE 10.3
The atmosphere consists of mainly nitrogen and oxygen gases with smaller amounts of various gases and aerosols.

humidity. Together, these elements create an overall atmospheric condition that we call "the weather."

Earth's present-day atmosphere is mostly a mixture of nitrogen and oxygen gas, with small percentages of water vapor, argon, methane, carbon dioxide, and other trace gases. Also, tiny suspended particles called *aerosols* are mixed into the atmosphere. The aerosols in the air include dust, ash, pollen, water droplets, and even air pollution such as soot. People typically call the atmosphere *air*, so we use the terms interchangeably here too.

The atmosphere is essential for life. It provides the oxygen and carbon dioxide that are required by living things. It provides the nitrogen that plants need. It protects organisms from the Sun's harmful high-energy ultraviolet waves, which damage not only the skin but also DNA. The atmosphere is an insulating blanket that traps heat and keeps temperatures sustainable for life—neither too hot nor too cold.

Climate is the general pattern of weather that occurs over a period of years. For instance, the weather in Anchorage, Alaska, may be clear, warm, and windy on a particular day, but the city has a cold, polar climate overall.

> You can get an idea of the thinness of our atmosphere by drawing a large circle that fills a regular sheet of paper. If the circle represents Earth, then its atmosphere fits inside your pencil mark!

Integrated Science 26A
PHYSICS

LEARNING OBJECTIVE
Describe how air pressure relates to the weight of air molecules.

Atmospheric Pressure

EXPLAIN THIS Explain why air pressure decreases with altitude.

The atmosphere is more than 100 miles thick, and it contains many trillions of molecules. Since these molecules have weight, the atmosphere has weight, and it therefore pushes against Earth's surface with a certain force per unit area—a pressure. The pressure that the atmosphere exerts on a surface due to the weight of the molecules above that surface is known as **atmospheric pressure**, or simply *air pressure*. (Again, we use the terms *air* and *atmosphere* interchangeably.)

UNIFYING CONCEPT

● *The Gravitational Force*
Section 5.3

FIGURE 10.4
Air density decreases with altitude; that is, there are more air molecules closer to Earth's surface than at higher altitudes. This is because air is compressible—"squishable." The weight of overlying air presses molecules downward, so they pack relatively tightly together near the ground.

FIGURE 10.5
Atmospheric pressure decreases with altitude.

UNIFYING CONCEPT

● *Density*
Section 2.3

MasteringPhysics®

VIDEO: Air Has Matter
VIDEO: Air Has Pressure
VIDEO: Air Has Weight

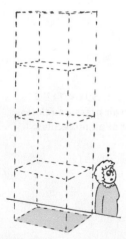

FIGURE 10.6
The weight of air that bears down on a 1-square-meter surface at sea level is about 100,000 N. So, the atmospheric pressure at sea level is about 10^5 N/m².

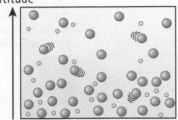
Altitude

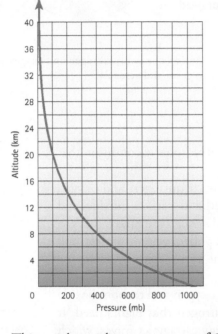

We have adapted so completely to the weight of the air around us that we don't notice it. Perhaps a fish "forgets" about the weight of water in the same way. The reason we don't feel the atmosphere's weight crushing against our bodies is that the pressure inside our bodies equals the pressure of the surrounding air. There is no net force acting on our skin.

If you have ever gone mountain climbing, you've noticed that the atmosphere gets thinner with altitude. There are fewer air molecules in a given volume of air up high, so it's harder to breathe. So, unlike the uniform density of water in a lake, the *density* of air in the atmosphere (its mass per volume) decreases with altitude (Figure 10.4).

Air pressure also decreases with altitude. This isn't surprising because air pressure is the weight of the overlying air. So, higher in the atmosphere, where the number of overlying molecules tapers off, air pressure also decreases (Figure 10.5). At sea level, air pressure is at its highest. What is the numerical value of air pressure at sea level? A column of air with a cross-sectional area of 1 square meter extending up through the atmosphere has a mass of about 10,000 kilograms. The weight of this air is about 100,000 newtons (10^5 N).

This weight produces a pressure of 100,000 newtons per square meter, so we estimate the atmospheric pressure at sea level to be 10^5 N/m² (Figure 10.6).

The SI unit of pressure is the pascal (Pa), and 1 Pa equals 1 N/m². Our estimate of atmospheric pressure thus may be stated as 100 kilopascals. Actually, the average atmospheric pressure at sea level is precisely 101.3 kilopascals (101.3 kPa), which is often expressed as 1 atmosphere (1 atm) of pressure. There are other popular units for atmospheric pressure. News programs report atmospheric pressure in *inches of mercury* or *millimeters of mercury*. These units refer to the mercury barometer, the instrument traditionally used to measure air pressure. Meteorologists often express air pressure in *bars* or *millibars* (mb). Conversion factors for air pressure are listed in Table 10.1.

TABLE 10.1	EQUIVALENT MEASUREMENTS FOR ATMOSPHERIC PRESSURE

1 standard atmosphere (1 atm)
101,325 pascals
1.013 bars
14.7 pounds per square inch (14.7 psi or 14.7 lb/in²)
760 torr
760 millimeters of mercury (760 mm Hg)

CHECK YOURSELF

1. Why doesn't the pressure of the atmosphere break windows?
2. The density of atmospheric gas molecules diminishes with altitude. How does this affect atmospheric pressure?

CHECK YOUR ANSWERS

1. Atmospheric pressure is exerted on both sides of a window, so no net force is exerted on the window. If, for some reason, the pressure is reduced on one side only, as in a strong wind, watch out!
2. Atmospheric pressure decreases due to the decreasing density of the atmospheric gas molecules.

10.2 The Structure of the Atmosphere

EXPLAIN THIS Explain why weather occurs only in the troposphere.

The atmosphere has four layers based on temperature: the troposphere, stratosphere, mesosphere, and thermosphere.

LEARNING OBJECTIVE
State the layers of the atmosphere, and describe their principal characteristics.

The Troposphere

As you have learned, most of Earth's atmospheric gas molecules are held close to Earth. They are concentrated in Earth's lowest atmospheric layer—the *troposphere*. The troposphere is quite dense but thin. It contains almost 90% of the atmosphere's total mass and has an average thickness of only 12 km (8 mi).

The troposphere contains almost all of the atmosphere's water vapor and suspended particles, and these create clouds and precipitation. For this reason, the troposphere is the layer where weather occurs.

The temperature in the troposphere decreases steadily (at 6°C per kilometer). At the top of the troposphere, the temperature averages a frigid −50°C. Certain gases of the troposphere absorb and retain warming energy from the Sun (we will give more details about this process in the next section). Therefore, as the density of air decreases, so does the troposphere's ability to retain heat (Figure 10.8). This is why high-altitude locations typically have cold climates.

Weather occurs in the troposphere. That's why commercial jets sometimes fly just above the troposphere. At this altitude, jets avoid turbulence caused by weather disturbances.

The Stratosphere

The *stratosphere* sits on top of the troposphere, from about 12 km to about 50 km above sea level. It is a thicker layer than the troposphere but much less dense. The bottom of the stratosphere is cold, only about

FIGURE 10.7
Earth's weather occurs in the troposphere—the lowest, thinnest, and densest layer of the atmosphere. This satellite image shows the thick, spiraling clouds over the Atlantic Ocean that accompanied Tropical Storm Xina in 1985.

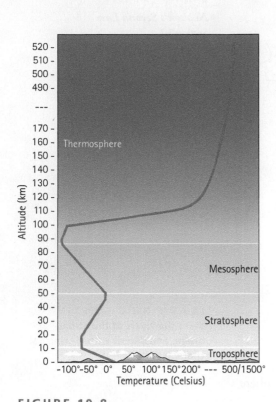

FIGURE 10.8
The average temperature of Earth's atmosphere varies in a zigzag pattern with altitude.

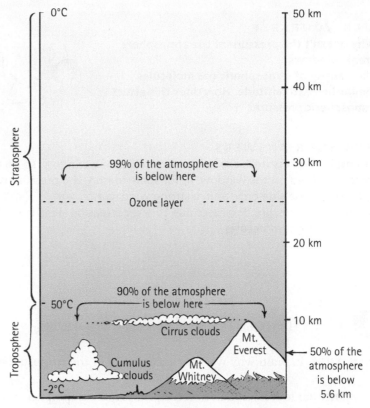

FIGURE 10.9
The two lowest layers of the atmosphere, the troposphere and the stratosphere, contain more than 99% of Earth's atmosphere.

MasteringPhysics®
ACTIVITY: Vertical Structure of the Atmosphere

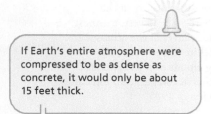

If Earth's entire atmosphere were compressed to be as dense as concrete, it would only be about 15 feet thick.

−60°C. However, the temperature rises steadily to about 0°C at the top of the stratosphere.

The temperature rises in the stratosphere because of *ozone*. Ozone (O_3), a molecule made of three oxygen atoms, accumulates in the stratosphere and absorbs solar energy. Ozone absorbs warming infrared radiation as well as the Sun's higher-energy ultraviolet (UV) radiation. Atmospheric ozone is critical to life on Earth because it absorbs UV radiation. UV radiation has many harmful effects, including sunburn, skin cancer, and eye damage. UV radiation also disrupts DNA, which may cause genetic mutations.

The Mesosphere

The *mesosphere* extends upward from the top of the stratosphere to an altitude of about 80 km. The gases that make up the mesosphere absorb little solar radiation. As a result, the temperature decreases from 0°C at the bottom of the mesosphere to about −90°C at the top. Very chilly indeed!

The Thermosphere

There is little air in the *thermosphere*, the next layer up in the atmosphere. However, the air that is there readily absorbs solar radiation. For this reason, temperatures are surprisingly high in the thermosphere, ranging from 500°C to 1500°C depending on solar activity.

The Ionosphere

The *ionosphere* isn't an atmospheric layer in the same sense that the other layers are. Instead, it is a region of the upper mesosphere and lower thermosphere that contains ions—gas molecules that have become electrically charged by absorbing solar energy. Near Earth's magnetic poles, fiery light displays called *auroras* occur as the solar wind (high-speed charged particles ejected by the Sun) strikes and excites particles in the ionosphere.

The atmosphere rises up from Earth's surface, but where does it end and outer space begin? There is no distinct boundary. The atmosphere thins rapidly with distance from Earth, then fades gradually. It finally terminates where there are too few molecules to detect hundreds of kilometers above Earth's surface.

CHECK YOURSELF

1. In recent years, scientists have found "holes" in the ozone layer—areas where atmospheric ozone has become very thin. Why are scientists concerned about this?
2. Why do mountainous areas generally have cold climates?

CHECK YOUR ANSWERS

1. Ozone protects life from damaging UV rays. Fortunately, the scientific and political communities have worked together and made great progress on the issue of the thinning ozone layer. By international agreement, the use of certain chemicals that damage the ozone layer has been restricted. Stratospheric ozone appears to be returning to healthy levels.
2. High-altitude places such as mountains have cold climates mainly because of the low density of the troposphere there.

FIGURE 10.10
The aurora borealis, or northern lights, is a beautiful display of light that occurs in the ionosphere when charged particles are excited by incoming solar radiation.

 Integrated Science 26B
PHYSICS

Solar Radiation and the Greenhouse Effect Drive Global Temperature

> **LEARNING OBJECTIVE**
> Describe how the greenhouse effect and solar radiation warm the atmosphere.

EXPLAIN THIS Explain why the visible radiation emitted by the Sun is not a cause of global warming.

Why does Earth have just the right temperature for life—neither too hot nor too cold? Two major factors work together to determine average global temperature: (1) the solar radiation that Earth absorbs, and (2) the concentration of greenhouse gases in its atmosphere.

The Sun emits **solar radiation**, which is energy in the form of electromagnetic waves. It moves outward from the Sun in all directions, like a light bulb. Earth intercepts a tiny part of it. We receive only about two-billionths of the total energy released by the Sun. This tiny fraction is the ultimate source of almost all of the energy used by everything on Earth. And it is also just the right amount of solar radiation required for sustaining temperatures suitable for life.

A bit less than half of the radiant energy from the Sun is in the form of visible light. As you know from physics, visible light is a portion of the

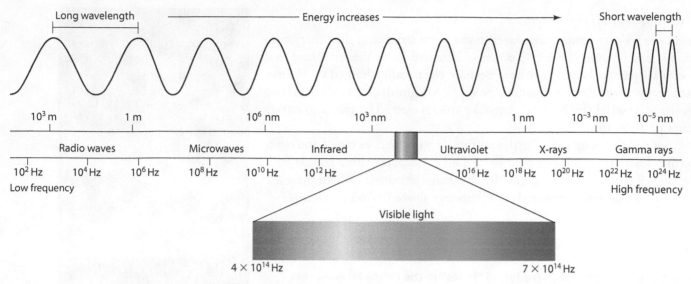

Long wavelength ← Energy increases → Short wavelength

| 10^3 m | 1 m | 10^6 nm | 10^3 nm | 1 nm | 10^{-3} nm | 10^{-5} nm |

| Radio waves | Microwaves | Infrared | | Ultraviolet | X-rays | Gamma rays |

| 10^2 Hz | 10^4 Hz | 10^6 Hz | 10^8 Hz | 10^{10} Hz | 10^{12} Hz | | 10^{16} Hz | 10^{18} Hz | 10^{20} Hz | 10^{22} Hz | 10^{24} Hz |

Low frequency   High frequency

Visible light

4×10^{14} Hz 7×10^{14} Hz

FIGURE 10.11
The electromagnetic spectrum consists of electromagnetic waves of different wavelengths.

UNIFYING CONCEPT

● **Waves**
Section 8.1

FIGURE 10.12
Some short-wavelength solar radiation is absorbed by the land, water, and atmosphere and eventually becomes heat. The rest is reflected back into space and doesn't affect temperature.

electromagnetic spectrum, a continuum of radiant energy waves. Electromagnetic waves have wavelengths ranging from thousands of kilometers to fractions of an atom (Figure 10.11). The longest waves are radio waves, then microwaves, infrared radiation, visible light, ultraviolet light, X-rays, and gamma rays. Energy and wavelength are related *inversely*—the longer the wavelength of a wave, the less energy it carries. Visible light has higher energy and shorter wavelength compared to *infrared radiation*, which is the radiant energy that warms our bodies and other forms of matter too, including many molecules of the atmosphere.

The atmosphere is transparent to visible light. Most of the light transmitted through the atmosphere is absorbed by the ground, although some of it is reflected back to space before it ever reaches Earth's surface (Figure 10.12).

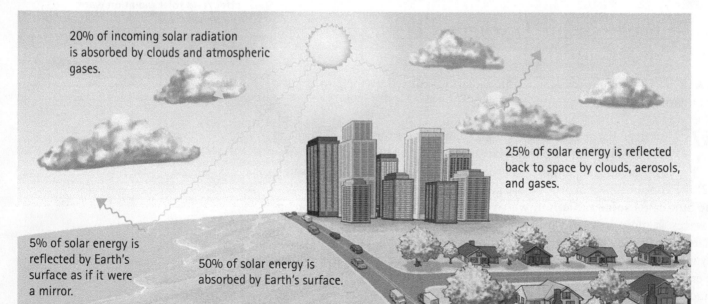

20% of incoming solar radiation is absorbed by clouds and atmospheric gases.

25% of solar energy is reflected back to space by clouds, aerosols, and gases.

5% of solar energy is reflected by Earth's surface as if it were a mirror.

50% of solar energy is absorbed by Earth's surface.

When the light energy that reaches the ground is absorbed, the ground in turn warms up and emits energy. But the energy that Earth's surface emits, which is called **terrestrial radiation**, has less energy and longer wavelengths than the incoming energy. Instead of being in the visible part of the spectrum, terrestrial radiation is infrared (Figure 10.13).

Although the atmosphere is transparent to short-wave visible light, it does not allow the infrared waves to freely pass through. As Figure 10.14 shows, carbon dioxide, water vapor, methane, and other "greenhouse gases" in the atmosphere absorb the warming terrestrial radiation, re-emit it, and re-absorb it many times before it can escape into space. Thus, energy becomes trapped in the atmosphere

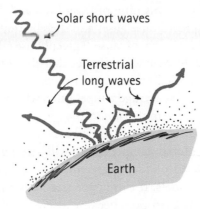

FIGURE 10.13
About 43% of the radiant energy from the Sun is in the visible part of the spectrum. The atmosphere is quite transparent to this radiation. Earth absorbs and Earth re-emits these waves as lower-energy, longer-wavelength infrared waves called terrestrial radiation.

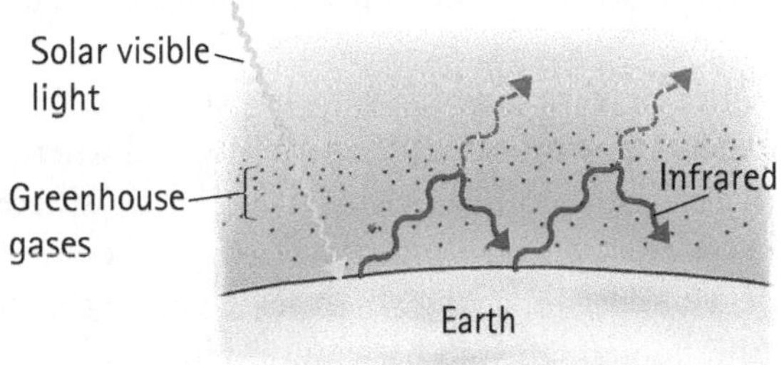

FIGURE 10.14
The greenhouse effect in Earth's atmosphere. Visible light is absorbed by the ground, which then emits infrared radiation. Carbon dioxide, water vapor, methane, and other greenhouse gases absorb and re-emit infrared radiation that would otherwise be radiated directly from Earth into space.

by greenhouse gases, and this causes the temperature to rise. The process of trapping terrestrial radiation leading to increased atmospheric temperature is called the **greenhouse effect**. The greenhouse effect is named for a florist's greenhouse, as shown in Figure 10.15.

The greenhouse effect is natural and beneficial to life on Earth. If greenhouse gases weren't present and able to trap heat, the planet's average temperature would be a frigid $-18°C$. The present concern, however, is that human activities,

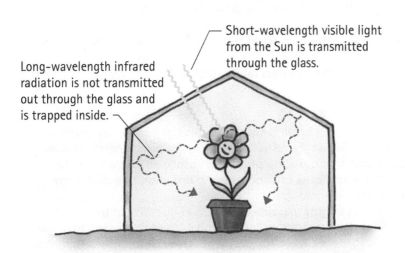

FIGURE 10.15
A florist's greenhouse is made of glass. Glass is transparent to visible light and opaque to infrared light just like the atmosphere is. Sunlight enters the greenhouse and warms the plants there. The plants then reradiate longer-wavelength infrared waves. The glass doesn't let the infrared waves pass through, so the infrared radiation builds up inside, increasing the temperature.

including the burning of fossil fuels and deforestation, produce high concentrations of greenhouse gases and thereby trap too much heat. As a result of this *anthropogenic* (human-caused) greenhouse effect, Earth is heating up too much and too quickly. Scientists predict that the complex ecosystems that have developed and diversified over tens of millions of years cannot be sustained. The sudden rise in Earth's average temperature, which threatens the biosphere, is called *global warming*, or simply *climate change*.

The United States Environmental Protection Agency (EPA) projects that average global temperatures will rise by 2°F to 11.5°F by 2100, depending on the level of future greenhouse gas emissions and the outcomes of various climate models. If this happens, ecosystems and human cultures worldwide will be severely disrupted because glaciers will melt and sea level will rise, there will be more frequent severe weather events, agriculture will de-stabilize, and there will be widespread economic impacts including the loss of habitable land along coastlines.

That being said, no one knows what the specific effects of global warming will be. Exactly how much will sea level rise and when? How severe and frequent will hurricanes be in different coastal regions? Where will drought, wildfires, and floods occur and how severe will they be compared to today? What will be the effect of climate change on disease-causing microbes and parasites when their natural habitats shift in basic ways? How will agricultural crops be affected when temperatures rise, soil dries out, and water for irrigation becomes scarce? There are many possible effects of climate change, and the problem is currently the focus of intense research and public interest. (More information on global climate change is provided in Chapter 11.)

UNIFYING CONCEPT

● *The Ecosystem*
Section 21.1

CHECK YOURSELF
1. Your friend says that it is mainly the ground that warms the atmosphere. Do you agree or disagree?
2. Which surface is a better emitter of terrestrial radiation—a snowy field or a black-topped road? Why?
3. How does the greenhouse effect relate to global warming?

CHECK YOUR ANSWERS
1. Your friend is right. The ground absorbs visible light and then reradiates it as terrestrial radiation. Terrestrial radiation is infrared energy, which is the wavelength that the atmosphere can absorb and be warmed by. Because of the greenhouse effect, terrestrial radiation is reused many times before escaping into space.
2. Fresh snow shines brightly because it reflects about 75% of the light that falls on it. A road, by contrast, reflects about 10% of the incoming radiation. The road therefore is a much better absorber of solar radiation and emitter of terrestrial radiation than the snowy field.
3. Global warming is principally caused by the greenhouse effect. But it's not the natural greenhouse effect that is the problem. It's the intensified greenhouse effect that is caused by human activities that put excessive amounts of greenhouse gases into the atmosphere.

10.3 Temperature Depends on Latitude

EXPLAIN THIS In terms of solar radiation, explain why you have a higher risk of getting a sunburn in Australia than in Canada.

Your house has a street address that identifies its unique location. Similarly, all points on Earth can be identified by their "address," a set of numbers called *longitude* and *latitude*.

Lines of longitude are imaginary lines that run north/south and pass through the poles (Figure 10.16). One of these lines, the one that passes through Greenwich, England, is called the *prime meridian*. The prime meridian, by international agreement, has a longitude of 0°. The longitude of any other location is its distance east or west from the prime meridian. Longitude is measured in degrees.

The equator is an imaginary circle that is halfway between the poles. It divides Earth into two halves: the Northern and Southern Hemispheres. Imaginary lines drawn around Earth parallel to the equator are called *lines of latitude*, or *parallels*. The equator has a latitude of 0°, and the latitudes of other locations are measured in degrees north or south from the equator. Figure 10.17 makes this clear.

Figure 10.18 shows how latitude relates to temperature. The world is divided into climate zones based on yearly temperature averages. Temperatures are highest in the latitudes nearest the equator, in the *tropical climate zone* (at sea level). In the tropical climate zone, temperature varies little throughout the year and averages higher than 18°C (or 64°F) even in the coldest months. At the middle latitudes, in the *temperate climate zone*, temperatures are neither very

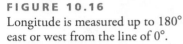
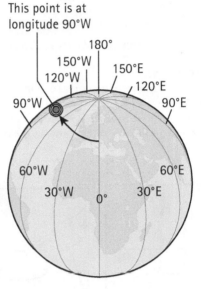

FIGURE 10.16
Longitude is measured up to 180° east or west from the line of 0°.

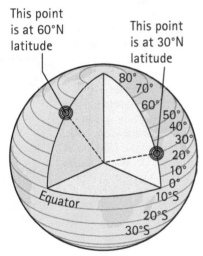

FIGURE 10.17
Latitude is a degree measurement that tells the angle between the center of Earth, the equator, and any particular point on Earth's surface.

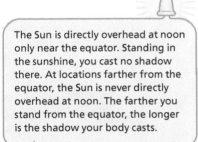

The Sun is directly overhead at noon only near the equator. Standing in the sunshine, you cast no shadow there. At locations farther from the equator, the Sun is never directly overhead at noon. The farther you stand from the equator, the longer is the shadow your body casts.

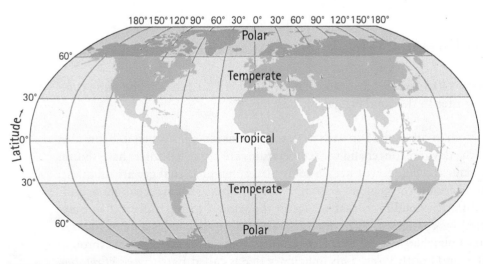

FIGURE 10.18
Yearly average temperatures vary in Earth's principal climate zones.

(a)

(b)

(c)

FIGURE 10.19
(a) Tropical rainforests, such as this one in Trinidad, are located in the tropical climate zone. (b) Temperate grasslands, such as the Oklahoma prairie, are found in the temperate climate zone. (c) The tundra is located in the polar climate zone. Here, within the Arctic Circle, grasses and tough shrubs grow in the frozen soil.

FIGURE 10.20
This simple demonstration shows why temperature depends on the angle at which the Sun's rays strike Earth.
(a) When the flashlight is held directly above at a right angle to the surface, the beam of light produces a bright circle. (b) When the light is held at an angle, the light beam elongates and forms an oval. The same amount of light energy as before is spread out over a larger area, so its intensity is reduced. High noon in equatorial regions is like a vertically held flashlight. High noon at higher latitudes is like the flashlight held at an angle.

hot nor very cold. Average monthly temperatures vary between 10°C and 18°C (between 50°F and 64°F) throughout the year, with much seasonal variation. The *polar climate zone* is located at high latitudes. Monthly temperatures remain lower than 10°C (50°F) there even in the warmest months.

Why does the temperature depend on latitude? Latitude affects temperature because the Sun's rays strike different latitudes at different angles. While the Sun's rays strike regions near the equator dead-on perpendicularly, the rays hit polar latitudes at a steep angle. Figure 10.20 demonstrates this. As you can see, when rays of light strike a surface at right angles, the rays strike the smallest possible area—they are most concentrated. That area has maximum **solar intensity**, or solar radiation per area. Equatorial regions have high temperatures because they experience maximum solar intensity. Solar intensity is at a minimum at the polar latitudes, so they are cold places.

LEARNING OBJECTIVE
In words and diagrams, show how Earth's tilted axis of rotation produces the seasons.

10.4 Earth's Tilted Axis—The Seasons

EXPLAIN THIS Why is it summer in the northern latitudes at the same time that it's winter in the southern latitudes?

As Earth orbits the Sun each year, the seasons change. When it is summer, the days are longer and the temperatures are higher. Winters have shorter days and colder weather. In some places, seasonal changes are dramatic; in other locations, the changes are mild. Why do these seasonal changes occur?

The different conditions that we see in the winter, spring, fall, and summer are caused by changes in solar intensity. The tilting of Earth's axis of rotation comes into play here. Recall that Earth rotates about an imaginary line through the North and South Poles. This imaginary line is called Earth's *axis of rotation* (Figure 10.21). The axis is not straight up and down. Instead, it is tilted at an

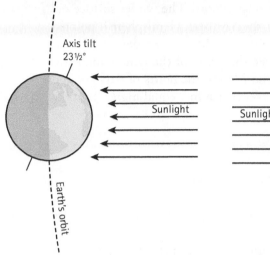

FIGURE 10.21
Earth spins about its axis of rotation while it orbits the Sun. The axis of rotation is not straight up and down—instead, it is tilted at an angle of $23\frac{1}{2}°$. When it is summer in the Northern Hemisphere, the Northern Hemisphere tilts toward the Sun.

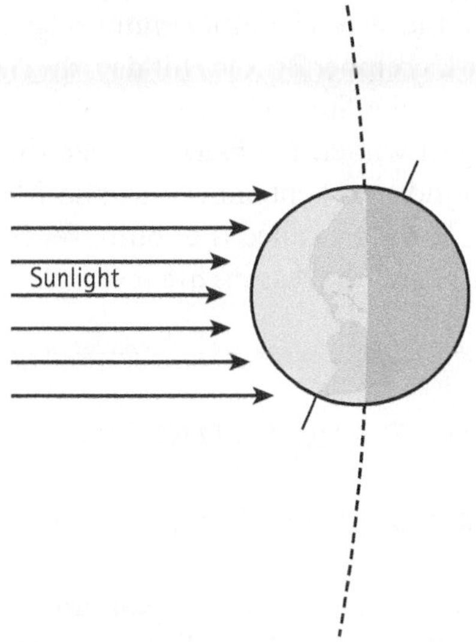

FIGURE 10.22
When it is winter in the Northern Hemisphere, the Northern Hemisphere tilts away from the Sun. In the winter, it gets dark earlier and the weather is cooler.

angle of $23\frac{1}{2}°$. Because Earth's axis is tilted, different points on Earth face the Sun differently as Earth travels around the Sun.

During the summer in the Northern Hemisphere, the Northern Hemisphere is tilted toward the Sun. You can see this in Figure 10.21. In the winter, the Northern Hemisphere is tilted away from the Sun (Figure 10.22). The hemisphere that is tilted toward the Sun receives the Sun's energy more directly and has longer days. This combination of more direct rays and longer days creates the warmth of summer.

As Figure 10.23 shows, the summer solstice occurs in the Northern Hemisphere on or about June 21. This is the longest day of the year as well as the first day of summer. On this day, the Northern Hemisphere is pointed directly

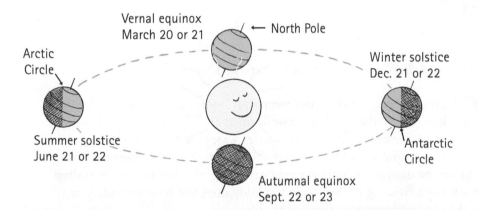

FIGURE 10.23
The tilt of Earth and the corresponding differences in the intensity of solar energy produce the yearly cycle of the seasons. Earth follows an elliptical (oval) path around the Sun and is farthest from the Sun when the Northern Hemisphere experiences summer. So, the angle of the Sun's rays, not the distance from the Sun, is most responsible for Earth's surface temperatures.

MasteringPhysics°
TUTORIAL: Seasons

toward the Sun, and it receives maximum solar energy. The winter solstice occurs on or about December 21. On this day, the Northern Hemisphere is pointed directly away from the Sun. The winter solstice is the shortest day of the year and the first day of winter. Halfway between the peaks of the winter and summer solstice, around mid-September and mid-March, the hours of daylight and night are equal. These are called the equinoxes (Latin for "equal nights"). In the Southern Hemisphere, the seasons are reversed.

LEARNING OBJECTIVE
Understand what wind is and how it relates to air pressure.

10.5 Flow of the Atmosphere—Wind

EXPLAIN THIS How is wind like air rushing from a tire that has a leak in it?

I f you have ever seen a tire go flat, you probably noticed the hissing sound of air escaping. If your hand was in front of the tire, you also felt air rushing out of the tire. Air moves naturally from a region of high pressure to a region of low pressure. A punctured tire is just one example of this. A popped balloon is another example. Wind is a third example of the same phenomenon. **Wind** is air flowing horizontally from a region of high pressure to a region of lower pressure.

Winds are caused by differences in air pressure, and bigger differences in air pressure produce stronger, faster winds. A gentle breeze, one that just rustles the grass, is air moving at 10–15 km/h. A wind strong enough to rattle power lines moves at 40–50 km/h. A hurricane blows more than 120 km/h. Winds are named according to the direction from which they blow, so a "30-km/h northwesterly wind" blows from the northwest at a speed of 30 km/h.

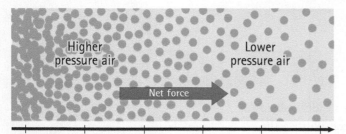

1010 mb	1008 mb	1006 mb	1004 mb	1002 mb	1000 mb

FIGURE 10.24
Air moves from a region of higher pressure to a region of lower pressure.

LEARNING OBJECTIVE
Obtain and interpret the data provided on a wind chill chart.

 Integrated Science 26C
BIOLOGY

Wind Chill

EXPLAIN THIS Explain why wind makes you feel cooler.

W arm air that transfers away from our bodies is held in place by our hair and clothes. This layer of warmed air keeps us warm. However, wind constantly blows this layer of warm air away. In the summer, the wind keeps us cool and this is a good thing. But, if it's cold outside, losing body heat can be dangerous. Extreme cold can bring on frostbite and hypothermia. Death from freezing occurs when the body does not have enough heat to perform the chemical reactions that sustain life.

The National Weather Service publishes a Wind Chill Index, a table that shows how air temperature and wind combine to produce a temperature that your body actually feels. A version of the Wind Chill Index is shown in Figure 10.25.

Temperature (°F)																	
Calm	**40**	**35**	**30**	**25**	**20**	**15**	**10**	**5**	**0**	**-5**	**-10**	**-15**	**-20**	**-25**	**-30**	**-35**	**-40**	**-45**
5	36	31	25	19	13	7	1	-5	-11	-16	-22	-28	-34	-40	-46	-52	-57	-63
10	34	27	21	15	9	3	-4	-10	-16	-22	-28	-35	-41	-47	-53	-59	-66	-72
15	32	25	19	13	6	0	-7	-13	-19	-26	-32	-39	-45	-51	-58	-64	-71	-77
20	30	24	17	11	4	-2	-9	-15	-22	-29	-35	-42	-48	-55	-61	-68	-74	-81
25	29	23	16	9	3	-4	-11	-17	-24	-31	-37	-44	-51	-58	-64	-71	-78	-84
30	28	22	15	8	1	-5	-12	-19	-26	-33	-39	-46	-53	-60	-67	-73	-80	-87
35	28	21	14	7	0	-7	-14	-21	-27	-34	-41	-48	-55	-62	-69	-76	-82	-89
40	27	20	13	6	-1	-8	-15	-22	-29	-36	-43	-50	-57	-64	-71	-78	-84	-91
45	26	19	12	5	-2	-9	-16	-23	-30	-37	-44	-51	-58	-65	-72	-79	-86	-93
50	26	19	12	4	-3	-10	-17	-24	-31	-38	-45	-52	-60	-67	-74	-81	-88	-95
55	25	18	11	4	-3	-11	-18	-25	-32	-39	-46	-54	-61	-68	-75	-82	-89	-97
60	25	17	10	3	-4	-11	-19	-26	-33	-40	-48	-55	-62	-69	-76	-84	-91	-98

Wind (mph)

Frostbite Times   ☐ 30 minutes   ☐ 10 minutes   ☐ 5 minutes

FIGURE 10.25
A wind chill chart. Wind speed and air temperature make the air feel colder to our bodies.

CHECK YOURSELF
1. (a) If it is 40°F and there is a gentle, 5-mi/h breeze, what is the effective temperature your body experiences? (b) If the wind is blowing at 35 mi/h and it is 40°F, what is the effective temperature?
2. How long will it take for you to develop frostbite if it is 5°F and the wind is blowing at 30 mi/h?

CHECK YOUR ANSWERS
1. (a) 36°F; (b) 28°F
2. 30 min

10.6 Local and Global Wind Patterns

LEARNING OBJECTIVE
Describe how and why temperature differences between polar and equatorial latitudes move the atmosphere.

EXPLAIN THIS Why do land breezes occur at night and sea breezes occur during the day?

There are two types of winds: *local winds* and *global winds*. Pressure differences over a small region create local winds. These winds blow short distances, and they can blow in any direction. Global winds, on the other hand, are part of a huge pattern of air circulation around the globe. Global winds blow consistently from the same direction. The wind where you live is a combination of local and global wind patterns.

Local Winds

Local temperature differences create wind where the geography varies—for example, where land meets water or where mountains meet valleys. Consider land and sea breezes (Figure 10.26). During the day, the land warms faster than the ocean because land has a lower specific heat capacity (specific heat capacity is "thermal inertia"—the resistance to a change in temperature). The hot air over the warmed land rises, creating an area of lower air pressure. The cooler,

During the day, a gentle, warm breeze moves from a valley floor upslope to mountain peaks. At night, a chilly breeze blows down the mountains as cold air sinks into the valley. The shapes of land features can produce local winds.

FIGURE 10.26
(a) Sea breeze. During the day, warm air above land rises, and cooler air moves in to replace it. (b) Land breeze. At night, the direction of airflow is reversed because then the water is warmer than the land.

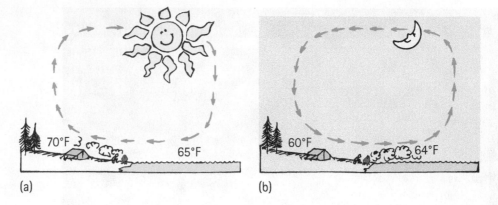

70°F   65°F

(a)

60°F   64°F

(b)

higher-pressure air from over the ocean then blows from the sea to the land. This is a *sea breeze*. But at night, the land cools off faster than the sea, again because of its lower specific heat capacity relative to water. Cooler air descends over the land and creates an area of higher pressure. Wind blows from the land to the sea. This is a *land breeze*. You may have experienced a refreshing sea breeze if you have spent time along the coast in the summer, or even near the shores of large lakes.

Global Winds

UNIFYING CONCEPT

● **Convection**
Section 6.9

All winds are created by differences in air pressure. Global winds are produced by planet-scale pressure differences that occur because of unequal heating of Earth at the equator and poles. At equatorial latitudes, Earth absorbs the Sun's rays directly. Air is warmed efficiently there, and it rises. The air flows toward the cooler poles but sinks back to Earth when it becomes too cold and dense to stay aloft. This creates an area of low pressure near the equator. At the poles, sinking cold air creates areas of high pressure. The unequal pressure causes the air to rise and sink, circulating in global patterns called *wind belts*. These wind belts are convection cells, and they move air in predictable patterns. As Figure 10.27 shows, there are six major convection cells: between the equator and latitudes of 30° north and south, between 30° and 60° north and south, and between 60° north and south and the poles. Global winds are the streams of horizontally moving air within these convection cells. Like land and sea breezes, global winds affect temperature patterns by transporting warming or cooling air.

The global winds that flow between 0° and 30° latitude are called the *trade winds*. The trade winds are named for their role in propelling trading ships centuries ago. The winds between the equator and 30°N latitude are called the *northeast trade winds* because European sailing ships used them as they traveled toward the New World and the coast of the British Colonies. Then the sailors caught the global winds called the "westerlies" back to Europe. The *westerlies*, as Figure 10.28 shows, blow from west to east from 30° to 60° latitudes. Note that winds are named according to the direction from which they blow. The *easterlies*

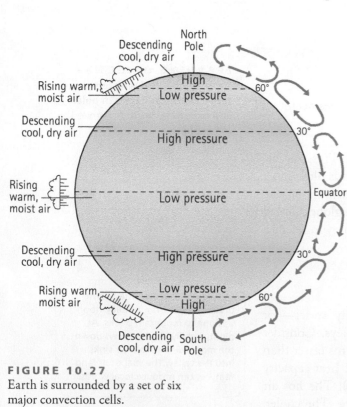

FIGURE 10.27
Earth is surrounded by a set of six major convection cells.

blow from east to west at the polar latitudes between 60° and 90° north and south.

Near the equator, where the trade winds die, there is a zone of still air. Sailors of long ago cursed the equatorial seas as their ships stalled for lack of wind, and they named the area the *doldrums*. Sailors were also frequently stalled in the calm air that occurs where convection cells meet at 30° north and south latitudes. According to legend, as food and water supplies dwindled, horses on board were either eaten or cast overboard to conserve fresh water. As a result, these regions became known as the *horse latitudes*.

There is another type of global wind—*jet streams*. Jet streams are narrow belts of high-speed wind that blow in the upper troposphere and lower stratosphere. Jet streams don't follow consistent paths around Earth as other global winds do. Instead, their altitude and latitude vary. Jet streams move very fast. In fact, jet streams were discovered by World War II pilots of high-altitude military aircraft. The pilots observed that they weren't flying forward because they were flying against winds blowing just as fast in the opposite direction!

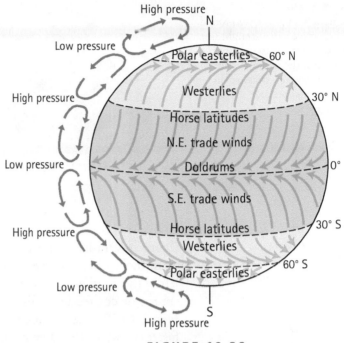

FIGURE 10.28
Note the locations of the major global winds: the trade winds, the westerlies, and the easterlies.

CHECK YOURSELF
1. How are land and sea breezes alike? How are they different?
2. A migrating bird flies west to east across the United States and then back again. Which trip is easier for the bird? Why?

CHECK YOUR ANSWERS
1. Both land breezes and sea breezes are local winds that occur where land is next to a large body of water. They are different in that a sea breeze blows from the sea to the land during the day, and a land breeze blows from the land to the sea at night.
2. The westerlies blow from west to east across the United States. This helps the bird when it flies from west to east but hinders the bird when it flies from east to west.

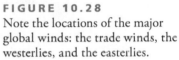

Why does Earth's atmosphere break up into six convection cells, instead of four, or nine, or 101? The number depends on how fast a planet rotates. Venus rotates slowly and has only two cells in each of its hemispheres. If Earth were to spin faster, like Jupiter, we would experience more air-circulation cells and faster mixing of our atmosphere.

 Integrated Science 26D
PHYSICS

The Coriolis Effect

LEARNING OBJECTIVE
Describe the pattern of global air circulation that arises due to the Coriolis effect.

EXPLAIN THIS Why do global winds appear to blow along curved paths when in fact the air molecules that make them up are traveling in straight-line paths?

If Earth didn't rotate, the global winds would blow straight in a north–south direction. High-altitude winds would blow from the equator to the poles, while low-altitude winds would blow from the poles back to the equator.

FIGURE 10.29
(a) On the nonrotating merry-go-round, a thrown ball travels in a straight line. (b) On the counterclockwise-rotating merry-go-round, the ball moves in a straight line. However, because the merry-go-round is rotating, the ball appears to move to the right.

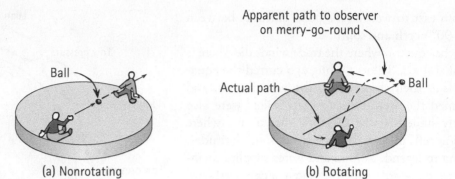

(a) Nonrotating   (b) Rotating

UNIFYING CONCEPT

● *Newton's First Law*
  Section 3.1

But this is not what happens because Earth *does* rotate. The **Coriolis effect** ("core-ee-OH-lis") is the tendency of moving bodies not attached to Earth (such as air molecules) to move to their right in the Northern Hemisphere and to their left in the Southern Hemisphere. Because of the Coriolis effect, air in the planet's six major convection cells turns in the directions indicated by the arrows in Figure 10.28. The Coriolis effect varies according to the speed of the wind: The faster the wind, the more it appears to turn.

To see how the Coriolis effect works, consider an analogy. Think of Earth as a large merry-go-round rotating in a counterclockwise direction (in the same direction Earth spins, as viewed from the North Pole). You and a friend are playing catch on this merry-go-round. When you throw the ball to your friend, the circular movement of the merry-go-round affects the direction the ball appears to travel. Although the ball really travels in a straight-line path, it appears to curve to the right, as shown in Figure 10.29.

CHECK YOURSELF

1. Why don't global winds flow in a straight direction between the equator and poles?
2. Which way does wind appear to turn in the Northern Hemisphere? In the Southern Hemisphere?

CHECK YOUR ANSWERS

1. Winds turn because moving air molecules are subject to the Coriolis effect. Molecules of air are not attached to Earth. Because Earth rotates beneath them, air molecules turn relative to Earth.
2. In the Northern Hemisphere, wind appears to turn to the right. In the Southern Hemisphere, it appears to turn to the left.

LEARNING OBJECTIVE
Describe how global winds create surface currents.

10.7 Ocean Currents Distribute Heat

EXPLAIN THIS How does warm ocean water from the equator warm up the air temperature in Norway and Great Britain?

In addition to latitude, elevation, atmospheric gases, and wind effects, another important factor in atmospheric temperature is ocean currents.

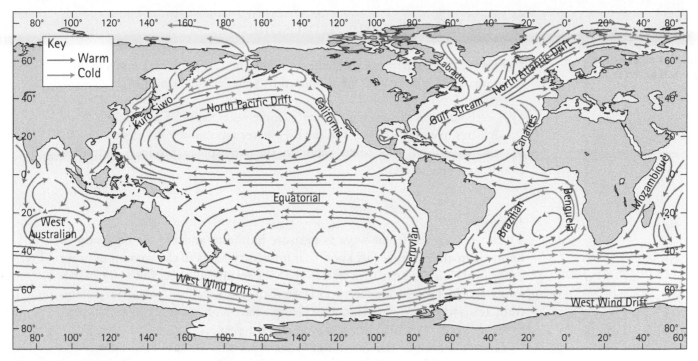

FIGURE 10.30
The ocean's major surface currents, shown by the arrows, closely match the pattern of global winds shown in Figure 10.31, except in regions where landmasses disrupt the water's flow.

Ocean water, like the fluid atmosphere, mixes and circulates. The oceans contain *currents*, streams of water that move relative to the larger ocean. **Surface currents** are usually created by global winds pushing water in the directions they blow. Compare Figure 10.30 closely with Figure 10.31. Notice that the surface currents match up quite well with the global winds if you take into account the interference of landmasses.

Surface currents, like the global winds, are turned and twisted along their path by Earth's rotation. Because of the Coriolis effect and other factors, surface water currents tend to form giant circular flow patterns called *gyres* (Figure 10.31).

Surface currents play a vital role in redistributing heat. The uneven heating of Earth's surface warms equatorial waters but leaves polar waters chilly. Surface currents redistribute heat by transporting waters far from their source. This circulation of the ocean affects not only water temperature but also atmospheric temperature. Consider the example of the Gulf Stream and how it warms Northern Europe.

Heat is transported in the North Atlantic Ocean as warm equatorial water flows westward into and around the Gulf of Mexico, then northward along the eastern coast of the United States. This warm-water current is called the *Gulf Stream*. As the Gulf Stream flows northward along the eastern coast of North America, global winds steer it toward Europe. When this warm water reaches the coasts of Great Britain and Norway, it cools and releases heat energy to the air. The heated air is carried by westerly winds over the lands of Great Britain and Norway.*

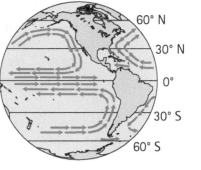

FIGURE 10.31
The world's major surface currents.

---

* Jet streams high in the atmosphere are also a major contributor to the warming of Europe.

LEARNING OBJECTIVE
Describe how the evaporation
and condensation of water
produce weather conditions.

10.8 Water in the Atmosphere

EXPLAIN THIS There are six elements of weather. Identify and describe the three weather elements that are produced by water in the atmosphere.

All air, even the driest air, contains some water vapor. *Water vapor* is water in the gaseous phase. You can't see water vapor, but you can feel and see its effects. The water vapor in the atmosphere produces humidity, clouds, and precipitation.

Humidity

There are a few different ways to measure humidity and it's not necessary to know them all. For now, just know that **humidity** refers to the amount of water vapor in the air. You can't see water vapor; it's an invisible gas. But you can certainly feel it. Humid weather is characteristic of Hawaii all year. Many states from Texas to New York to Illinois to Georgia have high humidity in the summer time. California is relatively dry throughout the year.

There is a limit to the amount of water vapor that air can hold. How much water vapor resides in air depends on the air's temperature. As the air temperature rises, the volume of the water vapor that it can hold increases too. That's why Earth's most humid locations are in the tropics and the dryest air is in the cold polar regions. Table 10.2 shows exactly how much air vapor can reside in air at various temperatures.

Weather reports describe humidity in terms of relative humidity. **Relative humidity** is the ratio of the amount of water vapor currently in the air to the largest amount of water vapor that it is possible for the air to hold at that temperature. You could say that relative humidity is a measurement of how full of water vapor the air is at a given temperature. Stated as an equation,

$$\text{Relative humidity} = \left(\frac{\text{water-vapor content}}{\text{water-vapor capacity}} \right) \times 100\%$$

Thus, if air contains 7 grams of water on a 25°C day, the relative humidity is expressed as 7/14, or 50%, because the water content of the air is half the amount that it can hold at a temperature of 25°C. Make sense?

The relative humidity of the air changes, of course, if the amount of water vapor in it changes or if the air's temperature changes. For instance, if the air temperature rises from 25°C to 40°C but 7 g of water vapor remains in the

TABLE 10.2	MAXIMUM AMOUNT OF WATER VAPOR THAT A 1-KG MASS OF AIR CAN HOLD AT DIFFERENT TEMPERATURES
Temperature (°C)	Grams of Water Vapor per kg of Air
−30	0.3
−20	0.75
−10	2
7	3.5
20	14
30	26.5
40	47

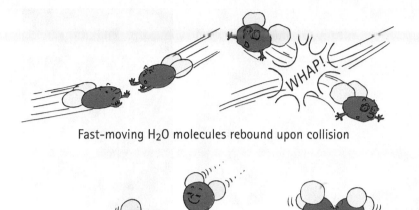

Fast-moving H₂O molecules rebound upon collision

Slow-moving H₂O molecules condense upon collision

FIGURE 10.32
Condensation of water molecules. Condensation occurs when water vapor reaches its dew point. At this temperature, the water molecules are moving slowly enough that they condense, rather than rebound, upon impact.

air, then the relative humidity decreases to $(7 \text{ g}/26.7 \text{ g}) \times 100\% = 26\%$ even though the actual quantity of water vapor in the air is unchanged.

When air contains as much water as it can possibly hold, the air is *saturated*. This is equivalent to saying that saturated air has 100% relative humidity. As an air mass cools, it can hold less and less water vapor before becoming saturated. If it cools down enough, the air mass reaches a point at which the water vapor present is the amount required to saturate the air at the lower temperature. This temperature, the temperature at which saturation occurs, is the **dew point**. Condensation occurs when the dew point is reached. Suppose, for example, that a certain mass of unsaturated air at 30°C is cooled to 15°C and that the air is saturated at that temperature. The dew point of this air is then 15°C; if the air is cooled further, its capacity for holding water vapor would be exceeded and the excess vapor would condense (Figure 10.32).

Water vapor condenses high in the atmosphere to form clouds. It condenses close to the ground as well. When condensation in the air occurs near Earth's surface, we call it *dew*, *frost*, or *fog*. On cool, clear nights, objects near the ground cool down more rapidly than the surrounding air. As the air cools to its dew point, it cannot hold as much water vapor as it could when it was warmer. Water from the now-saturated air condenses on any available surface—a twig, a blade of grass, or the windshield of a car. We often call this type of condensation early-morning dew. When the dew point is at or below freezing, we have frost. When a large mass of air cools to its dew point, its relative humidity approaches 100%. And this produces a cloud. This usually happens high in the atmosphere where the air is cold and so can't hold much water vapor. But it can also happen closer to the ground—and then we have *fog* (Figure 10.33).

When perspiration evaporates from your skin, your perspiration takes the energy it needs to change state from liquid to gas from your skin. This energy, water's *latent heat of vaporization*, thus leaves your body, and you become cooler as a result. In humid weather, perspiration doesn't cool you as well as it does in dry air because evaporation is slowed. This is why humid air feels so much hotter than dry air of the same temperature.

Clouds

As air rises, it expands and cools. As the air cools, water molecules move more slowly and condensation occurs. If there are larger and slower-moving particles or

(a)

(b)

(c)

(d)

FIGURE 10.33
Water vapor condenses from a mass of air when the air's dew point is exceeded. This results in the formation of (a) clouds, (b) fog, (c) dew, or (d) frost.

ions present in the air, water vapor condenses on these particles, and this creates a **cloud**—a visible collection of minute water droplets or tiny ice crystals.

In 1803, British weather observer Luke Howard was the first to classify clouds according to their shapes. He recognized three cloud forms: *cirrus* (Latin for "curl"); *cumulus* (L., "piled up"); and *stratus* (L., "spread out") (Figure 10.34). If you have searched for these basic shapes in the sky, however, you know that clouds do not usually come in these simple forms; instead, they usually occur as composites of these forms. For this reason, Howard's simple classification has been modified so that clouds are generally classified by their form as well as their altitude. This results in ten basic cloud types, each of which belongs to one of the four major cloud groups (Table 10.3).

High clouds form at altitudes above 6000 meters and are denoted by the prefix *cirro-*. The air at this elevation is quite cold and dry, so clouds this high are made up almost entirely of ice crystals. The most common high clouds are *cirrus* clouds, which are blown by strong, high-altitude winds into their classic wispy shapes, such as the "mare's tail" and "artist's brush." *Cirrocumulus* clouds are arrays of rounded white puffs that rarely cover more than a small patch of the sky (Figure 10.35a). Small ripples and a wavy appearance make the cirrocumulus

(a) (b) (c)

FIGURE 10.34
Clouds classified by shape: (a) "wispy" cirrus clouds, (b) "piled-up" cumulus clouds, and (c) "spread-out" stratus clouds.

TABLE 10.3	THE FOUR MAJOR CLOUD GROUPS		
1. High Clouds (above 6000 m)	**2. Middle Clouds** (2000–6000 m)	**3. Low Clouds** (below 2000 m)	**4. Clouds of** Vertical Development
Cirrus	Altostratus	Stratus	Cumulus
Cirrostratus	Altocumulus	Stratocumulus	Cumulonimbus
Cirrocumulus	Nimbostratus		

clouds look like the scaled body of a mackerel. Hence, cirrocumulus clouds make up what is often referred to as a "mackerel sky." Cirrus clouds usually indicate fair weather.

Middle clouds are denoted by the prefix *alto-*. They are made up of water droplets and, when temperature allows, ice crystals. *Altostratus* clouds are gray to blue-gray, and they often cover the sky for hundreds of square kilometers (Figure 10.35b). Altostratus clouds are often so thick that they diffuse incoming sunlight to the extent that objects on the ground don't produce shadows. Altostratus clouds often form before a storm. So, if you can't see your shadow when you're going on a picnic, cancel!

Low clouds are most often composed of water droplets, but they can contain ice crystals in colder climates. *Stratus* clouds tend to be the lowest of the low clouds. They are uniformly gray, and they cover the whole sky, often resembling a high fog. Stratus clouds are not associated with falling precipitation, but they sometimes generate a light drizzle or mist. *Nimbostratus* clouds are dark and foreboding (Figure 10.35c). They are a wet-looking cloud layer associated with rain and snow.

Clouds of vertical development do not fit into any of the three height categories. These clouds typically have their bases at low altitudes, but they reach up into the middle or high altitudes. Although cumulus clouds are fair-weather clouds, they are called "clouds of vertical development" because they can grow dramatically. Vertically moving air currents in them can produce a towering cloud with an anvil head—a *cumulonimbus* cloud (Figure 10.35d). Cumulonimbus clouds, popularly called "thunderheads," may produce heavy rain showers, thunder and lightning, and hail.

(a)   (b)   (c)   (d)

FIGURE 10.35
Clouds from each of the major cloud groups: (a) cirrocumulus, (b) altostratus, (c) nimbostratus, and (d) cumulonimbus.

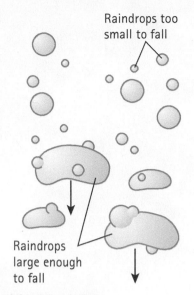

Raindrops too small to fall

Raindrops large enough to fall

FIGURE 10.36
Raindrops form when tiny water droplets in clouds collide and join together. Before a raindrop falls, it must grow to at least 100 times the size of average water droplets in clouds.

FIGURE 10.37
Snowflakes are built of many microscopic ice crystals.

Precipitation

Precipitation is water in the liquid or solid phase that returns to Earth's surface from the atmosphere. It is an essential part of the water cycle, which means that precipitation controls everything from the weathering of rock to the sustenance of Earth's organisms. Precipitation occurs as snow and rain, but there are other less common forms too: mist, drizzle, hail, freezing rain, and sleet (in the form of solid ice crystals). Mist and drizzle generally fall from stratus clouds. Rain falls from nimbostratus and cumulonimbus clouds. Air temperature controls what kind of precipitation occurs.

Rain, the most common kind of precipitation, is liquid water that falls from clouds through the air at above-freezing temperature. Rain falls when the tiny water droplets in clouds collide and join together, becoming so big and heavy that they can no longer stay suspended in the air (Figure 10.36).

Here's a challenge question: If clouds are made of water droplets and ice crystals, which are denser than air, why don't we see them sinking to the ground? The gravitational force pulling a droplet down *is* enough to make it fall. So, why don't all droplets in clouds fall to the ground? The answer has to do with updrafts—rising air currents. A typical cumulus cloud has an updraft speed of at least 1 meter per second, which is faster than the droplet can fall. Small droplets don't fall to Earth because they are supported by upward-rising air. Raindrops, on the other hand, are huge compared with typical cloud droplets. A drop of rain big enough to reach the ground contains about a million times more water than a cloud droplet. Raindrops fall faster than most updrafts can push upward.

Snow is composed of tiny, six-sided ice crystals. It forms when water vapor goes directly to the solid state at temperatures below freezing. Snowflakes grow into large and fanciful shapes by bumping into one another as they fall. When the air is very cold, snow is usually light and fluffy. When the air is near freezing, snow is sticky and wet. All snowflakes are six-sided, like the ice crystals from which they form.

Hail is sometimes very damaging. Hail forms only in cumulonimbus, or thunder, clouds. Particles of hail are *hailstones*—layered balls of ice. Hailstones form when drops of water freeze in a cloud but strong upward air currents keep them aloft for a prolonged time. As more drops of water collide with the hailstone and freeze, new layers are added on. Hailstones as big as golf balls can easily dent cars and hurt people they hit!

(a)

(b)

FIGURE 10.38
(a) Hail damage. (b) Hailstones are made up of layers of ice.

CHECK YOURSELF

1. Why is air in the tropics more humid than arctic air?
2. Why don't clouds fall to the ground?
3. In what way are snowflakes similar in shape to the ice crystals they contain?

CHECK YOUR ANSWERS

1. Tropical air is often humid because it contains water that has evaporated from warm equatorial waters. Arctic air is drier because there is less evaporation in cold Arctic air.
2. Rising air keeps clouds from falling. (When clouds are at ground level, we call them fog.)
3. Both the flakes and the crystals have six sides.

10.9 Changing Weather—Air Masses, Fronts, and Cyclones

LEARNING OBJECTIVE
Compare and contrast: cyclones versus anticyclones, warm fronts versus cold fronts, and maritime versus continental air masses.

EXPLAIN THIS Describe what happens when a cold air mass meets a warm air mass.

When a meteorologist says a high-pressure system is moving to your area, what kind of weather can you expect? Is it time to grab an umbrella? To understand changing weather and weather forecasts, you need to know about the movement of *air masses*, including *fronts* and *cyclones*.

Air Masses

An **air mass** is a large pool of air that has similar temperature and moisture characteristics throughout. Air masses form when a huge body of air stays in one place for a long enough time to take on the properties of that region. For example, an air mass forming over the coast of Florida will be warm and humid because this region is warm and wet. Air masses aren't completely stationary, however, because global winds drive them. As they move, they carry their weather conditions with them. As this occurs, the properties of an air mass change as it interacts with new environments.

Air masses are classified according to the latitude over which they form and whether they form over land or water. Figure 10.39 shows the air masses that have the biggest influence on weather in North America. Each air mass is represented by a two-letter code. The first letter represents moisture content, and the second letter represents temperature. Thus, the air mass developing over Florida is mT for *maritime tropical*. Maritime tropical air masses bring moist warm air. Air masses labeled (cP) are *continental polar* air masses. These carry cold, dry air from Alaska and Canada.

Fronts

Recall the directions of global winds from Section 26.6. Remember that convection cells move warm air away from the equator toward the poles; cold air moves

UNIFYING CONCEPT
● *Convection*
Section 6.9

FIGURE 10.39
The air masses that affect weather in North America, the regions they form over, and their typical directions of travel. Air masses keep their temperature and moisture characteristics as they move.

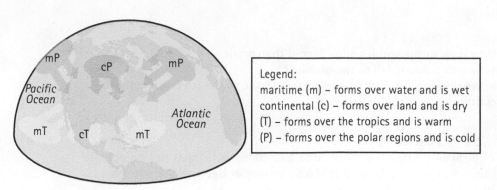

Legend:
maritime (m) – forms over water and is wet
continental (c) – forms over land and is dry
(T) – forms over the tropics and is warm
(P) – forms over the polar regions and is cold

UNIFYING CONCEPT

● *Density*
Section 2.3

from the poles to the equator. These movements set up global wind patterns that move air masses.

Just as global winds collide in the middle latitudes, so do air masses. And when air masses collide, they don't readily mix. Instead, air masses meet at a boundary that is called a *weather front*, or simply a **front**.

At a front, the less dense, warmer air mass flows upward over the denser, cooler air. The warmer air always rises vertically above the cooler air, but the horizontal movements of the air masses vary. Sometimes, the colder, denser air mass advances into and displaces a warm air mass. In this case, the contact zone between the air masses is called a *cold front* (Figure 10.40). But warm air can move into territory occupied by a cold air mass instead. In this case, the zone of contact is called a *warm front* (Figure 10.41). If neither of the air masses is moving, the contact zone is called a *stationary front*. An *occluded front* occurs when fast-moving cold air forces warm air up and traps it between two cold air masses. The warm air starts to cool and water vapor condenses. At the front—a region perhaps a few kilometers wide—there are often clouds, rain, winds, and storms.

You can generally predict that a cold front is moving in if you observe high cirrus clouds followed by alto and then stratus clouds, a shift in wind direction, and a drop in air pressure. As cold air moves into and displaces a warm air mass at the cold front, the warm air is forced upward, rises, and cools. If it is moist enough, the rising air can condense to form cumulonimbus clouds that produce thunderstorms with heavy showers and gusty winds. After the cold front passes, the lifted warm air cools and sinks, so pressure rises, and the rain stops. Except for a few fair-weather cumulus clouds, the skies clear and there is calm after the storm.

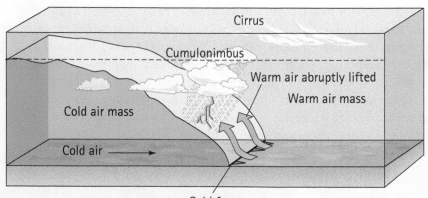

FIGURE 10.40
A cold front forms when a cold air mass moves into a warm air mass. The cold air forces the warm air upward, where it condenses to form clouds.

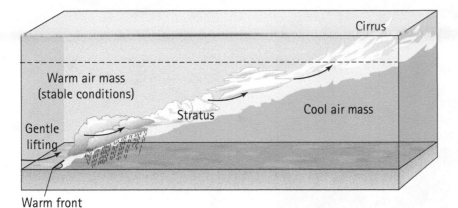

FIGURE 10.41
A warm front forms when a warm air mass moves into and displaces a cold air mass. The less-dense, warmer air rides up and over the colder, denser air.

A warm front may be coming if you see cirrus clouds in the sky followed by stratus clouds. A warm front separates an advancing mass of warm air from colder air ahead. As with a cold front, the different densities of cold and warm air discourage mixing of air masses so the warm air flows upward above the cold air mass. As the warm air rises and cools, water vapor in it may reach its dew point. Condensation and clouds ensue with light drizzle or fog along the front in summer and sleet at the front in the winter. Behind the front, the air is warm and the clouds scatter.

MasteringPhysics®
ACTIVITY: Cold Front
ACTIVITY: Warm Front

UNIFYING CONCEPT

● *Density*
Section 2.3

Cyclones

Air masses belong to gigantic *weather systems*, organized systems of moving air spanning a thousand or more square kilometers. Weather systems are organized around a center of either high pressure or low pressure.

A system of low pressure is called a **cyclone** (a *low-pressure system* or simply a *low*). Cyclones are associated with rough weather (Figure 10.42). A cyclone's center is the region of lowest pressure, so air flows into it in a spiral, but then the air is forced upward.

The rising air can produce clouds and precipitation. In the summer, cyclones often bring rain and thunderstorms. In the winter, thunderstorms and snow are

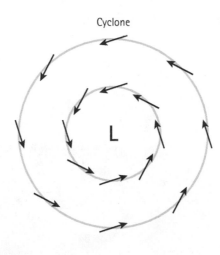

FIGURE 10.42
(a) A satellite image of a cyclone.
(b) In the Northern Hemisphere, winds blow counterclockwise into the cyclone. Air forced in and upward brings rough weather.

(a)   (b)

FIGURE 10.43
(a) A satellite image of an anticyclone. (b) In the Northern Hemisphere, winds blow clockwise away from the anticyclone. Anticyclones, or high-pressure systems, are associated with fair weather.

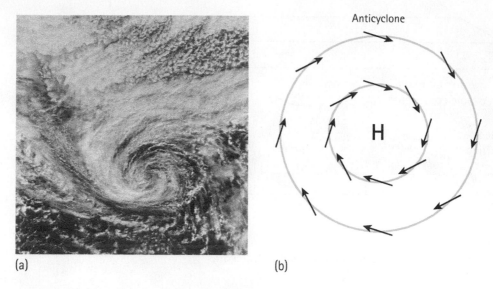

(a)   (b)

likely. Because of the Coriolis effect, the winds in a cyclone move counterclockwise in the Northern Hemisphere and clockwise in the Southern Hemisphere.

An **anticyclone** (a *high-pressure system* or simply a *high*) is an area of high pressure (Figure 10.43). Air moves from high pressure to low pressure, so the air moves outward from an anticyclone as well as downward. This sinking motion leads to generally fair skies and no precipitation near the high. (Does this make sense to you? Remember that clouds form where warm, moist air *rises* then condenses; *sinking* air is not the recipe for clouds and storms.) The Coriolis effect turns the moving air around a high-pressure center so that anticyclonic winds blow clockwise around a high in the Northern Hemisphere and counterclockwise around a high in the Southern Hemisphere.

Meteorologists plot the positions of fronts and pressure systems on weather maps to predict the weather (Figure 10.44). On a weather map, a high-pressure system is denoted with an *H*, and a low-pressure system is denoted with an *L*. The surface position of a warm front is shown as a line with semicircles on the side of cooler air. The surface position of a cold front is denoted by a line with triangles extending into the region of warmer air.

The weather map here, like the ones you see on television, is highly simplified. Weather forecasters build much more complex maps with computers in order to plot weather systems and calculate how fast the systems are moving. After all, it helps everyone—from farmers to astronauts—to know the weather!

FIGURE 10.44
Weather maps show pressure systems and fronts. In this weather map, a cold front moves southward and a warm front moves eastward.

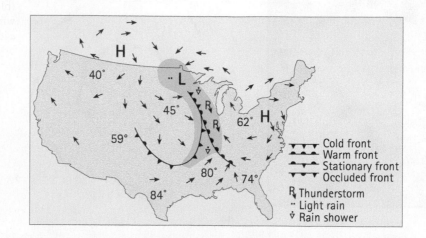

For instructor-assigned homework, go to www.masteringphysics.com (MP)

SUMMARY OF TERMS (KNOWLEDGE)

Air mass A large pool of air that has similar temperature and moisture characteristics throughout.

Anticyclone (*high-pressure system* or *high*) A weather system organized around an area of high pressure.

Atmosphere The thin envelope of gases, tiny solid particles, and liquid droplets surrounding the solid planet.

Atmospheric pressure The weight of all the air molecules in the atmosphere pressing down on Earth's surface.

Climate The general pattern of weather that occurs over a period of years.

Cloud A place in the atmosphere that contains enough water droplets or ice crystals to be visible.

Coriolis effect The tendency of moving bodies not attached to Earth (such as air molecules) to move to their right in the Northern Hemisphere and to their left in the Southern Hemisphere.

Cyclone (*low-pressure system* or *low*) A weather system organized around an area of low pressure.

Dew point The temperature at which the air becomes saturated.

Front (*weather front*) A boundary along which air masses meet.

Greenhouse effect The process by which certain gases warm the atmosphere by trapping infrared radiation that is emitted by Earth's surface.

Humidity The amount of water vapor in the air.

Precipitation Water in the liquid or solid state that returns to Earth's surface from the atmosphere.

Relative humidity The ratio of the water vapor actually in the air to the maximum water vapor the air can hold at that temperature.

Solar intensity Solar radiation per area.

Solar radiation Electromagnetic energy given off by the Sun.

Surface current A wind-driven, shallow ocean current.

Terrestrial radiation Infrared radiation emitted by Earth's surface.

Weather The state of the atmosphere at a particular time and place.

Wind Air flowing horizontally from an area of high pressure to an area of lower pressure.

READING CHECK (COMPREHENSION)

10.1 The Atmosphere

1. What is the difference between weather and climate?
2. What are the six elements of weather?
3. What two types of molecules make up more than 99% of the atmosphere?

10.2 The Structure of the Atmosphere

4. Name the four layers of the atmosphere.
5. Why does the stratosphere have a high temperature? Why does the mesosphere have a low temperature?

10.3 Temperature Depends on Latitude

6. Is San Francisco in the Northern or Southern Hemisphere? What is its approximate latitude?
7. How does latitude relate to temperature? Use the term *climate zone* in your answer.

10.4 Earth's Tilted Axis—The Seasons

8. Why are summer days warmer than winter days (on average)?
9. What is the winter solstice? The summer solstice? What are the equinoxes?

10.5 Flow of the Atmosphere—Wind

10. What is wind? What causes wind?
11. In what direction does wind blow?

10.6 Local and Global Wind Patterns

12. Give an example of a local wind pattern. Give an example of a global wind pattern.
13. How did the trade winds help traders in colonial America?

10.7 Ocean Currents Distribute Heat

14. What drives surface currents?
15. Do surface currents affect water temperature, air temperature, or both?

10.8 Water in the Atmosphere

16. What happens to the water vapor in the air when the air becomes saturated and its dew point is reached?
17. How do clouds form?
18. How do hailstones form?

10.9 Changing Weather—Air Masses, Fronts, and Cyclones

19. You hear of "low-pressure systems" on TV weather reports. What are two other names for a low-pressure system? What kind of weather are low-pressure systems associated with?
20. How do weather fronts develop?

THINK INTEGRATED SCIENCE

26A—Atmospheric Pressure

21. Why don't we feel atmospheric pressure?

22. Why is air pressure highest at sea level?

26B—Solar Radiation and the Greenhouse Effect Drive Global Temperature

23. About how much of solar radiation is intercepted by Earth? What portion of the solar energy intercepted by Earth is absorbed by the ground?

24. In what way is the greenhouse effect like a florist's greenhouse?

25. What is a greenhouse gas? Give three examples.

26. Distinguish between the natural greenhouse effect and global warming.

26C—Wind Chill

27. Why does wind generally make you feel cooler?

28. What is wind chill?

26D—The Coriolis Effect

29. What does the Coriolis effect do to the direction of global winds and ocean currents?

30. How is a ball tossed on a merry-go-round like the molecules in the atmosphere?

THINK AND DO (HANDS-ON APPLICATION)

31. Make a cloud—quickly. Simply open a can of soda and notice the cloud that forms for a moment over the opening. Why does the cloud form? The explanation is that bubbly drinks are held under pressure in cans. When you open the can, moist air escapes and quickly expands. Expanding air cools—to its dew point, as you can see.

32. Make a model of the greenhouse effect. You will need two nonmercury thermometers, one large plastic bag such as a produce bag, one small plastic bag such as a sandwich bag, and two twist ties. Place one thermometer in the small bag. Blow into the bag to inflate it, and tie it with a twist tie. Put the inflated bag inside the larger plastic bag. Inflate the large bag, and seal it with a twist tie. Now lay the bags containing the thermometer on a sunny windowsill or outside. Lay the unbagged thermometer next to it. Observe the temperature reading of both thermometers after 30 minutes. Explain your results.

33. The next time it rains, hold a sheet of black construction paper flat in the rain for a moment to catch a few raindrops. When you go inside, look at the marks the drops made. Are all raindrops the same size?

THINK AND COMPARE (ANALYSIS)

34. Suppose it's July 1. Rank the following locations in terms of the solar intensity they receive, from most to least: northern Africa, northern Canada, New York.

35. Rank the layers of the atmosphere in terms of density, from most dense to least dense.

36. Rank clouds classified as *alto*, *cirro*, and *stratus* according to their altitude, from highest to lowest.

THINK AND SOLVE (MATHEMATICAL APPLICATION)

37. Consider a house at sea level that has 2000 square feet of floor area. Show that the total force that the air inside the house exerts upward on the ceiling is 4.2×10^6 lb.

38. Suppose the air holds 75% of the water that it can hold at a given temperature before it becomes saturated. What is the relative humidity?

39. A tornado passes in front of a building, causing the pressure to drop there by 15% in 1 second. If a door on the side of the building is 6.5 feet tall and 3 feet wide, show that the net force on the closed door is 6200 lb.

40. At 50°C, the maximum amount of water vapor in the air is 9 g/m³. If the relative humidity is 40%, show that the mass of water vapor in 1 m³ of air is 3.6 g/m³. [Hint: Relative humidity = (water-vapor content)/(water-vapor capacity) × 100%.]

THINK AND EXPLAIN (SYNTHESIS)

41. The summer solstice is the longest day of the year. Does the summer solstice occur because Earth is closest to the Sun on this day? Explain.

42. Sometimes the atmosphere's temperature doesn't decrease with altitude in a normal way. Instead, warmer air sits on top of colder air in a temperature inversion. What effect can this have on local air pollution?

43. Clouds are made of tiny water droplets or ice crystals. These are heavier than air, so why don't clouds fall to the ground?

44. According to the graph, what is average atmospheric pressure at sea level? Why does atmospheric pressure change with altitude as shown in this graph?

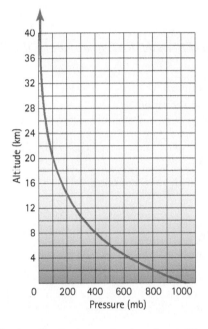

45. Identify the clouds shown in the photo. How are they formed? What kind of weather are they associated with?

46. After a day of skiing in the mountains, you decide to go indoors and get a cup of hot cocoa. As you enter the ski lodge, your eyeglasses fog up. Why?

47. Air is warmed and rises at the equator and then cools and sinks at the poles, as shown in the figure. Is this an accurate picture of the global circulation of air? Explain why or why not.

48. Why does warm, moist air blowing over cold water result in fog?

49. Why does atmospheric pressure typically drop before a storm comes?

50. What does convection in Earth's atmosphere produce? What does convection in Earth's mantle produce?

51. Why does the East Coast of the United States experience wider seasonal variation than the West Coast, even though both areas have oceans along their margins?

52. What role does the Sun play in ocean currents?

53. Explain why your ears pop when you climb to higher altitudes.

54. What is ozone? How might Earth be affected if there were no ozone layer in the stratosphere?

55. What are Earth's major climate zones? Describe each one.

56. Design an experiment to test the air pressure at different altitudes. What do you expect to observe?

57. When you go to school in the morning, the weather is sunny and warm. By lunchtime, it is cool, windy, and rainy. The weather front shown here has moved in. What kind of weather front is this—a cold front or a warm front?

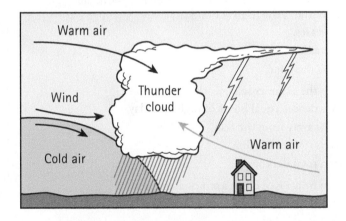

58. San Francisco, California, has mild winters. Springfield, Missouri, has cold winters. Yet San Francisco is farther north than Springfield. Is it surprising to learn then that Springfield is colder in the winter? Why? Why is San Francisco warm in the winter months?

59. At sea level, the air is about 23% oxygen. At the top of Mt. Everest, the air is still about 23% oxygen. So, why do almost all mountain climbers need to bring extra bottled oxygen to survive?

60. Identify which of these factors directly affect air temperature: altitude, latitude, proximity of water, ocean currents, the Coriolis effect.

61. As the air temperature decreases, does the relative humidity increase, decrease, or stay the same?

62. Why is it important that mountain climbers wear sunglasses and sunblock even when temperatures are below freezing?

THINK AND DISCUSS (EVALUATION)

63. When is the greenhouse effect a good thing? A bad thing?

64. The highest dew point ever recorded was 95°F, recorded in Saudi Arabia. Was the air humid or dry at that time? Explain your reasoning.

65. Do we see radiation emitted by the Earth? Do we feel it? Explain.

READINESS ASSURANCE TEST (RAT)

If you have a good handle on this chapter, if you really do, then you should be able to score 7 out of 10 on this RAT. If you score less than 7, you need to study further before moving on.

Choose the BEST answer to each of the following questions:

1. Earth's lower atmosphere is kept warm by
   (a) solar radiation.
   (b) terrestrial radiation.
   (c) shortwave radiation.

2. The wind blows because of
   (a) air pressure differences between different locations.
   (b) Earth's rotation.
   (c) the greenhouse effect.
   (d) differences in latitude.

3. If air temperature decreases but the water vapor in air stays constant, the relative humidity
   (a) increases.
   (b) decreases.
   (c) stays the same.

4. During the summer solstice, the North Pole
   (a) experiences equal hours of night and day.
   (b) leans away from the Sun.
   (c) leans toward the Sun.
   (d) is in total darkness.

5. Uneven heating of Earth's atmosphere produces
   (a) rain.
   (b) clouds.
   (c) air pressure.
   (d) wind.

6. The Gulf Stream redistributes heat from the Gulf of Mexico to
   (a) the North American coast, Great Britain, and Norway.
   (b) South America.
   (c) Japan.
   (d) Antarctica.

7. Air pressure is produced by
   (a) the weight of water vapor.
   (b) the weight of air.
   (c) the force of wind.
   (d) warm, moist air.

8. A maritime tropical air mass contains
   (a) cold, moist air.
   (b) cold, dry air.
   (c) warm, dry air.
   (d) warm, moist air.

9. High, wispy clouds that contain ice crystals and often bring rain are called
   (a) cumulus clouds.
   (b) cirrus clouds.
   (c) stratus clouds.
   (d) cumulonimbus clouds.

10. The relative humidity of air at its dew-point temperature is
    (a) 0%.
    (b) 10%.
    (c) 50%.
    (d) 100%.

Answers to RAT

1. b, 2. a, 3. a, 4. b, 5. d, 6. a, 7. b, 8. d, 9. b, 10. d

CHAPTER 11

Environmental Geology

W HEN DOES a natural event become a natural disaster? Floods, hurricanes, heat waves, volcanic eruptions, landslides, tsunami, etc. are natural events that become disasters when people are in the way. Sometimes it's possible to prevent natural disasters by staying out of the way. But sometimes, violent natural events occur where people live. In these cases, what can be done? Which violent natural events are preventable and how is this accomplished? When dangerous events can't be prevented, how can their impacts be mitigated? Disaster prediction, prevention, community preparedness, and emergency response all require state-of-the-art knowledge of environmental geology. In this chapter, we learn about the science that explains how environmental hazards work. We investigate climate change in particular depth because it's an environmental hazard of immediate and serious concern. This chapter is about serious science—the kind that saves lives!

LEARNING OBJECTIVE
Describe in detail what happens before, during, and after an earthquake.

UNIFYING CONCEPT

● *The Law of Conservation of Energy*
Section 4.10

● *Friction*
Section 2.8

● *Waves*
Section 8.1

● *Newton's Second Law*
Section 3.2

11.1 Earthquakes

EXPLAIN THIS What happens when the friction holding huge blocks of rock in place is overcome by tectonic forces?

It was just after 5:00 PM on a warm October afternoon. Suzanne Lyons, one of the authors of this book, was leaving work in Oakland, California. Just as she walked through her office door, the ground started shaking. Furniture toppled. As she stood in the swaying doorway, she saw waves roll through the pavement like swells on the open ocean. Was this "the big one"—the massive earthquake all Californians are warned about? No, but it was serious. It was the Loma Prieta earthquake, which shook the San Francisco Bay Area in 1989. Freeways collapsed, buildings were destroyed, 63 people died, and $6 billion of property damage was done.

An **earthquake**, as you learned in Chapter 8 on plate tectonics, happens when blocks of rock suddenly shift or break. Typically, earthquakes occur at plate boundaries. As the rocky plates grind beside one another, collide, or pull apart, their motion is usually steady and slow. In this case, the motion is called *creep*. But sometimes friction locks huge sections of rock together. Then, as force is applied to the rock, it cannot move freely and becomes compressed or stretched. When the force that is pushing or pulling the rock exceeds the friction that is holding it in place, or exceeds the strength of the rock, the stressed rock suddenly breaks loose and slips. Deformed rock snaps back elastically to its original position—a process called *elastic rebound* (Figure 11.2). The rock then releases its stored elastic energy in the form of **seismic waves**—mechanical waves that propagate through Earth. Geologists who study seismic waves and earthquakes are called *seismologists*.

When you bend a twig to the point that it breaks, you know that you have to put some energy into it. Imagine how much energy it takes to bend a rock. Now

FIGURE 11.1
This section of freeway collapsed during the 1989 Loma Prieta earthquake in California.

imagine the energy required to bend a slab of rock several kilometers long! This is the energy stored in rock before an earthquake. Where does this energy come from? The theory of *plate tectonics* provides the answer. Tectonic plates are huge sections of Earth's crust and upper mantle. Although they move slowly, their immense mass means that they carry enormous kinetic energy. (Recall that kinetic energy is proportional to mass times velocity squared: KE = ½ mv^2.) When huge zones of rock stick together because the plates are pushing against one another and locking, the rock's kinetic energy is converted into potential energy—energy that's stored in the rock.

The place where an earthquake starts is called the *focus* of the earthquake (Figure 11.3). Seismic waves radiate in all directions from the focus like sound from a ringing bell. The point at Earth's surface directly above the focus is the **epicenter**. Earthquakes generally occur at *faults*. A fault is a fracture where rocks on either side have moved relative to one another. Usually motion along a fault is smooth and slow; it's rapid only during an earthquake. Faults mostly exist at plate boundaries where extreme tectonic stresses crack the crust. But faults can occur in the middle of a plate too. Faults vary in length from a few centimeters to hundreds of kilometers. The amount of displacement along faults also varies greatly, again in a range of a few centimeters to many kilometers.

Fault

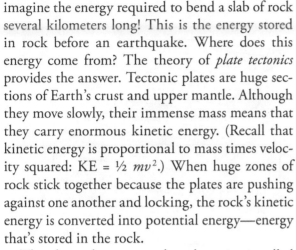

Sections of rock are forced in different directions though they are locked together by friction. The rock deforms.

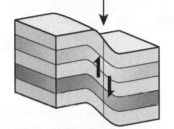

Stress builds in the rock as massive tectonic plates keep moving.

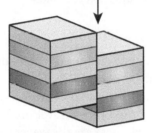

Rock slips along the fault and stress is released. Rocks rebound elastically–they return to their unstressed dimensions.

FIGURE 11.2
Huge blocks of rock moving under the influence of tectonic forces can become locked together through friction acting between them. When the force that is pushing or pulling the rocks exceeds the friction on them, the enormous zones of rock suddenly slip. The energy stored in them is released as seismic waves that travel through Earth and at its surface, shaking the ground.

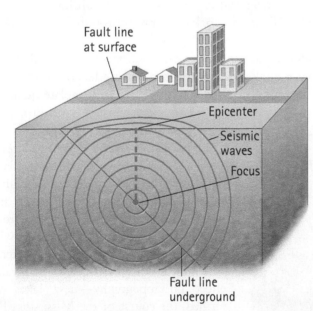

Fault line at surface

Epicenter

Seismic waves

Focus

Fault line underground

FIGURE 11.3
When rock suddenly moves in an earthquake, it is usually along a fault. The movement of rock generates seismic waves that radiate outward from the focus. The point at ground level directly above the focus is the epicenter.

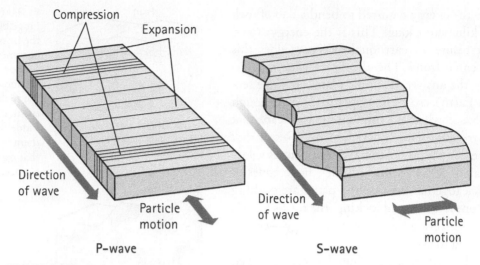

FIGURE 11.4

P-waves and S-waves are seismic waves known as *body waves*—they travel through Earth's interior. Notice that P-waves are longitudinal, whereas S-waves are transverse. They vibrate the rock they move through in different ways, as shown here. P-waves vibrate rock in the direction that they are traveling; S-waves vibrate the rock in a direction transverse (at right angles) to the direction of motion.

Faults are typically found in networks rather than as single cracks, and at shallow depths, usually within the top 10–15 km of Earth's crust.

There are two types of seismic waves. *Body waves* travel through Earth's interior, and *surface waves* travel on Earth's surface. Because surface waves travel at ground level, these are the waves that damage surface structures. They can shake things up and down or side to side. Body waves are classified as either primary waves (P-waves) or secondary waves (S-waves). P-waves are longitudinal waves that move quickly through rock, water, or air, compressing and expanding it as they travel, like the squeezing and expanding of an accordion. S-waves are transverse body waves that vibrate the rock they travel through from side to side (Figure 11.4).

Earthquakes occur all around the world. Although most happen along plate boundaries, *intraplate* earthquakes (which are not well understood) occur away from plate boundaries. An infamous series of three major intraplate quakes occurred in New Madrid, Missouri, in the winter of 1811–1812. The first of them occurred just after midnight on December 16. People emerging from their shaking homes that night observed the land rolling in waves up to 1 m high. These intense surface waves opened deep cracks in the ground. The subsequent two quakes occurred within several weeks and were of similar intensity. The New Madrid earthquakes had a major effect on topography—new lakes were formed, the course of the Mississippi River was changed, more than 150,000 acres of forest were destroyed, and the contours of the land were reshaped over a wide area.

Did you know that there are thousands of earthquakes every day? Most of them are minor—just the creeping of blocks of rock along a fault line. It's the sticking, bending, and slipping of giant blocks of rock that produce the big earthquakes that we can feel.

FIGURE 11.5

New Madrid, Missouri, was the site of more than 1000 small and large earthquakes in 1811–1812. The earthquakes ranged up to a Richter magnitude of 8.0, which is the highest recorded earthquake magnitude in the continental United States. The New Madrid earthquakes were intraplate quakes, which are rare in comparison to the earthquakes that occur at plate boundaries.

TABLE 11.1	EARTHQUAKE SEVERITY AND DEPTH RELATED TO TECTONIC SETTING (GENERAL TRENDS)
Plate Setting	**Focus Depth and Earthquake Intensity**
Diverging boundary	Shallow; mild
Subduction zone	Shallow to deep; high intensity
Continental–continental convergent boundary	Shallow to medium depth; moderate to high intensity
Transform boundary	Shallow; moderate to high intensity

Fortunately, because the region was sparsely settled at the time, there was little loss to human life and property.

Usually it's not the ground shaking itself but associated hazards that cause the most damage. Hazards associated with earthquakes include fire, landslides, tsunami, and *liquefaction*. What's liqufaction? When wet soil is shaken in an earthquake, soil particles are sometimes jarred apart and no longer locked together through friction. Then the soil is an unconsolidated slurry with insufficient strength to anchor buildings. Liquefaction is a major reason buildings topple over during earthquakes.

Intraplate quakes aside, most of the world's earthquakes—about 90%—are associated with movement along the boundaries of tectonic plates. In general, mild, shallow temblors occur at divergent plate boundaries. Earthquakes along transform plate boundaries are typically moderate. The strongest jolts mostly happen at convergent boundaries—especially at subduction zones where an oceanic plate slips under a plate that is less dense, as indicated in Table 11.1.

Most subduction occurs in the **Ring of Fire**, a horseshoe-shaped region of subduction zones that encircles much of the Pacific Ocean. About 80% of the world's big earthquakes occur in the Ring of Fire. Subduction produces volcanic activity as well as earthquakes. About 75% of the world's volcanoes are located in the Ring of Fire.

Earthquake Prediction

Can earthquakes be predicted? Yes, to some extent. Geologists can't predict exactly when or where an earthquake will occur, but they can measure the strain in rocks, and greater strain generally correlates with greater risk. Also, by mapping *seismic gaps*, scientists can identify which areas are most at risk within a timeframe of 30 to 100 years. Seismic gaps are stretches along major faults where little or no seismic activity has occurred for a long period of time even though the other regions of the fault are active. The dormant sections of the active fault—that is, the seismic gaps—are apparently dormant because they are locked by friction. In these areas, strain is building up rather than being released in small tremors. When the stress exceeds the friction holding the rock in place—snap! A large earthquake releases the strain. Figure 11.6 shows the locations of the major seismic gaps in the Western Hemisphere. Although the exact timing, location, and magnitude are impossible to predict, an understanding of seismic gaps allows scientists to prepare for future seismic activity. For example, scientists and policy officials used their knowledge of seismic gaps to prepare for the Loma Prieta earthquake by retrofitting buildings, enforcing new earthquake-safe building codes, and educating the local population about what to do when the quake hit.

UNIFYING CONCEPT

● *Friction*
Section 2.8

FIGURE 11.6
This map shows the major seismic gaps of the Western Hemisphere (note the shaded bands). Seismic gaps are dormant sections of active faults where stress is presumed to be accumulating.

UNIFYING CONCEPT

● *The Law of Conservation of Energy*
Section 4.10

CHECK YOURSELF

1. It takes a lot of energy to deform huge slabs of rock and cause an earthquake. Where does this energy come from?
2. Where do most severe earthquakes occur? Why are they so common there?
3. Suppose you live along a major fault zone but no seismic activity has occurred in your location for hundreds of years, even though small earthquakes are common elsewhere along the fault. Should you be confident that you live in a very safe, earthquake-proof zone?

CHECK YOUR ANSWERS

1. The energy that deforms rock comes from the motion of tectonic plates.
2. Most severe earthquakes occur along convergent plate boundaries where there is subduction. The Ring of Fire is where most of the subduction in the world is occurring.
3. No, you shouldn't feel especially safe. Check to see whether your location is in a seismic gap. If it is, you are in an especially hazardous portion of the fault. Practice earthquake preparedness!

The biggest earthquake to strike the United States occurred in Prince William Sound, Alaska, in 1964. It measured 9.2 on the Richter scale. By comparison, the Loma Prieta earthquake measured 7.0.

Earthquake Measurement

Geologists use a number of methods to determine the power of earthquakes. The *moment magnitude scale* measures *magnitude*, how much energy is released during an earthquake. This scale relies on actual measurements of a fault and the displacement of the plates along that fault. On this scale, each unit increase represents a 32-fold increase in the amount of energy released by the earthquake. In other words, a 4.0-magnitude earthquake has 32 times the energy of a 3.0-magnitude earthquake.

Although geologists use the moment magnitude scale, the media generally report the intensity of earthquakes in terms of the *Richter scale*. The Richter scale describes how much the ground shakes during an earthquake. On the Richter scale, each whole-number step represents a 10-fold increase in the amount of shaking that occurs. On the Richter scale, a 4.0 earthquake causes 10 times the shaking of a 3.0 earthquake.

Table 11.2 describes the intensity of earthquakes in terms of the Richter scale. Keep in mind, though, that two earthquakes assigned the same number may cause different amounts of damage. The amount of damage depends on whether the epicenter is near a populated area, how deep beneath the surface the focus is, the types of buildings located in the affected area, and other factors.

The moment magnitude scale is a more precise tool than the Richter scale, although both measure the size of an earthquake with a similar scale from 0 to 10.

The instrument used to measure the movement of Earth during an earthquake is called a *seismometer* (Figure 11.7). The stronger the earthquake, the harder the shaking and the greater the amplitude of the wave the seismometer records.

FIGURE 11.7
The standard seismometer records the shaking of the ground. Large-amplitude waves correspond to big shakes.

TABLE 11.2	THE RICHTER SCALE	
Intensity	Description	Effects
Less than 2.0	Microquake	Can be recorded by a seismometer
2.0–2.9	Minor	Potentially detectable by average person
3.0–3.9	Minor	May be felt near the epicenter; rarely causes damage
4.0–4.9	Light	Strong shaking and rattling
5.0–5.9	Moderate	Possible structural damage
6.0–6.9	Strong	Widespread damage
7.0–7.9	Major	Can cause serious damage over a large area; approximately 20 per year worldwide
8.0–8.9	Great	Can cause severe damage hundreds of miles from the epicenter; approximately 1 per year worldwide
9.0–9.9	Catastrophic	Devastating across areas thousands of miles in diameter; recorded once every 20 years on average

11.2 Tsunami

EXPLAIN THIS What is the best way to prevent loss of life due to tsunami?

LEARNING OBJECTIVE
Explain what causes tsunami and why tsunami are so destructive.

Occasionally, a strong earthquake causes a *tsunami*, which is Japanese for "harbor wave." A massive subduction earthquake in the Ring of Fire on December 26, 2004, triggered a catastrophic tsunami that killed more than 200,000 people in 14 countries. The earthquake focus was under the Indian Ocean, off the coast of Sumatra, where two plates meet at a subduction zone. The earthquake's magnitude was 9.1 on the moment magnitude scale. Although the quake itself was damaging, the **tsunami**—a huge seismic sea wave—was even more destructive than the quake.

UNIFYING CONCEPT

● *Waves*
Section 8.1

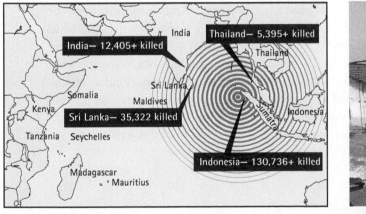

(a)   (b)

FIGURE 11.8
(a) The December 26, 2004, tsunami began with a strong subduction earthquake off the coast of Sumatra. (b) The tsunami strikes a coastline in Sri Lanka.

TABLE 11.3	CHARACTERISTICS OF A TSUNAMI VERSUS A TYPICAL OCEAN WAVE	
Wave Feature	Ocean Wave	Tsunami
Wave speed	8–10 km/h (5–60 mph)	800–1000 km/h (500–600 m/h)
Wave period	5–20 s	10–120 min
Wavelength	100–200 m (300–600 ft)	100–500 km (60–300 mi)
Initial disturbance	Wind	Earthquake, explosion, volcanic eruption, or meteor impact

Table 11.3 compares a tsunami with a typical ocean wave. As you can see, tsunami are long, fast-moving ocean waves triggered by a large disturbance—usually an earthquake. The 2004 tsunami was launched by a large but typical subduction earthquake: The subducting plate was sticking and bending along the overlying plate until friction no longer held it in place. When the bottom plate slipped, the overlying rock slab shot up like a piston with tremendous force. This force pushed a column of water upward above the surrounding sea level.

When a tsunami's initial bulge falls back down to sea level, it and subsequent ripples spread outward from the disturbance, traveling mostly underwater. The wave height of a tsunami is usually less than 1 m higher than the surface until it gets close to shore. However, close to shore, the shallower water and the shape of the shore compress the wave, which decreases its wavelength and greatly increases its amplitude. The Indonesian tsunami in 2004 reached a maximum height of nearly 30 feet above sea level.

Water is heavy, so a wall of water several stories high and moving at 500 miles per hour carries tremendous energy and packs giant force. The total energy released by the 2004 tsunami is estimated at five megatons of TNT. This is more than double the energy of all the bombs exploded in World War II, including the two atomic blasts. (Amazingly, the earthquake that triggered the tsunami possessed several orders of magnitude *more* energy than the tsunami!) Coastal buildings were smashed and seaside villages swept away when the tsunami reached coastal locations around the Pacific. And, since the tsunami inundated the land more than a mile past the shoreline, the killer wave had a significant impact inland as well as along the beach.

Another recent and catastrophic tsunami occurred in Japan on March 11, 2011. Over 20,000 people were reported killed or missing after a 9.0 Richter magnitude earthquake struck Honshu and triggered a huge tsunami. Adding to the misery, the tsunami flooded the Fukushima Daiichi nuclear power plant. This triggered fuel meltdowns at three of the plant's six reactors. At more than 40 feet high, the tsunami easily overtopped the Fukushima nuclear plant's 19-foot seawall, producing the worst nuclear disaster since the 1986 Chernobyl core meltdown in Russia. A radiation leak at Fukushima Daiichi displaced as many as 100,000 people. The Japanese government has said that some of the area around the plant will be uninhabitable for decades. The full effects of this disaster are still being assessed as of this writing.

LEARNING OBJECTIVE
Compare and contrast the three main kinds of volcanoes.

11.3 Volcanoes

EXPLAIN THIS Why are most volcanoes located along the Ring of Fire?

Temperature rises quickly with depth in Earth's interior. Between 30 and 150 miles below the surface, near the upper mantle, rock is so hot that it can exist as magma. Magma, a mixture of melted rock and trapped

(a)   (b)   (c)

FIGURE 11.9
(a) Kilauea is a shield volcano in Hawaii. Note the lava flowing gently down its broad sides.
(b) Mount St. Helens, a composite volcano in Washington State erupted violently in 1980.
(c) The Paricutin cinder cone in Mexico erupted in 1943.

gases, buoyantly rises toward Earth's surface, cooling all the while. Most of it crystallizes underground as igneous rock before it reaches the cool surface, but some magma makes it all the way to the surface without crystallizing. It then erupts through fissures and vents. Erupted magma, called *lava*, solidifies at cool surface temperatures to form volcanic rocks. Such rock, plus perhaps ash, cinders, and other erupted materials, can pile up in great masses to form a **volcano**.

There are three major types of volcanoes, each of which erupts different kinds of lava and other materials. The three types of volcanoes erupt in different ways, and they pose different hazards. The main categories of volcanoes are *shield volcanoes*, *composite volcanoes* (also known as *stratovolcanoes*), and *cinder cones* (Figure 11.9).

Shield volcanoes have broad, gentle slopes resembling a warrior's shield. Shield volcanoes erupt *basaltic* lava—a runny lava low in silica that hardens to make the iron- and magnesium-rich dark volcanic rock found on the ocean floor. Because shield volcanoes erupt smoothly flowing lava, they erupt quietly and steadily. On Hawaii, a shield volcano named *Kilauea* has been erupting almost continuously since 1983. Lava bubbles gently out of the ground at Kilauea and flows slowly enough downhill that you could outrun it most of the time.

In contrast, composite volcanoes erupt explosively. In 1980, *Mount St. Helens* in the state of Washington made history. Mount St. Helens is one of the majestic composite volcanoes that make up the Cascade Mountain Range. Most of the time, the snow-capped Cascade Range is a quiet place to hike or fish. However, on May 18, 1980, the top of Mount St. Helens blew off like a cork from a bottle in a giant eruption. A column of ash rose 60,000 feet into the air. Vegetation was charred 10 miles away. Burning, boulder-size **pyroclastics** ("pie-row-CLASS-ticks"), or debris fragments, were tossed into the air like popcorn. Composite volcanoes such as Mount St. Helens erupt thick, high-silica lava called *rhyolite* as well as a lava of intermediate consistency called *andesite*. Rhyolite and andesite are thick, chunky lavas that can clog up a volcano's vent. Trapped gases add to the pressure. When a composite volcano finally explodes, lava, toxic gases, ash, cinders, and pyroclastics hurl outward. Sometimes, exploding composite volcanoes trigger *lahars* ("LA-harz"), volcanic mudflows that can travel far and fast.

FIGURE 11.10
The Ring of Fire is a region of intense geologic activity. It is home to more than 75% of the world's volcanoes, and 90% of the world's earthquakes happen here. The reason? Convergent plate boundaries and subduction occur all along the Ring of Fire. Volcanoes are shown as red dots on this map.

Lahars have the consistency of wet cement as they flow and the consistency of dry cement when they come to rest.

A cinder cone is a small volcano with steep sides. Cinder cones are built up like heaps of assorted rubbish from basaltic, andesitic, or (less frequently) rhyolitic lava mixed together with various pyroclastics.

Most volcanoes are composite volcanoes. They form due to subduction, so they are mainly located in the Ring of Fire. As stated earlier, more than 75% of the world's volcanoes are composite volcanoes in the Ring of Fire (Figure 11.10). By contrast, shield volcanoes are usually formed over **hot spots**, which are randomly placed plumes of magma. Cinder cones are found anywhere volcanic activity occurs.

Sometimes cinder cones develop inside larger volcanoes. Wizard Island, for example, is a cinder cone sitting inside the composite volcano Mount Mazama, which erupted violently about 8000 years ago. Sometime after Mount Mazama blew, the Wizard Island cinder cone formed inside Mount Mazama's summit crater (or *caldera*). It is built of andesite lava, cinders, and other pyroclastics. Wizard Island, not surprisingly, sits within the Ring of Fire in Crater Lake National Park, Oregon (Figure 11.10).

A common misconception is that lava is the biggest hazard from volcanoes. In fact, lava is more threatening to structures than to people. Pyroclastics are more dangerous than lava. They are an impact hazard if they hit you, they can bury dwellings, and they create agricultural losses. Volcanic ash is also a burial hazard and an agricultural threat. Furthermore, volcanic ash causes lung damage. And, as you will read later in this chapter, ash can trigger climate change. The toxic gases that are released in volcanic eruptions are short-term hazards of volcanoes as well as causes of climate change.

FIGURE 11.11
Wizard Island, a cinder cone in Crater Lake National Park, Oregon. Wizard Island sits inside a caldera. Notice the dark, rugged lava rock encircling the island. That's Mount Mazama, the composite volcano that Wizard Island sits within.

SCIENCE AND SOCIETY

Disaster Warnings—When Do You Tell the People?

Figure 11.12 shows Mt. Vesuvius, a composite volcano that sits above Naples, Italy. This volcano erupted in AD 79, destroying the city of Pompeii. Mt. Vesuvius has erupted many times since. Today, geologists classify Mt. Vesuvius as one of the most dangerous volcanoes in the world. Like other composite volcanoes, it erupts explosively. A population of 3 million people has grown up around its base.

Predicting volcanic eruptions is far from certain. The most reliable approach is to constantly monitor them for signs of an impending eruption, such as bulging flanks. When there are clear signs of danger, disaster officials warn the population at risk. If there is sufficient evidence of an imminent eruption, officials order an evacuation.

Suppose you are a member of the International Volcanic Hazard Task Force. Your team has been monitoring Mt. Vesuvius carefully for many years. Also suppose that Mt. Vesuvius starts showing symptoms of an imminent eruption.

- When should your team warn people that they are at risk? What should you tell them? How will they react?

FIGURE 11.12
Mt. Vesuvius sits above Naples, a city of 3 million people.

- What will happen if you warn the people of an eruption but your indicators are wrong and the volcano goes quiet? What are some of the consequences of this "false alarm" to the local economy? To the people's trust in scientists and disaster officials?
- What will happen if you fail to issue a warning and the volcano blows sooner and more explosively than you predicted?

CHECK YOURSELF
1. **Where does lava come from?**
2. **Why are composite volcanoes more hazardous than shield volcanoes?**

CHECK YOUR ANSWERS
1. Lava is magma that erupts. Magma is melted rock that forms within the mantle.
2. Composite volcanoes erupt explosively. Both types of volcanoes erupt lava—which is a burn hazard. But in addition to lava, composite volcanoes emit toxic gases, pyroclastics, ash, and cinders. Also, composite volcanoes can trigger lahars—dangerous mudflows.

LEARNING OBJECTIVE
Explain the process by which hurricanes form.

11.4 Hurricanes

EXPLAIN THIS Why do hurricanes die when they move over dry land?

A hurricane is a large, rotating weather system with winds blowing at least 74 miles per hour (119 km/h). Hurricanes are the most powerful of all Earth's storms. They form over tropical seas and can be highly destructive if they reach land. As Figure 11.13 shows, hurricanes usually form between 5° and 20° north and south latitudes, where temperatures are warm. They vary from about 150 km to 1500 km in diameter, and they can travel for thousands of miles.

A hurricane starts as a storm over warm ocean water. The water needs to be at least 80°F down to a depth of 200 feet. As the Sun heats the ocean's surface, masses of warm, moist air move upward through the atmosphere, forming huge thunderclouds. More air is sucked into the warm, low-pressure air column beneath the storm clouds. The moving air is twisted by the Coriolis effect, so it turns in a spiral pattern around the low-pressure center. Figure 11.14 shows the pattern of

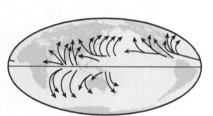

FIGURE 11.13
The map shows the places at risk for hurricanes. Hurricanes typically form at the tail of the arrow and track in the direction of the arrow to the arrowhead. The three regions that are most at risk for hurricane damage are the western Pacific Ocean, the Bay of Bengal (near India), and the Caribbean.

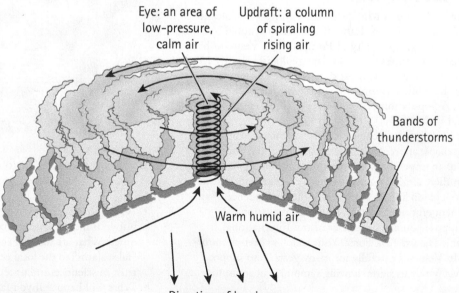

Eye: an area of low-pressure, calm air

Updraft: a column of spiraling rising air

Bands of thunderstorms

Warm humid air

Direction of hurricane

FIGURE 11.14
The low-pressure center of a hurricane is the eye. Moist air spirals around the eye and moves upward. Bands of rain and wind make it extend outward.

clouds and airflow that makes up a hurricane. Besides requiring warm water, warm air, and the Coriolis effect, hurricanes cannot exist in high-friction environments. So hurricanes are restricted to tropical seas.

UNIFYING CONCEPT

● *Friction*
Section 2.8

The warm air that is sucked into the bottom of a hurricane is rich in water vapor. As the air rises, it cools and the water vapor in it condenses to form liquid water. Do you remember that as a gas cools to a liquid it gives off energy to its surroundings? The energy stored by the gas and released upon condensation is called its *latent heat*. The condensation of the water vapor in a hurricane releases latent heat—and this is the energy that fuels a hurricane. Being a dynamic system, a hurricane eventually moves away from the tropics. The cooler temperatures it then encounters reduce the supply of warm, moist air so the hurricane diminishes or dies. If the storm hits land, it is no longer fed by condensing water vapor from the ocean, so it will certainly lose its fuel and die.

Figure 11.15 shows Hurricane Katrina on August 28, 2005, as it twisted through the Gulf of Mexico. When a hurricane moves toward shore, it creates a wall of water called a *storm surge*. The storm surge is a hammer of water and often the most destructive part of a hurricane. The 20-foot storm surge created by Katrina overwhelmed New Orleans' levee and sea wall system, bringing mass flooding to the city and nearby communities. Nearly 2000 people lost their lives in Hurricane Katrina and in the floods that followed. The storm is estimated to have caused more than $81 billion in damage, making it the costliest natural disaster in U.S. history.

Hurricanes are known by different names in different parts of the world. People in the western Pacific call these storms *typhoons*. In the Indian Ocean and western South Pacific, they are called *tropical cyclones*. By whatever the name,

(a)

(b)

FIGURE 11.15
(a) Hurricane Katrina in the Gulf of Mexico on August 28, 2005. (b) Hurricane Katrina hammered the city of New Orleans with a 20-ft storm surge. New Orleans sits below sea level and has been protected from flooding by an engineered system of levees and sea walls. But, when the hurricane battered these barrier walls, the structures gave way and seawater rushed into the city. The floodwaters, filthy with floating debris, remained trapped like soup in a bowl within the city walls until the water could be drained.

TABLE 11.4	SAFFIR–SIMPSON HURRICANE SCALE	
Category	Wind Speed (miles per hour)	Effects
No. 1	74–95	*Very dangerous winds produce some damage.* Examples: roofs damaged or destroyed; large tree branches snap; shallow-rooted trees topple; power lines and poles fall or break
No. 2	96–110	*Extremely dangerous winds cause extensive damage.* Examples: older mobile homes destroyed; some roofs removed; shallow-rooted trees uprooted blocking roads; long-term power loss
No. 3	111–130	*Devastating damage occurs.* Examples: electricity and water unavailable; extensive roof and siding damage; windows broken; high risk of injury or death due to flying and falling debris
No. 4	131–155	*Catastrophic damage occurs.* Examples: extensive structural damage to top floors; collapse of some masonry buildings; fallen trees and power poles isolate residential areas; long-term water shortages
No. 5	Greater than 155	*Catastrophic damage occurs.* Examples: people, livestock, and pets at very high risk of injury or death from falling or flying debris, even inside homes; many homes destroyed; nearly all trees uprooted; most of the area uninhabitable for weeks or months

hurricanes are by far most frequent in the Pacific Ocean. Hurricanes vary seasonally, as you might expect, because temperature varies seasonally. In the western Pacific, hurricane season peaks in late August/early September.

The severity of hurricanes can be compared using the *Saffir–Simpson Hurricane Scale* (Table 11.4). Hurricane Katrina was Category 5, an unusually severe event in terms of wind speed, height of the storm surge, and effects on land.

CHECK YOURSELF

1. Why do winds flow inward toward the eye of a hurricane?
2. Do you live in a place that is at high risk for hurricanes?

CHECK YOUR ANSWERS

1. The eye of a hurricane is a low-pressure zone. Air always moves from high to low pressure.
2. Look at the map in Figure 11.13. Is your home in the high-risk zone? If so, do you know what to do if a hurricane threatens your community?

Integrated Science 27A
PHYSICS, CHEMISTRY, BIOLOGY, AND ASTRONOMY

Climate Change

LEARNING OBJECTIVE
Describe how the use of fossil fuels over the past century has triggered a rise in global average temperature.

EXPLAIN THIS Explain why it's important that Edith's checkerspot butterfly has changed its range since the 1880s.

Signs of climate change—from melting sea ice, to increasingly frequent and severe hurricanes, to the relocation of native settlements away from flooded shorelines—are easy to find in the scientific literature and in the popular media. Climate change is here. But what exactly is climate change in the context of Earth's overall history? Is today's climate change natural or *anthropogenic* (human-caused)? What is the evidence that human activity is responsible for a recent spike in global temperature? What is planetary feedback? How is climate change affecting Earth systems, and what can be done in response? These questions frame our exploration of this important topic.

Paleoclimatology is the study of ancient climates. Paleoclimatological studies reveal a long history of climate change on our planet.

What Is Climate Change?

Weather is the state of the atmosphere at a particular time and place—its temperature, humidity, pressure, and precipitation, wind, and clouds. *Climate* is the weather pattern over several decades or longer. **Climate change**, then, is a lasting alteration to long-term weather patterns. One hot summer is not "global warming," nor is a single severe hurricane. Climate change is bigger than weather fluctuations—it's a lasting alteration to average weather conditions so new patterns of temperature, precipitation, storm intensity, and other weather features become established. As it's used in the popular media, the term *climate change* or *global warming* refers to the recent spike and projected future increase in average global temperature caused by an enhanced greenhouse effect. To understand climate change in a broad context, we begin by looking at how Earth's climate has varied throughout its history.

Earth's Climate Over Time Earth's climate has changed many times throughout its 4.6-billion-year history. The planet has withstood extremes. Figure 11.16 shows the geologic time scale, which divides Earth's long history into time units of different size. Today we are living in the Phanerozoic eon, the Cenozoic era, the Quaternary period, and the Holocene epoch. Most divisions of the geologic time scale mark major turning points in the history of geology or the history of life, such as mass extinctions. Many of these big turning points have involved, at least in part, a change in climate.

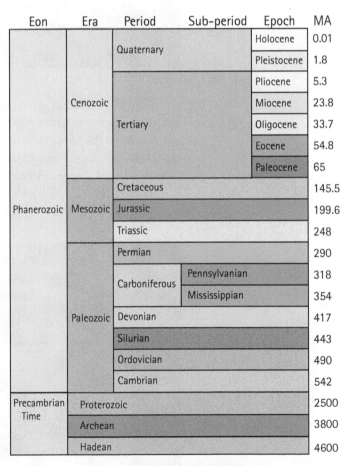

FIGURE 11.16
The geologic time scale divides Earth's history into time units of different size. The units on this scale are MA, or "millions of years ago." The Paleozoic era began about 542 Ma, or 542 million years ago, for example.

FIGURE 11.17
In the Hadean era, Earth's surface was mostly molten with a few fragments of crust.

In the Hadean eon, when Earth was newly formed, it was a scorching, lifeless sphere covered with churning, molten rock (Figure 11.17). About 600 million years ago, at the end of Precambrian time, the planet entered a frozen state called *Snowball Earth*. Ice completely covered it and life was sparse. In the Silurian period, about 400 million years ago, the global climate was stable and warm. Glaciers melted and warm shallow seas covered much of the globe, providing habitat for abundant species of marine life. A spectacular diversity of fishes evolved. Amphibians pushed the range of the animal kingdom onto the edge of land. Warm, moist forests developed as *gymnosperms*, plants bearing seeds, first appeared. The first animals to follow plants out of the water were wingless insects and scorpions. Later, in the Carboniferous period illustrated in Figure 11.18, reptiles appeared on land; they were able to survive in dry environments because they had developed the amniotic egg.

FIGURE 11.18
The Carboniferous period was marked by warm, moist, swampy forests. Reptiles first appeared in the Carboniferous period.

About 250 million years ago, at the end of the Permian period, a mass extinction destroyed almost 90% of the species living at the time. The Permian extinction is the most devastating extinction event in history. It coincided with the largest volcanic eruption ever—an eruption that lasted more than a million years and triggered two bouts of rapid climate change. Volcanic ash rapidly cooled the planet by blocking solar radiation (Figure 11.19). Then, as the

FIGURE 11.19
A million-year volcanic eruption at the end of the Permian period spewed huge amounts of ash into the air, thereby changing the world's climate.

eruption waned, Earth quickly warmed in a geologic whiplash. The two periods of rapid climate change—cooling and then warming—combined with disruption of the atmosphere's ozone layer, acid rain, the release of large amounts of carbon dioxide, and other factors are thought to have caused the huge die-off. Photosynthesizing species may have been most drastically affected first, with the effects of their death moving up the food chain. Although most species were destroyed in the Permian extinction, the reptiles that survived evolved and diversified to become the dominant animal species of the world—dinosaurs. Life flourished in many differentiated forms, driven by natural selection, until about 65 million years ago. Then, at the end of the Cretaceous period, about 60% of Earth's species were eliminated in the Cretaceous extinction. Famously, the dinosaurs were devastated. What caused this catastrophe?

The Mesozoic era is informally known as "The Age of the Dinosaurs" because of its famous reptilian species. Earth was warm and wet when the dinosaurs reigned.

Scientists agree that climate change was the key factor. Mild, warm Mesozoic climates suddenly turned cool. Sunlight dimmed. Ecosystems perished. According to most researchers, this round of climate change was triggered by an asteroid impact. In the rock record, there are widespread deposits of iridium, an element rare on Earth but characteristic of asteroids. The iridium layer in Earth's crust dates back to 65 million years ago—the time of the Cretaceous extinction. Apparently, a huge asteroid crashed into Earth and exploded over a large area, leaving its iridium "fingerprints" in rock strata. More important to the dinosaurs, though, the asteroid impact triggered wildfires that blanketed the atmosphere with soot and other particulates, and this blocked the Sun and altered the climate.

FIGURE 11.20
According to the impact hypothesis, a large asteroid triggered climate changes that caused a mass extinction at the end of the Cretaceous period.

CHECK YOURSELF
Among the survivors of the Cretaceous extinction are bottom-dwelling organisms such as clams. Why did they survive?

CHECK YOUR ANSWER
Bottom-dwelling communities were insulated from climate fluctuations that affected organisms closer to the atmosphere.

After the mass extinctions at the end of the Mesozoic era, many environmental niches were left vacant. They were filled in the Cenozoic era by new species. At the beginning of the Cenozoic era, tectonic events had cooled the climate. The supercontinent Pangaea had recently split apart. The breakup of Pangaea changed ocean circulation patterns by opening up seaways between landmasses. Cold-water currents could then cool the land. Subsequently, huge glaciers called *ice sheets* formed near the poles.

Ice Ages Geologic periods that are cold enough to support extensive glaciation are called **ice ages**. In an ice age, ice sheets and alpine glaciers are widespread.

FIGURE 11.21
This map shows how far glaciers (in blue) reached into North America during the Pleistocene epoch. Arrows show the directions of ice movement. The Pleistocene spanned the time from about 2 million years ago to about 10,000 years ago.

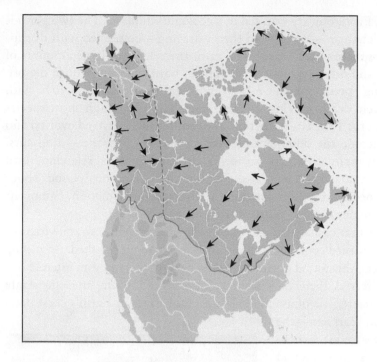

Antarctica and Greenland are largely covered by ice sheets today, the Arctic Sea is frozen most of the year, and alpine glaciers remain at high altitudes. Accordingly, Earth is now in an ice age. Within an ice age, pulses of especially cold climate are called *glacials*. Glacials are the coldest of cold climates. In a glacial, glaciers advance toward the equator. Sea level drops because glaciers take their water from the ocean. Figure 11.21 shows that much of North America was covered by a glacier during the most recent glacial period. Today, we live in an **interglacial period**, a pulse of warmer temperatures that lasts thousands of years and occurs within an ice age. In an interglacial period, glaciers melt back to high latitudes. This causes sea level to rise worldwide. The oscillations between glacials and interglacials within an ice age are called *glacial/interglacial cycles*.

Ice ages are rare compared to the warm periods in geologic history. Earth was warmer than it is today for most of its past. All of human existence, however, has occurred within an ice age. Humans evolved during the Pleistocene epoch at about the same time that mammoths, rhinoceroses, bison, reindeer, and musk oxen appeared. These creatures all evolved with warm, woolly coats for protection against the frigid cold. Lacking such a coat, *Homo sapiens* relied on intelligence to cope with the hardships of cold weather.

Following the Pleistocene epoch is the Holocene epoch. To see the Holocene environment, just look around. It is the most recent 10,000 years or so of Earth's history, including the present time. The transition from the Pleistocene to the Holocene, about 10,000 years ago, was marked by warming climate. It is this climate change, plus overhunting by humans, that apparently triggered the extinction of the large, cold-adapted mammals. From its beginning, the Holocene has been a warm and relatively stable interglacial period, allowing human culture to advance and population to grow exponentially.

To be sure, some climate variation has occurred even through the Holocene. Over the past 2000 years there have been three episodes of significant change: the Medieval Climate Anomaly (AD 900–1300), the Little Ice Age (AD 1500–1850), and the Industrial Era (AD 1900 to the present time). The Medieval Climate

You should have headed for Antarctica. You'd love the climate!

Anomaly was a warmer-than-average phase that affected large geographic expanses; the American West was very dry. The Little Ice Age was—as its name suggests—a cold period: Alpine glaciers advanced in Europe, which shortened growing seasons there and decreased agricultural productivity. Over the past 100 years, in the Industrial Era, the temperature has changed again. It has spiked: The average global temperature has increased by about 1.3°F or about 0.7°C in the last century. This may sound like a small variation, but the change has been very rapid in geologic terms. The temperature is rising exponentially, in fact: The eight warmest years on record (since 1880) have all occurred since 2001. The ecosystems we are part of and depend upon are adapted to a narrow temperature range of only a few degrees Celsius. The 1-degree global temperature increase of the Industrial Era has had many environmental effects—including the shift in the range of Edith's checkerspot butterfly (Figure 11.22).

(a)

(b)

FIGURE 11.22

(a) Edith's checkerspot butterfly (*Euphydryas editha*) is a resident species of western North America. Its range extends from Baja Mexico northward through the western United States to southwestern Canada. Because of its beauty and because it is slow moving and easy to catch, amateur and professional *lepidopterists* (butterfly scientists) have been observing and logging data on it for almost 150 years—since the dawn of the Industrial Revolution. These data provide the basis for comparing the present distribution of the *E. editha* to that of its past. (b) Dr. Camille Parmesan shared the 2007 Nobel Prize for her studies documenting the extinction of *E. editha* in the southern parts of its range. The record shows that the *E. editha*'s range has moved northward about 60 miles and upward in elevation about 300 feet. In more recent research, Parmesan has found that 800 of the 1500 species she studied worldwide were responding in some way to a warming global climate.

UNIFYING CONCEPT

● *Exponential Growth and Decay*
Appendix D

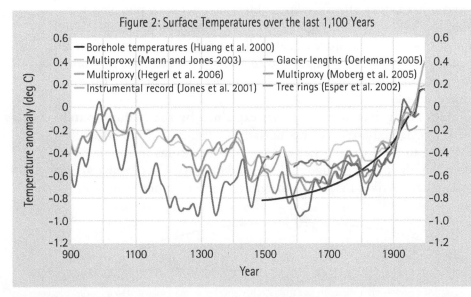

FIGURE 11.23

This graph tracks the average variations in surface temperatures in the Northern Hemisphere obtained from different research teams (in different colors). Can you find the Medieval Climate Anomaly, the Little Ice Age, and the Industrial Age on the graph?

Causes of Climate Change

What factors have driven Earth's climate swings? Paleoclimate researchers have identified several basic components. Some of the drivers are extraterrestrial in origin, whereas other factors originate here on Earth, as Figure 11.24 shows. Until recently, climate change occurred naturally. However, the temperature spike during the past hundred years, as well as projected near-term future climate warming, are mainly human-caused (*anthropogenic*). Anthropogenic climate change arises mostly from alterations to atmospheric chemistry that enhance the greenhouse effect.

FIGURE 11.24
Summary of factors that drive changes in Earth's climatic system.

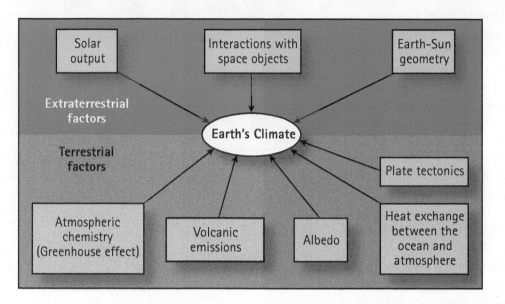

Natural Climate Change   Before discussing anthropogenic climate change, let's examine the factors that would make the climate change even if people weren't around. This is called *natural climate change*. Note that the diagram of climate change drivers shows that Earth's temperature is controlled by the Sun's output. The amount of energy transmitted by the Sun is not truly constant. Sunspots and other factors affect the incoming solar energy to our planet. As you'd expect, low solar output corresponds with low average global temperature. Matter in near space and deep space can also affect Earth's climate from time to time. For example, you read that an asteroid collision ended the dinosaurs' reign 65 million years ago. Clouds of interstellar dust have cooled Earth by blocking solar radiation as well.

The comings and goings of ice ages are explained by the **Milankovitch theory**, which is named after its Yugoslavian discoverer, Milutin Milankovitch. According to the Milankovitch theory, slow variations in the shape of Earth's orbit, the tilt of its axis (Figure 11.25), and the path of its wobble affect the way solar energy strikes Earth and therefore alter its temperature.

Earth's orbit around the Sun is an ellipse, an elongated loop. Over a 100,000-year period, the orbit changes from a more circular path to a more elliptical one and back again. Can you see that, the more elliptical Earth's orbit is, the farther away from the Sun it can be? This affects its climate.

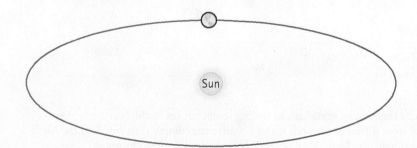

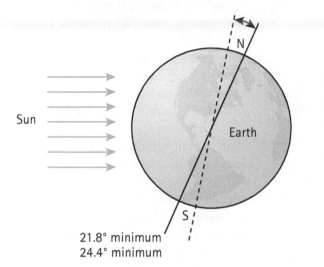

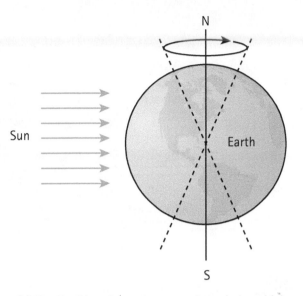

(a) The tilt of Earth's axis changes. Today, Earth is inclined at an angle of 23.5° but it varies between 22° and 25° every 41,000 years. When the tilt is 22°, Earth is most upright. Then, sunlight hits all parts of the Earth most evenly so seasonal intensity is reduced. This makes for cooler summers, which allows glaciers to build up year upon year.

(b) The Earth's axis traces a complete circle, which affects its position in space and the solar energy it receives. Earth's axis completes a full circle every 26,000 years. The variation affects the amount of solar radiation it receives and therefore affects its climate.

FIGURE 11.25
Changes in Earth's orbital shape from elliptical to increasingly circular, (a) the tilt of its axis, and (b) the path of its wobble affect its climate and account for ice age changes, according to the Milankovitch theory.

The changes in Earth's orbit and axial spin occur in cycles of differing length. Sometimes changes that act toward a warming trend are canceled by other changes that act toward a cooling trend. But sometimes the effects all push climate in the same direction. Then the factors add together to cause extreme warming or cooling. Milankovitch proposed that ice ages occur when cooling effects occur at the same time and add up. Evidence shows that he was probably right.

CHECK YOURSELF
Do the changes in Earth's tilt, wobble, and orbital shape work together or separately to produce ice ages?

CHECK YOUR ANSWER
The variations work together—sometimes canceling and sometimes reinforcing one another. When several changes that produce cooling add up, ice ages occur.

Most of the causes of climate change originate here on Earth rather than in space. An important terrestrial component is volcanic emissions. Volcanic eruptions affect climate by filling the atmosphere with ash, dust, and gases that block the solar radiation received by Earth. Volcanic emissions can also work in the opposite direction—warming Earth rather than cooling it—because volcanoes emit carbon dioxide, a greenhouse gas.

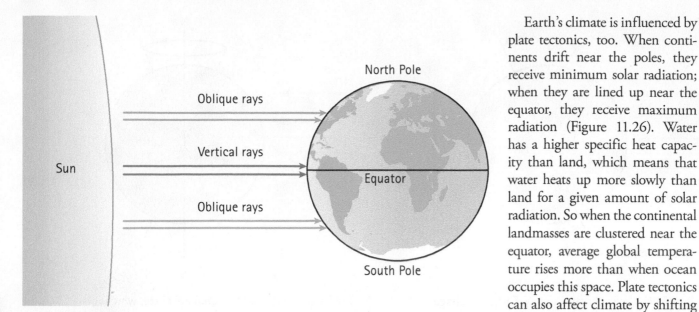

FIGURE 11.26
This diagram shows why latitude influences climate. Solar radiation is more intense at low latitudes because the Sun's rays strike Earth most directly there.

Earth's climate is influenced by plate tectonics, too. When continents drift near the poles, they receive minimum solar radiation; when they are lined up near the equator, they receive maximum radiation (Figure 11.26). Water has a higher specific heat capacity than land, which means that water heats up more slowly than land for a given amount of solar radiation. So when the continental landmasses are clustered near the equator, average global temperature rises more than when ocean occupies this space. Plate tectonics can also affect climate by shifting the path of ocean currents as they move around landmasses.

There is a continual exchange of heat between the oceans and atmosphere so the way in which ocean currents flow significantly affects the temperature. Surface currents move streams of warm and cold water around the world in response to global winds. There is another set of ocean currents, too. Cold, salty water sinks in the Arctic and is replaced by warm surface water circulating toward the poles from the tropics. This process is called *thermohaline circulation*. It is the basis of the "ocean conveyor belt," the circulation of seawater due to salinity and temperature differences that distributes heat around the globe. Perturbations in thermohaline circulation both result from and produce more changes to the global climate.

Reflectivity is another climate control. The fraction of solar radiation arriving at a surface and reflected is its **albedo**. Albedo depends on two factors: color and chemical composition, so it varies from surface to surface. The dark, blue ocean has a much lower albedo than the white ice caps of the poles, so the ocean absorbs a higher percentage of incoming energy and reflects less compared to

FIGURE 11.27
Thermohaline circulation: global ocean circulation pattern driven by density currents.

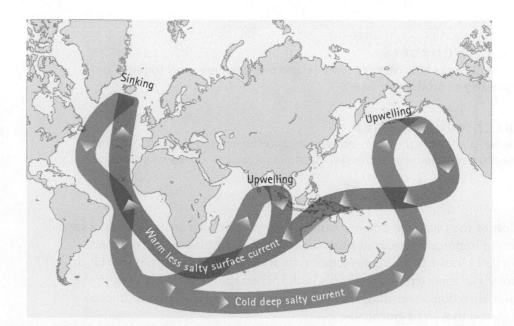

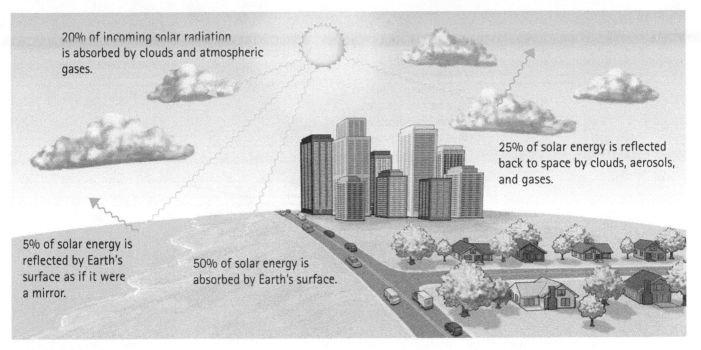

20% of incoming solar radiation is absorbed by clouds and atmospheric gases.

25% of solar energy is reflected back to space by clouds, aerosols, and gases.

5% of solar energy is reflected by Earth's surface as if it were a mirror.

50% of solar energy is absorbed by Earth's surface.

FIGURE 11.28
Earth's overall surface reflectivity or albedo is about 0.3, or 30%. This means that about 70% of incident radiation is absorbed by the land, water, and atmosphere and eventually becomes heat. The rest (30%) is reflected back to space and doesn't affect temperature.

the ice caps. Earth's total albedo varies mainly due to changes in cloud cover, snow and ice cover, human developments, and vegetation cover. Paving surfaces decrease their reflectivity. Asphalt absorbs nearly all of the energy incident on it. During ice ages, when glaciation is at its maximum, Earth's total albedo is very high. When albedo decreases due to, say, melting of the ice caps, Earth's global average temperature rises.

CHECK YOURSELF
1. How does astronomy relate to climate change?
2. How do catastrophic events relate to climate change?
3. How does plate tectonics relate to climate change?
4. Which has a higher albedo—a mirror or Earth as a whole?

CHECK YOUR ANSWERS
1. The intensity of solar radiation received, which affects Earth's temperature, depends on Earth's orbit and the tilt of its axis.
2. Asteroid impacts and volcanic eruptions throw gases and particles into the air that block sunlight and cool the climate.
3. There are many ways. A few of them are mentioned in this book. For example, the effects of continental drift include disruption of ocean currents and redistribution of continents to cold polar latitudes as well as increased reflection of incoming solar radiation by landmasses gathered along the equator.
4. A mirror's albedo is 100% because it's a virtually perfect reflector. Earth's albedo is only about 30%. Thus, about 70% of all incident solar radiation is absorbed by Earth and 30% is reflected.

FIGURE 11.29
The greenhouse effect in a car.

FIGURE 11.29
The greenhouse effect in a car.

Step 2
The interior absorbs incoming light then reradiates it as lower-energy infrared radiation. Glass won't let infrared radiation pass through so it stays inside the car.

Step 1
Glass windows allow electromagnetic waves from the Sun in the visible range to pass through.

Step 3
Temperature rises.

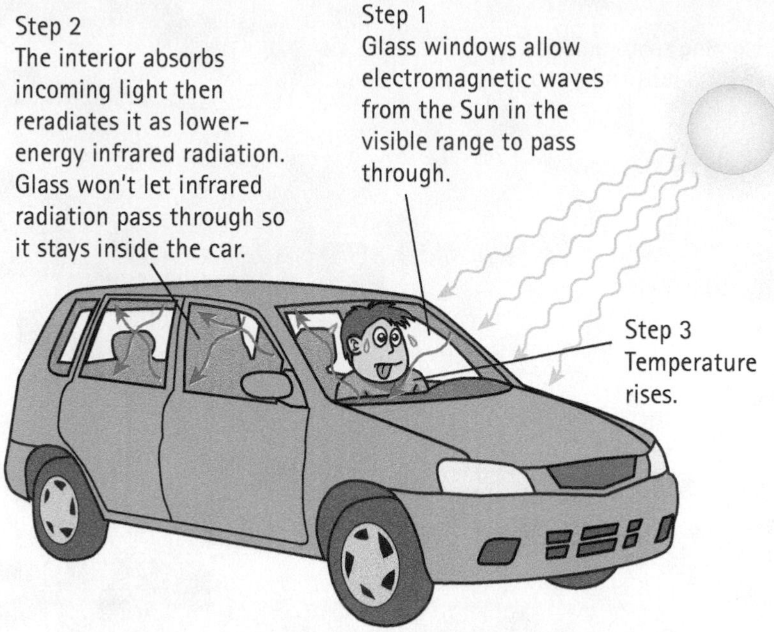

Last but certainly not least among natural climate controls is atmospheric chemistry. The atmosphere is an envelope of nitrogen gas (78%) and oxygen gas (21%) plus hundreds of species of trace gases; suspended particles (such as soot, ash, and dust); and water droplets and other liquids. Water vapor, carbon dioxide, and methane are important trace gases because they are potent *greenhouse gases*.

The greenhouse effect is a major mechanism by which Earth maintains its "Goldilocks climate"—not too hot, not too cold, but just right for life. Without the greenhouse effect, the planet's average temperature would be a frigid $-18°C$. The atmosphere's greenhouse effect works much like the glass of a florist's greenhouse or the glass windows of your car on a sunny day (Figure 11.29). Greenhouse gases in the atmosphere allow short-wave visible light from the Sun to pass through (Figure 11.30). The ground absorbs the light, then reradiates it. But the reradiated energy is no longer in the visible range. It's longer-wavelength *infrared radiation*—heat. When the infrared rays move away from the ground toward space, greenhouse gas molecules absorb and re-emit them many times before the waves finally escape. Every time the infrared radiation is absorbed, it heats the atmospheric gases a little more. The atmosphere is warmed up—just like the interior of your car on a sunny day. Eventually, the infrared radiation escapes to space, leaving a warmed Earth behind.

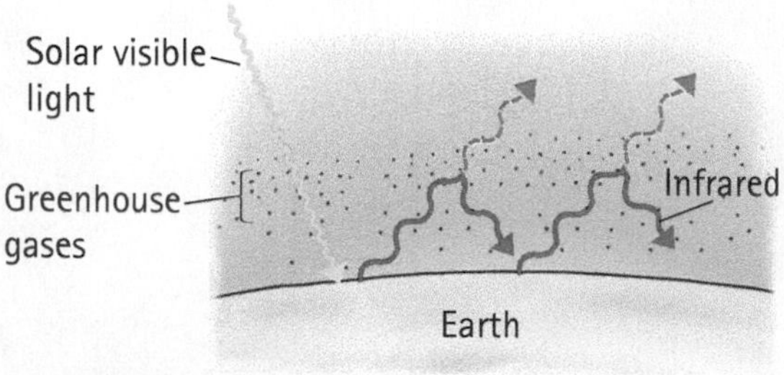

Solar visible light

Greenhouse gases

Infrared

Earth

FIGURE 11.30
The greenhouse effect in Earth's atmosphere. Visible light is absorbed by the ground, which emits infrared radiation. Carbon dioxide, water vapor, methane, and other greenhouse gases absorb and re-emit the infrared radiation that would otherwise be radiated directly from Earth into space.

Anthropogenic Climate Change There is more agreement about anthropogenic climate change among scientists than there is about almost any other scientific issue: temperature has risen sharply since the beginning of the Industrial Era and most of the increase has occurred during the past three decades due to the buildup of carbon dioxide (and, to a lesser extent, other greenhouse gases) in Earth's atmosphere. Carbon dioxide levels are higher today than at any time in the past 800,000 years. Carbon dioxide is released naturally by decaying organisms and volcanic emissions. But analysis of the isotopic composition of carbon dioxide in today's atmosphere shows that it comes mainly from burning fossil fuels, not from natural sources.

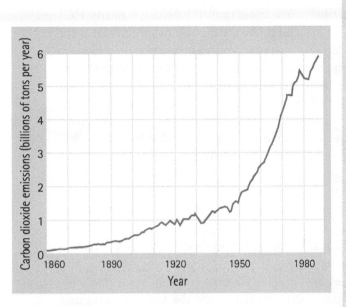

FIGURE 11.31
Carbon dioxide emissions from the burning of fossil fuels have increased exponentially since the time of the Industrial Revolution.

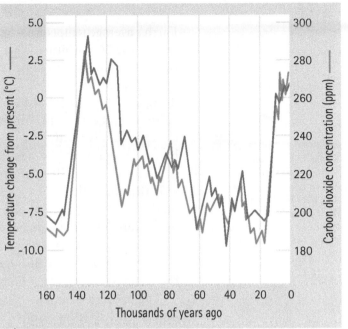

FIGURE 11.32
Carbon dioxide level and temperature have shown a close correlation for many thousands of years.

How does burning fossil fuels put carbon dioxide into the air? Fossil fuels—by which we mean petroleum (crude oil and natural gas) and coal—are formed from animals and plants that died millions of years ago but did not decay completely. Instead, they were buried by sand and silt. Biomolecules, rich in chemical energy as well as carbon, remained buried. Over time, heat and pressure converted the biomass into fossil fuels. When these fossil fuels are extracted and then burned for energy, they release their stored carbon as carbon dioxide. Millions of tons of carbon dioxide are exhausted into the atmosphere every day from power plants that burn coal or oil, from trucks and cars that burn gas, and from other human activities.

Figure 11.31 shows the dramatic rise in carbon dioxide emissions since the mid-1800s, when humans began burning the fossil fuels that seemed abundant at the time. Burning coal, oil, and natural gas produces carbon dioxide as a waste product. Figure 11.32 shows that atmospheric carbon dioxide levels and temperatures have been closely correlated for many thousands of years. As CO_2 levels increase, so do temperatures.

Besides burning fossil fuels, people increase atmospheric carbon dioxide levels through *deforestation*. Deforestation is the clearing of forests, as shown in Figure 11.33. In many countries around the world, forests are being cleared to obtain firewood, build roads, and open up land for agriculture to feed a large and growing human population. Plants take carbon dioxide out of the air to perform photosynthesis, making them *carbon sinks*. So, a net loss of trees means a net gain of carbon dioxide in the atmosphere. Plus, if the trees are burned when they are cut down, they give off carbon dioxide right away through combustion.

UNIFYING CONCEPT
● *Exponential Growth and Decay*
Appendix D

Burning fossil fuels keeps many factories humming, but it also puts a lot of carbon dioxide into the air.

FIGURE 11.33
This deforested landscape was once rainforest. The forest was cut down to harvest palm oil in Indonesia.

Current and Future Effects of Climate Change

Earth's average temperature has risen a little more than 1°F (which is nearly 1°C) during the 20th century. That doesn't sound like much, but it's an unusual event in history. The rapid rise has effects we can observe and measure today: Flowers and trees are blooming earlier in the year. Plant and animal ranges have shifted to higher elevations and higher latitudes. Glaciers have melted back to higher latitudes and elevations. Amounts of arctic sea ice are at a record low. Ice on rivers and lakes is melting earlier in the year. Tropical storms and heat waves have become more intense. Permafrost (permanently frozen ground at high latitudes) is melting, which allows buried stores of the greenhouse gas methane to escape into the atmosphere. Sea level has risen as melting glaciers and sea ice release liquid water into the sea and as the volume of seawater increases due to thermal expansion. The first climate refugees have begun moving away from inundated shoreline settlements. For example, Bhola Island (a region of the Asian nation Bangladesh) became half-submerged by rising sea levels in 1995. Five hundred thousand people were left homeless.

The Intergovernmental Panel on Climate Change (IPCC) is a global volunteer organization of more than 1300 scientists from the United States and other countries. The IPCC reviews the credible scientific research on climate change and summarizes its findings in reports for policy makers and the public. The IPCC forecasts a temperature rise of 2.5°F to 10°F over the next century. The principal scientific agencies of the United States, including the Environmental Protection Agency (EPA) and the National Oceanic and Atmospheric Administration (NOAA), have published estimates that agree with the IPCC. There is high confidence and agreement among IPCC and other scientists that global temperatures will continue to rise precipitously, largely due to greenhouse gases produced by human activities. What will be the effects of this future warming?

It is impossible to predict what the particular future effects of global warming will be. There are too many factors involved to make specific forecasts. The IPCC has issued some predictions, however, and assigned probabilities to them; see Table 11.5.

One of the reasons it's so hard to predict future global warming and its effects is that climate is a *system*—a functioning unit made up of parts and processes

> Why does sea level rise when the climate warms? Glaciers and sea ice melt when the temperature warms, and they release their water into the sea. Also, heat makes water expand. A warmer ocean takes up more space. Sea level rises.

(a)

(b)

FIGURE 11.34

(a) A glacier-topped mountain. (b) A glacier that has almost completely melted. Where did the glacier's ice go? How does this relate to the rise in sea level that accompanies global warming?

TABLE 11.5 GLOBAL CLIMATE CHANGE: FUTURE TRENDS	
Phenomena	**Likelihood of Trend**
Contraction of snow cover areas, increased thaw in permafrost regions, decrease in sea ice extent	Virtually certain
Increased frequency of hot extremes, heat waves, and heavy precipitation	Very likely to occur
Increase in hurricane intensity	Likely to occur
Precipitation increases in high latitudes	Very likely to occur
Precipitation decreases in subtropical land regions	Very likely to occur
Decreased water resources in many semi-arid areas, including western U.S. and Mediterranean basin	High confidence

Definitions of likelihood ranges used to express the assessed probability of occurrence: *virtually certain* > 99%, *very likely* > 90%, *likely* > 66%.

Source: *Global Climate Change, Vital Signs of the Planet, NASA, 2011* and *Summary for Policymakers, IPCC Synthesis Report, November 2007,* http://www.ipcc.ch/

that interact with one another. There are many, many interacting components in Earth's overall climate system. Interacting variables aren't restricted to the atmosphere   the atmosphere, hydrosphere, biosphere, and lithosphere are all involved. The interconnections among the parts of a system are called *feedbacks* or **feedback loops**. In climatology, we call the interactions among climate variables *planetary feedbacks*.

The simplest feedback loop consists of just two variables, as shown in Figure 11.35. In a feedback loop, changes in one variable affect the other variable, *and* changes in the second variable in turn affect the first variable. Some feedbacks tend to inhibit change in the system, while other feedback relationships tend to support further changes to the system. Feedbacks that inhibit future change are called *negative feedbacks*. Negative feedback relationships among the variables in a system tend to stabilize the system because, when the second variable responds to changes in the first variable, it tends to suppress further change in the first variable. On the other hand, feedbacks that amplify the change in the initial variable are called *positive feedbacks*. Positive feedbacks are destabilizing—the changes in the interacting variables don't balance one another out; they amplify each other and change is exponential. In the real world, feedback loops are much more complicated than these simplified two-variable examples suggest. Planetary feedback is too complex even for today's sophisticated climate models to fully track.

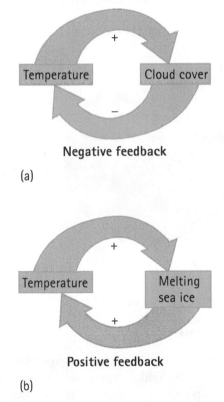

Negative feedback

(a)

Positive feedback

(b)

FIGURE 11.35
Diagram of a possible negative feedback loop between cloud cover and Earth's surface temperature. As the surface temperature increases, evaporation increases, which promotes the development of clouds. But the clouds can work against further temperature increases because they reflect sunlight, which cools the air. (b) Diagram of a positive feedback relationship between sea ice and temperature. As temperatures increase, sea ice melts. But, since sea ice is very reflective (it has a high albedo), melting sea ice drives Earth's temperature higher.

UNIFYING CONCEPT

● *Feedback Regulation*
  Section 19.2

To me and other animals who need cold temperatures, global warming just isn't cool.

Although numerous difficulties surely accompany climate change, there may be some positive effects for certain locations. Perhaps global warming will improve the potential for growing crops in areas that are now too cold. The effects simply cannot be predicted with confidence. But, on the whole, the forecast is for challenges ahead. Global warming is one risky experiment that we would rather not conduct.

Responding to Climate Change

There is no single solution to climate change. We need knowledge and we need wisdom too. We need Earth scientists to keep working hard and reporting their findings accurately. We need policy officials who understand the science and formulate laws and regulations that foster sustainability. We need citizens who care for and act on behalf of the planet and one another. Everyone has a part to play in protecting the big blue planet that is our home, our Mother Earth. What will be your role?

As you move ahead, here are three guidelines to help you exert a positive effect on Earth, particularly the changing climate. You'll find that these simple practices can benefit your personal life too.

FIGURE 11.36
A "carbon footprint" is the total amount of greenhouse gas emissions that support human activities. It's often expressed as tons of carbon dioxide emitted during one year. This pie chart shows constituents of a typical American citizen's carbon footprint.

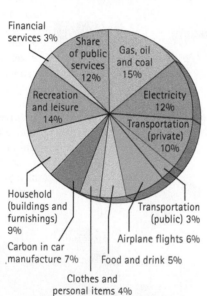

Sample Carbon Footprint

Financial services 3%
Share of public services 12%
Gas, oil and coal 15%
Recreation and leisure 14%
Electricity 12%
Transportation (private) 10%
Household (buildings and furnishings) 9%
Transportation (public) 3%
Carbon in car manufacture 7%
Airplane flights 6%
Clothes and personal items 4%
Food and drink 5%

1. **Learn more.** You've studied this chapter—that's great. Now find out more! Tap whatever resources you have access to. Subscribe to NASA, NOAA, NSF, EPA, and other scientific and educational Web sites. Investigate citizen science programs to get involved in research projects right now. Find out about opportunities that appeal to you in your local community. Keep an open mind and ask questions until you get answers.

2. **Reduce your carbon footprint.** The average American emits 22 tons of carbon dioxide each year. Your transportation, dietary, and lifestyle choices do have an impact. Calculate your carbon footprint—a good measure of your impact on the climate—by visiting www.epa.gov/climatechange/ghgemissions/ind_calculator.html. Consider Figure 11.36, which represents a typical American citizen's carbon footprint. Develop a plan to reduce yours. Chances are, you'll be healthier and happier in the long run if you make Earth-wise choices.

3. **Stay connected to Earth.** Know enough science to understand and contribute to the public discussion on climate change. Learn more science still to empower yourself even more. Speak, vote, and live your values. Say what you think. Listen to others. Work with them too. Maintain your connection to nature through sports, the food you eat, and music and the arts. Use your talents and opportunities for the benefit of the biosphere. Enjoy a healthy and happy relationship with your home in space—beautiful planet Earth!

FIGURE 11.37
To live sustainably, remember these guidelines: Learn more. Understand your impact. Care for your home, planet Earth.

CHECK YOURSELF

1. Your friend tells you not to worry about global warming because the greenhouse effect is a natural process that dates back to early Earth. What does he *not understand* about how global warming works?

2. Another friend tells you to just give up and plan on moving to Antarctica, where temperatures will rise and crops will thrive. What does she *not understand* about global warming?

3. A third friend tells you that people should find ways to reduce greenhouse gas emissions to minimize global warming. What does he likely *understand* about global warming?

CHECK YOUR ANSWERS

1. In moderation, the greenhouse effect is beneficial to life. However, large concentrations of greenhouse gases in the atmosphere trap so much heat so quickly that ecosystems can't adapt to the temperature rise.

2. The regional effects of global warming are unknown.

3. When it comes to greenhouse gases, less is more. The less greenhouse gas people deposit in the air, the more likely it is that Earth's climate will continue to support a diverse biosphere.

For instructor-assigned homework, go to www.masteringphysics.com **MP**

SUMMARY OF TERMS (KNOWLEDGE)

Albedo The fraction of solar radiation arriving at a surface and reflected by it.

Earthquake The sudden ground motion and energy release that occur when rocks slip along a fault.

Epicenter The point at Earth's surface directly above the focus of an earthquake.

Climate change (global warming) A long-term rise in average global temperature that results from an increase in the greenhouse effect.

Feedback loop A path between the parts of a system such that one part affects a second part and the second part in turn affects the initial part. Regarding climate change, positive feedback accelerates climate change, while negative feedback decelerates it.

Hot spots A place on Earth's surface that sits directly above a rising column of magma that extends to the lower mantle.

Hurricane A large rotating tropical storm with wind speeds of at least 119 km/h.

Ice age A time period that is cold enough so that glaciers collect at high latitudes and move toward lower latitudes.

Interglacial period A period within an ice age that is warm enough so that glaciers melt back to polar latitudes.

Milankovitch theory The idea that slow variations in Earth's orbit, the tilt of its axis, and the path of its wobble affect the way sunlight strikes Earth and therefore alter its temperature.

Pyroclastics Lava and rock fragments ejected into the atmosphere during a violent volcanic eruption.

Ring of Fire A horseshoe-shaped zone of frequent earthquakes and volcanic eruptions that encircles the basin of the Pacific Ocean.

Seismic waves Mechanical waves produced by an earthquake that propagate through Earth.

Tsunami A huge seismic sea wave.

Volcano A mountain that forms when lava or pyroclastic materials pile up around a volcano vent.

READING CHECK (COMPREHENSION)

11.1 Earthquakes

1. What does the Richter scale measure?

2. Why do earthquakes produce seismic waves?

3. Where do earthquakes occur?

4. What method uses records of past earthquakes to predict future earthquakes? What are the limitations of this method?

11.2 Tsunami

5. How is a tsunami similar to a ripple in a pond? How do they differ?

6. What causes a tsunami?

7. Describe two devastating tsunami that have occurred since the year 2000. Tell when they occurred and why they were costly in terms of lives and property.

11.3 Volcanoes

8. What are the three major kinds of volcanoes?

9. Which types of volcanoes erupt quietly? Which erupt most explosively?

10. What are the hazards associated with volcanoes?

11.4 Hurricanes

11. What is the source of a hurricane's energy?

12. Where do hurricanes form? Describe how they travel.

13. What was the costliest natural disaster in U.S. history?

THINK INTEGRATED SCIENCE

27A—Climate Change

14. What astronomical changes produce climate change on Earth?

15. Can continental drift cause climate change? Provide an example.

16. Cite two kinds of catastrophes that occur naturally and can alter climate.

17. Relate the greenhouse effect to global warming.

18. What are greenhouse gases?

19. Besides burning fossil fuels, what causes carbon dioxide buildup?

20. How do planetary feedbacks affect climate change?

21. What is it about the Industrial Era that has apparently caused the average global temperature to increase?

22. Explain why melting ice caps cause Earth's temperature to rise. (Hint: Use the term *albedo*.)

23. Give two examples of mass extinctions that apparently were related to climate change.

24. What does albedo depend upon?

25. Why is the greenhouse effect a good thing for life on Earth? Why is it a bad thing?

26. Why is melting permafrost a climate concern?

27. Why is sea level expected to rise as global temperature climbs?

28. By how much did the average global temperature rise during the past century?

29. Burning a plant releases carbon dioxide in two ways. What are they?

30. What is the IPCC? By how much does the IPCC predict climate will change over the next century?

THINK AND DO (HANDS-ON APPLICATION)

31. Use your hands to simulate motion along a fault. Press your palms together and move your hands in opposite directions, as shown in the figure. Notice that friction keeps them "locked" together until the opposing 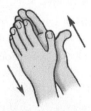 forces no longer balance, friction no longer holds, and your palms slip suddenly past each other. This demonstration nicely models the sticking and slipping that occur along a transform fault.

THINK AND SOLVE (MATHEMATICAL APPLICATION)

32. The Richter scale measures how much the ground shakes in an earthquake. Note that this is not equal to the energy released by an earthquake. However, there is a simple relationship between Richter magnitude and earthquake energy.

    A 1-point increase on the Richter scale corresponds to an energy increase of about 30 times. Thus a 5.0-magnitude earthquake releases about 30 times as much energy as a 4.0-magnitude earthquake. The 5.0-magnitude earthquake releases about 900 (30 × 30) times the energy of a 3.0-magnitude quake.

    (a) How much more energy does an 8.0-magnitude earthquake release than a 7.0-magnitude earthquake?

    (b) How much more energy does a 7.0-magnitude earthquake release than a 5.0-magnitude earthquake?

    (c) How much more energy does a 7.0-magnitude earthquake release than a 4.0-magnitude earthquake?

    (d) How much *less* energy does a 6.0-magnitude earthquake release than a 7.0-earthquake?

33. Investigate your carbon footprint. Go to the Environmental Protection Agency Web site (http://www.epa.gov/climatechange/kids/calc/index.html) and use the Global Climate Change Calculator. Calculate the impact you have through simple actions, such as turning off electric lights, on atmospheric carbon dioxide concentration.

THINK AND EXPLAIN (SYNTHESIS)

34. Why do shield volcanoes have broader bases than cinder cone volcanoes?

35. Why do hurricanes die when they reach land?

36. Have volcanoes been more of a threat in modern times or in ancient times? State your reasons.

37. How is rock before an earthquake like a compressed or stretched Slinky?

38. Briefly describe how a tsunami develops.

39. Heat waves kill more people in the United States than all of the other natural disasters combined. Why do heat waves mainly kill people who live in cities?

40. Name three natural hazards discussed in this chapter that affect coastal regions more than inland areas.

41. The use of fossil fuels contributes to global climate change. Are there other reasons to reduce our consumption of fossil fuels? If so, describe them.

42. Why have levels of carbon dioxide in the atmosphere increased sharply since the latter part of the 19th century?

43. What are some likely effects of global warming?

44. As technological society advances, humans use increasing amounts of energy. Does this violate the law of conservation of energy? Why or why not?

45. In what way do plants reduce the threat of global warming?

46. Can the problems associated with fossil fuels be cured by planting enough trees? Explain your reasoning.

47. How is a volcano like a shaken bottle of soda?

48. If you had to live near a composite volcano or a shield volcano, which type would you choose? Why?

49. Where is the Ring of Fire, and how did it earn its name?

50. What would eventually happen to a volcano that formed over a hot spot? (*Hint:* Think about plate movement.)

51. Some engineers have suggested burying radioactive wastes in ocean trenches at subduction zones. Why do you think they have proposed this? What hazards could this create?

52. Drowning causes the most deaths in a hurricane. Explain why, using the term *storm surge* in your answer.

53. Suppose geologists report that the stress in Earth's crust has increased where you live. Should you move? If so, how soon? Explain the reasons for your answer.

54. Draw a feedback loop with two variables: melting sea ice and temperature. Is this a positive or negative feedback loop? Does it enhance climate change or balance Earth's climatic system?

55. Which of these graphs represents feedback that destabilizes climate?

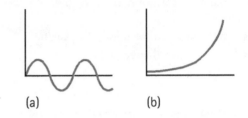

(a)   (b)

56. Do greenhouse gases truly trap the infrared radiation emitted by Earth or do they simply delay its transmission to space?

57. Why does paving the ground contribute to planetary warming?

58. Earth emits radiation. Is this the reason we can see Earth? Explain your answer.

59. Name one preventable natural disaster. Name one nonpreventable disaster.

60. What are three hazards associated with living in the Ring of Fire?

61. Why can't Arctic species use the same strategy to adapt to a warming climate that Edith's checkerspot butterfly used?

62. Earth has usually been much warmer than it is today. During the high point of the Mesozoic era, in fact, the sea surface temperature may have been 31°F warmer than at present. Yet life was abundant on planet Earth in the Mesozoic era. Why then do we worry about high surface temperatures today?

63. Why are hurricanes expected to become more frequent as the climate warms?

64. How do andesitic and basaltic lava differ from one another?

65. How does the type of magma in a volcano affect how the volcano erupts?

66. How did an earthquake in Japan in 2011 lead to the worst nuclear reactor accident since 1986?

THINK AND DISCUSS (EVALUATION)

67. Is climate change natural or anthropogenic? Give a thorough response.

68. How is the large human population a contributing cause to climate change?

69. Climate change is controversial even though the overwhelming majority of scientists agree that it is real and that it is human-caused. Why is the issue so controversial?

70. Seismic gap analysis shows that a densely populated region is at high risk for an earthquake. Should disaster officials warn the public? What are your reasons?

READINESS ASSURANCE TEST (RAT)

If you have a good handle on this chapter, if you really do, then you should be able to score 7 out of 10 on this RAT. If you score less than 7, you need to study further before moving on.

Choose the BEST answer to the following questions.

1. Which of these statements about hurricanes are true?
   (a) The source of hurricanes is warm, moist air over tropical oceans.
   (b) Hurricanes have wind speeds of at least 119 km/h.
   (c) Hurricanes dissipate when they reach land.
   (d) All are true.

2. Climate change
   (a) is a subject most scientists disagree about.
   (b) refers to the effect of greenhouse gases on atmospheric temperature.
   (c) refers to temperature increases in all of Earth's climate zones.
   (d) is not related to human activities.

3. Climates farther from the equator usually have
   (a) lower average temperatures.
   (b) higher solar intensity.
   (c) more precipitation.
   (d) more water.

4. Ice ages occur because of
   (a) chemicals people put into the atmosphere.
   (b) variations in Earth's tilt and orbit.
   (c) asteroids crashing into Earth.
   (d) changes in the temperature of Earth's core.

5. In an ice age, glaciers
   (a) advance.
   (b) retreat.
   (c) cause sea level to rise.
   (d) reflect incoming solar radiation.

6. Earthquakes occur because
   (a) tectonic plates shift as Earth cools.
   (b) tectonic plates shift as Earth warms.
   (c) seismic waves escape Earth's interior.
   (d) Pangaea continues to break up into smaller pieces.

7. Tsunami
   (a) are usually caused by hurricanes.
   (b) are usually caused by global warming.
   (c) are usually caused by the Milankovitch cycles.
   (d) are usually caused by earthquakes.

8. What can scientists do to predict earthquakes?
   (a) nothing
   (b) measure the strain in rocks and map inactive sections of active fault zones
   (c) measure the elasticity of rock
   (d) measure the distance from a certain location to the nearest subduction zone

9. Hurricanes are related to
   (a) heat, pressure, and water.
   (b) earthquakes.
   (c) tsunami.
   (d) volcanoes.

10. Which of the following is a sign that a volcano may soon erupt?
    (a) bulging of its flanks
    (b) climate change
    (c) warming of its base and flanks
    (d) odd animal behavior

Answers to RAT:
1. d, 2. b, 3. a, 4. b, 5. a, 6. a, 7. d, 8. b, 9. a, 10. a

12 Earth's Evolution Through Geologic Time

Grand Prismatic Pool in Yellowstone National Park This hot-water pool gets its blue color from several species of heat-tolerant cyanobacteria. Microscopic fossils of organisms similar to modern cyanobacteria are among Earth's oldest fossils. (Photo by Michael Collier)

Earth has a long and complex history. Time and again, the splitting and collision of continents has resulted in the formation of new ocean basins and the creation of great mountain ranges. Furthermore, the nature of life on our planet has experienced dramatic changes through time.

12.1 | IS EARTH UNIQUE?

List the principal characteristics that make Earth unique among the planets.

There is only one place in the universe, as far as we know, that supports life—a modest-sized planet called Earth that orbits an average-sized star, the Sun. Life on Earth is ubiquitous; it is found in boiling mudpots and hot springs, in the deep abyss of the ocean, and even under the Antarctic Ice Sheet. Living space on our planet, however, is significantly limited when we consider the needs of individual organisms, particularly humans. The global ocean covers 71 percent of Earth's surface, but only a few hundred meters below the water's surface, pressures are so intense that humans cannot survive without an atmospheric diving suit. In addition, many continental areas are too steep, too high, or too cold for us to inhabit (**FIGURE 12.1**). Nevertheless, based on what we know about other bodies in the solar system—and the hundreds of planets recently discovered orbiting around other stars—Earth is still by far the most accommodating.

What fortuitous events produced a planet so hospitable to life? Earth was not always as we find it today. During its formative years, our planet became hot enough to support a magma ocean. It also survived a several-hundred-million-year period of extreme bombardment by asteroids, to which the heavily cratered surfaces of Mars and the Moon testify. The oxygen-rich atmosphere that makes higher life-forms possible developed relatively recently. Serendipitously, Earth seems to be the right planet, in the right location, at the right time.

The Right Planet

What are some of the characteristics that make Earth unique among the planets? Consider the following:

- If Earth were considerably larger (more massive), its force of gravity would be proportionately greater. Like the giant planets, Earth would have retained a thick, hostile atmosphere consisting of ammonia and methane, and possibly hydrogen and helium.

- If Earth were much smaller, oxygen, water vapor, and other volatiles would escape into space and be lost forever. Thus, like the Moon and Mercury, both of which lack atmospheres, Earth would be void of life.

- If Earth did not have a rigid lithosphere overlaying a weak asthenosphere, plate tectonics would not operate. The continental crust (Earth's "highlands") would not have formed without the recycling of plates. Consequently, the entire planet would likely be covered by an ocean a few kilometers deep. As author Bill Bryson so aptly stated, "There might be life in that lonesome ocean, but there certainly wouldn't be baseball."[1]

- Most surprisingly, perhaps, is the fact that if our planet did not have a molten metallic core, most of the life-forms on Earth would not exist. Fundamentally, without the flow of iron in the core, Earth could not support a magnetic field. It is the magnetic field that prevents lethal cosmic rays from showering Earth's surface and from stripping away our atmosphere.

FIGURE 12.1 Much of Earth's Surface Is Uninhabitable Climbers near the top of Mount Everest. At this altitude, the level of oxygen is only one-third the amount available at sea level. (Photo by STR/AFP/Getty Images)

[1]*A Short History of Nearly Everything* (Broadway Books, 2003).

The Right Location

One of the primary factors that determine whether a planet is suitable for higher life-forms is its location in the solar system. The following scenarios substantiate Earth's advantageous position:

- If Earth were about 10 percent closer to the Sun, our atmosphere would be more like that of Venus and consist mainly of the greenhouse gas carbon dioxide. As a result, Earth's surface temperature would be too hot to support higher life-forms.

- If Earth were about 10 percent farther from the Sun, the problem would be reversed—it would be too cold. The oceans would freeze over, and Earth's active water cycle would not exist. Without liquid water, all life would perish.

- Earth is near a star of modest size. Stars like the Sun have a life span of roughly 10 billion years. During most of this time, radiant energy is emitted at a fairly constant level. Giant stars, on the other hand, consume their nuclear fuel at very high rates and "burn out" in a few hundred million years. Therefore, Earth's proximity to a modest-sized star allowed enough time for the evolution of humans, who first appeared on this planet only a few million years ago.

The Right Time

The last, but certainly not the least, fortuitous factor for Earth is timing. The first organisms to inhabit Earth were extremely primitive and came into existence roughly 3.8 billion years ago. From that point in Earth's history, innumerable changes occurred—life-forms came and went, and there were many changes in the physical environment of our planet. Consider two of the many timely Earth-altering events:

- Earth's atmosphere has developed over time. Earth's primitive atmosphere is thought to have been composed mostly of methane, water vapor, ammonia, and carbon dioxide—but no free oxygen. Fortunately, microorganisms evolved that released oxygen into the atmosphere through the process of *photosynthesis*. About 2.5 billion years ago, an atmosphere with free oxygen came into existence. The result was the evolution of the ancestors of the vast array of organisms that occupy Earth today.

- About 65 million years ago, our planet was struck by an asteroid 10 kilometers (6 miles) in diameter. This impact likely caused a mass extinction during which nearly three-quarters of all plant and animal species were obliterated—including dinosaurs (**FIGURE 12.2**). Although this may not seem fortuitous, the extinction of dinosaurs opened new habitats for small mammals that survived the impact. These habitats, along with evolutionary forces, led to the development of many large mammals that occupy our modern world. Without this event, mammals may not have evolved beyond the small rodent-like creatures that live in burrows.

FIGURE 12.2
Paleontologist and Technicians Excavating a Dinosaur Known as *Titanosaurus* in Southern Argentina (Photo by BERNARDO GONZALEZ RIGA/EPA/Newscom)

As various observers have noted, Earth developed under "just right" conditions to support higher life-forms. Astronomers refer to this as the *Goldilocks scenario*. Like the classic "Goldilocks and the Three Bears" fable, Venus is too hot (Papa Bear's porridge), Mars is too cold (Mama Bear's porridge), but Earth is just right (Baby Bear's porridge).

Viewing Earth's History

The remainder of this chapter focuses on the origin and evolution of planet Earth—the one place in the universe we know fosters life. Using these tools, as well as clues contained in the rock record, scientists continue to unravel many complex events of the geologic past. The goal of this chapter is to provide a brief overview of the history of our planet and its life-forms—a journey that takes us back about 4.6 billion years, to the formation of Earth. Later, we will consider how our physical world assumed its present state and how Earth's inhabitants changed through time. We suggest that you reacquaint yourself with the *geologic time scale* presented in **FIGURE 12.3** and refer to it throughout the chapter.

12.1 CONCEPT CHECKS

1 In what way is Earth unique among the planets of our solar system?

2 Explain why Earth is just the right size.

3 Why is Earth's molten, metallic core important to humans living today?

4 Why is Earth's location in the solar system ideal for the development of higher life-forms?

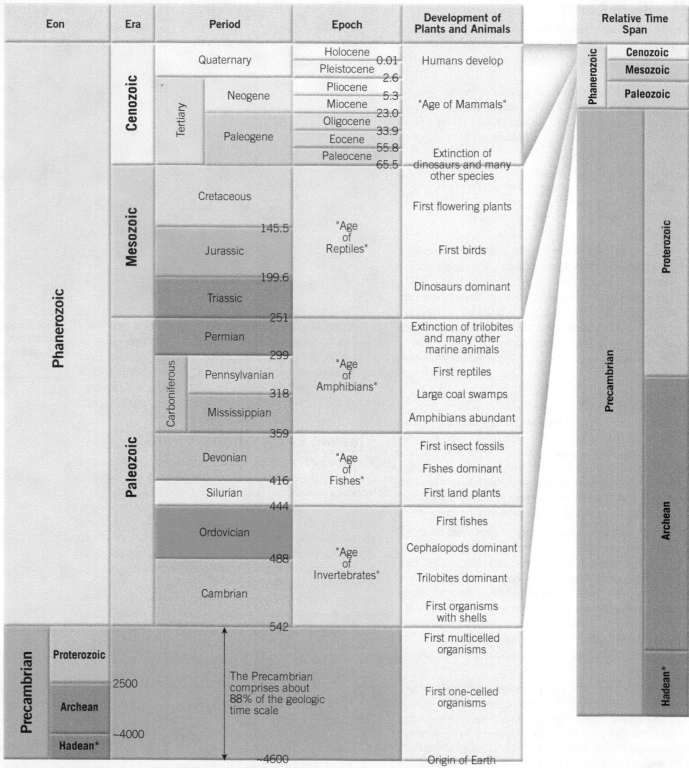

Eon	Era	Period	Epoch	Development of Plants and Animals
Phanerozoic	Cenozoic	Quaternary	Holocene — 0.01	Humans develop
			Pleistocene — 2.6	
		Tertiary — Neogene	Pliocene — 5.3	"Age of Mammals"
			Miocene — 23.0	
		Tertiary — Paleogene	Oligocene — 33.9	
			Eocene — 55.8	
			Paleocene — 65.5	Extinction of dinosaurs and many other species
	Mesozoic	Cretaceous	"Age of Reptiles"	First flowering plants
		— 145.5		
		Jurassic		First birds
		— 199.6		
		Triassic		Dinosaurs dominant
		— 251		
	Paleozoic	Permian	"Age of Amphibians"	Extinction of trilobites and many other marine animals
		— 299		
		Carboniferous — Pennsylvanian		First reptiles
		— 318		Large coal swamps
		Carboniferous — Mississippian		Amphibians abundant
		— 359		
		Devonian	"Age of Fishes"	First insect fossils
				Fishes dominant
		— 416		First land plants
		Silurian		
		— 444		
		Ordovician	"Age of Invertebrates"	First fishes
				Cephalopods dominant
		— 488		Trilobites dominant
		Cambrian		First organisms with shells
		— 542		First multicelled organisms
Precambrian	Proterozoic	The Precambrian comprises about 88% of the geologic time scale		
	— 2500			First one-celled organisms
	Archean			
	~4000			
	Hadean*			
	~4600			Origin of Earth

Relative Time Span

Phanerozoic	Cenozoic
	Mesozoic
	Paleozoic
Precambrian	Proterozoic
	Archean
	Hadean*

* Hadean is the informal name for the span that begins at Earth's formation and ends with Earth's earliest-known rocks.

FIGURE 12.3 The Geologic Time Scale Numbers represent time in millions of years before the present. The Precambrian accounts for about 88 percent of geologic time.

12.2 | BIRTH OF A PLANET Outline the major stages in the evolution of Earth, from the Big Bang to the formation of our planet's layered internal structure.

The universe had been evolving for several billion years before our solar system and Earth began to form. The universe began about 13.7 billion years ago, with the Big Bang, when all matter and space came into existence. Shortly thereafter, the two simplest elements, hydrogen and helium, formed. These basic elements were the ingredients for the first star systems. Several billion years later, our home galaxy, the Milky Way, came into existence. It was within a band of stars and nebular debris in an arm of this spiral galaxy that the Sun and planets took form nearly 4.6 billion years ago.

From the Big Bang to Heavy Elements

According to the Big Bang theory, the formation of our planet began about 13.7 billion years ago, with a cataclysmic explosion that created all matter and space (**FIGURE 12.4**). Initially, subatomic particles (protons, neutrons, and electrons) formed. Later, as this debris cooled, atoms of hydrogen and helium, the two lightest elements, began to form. Within a few hundred million years, clouds of these gases condensed and coalesced into stars that compose the galactic systems we now observe.

As these gases contracted to become the first stars, heating triggered the process of *nuclear fusion*. Within the interiors of stars, hydrogen nuclei convert to helium nuclei, releasing enormous amounts of radiant energy (heat, light, cosmic rays). Astronomers have determined that in stars more massive than our Sun, other thermonuclear reactions occur that generate all the elements on the periodic table up to number 26, iron. The heaviest elements (beyond number 26) are created only at extreme temperatures during the explosive death of a star eight or more times as massive as the Sun. During these cataclysmic **supernova** events, exploding stars produce all the elements heavier than iron and spew them into interstellar space. It is from such debris that our Sun and solar system formed. According to the Big Bang scenario, atoms in your body were produced billions of years ago, in the hot interior of now-defunct stars, and the gold in your jewelry was produced during a supernova explosion that occurred in some distant place.

From Planetesimals to Protoplanets

Recall that the solar system, including Earth, formed about 4.6 billion years ago, from the **solar nebula**, a large rotating cloud of interstellar dust and gas (see Figure 12.4E). As the solar nebula contracted, most of the matter collected in the center to create the hot *protosun*. The remaining materials formed a thick, flattened, rotating disk, within which matter gradually cooled and condensed into grains and clumps of icy, rocky, and metallic material. Repeated collisions resulted in most of the material eventually collecting into asteroid-sized objects called **planetesimals**.

The composition of planetesimals was largely determined by their proximity to the protosun. As you might expect, temperatures were highest in the inner solar system and decreased toward the outer edge of the disk. Therefore, between the present orbits of Mercury and Mars, the planetesimals were composed mainly of materials with high melting temperatures—metals and rocky substances. The planetesimals that formed beyond the orbit of Mars, where temperatures are low, contained high percentages of ices— water, carbon dioxide, ammonia, and methane—as well as smaller amounts of rocky and metallic debris.

Through repeated collisions and accretion (sticking together), these planetesimals grew into eight **protoplanets** and their moons (see Figure 12.4G). During this process, the same amount of matter was concentrated into fewer and fewer bodies, each having greater and greater masses.

At some point in Earth's evolution, a giant impact occurred between a Mars-sized object and a young, semi-molten Earth. This collision ejected huge amounts of debris into space, some of which coalesced to form the Moon (see Figure 12.4J,K,L).

Earth's Early Evolution

As material continued to accumulate, the high-velocity impact of interplanetary debris (planetesimals) and the decay of radioactive elements caused the temperature of our planet to steadily increase. This early period of heating resulted in a magma ocean, perhaps several hundred kilometers deep. Within the magma ocean, buoyant masses of molten rock rose toward the surface and eventually solidified to produce thin rafts of crustal rocks. Geologists call this early period of Earth's history the **Hadean**, which began with the formation of Earth about 4.6 billion years ago and ended roughly 3.8 billion years ago (**FIGURE 12.5**). The name *Hadean* is derived from the Greek word *Hades*, meaning "the underworld," referring to the "hellish" conditions on Earth at the time.

During this period of intense heating, Earth became hot enough that iron and nickel began to melt. Melting produced liquid blobs of heavy metal that sank under their own weight. This process occurred rapidly on the scale of geologic time and produced Earth's dense iron-rich core. The

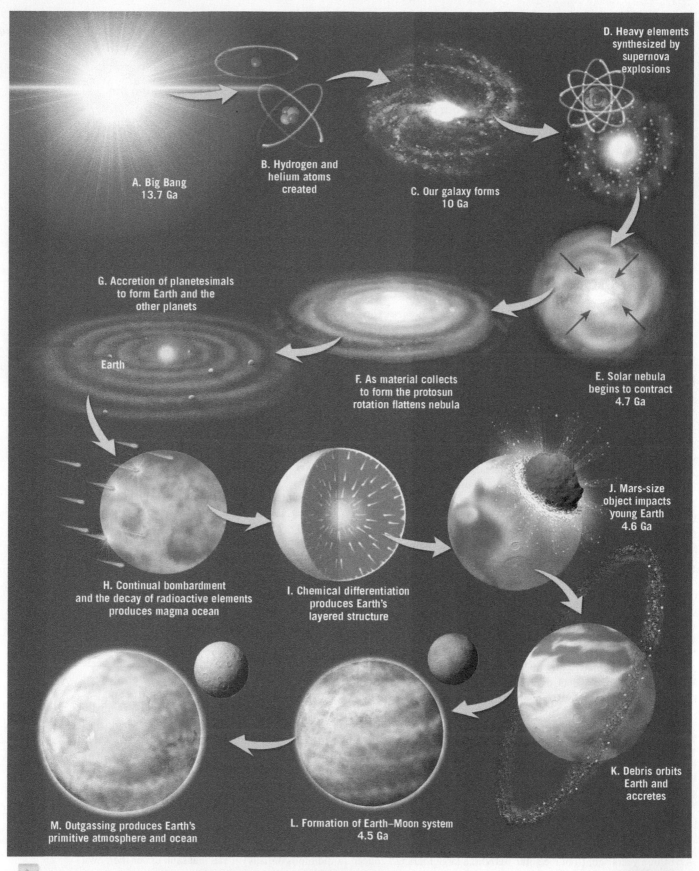

SmartFigure 12.4 Major Events That Led to the Formation of Early Earth

FIGURE 12.5 Artistic Depiction of Earth During the Hadean The Hadean is an unofficial eon of geologic time that occurred before the Archean. Its name refers to the "hellish" conditions on Earth. During the Hadean, Earth had a magma ocean and experienced intense bombardment by nebular debris.

formation of a molten iron core was the first of many stages of chemical differentiation in which Earth converted from a homogeneous body, with roughly the same matter at all depths, to a layered planet with material sorted by density (see Figure 12.4I).

This period of chemical differentiation established the three major divisions of Earth's interior—the iron-rich *core*; the thin *primitive crust*; and Earth's thickest layer, the *mantle*, located between the core and the crust. In addition, the lightest materials—including water vapor, carbon dioxide, and other gases—escaped to form a primitive atmosphere and, shortly thereafter, the oceans.

12.2 CONCEPT CHECKS

1 What two elements made up most of the very early universe?

2 What is the name of the cataclysmic event in which an exploding star produces all the elements heavier than iron?

3 Briefly describe the formation of the planets from the solar nebula.

4 Describe the conditions on Earth during the Hadean.

12.3 | ORIGIN AND EVOLUTION OF THE ATMOSPHERE AND OCEANS

Describe how Earth's atmosphere and oceans have formed and evolved through time.

We can be thankful for our atmosphere; without it, there would be no greenhouse effect, and Earth would be nearly 60°F colder. Earth's water bodies would be frozen over, and the hydrologic cycle would be nonexistent.

The air we breathe is a stable mixture of 78 percent nitrogen, 21 percent oxygen, about 1 percent argon (an inert gas), and small amounts of gases such as carbon dioxide and water vapor. However, our planet's original atmosphere 4.6 billion years ago was substantially different.

Earth's Primitive Atmosphere

Early in Earth's formation, its atmosphere likely consisted of gases most common in the early solar system: hydrogen, helium, methane, ammonia, carbon dioxide, and water vapor. The lightest of these gases—hydrogen and helium—most likely escaped into space because Earth's gravity was too weak to hold them. The remaining gases—methane, ammonia, carbon dioxide, and water vapor—contain the basic ingredients of life: carbon, hydrogen, oxygen, and nitrogen. This early atmosphere was enhanced by a process called **outgassing**, through which gases trapped in the planet's interior are released. Outgassing from hundreds of active volcanoes still remains an important planetary function worldwide (**FIGURE 12.6**). However, early in Earth's history, when massive heating and fluidlike motion occurred in the mantle, the gas output would likely have

been immense. These early eruptions probably released mainly water vapor, carbon dioxide, and sulfur dioxide, with minor amounts of other gases. Most importantly, free oxygen was not present in Earth's primitive atmosphere.

Oxygen in the Atmosphere

As Earth cooled, water vapor condensed to form clouds, and torrential rains began to fill low-lying areas, which became

FIGURE 12.6 Outgassing Produced Earth's First Enduring Atmosphere Outgassing continues today from hundreds of active volcanoes like this one in Iceland. (Photo by Lee Frost/Robert Harding)

the oceans. In those oceans, nearly 3.5 billion years ago, photosynthesizing bacteria began to release oxygen into the water. During *photosynthesis*, organisms use the Sun's energy to produce organic material (energetic molecules of sugar containing hydrogen and carbon) from carbon dioxide (CO_2) and water (H_2O). The first bacteria probably used hydrogen sulfide (H_2S) rather than water as the source of hydrogen. One of the earliest-known bacteria, *cyanobacteria* (once called blue-green algae), began to produce oxygen as a by-product of photosynthesis.

Initially, the newly released free oxygen was readily captured by chemical reactions with organic matter and dissolved iron in the ocean. It seems that large quantities of iron were released into the early ocean through submarine volcanism and associated hydrothermal vents. Iron has tremendous affinity for oxygen. When these two elements join, they become iron oxide (rust). As it accumulated on the seafloor, these early iron oxide deposits created alternating layers of iron-rich rocks and chert, called **banded iron formations**. Most banded iron deposits accumulated in the Precambrian, between 3.5 and 2 billion years ago, and represent the world's most important reservoir of iron ore.

As the number of oxygen-generating organisms increased, oxygen began to build in the atmosphere. Chemical analysis of rock suggests that oxygen first appeared in significant amounts in the atmosphere around 2.5 billion years ago, a phenomenon referred to as the **Great Oxygenation Event**. For the next billion years, oxygen levels in the atmosphere probably fluctuated but remained below 10 percent of current levels. Prior to the start of the Cambrian period 542 million years ago, which coincided with the evolution of complex life-forms, the level of free oxygen in the atmosphere began to climb. The availability of abundant oxygen in the atmosphere contributed to the proliferation of aerobic life-forms (oxygen-consuming organisms). One apparent spike in oxygen levels occurred during the Pennsylvanian period (300 million years ago), when oxygen made up about 35 percent of the atmosphere, compared to modern levels of only 21 percent. The large size of insects and amphibians during the Pennsylvanian period has been attributed to this abundance of oxygen.

Another positive benefit of the Great Oxygenation Event is that oxygen molecules (O_2) readily absorb ultraviolet radiation and form *ozone* (O_3), an oxygen molecule composed of three oxygen atoms. Ozone is concentrated between 10 and 50 kilometers (6 and 30 miles) above Earth's surface, in a layer called the *stratosphere*, where it absorbs much of the harmful ultraviolet radiation before it reaches the surface. For the first time, Earth's landmasses were protected from this form of solar radiation, which is particularly harmful to DNA—the stuff of which living organisms are made. Marine organisms had always been shielded from harmful ultraviolet radiation by seawater, but with the development of the atmosphere's protective ozone layer, the continents became more hospitable to plants and animals.

Evolution of the Oceans

When Earth cooled sufficiently to allow water vapor to condense, rainwater fell and collected in low-lying areas. By 4 billion years ago, it is estimated that as much as 90 percent of the current volume of seawater was contained in the developing ocean basins. Because volcanic eruptions released into the atmosphere large quantities of sulfur dioxide, which readily combines with water to form hydrochloric acid, the earliest rainwater was highly acidic. The level of acidity was even greater than the acid rain that damaged lakes and streams in eastern North America during the latter part of the twentieth century. Consequently, Earth's rocky surface weathered at an accelerated rate. The products released by chemical weathering included atoms and molecules of various substances—including sodium, calcium, potassium, and silica—that were carried

FIGURE 12.7 White Chalk Cliffs, England Similar deposits are also found in northern France. (Photo by Stuart Black/Robert Harding)

These prominent chalk cliffs are composed largely of tiny shells of marine organisms, such as foraminifera.

into the newly formed oceans. Some of these dissolved substances precipitated to become chemical sediment that mantled the ocean floor. Other substances formed soluble salts, which increased the salinity of seawater. Research suggests that the salinity of the oceans increased rapidly at first but has remained constant over the past 2 billion years.

Earth's oceans also serve as a repository for tremendous volumes of carbon dioxide, a major constituent in the primitive atmosphere. This is significant because carbon dioxide is a greenhouse gas that strongly influences the heating of the atmosphere. Venus, once thought to be very similar to Earth, has an atmosphere composed of 97 percent carbon dioxide that produced a "runaway" greenhouse effect. As a result, its surface temperature is 475°C (900°F).

Carbon dioxide is readily soluble in seawater, where it often joins other atoms or molecules to produce various chemical precipitates. The most common compound generated by this process is calcium carbonate ($CaCO_3$), which makes up limestone, the most abundant chemical sedimentary rock. About 542 million years ago, marine organisms began to extract calcium carbonate from seawater to make their shells and other hard parts. Included were trillions of tiny marine organisms, such as foraminifera, whose shells were deposited on the seafloor at the end of their life cycle. Today, some of these deposits can be observed in the chalk beds exposed along the White Cliffs of Dover, England, shown in **FIGURE 12.7**. By "locking up" carbon dioxide, these limestone deposits store this greenhouse gas so it cannot easily re-enter the atmosphere.

12.3 CONCEPT CHECKS

1 What is meant by *outgassing*, and what modern phenomenon serves that role today?

2 Identify the most abundant gases that were added to Earth's early atmosphere through the process of outgassing.

3 Why is the evolution of a type of bacteria that used photosynthesis to produce food important to most modern organisms?

4 Why was rainwater highly acidic early in Earth's history?

5 How does the ocean remove carbon dioxide from the atmosphere? What role do tiny marine organisms, such as foraminifera, play?

12.4 | PRECAMBRIAN HISTORY: THE FORMATION OF EARTH'S CONTINENTS
Explain the formation of continental crust, how continental crust becomes assembled into continents, and the role that the supercontinent cycle has played in this process.

Earth's first 4 billion years are encompassed in the time span called the *Precambrian*. Representing nearly 90 percent of Earth's history, the Precambrian is divided into the *Archean eon* ("ancient age") and the *Proterozoic eon* ("early life"). Our knowledge of this ancient time is limited because much of the early rock record has been obscured by the very Earth processes you have been studying, especially plate tectonics, erosion, and deposition. Most Precambrian rocks lack fossils, which hinders correlation of rock units. In addition, rocks this old are often metamorphosed and deformed, extensively eroded, and frequently concealed by younger strata. Indeed, Precambrian history is written in scattered, speculative episodes, like a long book with many missing chapters.

Earth's First Continents

Geologists have discovered tiny crystals of the mineral zircon that formed 4.4 billion years ago—evidence that crustal rocks began to form early in Earth's history. What differentiates

EYE ON EARTH

The oldest-known sample of Earth is a 4.4-billion-year-old zircon crystal found in a metaconglomerate in the Jack Hills area of western Australia. Zircon is a silicate mineral that commonly occurs in trace amounts in most granitic rocks. (Photo by John W. Valley/NSF)

QUESTION 1 What is the parent rock of a metaconglomerate?

QUESTION 2 Assuming that this zircon crystal originated as part of a granite intrusion, briefly describe its journey from the time of its formation until it was discovered in Jack Hill.

QUESTION 3 Is this zircon crystal younger or older than the metaconglomerate in which it was found? Explain.

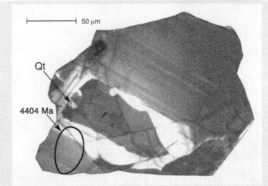

50 µm

Qt

4404 Ma

FIGURE 12.8 Earth's Early Crust Was Continually Recycled (Photo by Mood Board/AGE Fotostock)

The crust covering this lava lake is continually being replaced with fresh lava from below, much like Earth's crust was recycled early in its history.

Making Continental Crust

Earth's first crust was probably ultramafic in composition, but because physical evidence no longer exists, we are not certain. The hot, turbulent mantle that most likely existed during the Archean eon recycled most of this material back into the mantle. In fact, it may have been continuously recycled, in much the same way that the "crust" that forms on a lava lake is repeatedly replaced with fresh lava from below (**FIGURE 12.8**).

The oldest preserved continental rocks occur as small, highly deformed terranes, which are incorporated within somewhat younger blocks of continental crust (**FIGURE 12.9**). One of the oldest of these is the 4-billion-year-old Acasta gneiss, located in Canada's Northwest Territories. Older crustal rocks may exist in the Nuvvuagittuq Greenstone Belt in Quebec, but the technique used to date them is controversial.

oceanic crust from continental crust? Recall that oceanic crust is a relatively dense (3.0 g/cm³) homogeneous layer of basaltic rocks derived from partial melting of the rocky upper mantle. In addition, oceanic crust is thin, averaging only 7 kilometers (4.3 miles) thick. Continental crust, on the other hand, is composed of a variety of rock types, has an average thickness of nearly 40 kilometers (25 miles), and contains a large percentage of low-density (2.7 g/cm³), silica-rich rocks such as granite.

The significance of the differences between continental crust and oceanic crust cannot be overstated in a review of Earth's geologic evolution. Oceanic crust, because it is relatively thin and dense, is found several kilometers below sea level—unless of course it has been pushed onto a landmass by tectonic forces. Continental crust, because of its great thickness and lower density, may extend well above sea level. Also, recall that oceanic crust of normal thickness readily subducts, whereas thick, buoyant blocks of continental crust resist being recycled into the mantle.

The formation of continental crust is a continuation of the gravitational segregation of Earth materials that began during the final stage of our planet's formation. Dense metallic material, mainly iron and nickel, sank to form Earth's core, leaving behind the less dense rocky material of which the mantle is composed. It is from Earth's rocky mantle that low-density, silica-rich minerals were gradually distilled to form continental crust. This process is analogous to making sour mash whiskeys. In the production of whiskeys, various grains, such as corn, are fermented to generate alcohol, with sour mash being the byproduct. This mixture is then heated or distilled, which drives off the lighter material (alcohol) and leaves behind the sour mash. In a similar manner, partial melting of mantle rocks generates low-density, silica-rich materials that buoyantly rise to the surface to form Earth's crust, leaving behind the dense mantle rocks. However, little is known about the details of the mechanisms that generated these silica-rich melts during the Archean.

Some geologists think that some type of plate-like motion operated early in Earth's history. In addition, hot-spot volcanism was likely active during this time. However, because the mantle was hotter in the Archean than it is today, both of these phenomena would have progressed at higher rates than their modern counterparts. Hot-spot volcanism is thought to

FIGURE 12.9 Earth's Oldest Preserved Continental Rocks Are About 4 Billion Years Old (Photo courtesy of James L. Amos/ CORBIS)

These rocks at Isua, Greenland, some of the world's oldest, have been dated at 3.8 billion years.

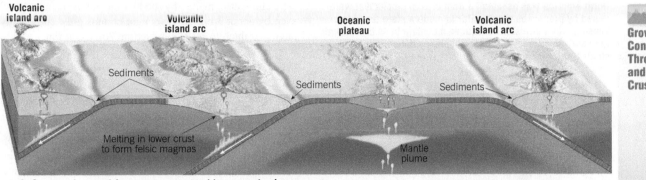

SmartFigure 12.10
Growth of Large Continental Masses Through the Collision and Accretion of Smaller Crustal Fragments

A. Scattered crustal fragments separated by ocean basins

B. Collision of volcanic island arcs and oceanic plateau to form a larger crustal block

have created immense shield volcanoes as well as oceanic plateaus. Simultaneously, subduction of oceanic crust generated volcanic island arcs. Collectively, these relatively small crustal fragments represent the first phase in creating stable, continent-size landmasses.

From Continental Crust to Continents The growth of larger continental masses was accomplished through collision and accretion of various types of crustal fragments, as illustrated in FIGURE 12.10. This type of collision tectonics deformed and metamorphosed sediments caught between converging crustal fragments, thereby shortening and thickening the developing crust. In the deepest regions of these collision zones, partial melting of the thickened crust generated silica-rich magmas that ascended and intruded the rocks above. The result was the formation of large crustal provinces that, in turn, accreted with others to form even larger crustal blocks called **cratons**.

The portion of a modern craton that is exposed at the surface is referred to as a **shield**. The assembly of a large craton involves the accretion of several crustal blocks that cause major mountain-building episodes similar to India's collision with Asia. FIGURE 12.11 shows the extent of crustal material

FIGURE 12.11
Distribution of Crustal Material Remaining from the Archean and Proterozoic Eons

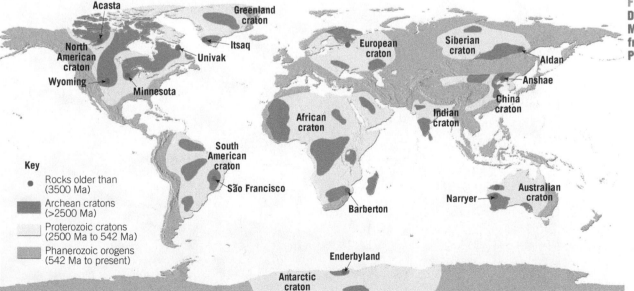

Key
- • Rocks older than (3500 Ma)
- Archean cratons (>2500 Ma)
- Proterozoic cratons (2500 Ma to 542 Ma)
- Phanerozoic orogens (542 Ma to present)

SmartFigure 12.12
The Major Geologic Provinces of North America and Their Ages in Billions of Years (Ga)

North America was assembled from crustal blocks that were joined by processes very similar to modern plate tectonics. These ancient collisions produced mountain belts that include remnant volcanic island arcs, trapped by the colliding continental fragments.

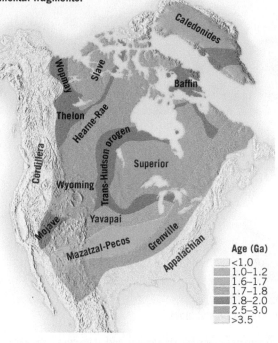

Age (Ga)
<1.0
1.0–1.2
1.6–1.7
1.7–1.8
1.8–2.0
2.5–3.0
>3.5

that was produced during the Archean and Proterozoic eons. This was accomplished by the collision and accretion of many thin, highly mobile terranes into nearly recognizable continental masses.

Although the Precambrian was a time when much of Earth's continental crust was generated, a substantial amount of crustal material was destroyed as well. Crust can be lost either by weathering and erosion or by direct reincorporation into the mantle through subduction. Evidence suggests that during much of the Archean, thin slabs of continental crust

were eliminated, mainly by subduction into the mantle. However, by about 3 billion years ago, cratons grew sufficiently large and thick to resist subduction. After that time, weathering and erosion became the primary processes of crustal destruction. By the close of the Precambrian, an estimated 85 percent of the modern continental crust had formed.

The Making of North America

North America provides an excellent example of the development of continental crust and its piecemeal assembly into a continent. Notice in **FIGURE 12.12** that very little continental crust older than 3.5 billion years remains. In the late Archean, between 3 and 2.5 billion years ago, there was a period of major continental growth. During this span, the accretion of numerous island arcs and other fragments generated several large crustal provinces. North America contains some of these crustal units, including the Superior and Hearne/Rae cratons shown in Figure 12.12. It remains unknown where these ancient continental blocks formed.

About 1.9 billion years ago, these crustal provinces collided to produce the Trans-Hudson mountain belt (see Figure 12.12). (Such mountain-building episodes were not restricted to North America because ancient deformed strata of similar age are also found on other continents.) This event built the North American craton, around which several large and numerous small crustal fragments were later added (**FIGURE 12.13**). One of these late arrivals is the Piedmont province of the Appalachians. In addition, several terranes were added to the western margin of North America during the Mesozoic and Cenozoic eras to generate the mountainous North American Cordillera.

Supercontinents of the Precambrian

At different times, parts of what is now North America have combined with other continental landmasses to form a supercontinent. **Supercontinents** are large landmasses that

FIGURE 12.13 Rocky Shoreline in the Superior Province The Superior province is part of the North American craton, around which several crustal fragments were later added. (Photo by Peter Van Rhijn/Getty Images)

contain all, or nearly all, the existing continents. Pangaea was the most recent, but certainly not the only, supercontinent to exist in the geologic past. The earliest well-documented supercontinent, *Rodinia*, formed during the Proterozoic eon, about 1.1 billion years ago. Although its reconstruction is still being researched, it is clear that Rodinia's configuration was quite different from Pangaea's (FIGURE 12.14). One obvious distinction is that North America was located near the center of this ancient landmass.

Between 800 and 600 million years ago, Rodinia gradually split apart. By the end of the Precambrian, many of the fragments reassembled, producing a large landmass in the Southern Hemisphere called *Gondwana*, comprised mainly of present-day South America, Africa, India, Australia, and Antarctica (FIGURE 12.15). Other continental fragments also developed—North America, Siberia, and Northern Europe. We consider the fate of these Precambrian landmasses later in the chapter.

Supercontinent Cycle
The idea that rifting and dispersal of one supercontinent is followed by a long period during which the fragments are gradually reassembled into a new supercontinent with a different configuration is called the **supercontinent cycle**. The assembly and dispersal of supercontinents had a profound impact on the evolution of Earth's continents. In addition, this phenomenon greatly influenced global climates and contributed to periodic episodes of rising and falling sea level.

Supercontinents, Mountain Building, and Climate
As continents move, the patterns of ocean currents and global winds change, which influences the global distribution of temperature and precipitation. One example of how a supercontinent's dispersal influenced climate is the formation of the Antarctic Ice Sheet. Although eastern Antarctica remained over the South Pole for more than 100 million years, it was not glaciated until about 25 million years ago. Prior to this period of glaciation, South America was connected to the Antarctic Peninsula. This arrangement of landmasses helped maintain a circulation pattern in which warm ocean currents reached the coast of Antarctica, as shown in FIGURE 12.16A. This is similar to the way in which the modern Gulf Stream keeps Iceland mostly ice free, despite its name. However, as South America separated from Antarctica, it moved northward, permitting ocean circulation to flow from west to east around the entire continent of Antarctica (FIGURE 12.16B). This cold current, called the West Wind Drift, effectively isolated the entire Antarctic coast from the warm,

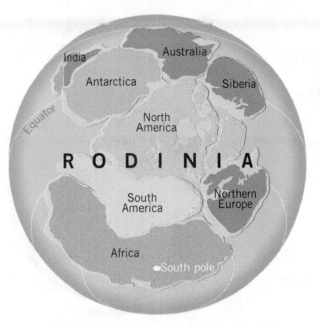

FIGURE 12.14 **One of Several Possible Configurations of the Supercontinent Rodinia** For clarity, the continents are drawn with somewhat modern shapes, not their actual shapes from 1 billion years ago. (After P. Hoffman, J. Rogers, and others)

poleward-directed currents in the southern oceans. As a result, most of the Antarctic landmass became covered with glacial ice.

Local and regional climates have also been impacted by large mountain systems created by the collision of large cratons. Because of their high elevations, mountains exhibit markedly lower average temperatures than surrounding lowlands. In addition, when air rises over these lofty structures, lifting "squeezes" moisture from the air, leaving the region downwind relatively dry. A modern analogy is the wet, heavily forested western slopes of the Sierra Nevada compared to the dry climate of the Great Basin Desert that lies directly to the east.

Supercontinents and Sea-Level Changes
Significant and numerous sea-level changes have been documented in geologic history, and many of them appear to be related to the assembly and dispersal of supercontinents. If sea level rises, shallow seas advance onto the continents. Evidence for periods when the seas advanced onto the continents include

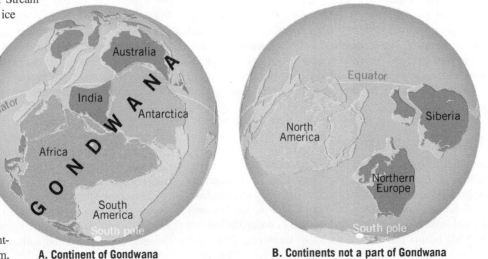

A. Continent of Gondwana

B. Continents not a part of Gondwana

FIGURE 12.15 **Reconstruction of Earth as It May Have Appeared in Late Precambrian Time** The southern continents were joined into a single landmass called Gondwana. Other landmasses that were not part of Gondwana include North America, northwestern Europe, and northern Asia. (After P. Hoffman, J. Rogers, and others)

50 million years ago warm ocean currents kept Antarctica nearly ice free.

As South America separated from Antarctica, the West Wind Drift developed. This newly formed ocean current effectively cut Antarctica off from warm currents and contributed to the formation of its vast ice sheets.

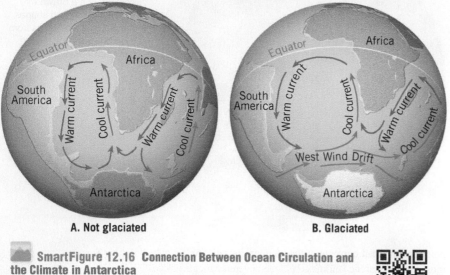

A. Not glaciated

B. Glaciated

 SmartFigure 12.16 Connection Between Ocean Circulation and the Climate in Antarctica

thick sequences of ancient marine sedimentary rocks that blanket large areas of modern landmasses—including much of the eastern two-thirds of the United States.

The supercontinent cycle and sea-level changes are directly related to rates of *seafloor spreading*. When the rate of spreading is rapid, as it is along the East Pacific Rise today, the production of warm oceanic crust is also high. Because warm oceanic crust is less dense (takes up more space) than cold crust, fast-spreading ridges occupy more volume in the ocean basins than do slow-spreading centers. (Think of getting into a tub filled with water.) As a result, when the rates of seafloor spreading increase, more seawater is displaced, which results in the sea level rising. This, in turn, causes shallow seas to advance onto the low-lying portions of the continents.

12.4 CONCEPT CHECKS

1 Briefly explain how low-density continental crust was produced from Earth's rocky mantle.

2 Describe how cratons came into being.

3 How can the movement of continents trigger climate change?

4 What is the supercontinent cycle? What supercontinent preceded Pangaea?

5 Explain how seafloor-spreading rates are related to sea-level changes.

12.5 | GEOLOGIC HISTORY OF THE PHANEROZOIC: THE FORMATION OF EARTH'S MODERN CONTINENTS List and discuss the major geologic events in the Paleozoic, Mesozoic, and Cenozoic eras.

The time span since the close of the Precambrian, called the *Phanerozoic eon*, encompasses 542 million years and is divided into three eras: *Paleozoic*, *Mesozoic*, and *Cenozoic*. The beginning of the Phanerozoic is marked by the appearance of the first life-forms with hard parts such as shells, scales, bones, or teeth—all of which greatly enhance the chances for an organism to be preserved in the fossil record. Thus, the study of Phanerozoic crustal history was aided by the availability of fossils, which improved our ability to date and correlate geologic events. Moreover, because every organism is associated with its own particular niche, the greatly improved fossil record provided invaluable information for deciphering ancient environments.

Paleozoic History

As the Paleozoic era opened, North America hosted no living things, neither plant nor animal. There were no Appalachian or Rocky Mountains; the continent was largely a barren lowland. Several times during the early Paleozoic, shallow seas moved inland and then receded from the continental interior and left behind the thick deposits of limestone, shale, and clean sandstone that mark the shorelines of these previously midcontinent shallow seas.

Formation of Pangaea One of the major events of the Paleozoic was the formation of the supercontinent Pangaea, which began with a series of collisions that gradually joined North America, Europe, Siberia, and other smaller crustal fragments (**FIGURE 12.17**). These events eventually generated a large northern continent called *Laurasia*. This tropical landmass supported warm wet conditions that led to the formation of vast swamps that eventually converted to coal.

Simultaneously, the vast southern continent of *Gondwana* encompassed five continents—South America, Africa, Australia, Antarctica, and India—and perhaps portions of China. Evidence of extensive continental glaciation places this landmass near the South Pole. By the end of the Paleozoic, Gondwana had migrated northward and collided with Laurasia, culminating in the formation of the supercontinent *Pangaea*.

The accretion of Pangaea spans more than 300 million years and resulted in the formation of several mountain belts. The collision of Northern Europe (mainly Norway) with Greenland produced the Caledonian Mountains, whereas the joining of northern Asia (Siberia) and Europe created the Ural Mountains, Northern China is also thought to have accreted to Asia by the end of the Paleozoic, whereas southern China may not have become part of Asia until after Pangaea had begun to rift. (Recall that India did not begin to accrete to Asia until about 50 million years ago.)

Pangaea reached its maximum size about 250 million years ago, as Africa collided with North America (see Figure 12.17D). This event marked the final and most intense period of mountain building in the long history of the Appalachian Mountains (**FIGURE 12.18**).

Mesozoic History

Spanning about 186 million years, the Mesozoic era is divided into three periods: the *Triassic, Jurassic,* and *Cretaceous.* Major geologic events of the Mesozoic include the breakup of Pangaea and the evolution of our modern ocean basins.

Changes in Sea Levels The Mesozoic era began with much of the world's continents above sea level. The exposed Triassic strata are primarily red sandstones and mudstones that lack marine fossils, features that indicate a terrestrial environment. (The red color in sandstone comes from the oxidation of iron.)

As the Jurassic period opened, the sea invaded western North America. Adjacent to this shallow sea, extensive continental sediments were deposited on what is now the Colorado Plateau. The most prominent is the Navajo Sandstone, a cross-bedded, quartz-rich layer that in some places approaches 300 meters (1000 feet) thick. These remnants of massive dunes indicate that an enormous desert occupied much of the American Southwest during early Jurassic times (**FIGURE 12.19**). Another well-known Jurassic deposit is the Morrison Formation—the world's richest storehouse of dinosaur fossils. Included are the fossilized bones of massive dinosaurs such as *Apatosaurus* (formerly *Brontosaurus*), *Brachiosaurus,* and *Stegosaurus.*

Coal Formation in Western North America As the Jurassic period gave way to the Cretaceous, shallow seas again encroached upon much of western North America, as well as the Atlantic and Gulf coastal regions. This led to the formation of "coal swamps" similar to those of the Paleozoic era. Today, the Cretaceous coal deposits in the western United States and Canada are economically important. For example, on the Crow Native American reservation in Montana, there are nearly 20 billion tons of high-quality, Cretaceous-age coal.

The Breakup of Pangaea Another major event of the Mesozoic era was the breakup of Pangaea. About 185 million years ago, a rift developed between what is now North America and western Africa, marking the birth of the Atlantic Ocean. As Pangaea gradually broke apart, the westward-moving North American plate began to override the Pacific basin. This tectonic event triggered a continuous wave of

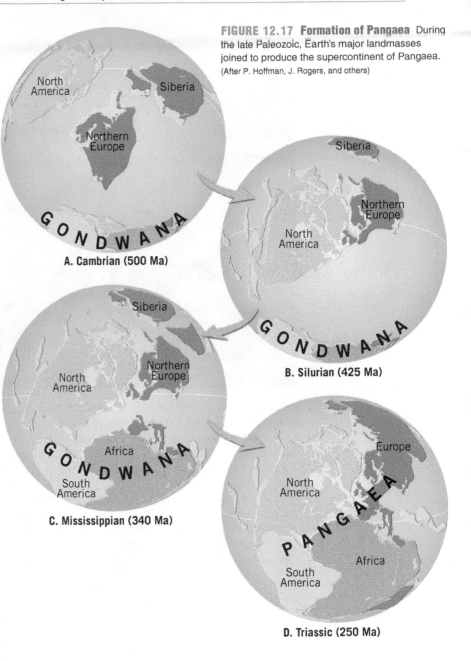

FIGURE 12.17 Formation of Pangaea During the late Paleozoic, Earth's major landmasses joined to produce the supercontinent of Pangaea. (After P. Hoffman, J. Rogers, and others)

A. Cambrian (500 Ma)

B. Silurian (425 Ma)

C. Mississippian (340 Ma)

D. Triassic (250 Ma)

deformation that moved inland along the entire western margin of North America.

Formation of the North American Cordillera By Jurassic times, subduction of the Pacific basin under the North American plate began to produce the chaotic mixture of rocks that exist today in the Coast Ranges of California. Further inland, igneous activity was widespread, and for more than 100 million years, volcanism was rampant as huge masses of magma rose within a few miles of Earth's surface. The remnants of this activity include the granitic plutons of the Sierra Nevada, as well as the Idaho batholith and British Columbia's Coast Range batholith.

The subduction of the Pacific basin under the western margin of North America also resulted in the piecemeal

addition of crustal fragments to the entire Pacific margin of the continent—from Mexico's Baja Peninsula to northern Alaska. Each collision displaced earlier accreted terranes further inland, adding to the zone of deformation as well as to the thickness and lateral extent of the continental margin.

Compressional forces moved huge rock units in a shingle-like fashion toward the east. Across much of North America's western margin, older rocks were thrust eastward over younger strata, for distances exceeding 150 kilometers (90 miles). Ultimately, this activity was responsible for generating a vast portion of the North American Cordillera that extends from Wyoming to Alaska.

Toward the end of the Mesozoic, the southern portions of the Rocky Mountains developed. This mountain-building event, called the *Laramide Orogeny*, occurred when large blocks of deeply buried Precambrian rocks were lifted nearly vertically along steeply dipping faults, upwarping the overlying younger sedimentary strata. The mountain ranges produced by the Laramide Orogeny include Colorado's Front Range, the Sangre de Cristo of New Mexico and Colorado, and the Bighorns of Wyoming.

FIGURE 12.19 Massive, Cross-Bedded Sandstone Cliffs in Zion National Park These sandstone cliffs are the remnants of ancient sand dunes that were part of an enormous desert during the Jurassic period. (Photo by Michael Collier)

Cenozoic History

The Cenozoic era, or "era of recent life," encompasses the past 65.5 million years of Earth history. It was during this span that the physical landscapes and life-forms of our modern world came into existence. The Cenozoic era represents a considerably smaller fraction of geologic time than either the Paleozoic or the Mesozoic. Nevertheless, much more is known about this time span because the rock formations are more widespread and less disturbed than those of any preceding era.

Most of North America was above sea level during the Cenozoic era. However, the eastern and western margins of the continent experienced markedly contrasting events because of their different plate boundary relationships. The Atlantic and Gulf coastal regions, far removed from an active plate boundary, were tectonically stable. By contrast, western North America was the leading edge of the North American plate. As a result, plate interactions during the Cenozoic account for many events of mountain building, volcanism, and earthquakes.

Eastern North America The stable continental margin of eastern North America was the site of abundant marine sedimentation. The most extensive deposition surrounded the Gulf of Mexico, from the Yucatan Peninsula to Florida, where a massive buildup of sediment caused the crust to downwarp. In many instances, faulting created structures in which oil and natural gas accumulated. Today, these and other petroleum traps are the Gulf Coast's most economically important resource, evidenced by numerous offshore drilling platforms.

By early Cenozoic time, the Appalachians had eroded to create a low plain. Later, isostatic adjustments again raised the region and rejuvenated its rivers. Streams eroded with renewed vigor, gradually sculpting the surface into its present-day topography. Sediments from this erosion were deposited along the eastern continental margin, where they accumulated to a thickness of many kilometers. Today, portions of the strata deposited during the Cenozoic are exposed as the gently sloping Atlantic and Gulf coastal plains, where a large percentage of the eastern and southeastern U.S. population resides.

Western North America In the West, the Laramide Orogeny responsible for building the southern Rocky Mountains was coming to an end. As erosional forces lowered the mountains, the basins between uplifted ranges began to fill with sediment. East of the Rockies, a large wedge of sediment from the eroding mountains created the gently sloping Great Plains.

Beginning in the Miocene epoch, about 20 million years ago, a broad region from northern Nevada into Mexico experienced crustal extension that created more than 100 fault-block mountain ranges. Today, they rise abruptly above the adjacent basins, forming the Basin and Range Province.

During the development of the Basin and Range Province, the entire western interior of the continent gradually uplifted. This event reelevated the Rockies and rejuvenated many of the West's major rivers. As the rivers became incised, many spectacular gorges were created, including the Grand Canyon of

FIGURE 12.20 Mount Shasta, California This volcano is one of several large composite cones that comprise the Cascade Range. (Photo by Michael Collier)

the Colorado River, the Grand Canyon of the Snake River, and the Black Canyon of the Gunnison River.

Volcanic activity was also common in the West during much of the Cenozoic. Beginning in the Miocene epoch, great volumes of fluid basaltic lava flowed from fissures in portions of present-day Washington, Oregon, and Idaho. These eruptions built the extensive (3.4-million-square-kilometer [1.3-million-square–mile]) Columbia Plateau. Immediately west of the Columbia Plateau, volcanic activity was different in character. Here, more viscous magmas with higher silica content erupted explosively, creating the Cascades, a chain of stratovolcanoes extending from northern California into Canada, some of which are still active (**FIGURE 12.20**).

As the Cenozoic was drawing to a close, the effects of mountain building, volcanic activity, isostatic adjustments, and extensive erosion and sedimentation created the physical landscape we know today. All that remained of Cenozoic time was the final 2.6-million-year episode called the Quaternary period. During this most recent, and ongoing, phase of Earth's history, humans evolved, and the action of glacial ice, wind, and running water added to our planet's long, complex geologic history.

12.5 CONCEPT CHECKS

1 During which period of geologic history did the supercontinent Pangaea come into existence?

2 Where is most Cretaceous age coal found today in the United States?

3 During which period of geologic history did Pangaea begin to break apart?

4 Describe the climate during the early Jurassic period.

5 Compare and contrast eastern and western North America during the Cenozoic era.

12.6 | EARTH'S FIRST LIFE Describe some of the hypotheses on the origin of life and the characteristics of early prokaryotes, eukaryotes, and multicelled organisms.

The oldest fossils provide evidence that life on Earth was established at least 3.5 billion years ago. Microscopic fossils similar to modern cyanobacteria have been found in silica-rich chert deposits worldwide. Notable examples include southern Africa, where rocks date to more than 3.1 billion years, and the Lake Superior region of western Ontario and northern Minnesota, where the Gunflint Chert contains some fossils that are older than 2 billion years. Chemical traces of organic matter in rocks of greater age have led paleontologists to strongly suggest that life may have existed as early as 3.8 billion years ago.

Origin of Life

How did life begin? This question sparks considerable debate, and hypotheses abound. Requirements for life, assuming the presence of a hospitable environment, include the chemical raw materials that are found in essential molecules such as proteins. Proteins are made from organic compounds called *amino acids*. The first amino acids may have been synthesized from methane and ammonia, both of which were plentiful in Earth's primitive atmosphere. Some scientists suggest that these gases could have been easily reorganized into useful organic molecules by ultraviolet light. Others consider lightning to have been the impetus, as the well-known experiments conducted by Stanley Miller and Harold Urey attempted to demonstrate.

Still other researchers suggest that amino acids arrived "ready made," delivered by asteroids or comets that collided with a young Earth. A group of meteorites (debris from asteroids and comets that strike Earth) called *carbonaceous chrondrites*, known to contain amino acid–like organic compounds, led to a hypothesis which concludes that early life had an extraterrestrial beginning.

Yet another hypothesis proposes that the organic material needed for life came from the methane and hydrogen sulfide that spews from deep-sea hydrothermal vents (black smokers). It is also possible that life originated in hot springs similar to those found in Yellowstone National Park.

Earth's First Life: Prokaryotes

Regardless of where or how life originated, it is clear that the journey from "then" to "now" involved change. The first known organisms were simple single-cell bacteria called **prokaryotes**, which means their genetic material (DNA) is *not separated* from the rest of the cell by a nucleus. Because oxygen was largely absent from Earth's early atmosphere and oceans, the first organisms employed anaerobic (without oxygen) metabolism to extract energy from "food." Their food source was likely organic molecules in their surroundings, but that supply was very limited. Later, bacteria evolved that used solar energy to synthesize organic compounds (sugars). This event was an important turning point in biological evolution: For the first time, organisms had the capability of producing food for themselves as well as for other life-forms.

Recall that photosynthesis by ancient cyanobacteria, a type of prokaryote, contributed to the gradual rise in the level of oxygen, first in the ocean and later in the atmosphere. It was these early organisms, which began to inhabit Earth 3.5 billion years ago, that dramatically transformed our planet. Fossil evidence for the existence of these microscopic bacteria includes distinctively layered mats, called **stromatolites**, composed of slimy material secreted by these organisms, along with trapped sediments (**FIGURE 12.21A**). What is known about these ancient fossils comes mainly from the study of

FIGURE 12.21
Stromatolites Are Among the Most Common Precambrian Fossils A. Cross-section though fossil stromatolites deposited by cyanobacteria. (Photo by Sinclair Stammers/Science Source) **B.** Modern stromatolites exposed at low tide in western Australia. (Photo by Bill Bachman/Science Source)

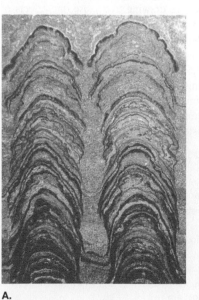

A.

B.

modern stromatolites like those found in Shark Bay, Australia (**FIGURE 12.21B**). Today's stromatolites look like stubby pillars built as microbes slowly move upward to avoid being buried by sediment that is continually being deposited on them.

Evolution of Eukaryotes The oldest fossils of more advanced organisms, called **eukaryotes**, are about 2.1 billion years old. The first eukaryotes were microscopic, single-cell organisms, but unlike prokaryotes, eukaryotes contain nuclei. This distinctive cellular structure is what all multicellular organisms that now inhabit our planet—trees, birds, fish, reptiles, and humans—have in common.

During much of the Precambrian, life consisted exclusively of single-celled organisms. It wasn't until perhaps 1.2 billion years ago that multicelled eukaryotes evolved. Green algae, one of the first multicelled organisms, contained chloroplasts (used in photosynthesis)

FIGURE 12.22 Ediacaran Fossil The Ediacarans are a group of sea-dwelling animals that may have come into existence about 600 million years ago. These soft-bodied organisms were up to 1 meter in length and are the oldest animal fossils so far discovered. (Photo by Sinclair Stammers/Science Source)

and were the likely ancestors of modern plants. The first primitive marine animals did not appear until somewhat later, perhaps 600 million years ago (**FIGURE 12.22**).

Fossil evidence suggests that organic evolution progressed at an excruciatingly slow pace until the end of the Precambrian. At that time, Earth's continents were largely barren, and the oceans were populated by small organisms, many too small to be seen with the naked eye. Nevertheless, the stage was set for the evolution of larger and more complex plants and animals.

12.6 CONCEPT CHECKS

1 What group of organic compounds are essential for the formation of DNA and RNA and therefore necessary for life as we know it?

2 Why do some researchers think that a type of asteroid, called *carbonaceous chondrites*, played an important role in the development of life on Earth?

3 What are stromatolites? What group of organisms is thought to have produced them?

4 Compare *prokaryotes* with *eukaryotes*. Within which of these two groups do all multicelled organisms belong?

12.7 | PALEOZOIC ERA: LIFE EXPLODES

Discuss the major developments in the history of life during the Paleozoic era.

The Cambrian period marks the beginning of the Paleozoic era, a time span that saw the emergence of a spectacular variety of new life-forms. All major invertebrate (animals lacking backbones) groups made their appearance, including jellyfish, sponges, worms, mollusks (clams and snails), and arthropods (insects and crabs). This huge expansion in biodiversity is often referred to as the **Cambrian explosion**.

Early Paleozoic Life-Forms

The Cambrian period was the golden age of *trilobites* (**FIGURE 12.23**). Trilobites developed a flexible exoskeleton of a protein called chitin (similar to a lobster shell), which permitted them to be mobile and search for food by burrowing through soft sediment. More than 600 genera of these mud-burrowing scavengers flourished worldwide.

The Ordovician marked the appearance of abundant cephalopods—mobile, highly developed mollusks that became the major predators of their time (**FIGURE 12.24**). Descendants of these cephalopods include the squid, octopus, and chambered nautilus that inhabit our modern oceans. Cephalopods were

the first truly large organisms on Earth, including one species that reached a length of nearly 10 meters (30 feet).

The early diversification of animals was driven, in part, by the emergence of predatory lifestyles. The larger mobile cephalopods preyed on trilobites that were typically smaller than a child's hand. The evolution of efficient movement was often associated with the development of greater sensory

FIGURE 12.23 Fossil of a Trilobite Trilobites dominated the early Paleozoic ocean, scavenging food from the bottom. (Photo by Ed Reschke/Getty Images)

Evolution of Life Through Geologic Time

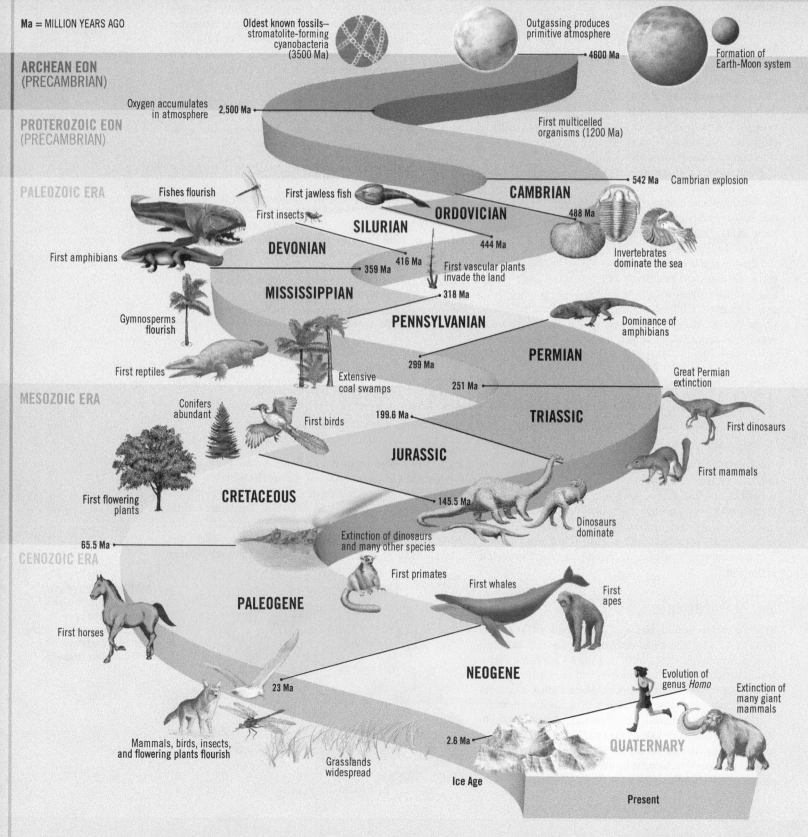

Ma = MILLION YEARS AGO

Oldest known fossils— stromatolite-forming cyanobacteria (3500 Ma)

Outgassing produces primitive atmosphere

4600 Ma

Formation of Earth-Moon system

ARCHEAN EON (PRECAMBRIAN)

Oxygen accumulates in atmosphere — 2,500 Ma

PROTEROZOIC EON (PRECAMBRIAN)

First multicelled organisms (1200 Ma)

PALEOZOIC ERA

542 Ma Cambrian explosion

CAMBRIAN

Fishes flourish

First jawless fish

ORDOVICIAN

488 Ma

First insects

SILURIAN

444 Ma

Invertebrates dominate the sea

DEVONIAN

416 Ma

First amphibians

359 Ma

First vascular plants invade the land

MISSISSIPPIAN

318 Ma

Gymnosperms flourish

PENNSYLVANIAN

Dominance of amphibians

First reptiles

PERMIAN

299 Ma

Extensive coal swamps

251 Ma

Great Permian extinction

MESOZOIC ERA

Conifers abundant

First birds

199.6 Ma

TRIASSIC

First dinosaurs

JURASSIC

First mammals

First flowering plants

CRETACEOUS

145.5 Ma

Dinosaurs dominate

65.5 Ma

Extinction of dinosaurs and many other species

CENOZOIC ERA

First primates

First whales

First apes

PALEOGENE

First horses

NEOGENE

Evolution of genus *Homo*

Extinction of many giant mammals

23 Ma

2.6 Ma

QUATERNARY

Mammals, birds, insects, and flowering plants flourish

Grasslands widespread

Ice Age

Present

FIGURE 12.24 Artistic Depiction of a Shallow Ordovician Sea During the Ordovician period (488–444 million years ago), the shallow waters of an inland sea over central North America contained an abundance of marine invertebrates. Shown in this reconstruction are 1) corals, 2) trilobites, 3) snails, 4) brachiopods, and 5) straight-shelled cephalopods. (Field Museum/Getty Images)

capabilities and more complex nervous systems. These early animals developed sensory devices for detecting light, odor, and touch.

Approximately 400 million years ago, green algae that had adapted to survive at the water's edge gave rise to the first multicellular land plants. The primary difficulty in sustaining plant life on land was obtaining water and staying upright, despite gravity and winds. These earliest land plants were leafless, vertical spikes about the size of a human index finger (**FIGURE 12.25**). However, the fossil record indicates that by the beginning of the Mississippian period, there were forests with trees tens of meters tall (see Figure 12.25).

In the ocean, fish perfected an internal skeleton as a new form of support, and they were the first creatures to have jaws. Armor-plated fish that evolved during the Ordovician continued to adapt. Their armor plates thinned to lightweight scales that increased their speed and mobility. Other fish evolved during the Devonian, including primitive sharks with cartilage skeletons and bony fish—the groups in which many modern fish are classified. Fish, the first large vertebrates, proved to be faster swimmers than invertebrates and possessed more acute senses and larger brains. They became the dominant predators of the sea,

FIGURE 12.25 Land Plants of the Paleozoic The Silurian saw the first upright-growing (vascular) plants. Plant fossils became increasingly common from the Devonian onward.

Small upright-growing, vascular plants begin to invade the land

SILURIAN PERIOD

First tree-size plants become common

DEVONIAN PERIOD

Extensive forests cover vast areas of the continents

MISSISSIPPIAN PERIOD

TIME

EYE ON EARTH

The rocks shown here are Cambrian-age stromatolites of the Hoyt Limestone, exposed at Lester Park, near Saratoga Springs, New York. (Michael C. Rygel)

QUESTION 1 Using Figure 12.3, determine approximately how many years ago these rocks were deposited.

QUESTION 2 What is the name of the group of organisms that likely produced these limestone deposits?

QUESTION 3 What was the environment like in this part of New York when these rocks were deposited?

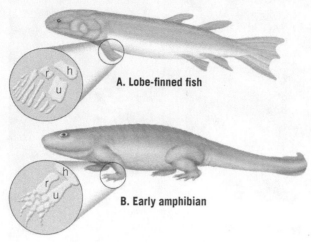

FIGURE 12.26 Comparison of the Anatomical Features of the Lobe-Finned Fish and Early Amphibians **A.** The fins on the lobe-finned fish contained the same basic elements (*h*, humerus, or upper arm; *r*, radius; and *u*, ulna, or lower arm) as those of the amphibians. **B.** This amphibian is shown with the standard five toes, but early amphibians had as many as eight toes. Eventually the amphibians evolved to have a standard toe count of five.

A. Lobe-finned fish

B. Early amphibian

which is why the Devonian period is often referred to as the "Age of the Fishes."

Vertebrates Move to Land

During the Devonian, a group of fish called the *lobe-finned fish* began to adapt to terrestrial environments (FIGURE 12.26). Lobe-finned fish had internal sacks that could be filled with air to supplement their "breathing" through gills. One group of lobe-finned fish probably occupied freshwater tidal flats or small ponds. Some began to use their fins to move from one pond to another in search of food or to evacuate deteriorating ponds. This favored the evolution of a group of animals able to stay out of water longer and move on land more efficiently. By the late Devonian, lobe-finned fish had evolved into air-breathing amphibians with strong legs yet retained a fishlike head and tail (see Figure 12.26).

Modern amphibians, such as frogs, toads, and salamanders, are small and occupy limited biological niches.

However, conditions during the late Paleozoic were ideal for these newcomers to land. Large tropical swamps that were teeming with large insects and millipedes extended across North America, Europe, and Siberia (FIGURE 12.27). With virtually no predatory risks, amphibians diversified rapidly. Some even took on lifestyles and forms similar to modern reptiles such as crocodiles.

Despite their success, amphibians were not fully adapted to life out of water. In fact, *amphibian* means "double life" because these animals need both the water from where they came and the land to which they moved. Amphibians are born in water, as exemplified by tadpoles, complete with gills and tails. These features disappear during the maturation process, resulting in air-breathing adults with legs.

Reptiles: The First True Terrestrial Vertebrates

Reptiles were the first true terrestrial animals with improved lungs for active lifestyles and "waterproof" skin that helped prevent the loss of body fluids. Most importantly, reptiles developed shell-covered eggs laid on land. The elimination of a water-dwelling stage (like the tadpole stage in frogs) was an important evolutionary step. Vertebrates advance from water-dwelling lobe-finned fish, to amphibians, to reptiles—the first true terrestrial vertebrates (FIGURE 12.28).

Of interest is the fact that the watery fluid within the reptilian egg closely resembles seawater in chemical composition. Because the reptile embryo develops in this watery environment, the shelled egg has been characterized as a "private aquarium" in which the embryos of these land vertebrates spend their water-dwelling stage of life. With this "sturdy egg," the remaining ties to the water were broken, and reptiles moved inland.

FIGURE 12.27 Artistic Depiction of a Pennsylvanian-Age Coal Swamp Shown are scale trees (left), seed ferns (lower left), and scouring rushes (right). Also note the large dragonfly. (Field Museum/Getty Images)

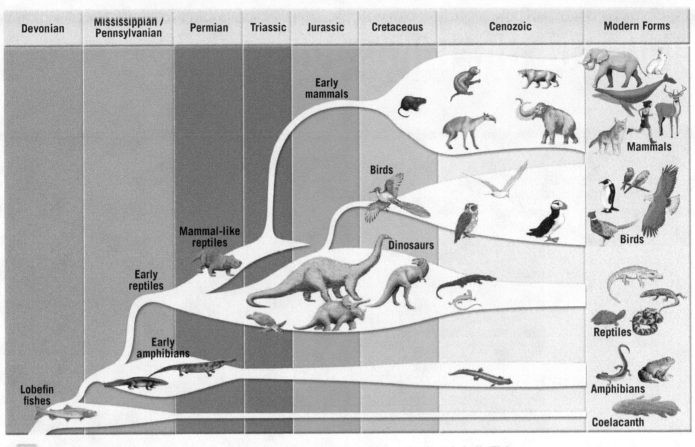

Devonian	Mississippian / Pennsylvanian	Permian	Triassic	Jurassic	Cretaceous	Cenozoic	Modern Forms

SmartFigure 12.28 Relationships of Vertebrate Groups and Their Divergence from Lobefin Fish

The Great Permian Extinction

By the close of the Permian period, a **mass extinction** occurred in which a large number of Earth's species became extinct. During this mass extinction, 70 percent of all land-dwelling vertebrate species and perhaps 90 percent of all marine organisms were obliterated; it was the most significant of five mass extinctions that occurred over the past 500 million years. Each extinction wreaked havoc with the existing biosphere, wiping out large numbers of species. In each case, however, survivors entered new biological communities that were ultimately more diverse. Therefore, mass extinctions actually invigorated life on Earth, as the few hardy survivors eventually filled more environmental niches than those left behind by the victims.

Several mechanisms have been proposed to explain these ancient mass extinctions. Initially, paleontologists believed they were gradual events caused by a combination of climate change and biological forces, such as predation and competition. Other research groups have attempted to link certain mass extinctions to the explosive impact of a large asteroid striking Earth's surface.

The most widely held view is that the Permian mass extinction was driven mainly by volcanic activity because it coincided with a period of voluminous eruptions of flood basalts that blanketed about 1.6 million square kilometers (624,000 square miles), an area nearly the size of Alaska. This event, which lasted roughly 1 million years, occurred in northern Russia, in an area called the Siberian Traps. It was the largest volcanic eruption in the past 500 million years. The release of huge amounts of carbon dioxide likely generated a period of accelerated greenhouse warming, while the emissions of sulfur dioxide is credited with producing copious amounts of acid rain. These drastic changes in the environment likely put excessive stress on many of Earth's life-forms.

12.7 CONCEPT CHECKS

1 What is the Cambrian explosion?

2 What animal group was dominant in Cambrian seas?

3 What did plants have to overcome in order to move onto land?

4 What group of animals is thought to have left the ocean to become the first amphibians?

5 Why are amphibians not considered "true" land animals?

6 What major development allowed reptiles to move inland?

Demise of the Dinosaurs

The geologic time scale marks the transitions, or boundaries, of significant periods of geological and/or biological change. Of special interest to geoscientists is the boundary between the Mesozoic Era and the Cenozoic Era, about 65.5 million years ago, when roughly 70 percent of all plant and animal species died out in a mass extinction.

UNITED STATES

Gulf of Mexico

CHICXULUB CRATER

Yucatán

MEXICO

The most widely accepted hypothesis on the demise of the dinosaurs proposes that about 65.5 million years ago, Earth was struck by an asteroid—a relict from the formation of the solar system. The errant mass of rock was approximately 10 kilometers in diameter and struck Earth with 100 million megatons of force.

This asteroid struck a shallow tropical sea in the area of Mexico's Yucatan Peninsula and generated Chicxulub crater, which is about 180 kilometers in diameter and 10 kilometers deep. Much of the plant and animal life that survived the initial impact likely fell victim to firestorms triggered by atmospheric heating. Following the impact, the huge amount of debris ejected into the atmosphere greatly reduced the amount of sunlight reaching Earth's surface. This resulted in an extended period of global cooling that inhibited photosynthesis, which ultimately caused the demise of the dinosaurs.

Artistic recreation of Chicxulub crater

Detlev van Ravenswaay/Science Source

The transition from the Mesozoic to the Cenozoic era marks the end of the dinosaurs, a group that had dominated the landscape for more than 100 million years, and the beginning of the era when mammals became the most prominent land animals.

Photri Inc./AGE Fotostock

What evidence supports a massive, catastrophic impact more than 65 million years ago? A thin layer of sediment has been discovered worldwide at Earth's physical boundary separating the Mesozoic and Cenozoic eras. This sediment contains a high level of iridium, an element that is rare in Earth's crust but is found in much higher proportions in stony meteorites. Scientists believe this layer contains debris from the impact.

Mesozoic rocks

IRIDIUM LAYER

Cenozoic rocks

Nationalparks

Oleg Znamenskiy/Shutterstock

The mass extinction of the dinosaurs opened habitats for the small mammals that survived the impact. These new habitats, along with evolutionary forces, led to the development of the large mammals that occupy our modern world.

Wesley Aston/Shutterstock

VikOl/Shutterstock

12.8 | MESOZOIC ERA: AGE OF THE DINOSAURS

Discuss the major developments in the history of life during the Mesozoic era.

As the Mesozoic era dawned, its life-forms were the survivors of the great Permian extinction. These organisms diversified in many ways to fill the biological voids created at the close of the Paleozoic. While life on land underwent a radical transformation with the rise of the dinosaurs, life in the sea also entered a dramatic phase of transformation that produced many of the animal groups that prevail in the oceans today, including modern groups of predatory fish, crustaceans, mollusks, and sand dollars.

Gymnosperms: The Dominant Mesozoic Trees

On land, conditions favored organisms that could adapt to drier climates. One such group of plants, **gymnosperms**, produced "naked" seeds that are exposed on modified leaves that usually form cones. The seeds are not enclosed in fruits as, for example, are apple seeds. Unlike the first plants to invade the land, seed-bearing gymnosperms did not depend on free-standing water for fertilization. Consequently, these plants were not restricted to a life near the water's edge.

The gymnosperms quickly became the dominant trees of the Mesozoic. Examples of this group include cycads that resembled large pineapple plants (**FIGURE 12.29**); ginkgo plants that had fan-shaped leaves, much like

FIGURE 12.30 Petrified Logs of Triassic Age, Arizona's Petrified Forest National Park (Photo by Bernd Siering/AGE Fotostock)

their modern relatives; and the largest plants, the conifers, whose modern descendants include the pines, firs, and junipers. The best-known fossil occurrence of these ancient trees is in northern Arizona's Petrified Forest National Park. Here, huge petrified logs lie exposed at the surface, having been weathered from rocks of the Triassic Chinle Formation (**FIGURE 12.30**).

Reptiles: Dominating the Land, Sea, and Sky

Among the animals, reptiles readily adapted to the drier Mesozoic environment, thereby relegating amphibians to the swamps and wetlands, where most remain today. The first reptiles were small, but larger forms evolved rapidly, particularly the dinosaurs. One of the largest was *Apatosaurus*, which weighed more than 30 tons and measured over 25 meters (80 feet) from head to tail. Some of the largest dinosaurs were carnivorous (for example, *Tyrannosaurus*), whereas others were herbivorous (like ponderous *Apatosaurus*).

Some reptiles evolved specialized characteristics that enabled them to occupy drastically different environments. One group, the pterosaurs, became airborne. These "dragons of the sky" possessed huge membranous wings that allowed them rudimentary flight. How the largest pterosaurs (some had wing spans of 8 meters [26 feet] and weighed 90 kilograms [200 pounds]) took flight is still unknown. Another group, exemplified by

FIGURE 12.29 Cycads, a Type of Gymnosperm That Was Very Common in the Mesozoic These plants have palm-like leaves and large cones. (Photo by Jiri Loun/ Science Source)

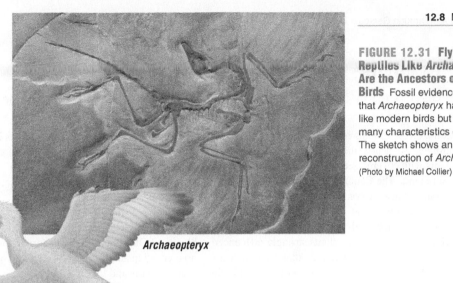

FIGURE 12.31 Flying Reptiles Like *Archaeopteryx* Are the Ancestors of Modern Birds Fossil evidence indicates that *Archaeopteryx* had feathers like modern birds but retained many characteristics of reptiles. The sketch shows an artist's reconstruction of *Archaeopteryx*. (Photo by Michael Collier)

Toothed beak
(reptilian feature)

Wing claws
(reptilian feature)

Archaeopteryx

Tail feathers
(bird feature)

Airfoil wings with feathers
(bird feature)

Long tail with vertebrae
(reptilian feature)

the fossil *Archaeopteryx*, led to more successful flyers—birds (**FIGURE 12.31**). These ancestors of modern birds had feathered wings but retained reptilian characteristics, such as sharp teeth, clawed digits in the wings, and a long tail with many vertebrae. A recent study concluded that *Archaeopteryx* were unable to use flapping flight. Rather, by running and leaping into the air, these bird-like reptiles escaped predators with glides and downstrokes. Other researchers disagree and see them as climbing animals that glided down to the ground, following the idea that birds evolved from tree-dwelling gliders. Whether birds took to the air from the ground *up* or from the trees *down* is a question scientists continue to debate.

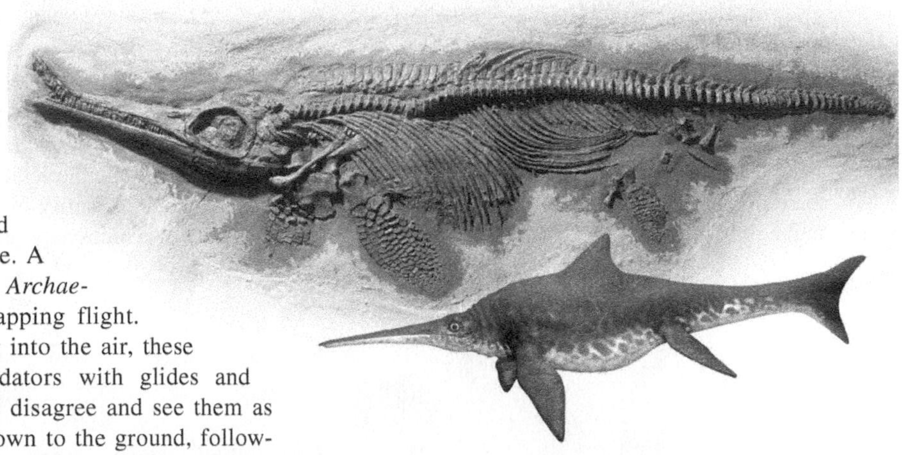

Other reptiles returned to the sea, including fish-eating *plesiosaurs* and *ichthyosaurs* (**FIGURE 12.32**). These reptiles became proficient swimmers but retained their reptilian teeth and breathed by means of lungs rather than gills.

For nearly 160 million years, dinosaurs reigned supreme. However, by the close of the Mesozoic, like many reptiles, they became extinct. Select reptile groups survived to recent times, including turtles, snakes, crocodiles, and lizards. The huge, land-dwelling dinosaurs, the marine plesiosaurs, and the flying pterosaurs are known only through the fossil record. What caused this great

FIGURE 12.32 During the Mesozoic, Some Reptiles Returned to the Sea Reptiles, including *Ichthyosaur*, became the dominant marine animals. (Photo by Chip Clark/Fundamental Photographs, NYC)

extinction? The GEOgraphics on page 354 provides the most plausible answer to this question.

12.8 CONCEPT CHECKS

1 What group of plants became the dominant trees during the Mesozoic era? Name a modern descendant of this group.

2 What group of reptiles led to the evolution of modern birds?

3 What was the dominant reptile group on land during the Mesozoic?

4 Name two reptiles that returned to life in the sea.

12.9 | CENOZOIC ERA: AGE OF MAMMALS

Discuss the major developments in the history of life during the Cenozoic era.

During the Cenozoic, mammals replaced reptiles as the dominant land animals. At nearly the same time, **angiosperms** (flowering plants with covered seeds) replaced gymnosperms as the dominant plants. The Cenozoic is often called the "Age of Mammals" but can also be considered the "Age of Flowering Plants" because, in the plant world, angiosperms enjoy a status similar to that of mammals in the animal world.

The development of flowering plants strongly influenced the evolution of both birds and mammals that feed on seeds and fruits, as well as many insect groups. During the middle of the Cenozoic, another type of angiosperm, grasses, developed and spread rapidly over the plains (**FIGURE 12.33**). This fostered the emergence of herbivorous (plant-eating) mammals, which, in turn, provided the evolutionary foundation for large predatory mammals.

During the Cenozoic, the ocean was teeming with modern fish such as tuna, swordfish, and barracuda. In addition, some mammals, including seals, whales, and walruses, took up life in the sea.

From Reptiles to Mammals

The earliest mammals coexisted with dinosaurs for nearly 100 million years but were small rodent-like creatures that gathered food at night, when dinosaurs were probably less active. Then, about 65 million years ago, fate intervened when a large asteroid collided with Earth and dealt a crashing blow to the reign of the dinosaurs. This transition, during which one dominant group is replaced by another, is clearly visible in the fossil record.

Mammals are distinct from reptiles in that they give birth to live young that suckle on milk and are warm blooded. This latter adaptation allowed mammals to lead more active lives and to occupy more diverse habitats than reptiles because they could survive in cold regions. (Modern reptiles are cold blooded and dormant during cold weather. However, recent studies suggest that dinosaurs may have been warm blooded.) Other mammalian adaptations included the development of insulating body hair and more efficient organs, such as hearts and lungs.

With the demise of the large Mesozoic reptiles, Cenozoic mammals diversified rapidly. The many forms that exist today evolved from small primitive mammals that were characterized by short legs; flat, five-toed feet; and small brains. Their development and specialization took four principal directions: increase in size, increase in brain capacity, specialization of teeth to better accommodate their diet, and specialization of limbs to be better equipped for a particular lifestyle or environment.

Marsupial and Placental Mammals

Two groups of mammals, the marsupials and the placentals, evolved and diversified during the Cenozoic. The groups differ principally in their modes of reproduction. Young marsupials are born live at a very early stage of development. At birth, the tiny and immature young enter the mother's pouch to suckle and complete their development. Today, marsupials are found primarily in Australia, where they underwent a separate evolutionary expansion, largely isolated from

FIGURE 12.33
Angiosperms Became the Dominant Plants During the Cenozoic This plant group, commonly known as flowering plants, consists of seed plants that have reproductive structures called flowers and fruits. **A.** The most diverse and widespread of modern plants, many angiosperms display easily recognizable flowers. **B.** Some angiosperms, including grasses, have very tiny flowers. The expansion of the grasslands during the Cenozoic era greatly increased the diversity of grazing mammals and the predators that feed on them. (Photo A by WDG Photo/Shutterstock; photo B by Torleif Svensson/Corbis)

FIGURE 12.34 Kangaroos, Examples of Marsupial Mammals After the breakup of Pangaea, the Australian marsupials evolved differently than their relatives in the Americas. (Photo by Martin Harvey/Getty Images)

placental mammals. Modern marsupials include kangaroos, opossums, and koalas (FIGURE 12.34).

Placental mammals (eutherians), conversely, develop within the mother's body for a much longer period, so birth occurs when the young are comparatively mature. Members of this group include wolves, elephants, bats, manatees, and monkeys. Most modern mammals, including humans, are placental.

Humans: Mammals with Large Brains and Bipedal Locomotion

Both fossil and genetic evidence suggest that around 7 or 8 million years ago in Africa, several populations of anthropoids (informally called apes) diverged. One line would eventually produce modern apes such as gorillas, orangutans, and chimpanzees, while the other population would produce several varieties of human ancestors. We have a good record of this evolution in fossils found in several sedimentary basins in Africa, in particular the rift valley system in East Africa.

The genus *Australopithecus*, which came into existence about 4.2 million years ago, showed skeletal characteristics that were intermediate between our apelike ancestors and modern humans. Over time, these human ancestors evolved features that suggest an upright posture and therefore a habit of walking around on two legs, rather than four. Evidence for this bipedal stride includes footprints preserved in 3.2-million-year-old ash deposits at Laetoli, Tanzania (FIGURE 12.35). This new way of moving around is correlated with our human ancestors leaving forest habitat in Africa and moving to open grasslands for hunting and gathering food.

The earliest fossils of our genus *Homo* include *Homo habilis*, nicknamed "handy man" because their remains were often found with sharp stone tools in sedimentary deposits

from 2.4 to 1.5 million years ago, *Homo habilis* had a shorter jaw and a larger brain than its ancestors. The development of a larger brain size is thought to be correlated with an increase in tool use.

During the next 1.3 million years of evolution, our ancestors developed substantially larger brains and long slender legs with hip joints adapted for long-distance walking. These species (including *Homo erectus*) ultimately gave rise to our species, *Homo sapiens*, as well as some extinct related species, including the Neanderthals (*Homo neanderthalis*). Despite having the same-sized brain as present-day humans and being able to fashion hunting tools from wood and stone, Neanderthals became extinct about 28,000 years ago. At one time, Neanderthals were considered a stage in the evolution of *Homo sapiens*, but that view has largely been abandoned.

Based on our current understanding, humans (*Homo sapiens*) originated in Africa about 200,000 years ago and began to spread around the globe. The oldest-known fossils of *Homo sapiens* outside Africa were found in the Middle East and date back to 115,000 years ago. Humans are also known to have coexisted with Neanderthals and other prehistoric populations, remains of which have been found in Siberia, China, and Indonesia. Further, there is mounting genetic evidence that our ancestors may have interbred with members of some of these groups. By 36,000 years ago, humans were producing spectacular cave paintings in Europe (FIGURE 12.36). About 11,500 years ago all prehistoric populations, except for modern humans (*Homo sapiens*), died out.

Large Mammals and Extinction

During the rapid mammal diversification of the Cenozoic era, some groups became very large. For example, by the Oligocene epoch, a hornless rhinoceros evolved that stood nearly 5 meters (16 feet) high. It is the largest land mammal known to have existed. As time passed, many other mammals evolved to larger forms—more, in fact, than now exist. Many of these large forms were common as recently as 11,000 years ago.

FIGURE 12.35 Footprints of *Australopithecus*, Human-Like Apes in Ash Deposits at Laetoli, Tanzania (Photo by John Reader/Science Source)

FIGURE 12.36 Cave Painting of Animals by Early Humans (Photo courtesy of Sisse Brimberg/National Geographic Stock)

However, a wave of late Pleistocene extinctions rapidly eliminated these animals from the landscape.

North America experienced the extinction of mastodons and mammoths, both huge relatives of the modern elephant (**FIGURE 12.37**). In addition, saber-toothed cats, giant beavers, large ground sloths, horses, giant bison, and others died out. In Europe, late Pleistocene extinctions included woolly rhinos, large cave bears, and Irish elk. Scientists remain puzzled about the reasons for this recent wave of extinctions of large animals. Because these large animals survived several major glacial advances and interglacial periods, it is difficult to ascribe extinctions of these animals to climate change. Some scientists hypothesize that early humans hastened the decline of these mammals by selectively hunting large forms.

12.9 CONCEPT CHECKS

1 What animal group became the dominant land animals of the Cenozoic era?

2 Explain how the demise of the large Mesozoic reptiles impacted the development of mammals.

3 Where has most of the evidence for the early evolution of our ancestors been discovered?

4 What two characteristics best separate humans from other mammals?

5 Describe one hypothesis that explains the extinction of large mammals in the late Pleistocene.

FIGURE 12.37 Mammoths These relatives of modern elephants were among the large mammals that became extinct at the close of the Ice Age. (Image courtesy of INTERFOTO/Alamy)

12 CONCEPTS IN REVIEW | Earth's Evolution Through Geologic Time

12.1 IS EARTH UNIQUE?

List the principal characteristics that make Earth unique among the planets.

■ As far as we know, Earth is unique among planets in the fact that it hosts life. The planet's size, composition, and location all contribute to conditions that support life (or at least our kind of life).

Q If you worked for NASA as an astrobiologist, what characteristics would you look for in a newly discovered planet as you considered whether it might host living organisms?

12.2 BIRTH OF A PLANET

Outline the major stages in the evolution of Earth, from the Big Bang to the formation of our planet's layered internal structure.

KEY TERMS: supernova, solar nebula, planetesimal, protoplanet, Hadean

■ The universe is thought to have formed around 13.7 billion years ago, with the Big Bang, which generated space, time, energy, and matter. Early stars grew from the lightest elements, hydrogen and helium, and the process of nuclear fusion produced the other low mass elements. Some large stars exploded in supernovae, generating heavier atoms and spewing them into space.

■ The story of Earth and the solar system began around 4.6 billion years ago, with the contraction of a solar nebula under the influence of gravity. Collisions between clumps of matter in this spinning disc resulted in the growth of planetesimals and then protoplanets. Over time, the matter of the solar nebula was concentrated into a smaller number of larger bodies: the Sun, the rocky inner planets, the gassy outer planets, moons, comets, and asteroids.

■ Heat production within Earth during its formative years was much higher than it is today, thanks to the kinetic energy of impacting asteroids and planetesimals, as well as decay of short-lived radioactive isotopes. The high temperatures of our young Earth caused rock and iron to melt. This allowed iron to sink to form Earth's core and rocky material to rise to form the mantle and crust. This began the "hellish" first span of geologic time, the Hadean.

Q The photo shows Comet Shoemaker-Levy 9 impacting Jupiter in 1994. After this event, what happened to Jupiter's total mass? How was the number of objects in the solar system affected? Relate this example to the nebular theory and evolution of the solar system.

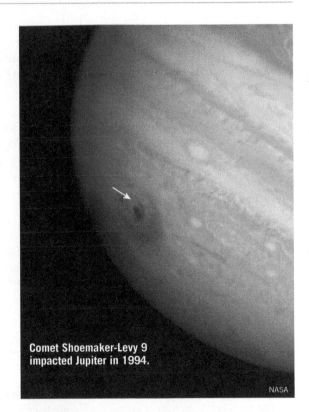

Comet Shoemaker-Levy 9 impacted Jupiter in 1994.

NASA

12.3 ORIGIN AND EVOLUTION OF THE ATMOSPHERE AND OCEANS

Describe how Earth's atmosphere and oceans have formed and evolved through time.

KEY TERMS: outgassing, banded iron formation, Great Oxygenation Event

■ Earth's atmosphere is essential for life. It evolved as volcanic outgassing added mainly water vapor and carbon dioxide to the primordial atmosphere of gases common in the early solar system: methane and ammonia.

■ Free oxygen began to accumulate partly through photosynthesis by cyanobacteria, which released oxygen as a waste product. Much of this early oxygen immediately reacted with iron dissolved in seawater and settled to the ocean floor as chemical sediments called banded iron formations. The Great Oxygenation Event of 2.5 billion years ago marks the first evidence of appreciable amounts of free oxygen in the atmosphere.

■ Earth's oceans formed after the planet's surface had cooled. Soluble ions weathered from the crust were carried to the ocean, making it salty. The oceans also absorbed tremendous amounts of carbon dioxide from the atmosphere.

12.4 PRECAMBRIAN HISTORY: THE FORMATION OF EARTH'S CONTINENTS

Explain the formation of continental crust, how continental crust becomes assembled into continents, and the role that the supercontinent cycle has played in this process.

KEY TERMS: craton, shield, supercontinent, supercontinent cycle

- The Precambrian includes the Archean and Proterozoic eons. However, the geologic records of these eons are rather limited because the rock cycle operating over billions of years has destroyed much of the evidence.
- Continental crust was produced over time through the recycling of basaltic (mafic) crust in an early version of plate tectonics. Small crustal fragments formed and accreted to one another, amalgamating over time into large crustal provinces called cratons. Over time, North America and other continents grew through the accretion of new terranes around the edges of their central "nucleus" of crust.
- Early cratons not only merged but sometimes rifted apart, too. The supercontinent Rodinia formed around 1.1 billion years ago and then rifted apart, opening new ocean basins. In time, these also closed and formed a new supercontinent called Pangaea around 300 million years ago. Like Rodinia before it, Pangaea broke up as part of the ongoing supercontinent cycle.
- The formation of elevated oceanic ridges upon the breakup of a supercontinent displaced enough water that sea level rose, and shallow seas flooded low-lying portions of the continents. The breakup of continents also influenced the direction of ocean currents, with important consequences for climate.

Q Consult Figure 12.12 and use it to give a history of the North American continent's assembly over the past 3.5 billion years. Which pieces of the continent were added at what times?

12.5 GEOLOGIC HISTORY OF THE PHANEROZOIC: THE FORMATION OF EARTH'S MODERN CONTINENTS

List and discuss the major geologic events in the Paleozoic, Mesozoic, and Cenozoic eras.

- The Phanerozoic eon encompasses the most recent 542 million years of geologic time.
- In the Paleozoic era, North America experienced a series of collisions that resulted in the rise of the young Appalachian mountain belt and the assembly of Pangaea. High sea levels caused the ocean to cover vast areas of the continent and resulted in a thick sequence of sedimentary strata.
- In the Mesozoic, Pangaea broke up, and the Atlantic Ocean began to form. As the continent moved westward, the Cordillera began to rise due to subduction and the accretion of terranes along the west coast of North America. In the Southwest, vast deserts deposited thick layers of dune sand, while environments in the east were conducive to the formation and subsequent burial of coal swamps.
- In the Cenozoic era, a thick sequence of sediments was deposited along the Atlantic margin and the Gulf of Mexico. Meanwhile, western North America experienced an extraordinary episode of crustal extension; the Basin and Range Province resulted.

Q Contrast the tectonics of eastern and western North America during the Mesozoic era.

12.6 EARTH'S FIRST LIFE

Describe some of the hypotheses on the origin of life and the characteristics of early prokaryotes, eukaryotes, and multicelled organisms.

KEY TERMS: prokaryote, stromatolite, eukaryote

- Life began from nonlife. Whether the genetic code of life (DNA and RNA) or biologically active molecules (proteins) came first is a matter of some controversy. Amino acids are a necessary building block for proteins. They may have been assembled with energy from ultraviolet light or lightning, or in a hot spring, or on another planet, only to be delivered later to Earth on meteorites.
- The first organisms were relatively simple single-celled prokaryotes that thrived in low-oxygen environments. They formed around 3.8 billion years ago. The advent of photosynthesis allowed microbial mats to build up and form stromatolites.
- Eukaryotes have larger, more complex cells than prokaryotes. The oldest eukaryotic cells formed around 2.1 billion years ago. Eventually, some eukaryotic cells linked together and differentiated their structures and functions, producing the earliest multicellular organisms.

Q Are these stromatolites right-side up, or have they been flipped upside-down by folding of the crust? Explain.

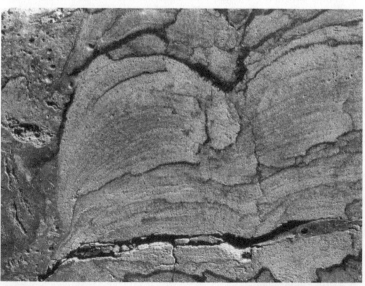

Biophoto Associates/Science Source

12.7 PALEOZOIC ERA: LIFE EXPLODES

Discuss the major developments in the history of life during the Paleozoic era.

KEY TERMS: Cambrian explosion, mass extinction

- At the beginning of the Cambrian period, abundant fossil hard parts appear in sedimentary rocks. The source of these shells and other skeletal material were a profusion of new animals, including trilobites and cephalopods.
- Plants colonized the land around 400 million years ago and soon diversified into forests.
- In the Devonian, some lobe-finned fish began to spend time out of water and gradually evolved into the first amphibians. A subset of the amphibian population evolved waterproof skin and eggs and split off to become the reptile line.
- The Paleozoic era ended with the largest mass extinction in the geologic record. This deadly event may have been related to the eruption of the Siberian Traps flood basalts.

Q What advantages do reptiles have over amphibians? What advantages do amphibians have over fish? Suggest a reason that fish would still exist in a world that also contains reptiles.

12.8 MESOZOIC ERA: AGE OF THE DINOSAURS

Discuss the major developments in the history of life during the Mesozoic era.

KEY TERM: gymnosperm

- Plants diversified during the Mesozoic. The flora of that time was dominated by gymnosperms, the first plants with seeds that allowed them to migrate beyond the edge of water bodies.
- Reptiles diversified, too. The dinosaurs came to dominate the land, the pterosaurs dominated the air, and a suite of several different marine reptiles swam the seas. The first birds evolved during the Mesozoic, exemplified by *Archaeopteryx*, a transitional fossil.
- As with the Paleozoic, the Mesozoic ended with a mass extinction, probably due to a massive meteorite impact in what is now Chicxulub, Mexico.

Q Would a paleontologist be likely to announce that some dinosaurs ate apples? Explain.

12.9 CENOZOIC ERA: AGE OF MAMMALS

Discuss the major developments in the history of life during the Cenozoic era.

KEY TERM: angiosperm,

- After the giant Mesozoic reptiles were extinct, mammals were able to diversify on the land, in the air, and in the oceans. Mammals are warm blooded, have hair on their bodies, and nurse their young with milk. Marsupial mammals are born very young and then move to a pouch on the mother, while placental mammals spend a longer time *in utero* and are born in a relatively mature state compared to marsupials.
- Flowering plants, called angiosperms, diversified and spread around the world through the Cenozoic era.
- Humans evolved from primate ancestors in Africa over a period of 8 million years. They are distinguished from their ape ancestors by an upright, bipedal posture, large brains, and tool use. The oldest anatomically modern human fossils are 200,000 years old. Some of these humans migrated out of Africa and coexisted with Neanderthals and other related populations.

GIVE IT SOME **THOUGHT**

1. Refer to the geologic time scale in Figure 12.3. The Precambrian accounts for nearly 90 percent of geologic time. Why do you think it has fewer divisions than the rest of the time scale?
2. Referring to Figure 12.4, write a brief summary of the events that led to the formation of Earth.
3. Describe two ways in which the sudden appearance of oxygen in the atmosphere about 2.5 billion years ago influenced the development of modern life-forms.
4. The accompanying photograph shows layered iron-rich rocks called banded iron formations. What does the existence of these 2.5-billion-year-old rocks tell us about the evolution of Earth's atmosphere?

Blue Gum Pictures/Alamy

5. Five mass extinctions, in which 50 percent or more of Earth's marine species became extinct, are documented in the fossil record. Use the accompanying graph, which depicts the time and extent of each mass extinction, to answer the following:

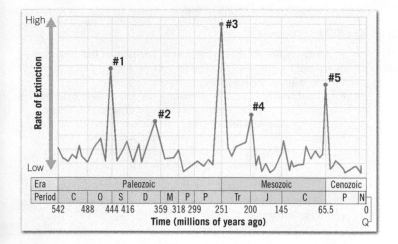

a. Which of the five mass extinctions was the *most extreme*? Identify this extinction by name and when it occurred.

b. What group of animals was most affected by the extinction referred to in Question a?

c. When did the *most recent* mass extinction occur?

d. During the most recent mass extinction, what prominent animal group was eliminated?

e. What animal group experienced a major period of diversification following the most recent mass extinction?

6. Currently, oceans cover about 71 percent of Earth's surface. This percentage was much higher early in Earth history. Explain.

7. Contrast the eastern and western margins of North America during the Cenozoic era in terms of their relationships to plate boundaries.

8. Suggest at least one reason plants moved onto land before large animals.

9. Some scientists have proposed that the environments around black smokers may be similar to the extreme conditions that existed early in Earth history. Therefore, these scientists look to the unusual life that exists around black smokers for clues about how earliest life may have survived. Compare and contrast the environment of a black smoker to the environment on Earth approximately 3 to 4 billion years ago. Do you think there are parallels between the two? If so, do you think black smokers are good examples of the environment that earliest life may have experienced? Explain.

10. About 250 million years ago, plate movement assembled all the previously separated landmasses together to form the supercontinent Pangaea. The formation of Pangaea resulted in deeper ocean basins, which caused a drop in sea level and caused shallow coastal areas to dry up. Thus, in addition to rearranging the geography of our planet, continental drift had a major impact on life on Earth. Use the accompanying diagram to answer the following:

a. Which of the following types of habitats would likely diminish in size during the formation of a supercontinent: deep-ocean habitats, wetlands, shallow marine environments, or terrestrial (land) habitats? Explain.

b. During the breakup of a supercontinent, what would happen to sea level? Would it remain the same, rise, or fall?

c. Explain how and why the development of an extensive oceanic ridge system that forms during the breakup of a supercontinent affects sea level.

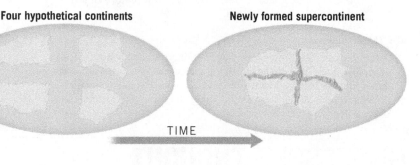

Four hypothetical continents   **Newly formed supercontinent**

TIME

11. Suggest a geologic reason why the rift valley system of East Africa is so rich in human ancestor fossils.

EXAMINING THE **EARTH SYSTEM**

1. The Earth system has been responsible for both the conditions that favored the evolution of life on this planet and for the mass extinctions that have occurred throughout geologic time. Describe the role of the biosphere, hydrosphere, and solid Earth in forming the current level of atmospheric oxygen. How did Earth's outer-space environment interact with the atmosphere and biosphere to contribute to the great mass extinction that marked the end of the dinosaurs?

2. Most of the vast North American coal resources located from Pennsylvania to Illinois began forming during the Pennsylvanian and Mississippian periods of Earth history. (This time period is also referred to as the Carboniferous period.) Using Figure 12.27, a restoration of a Pennsylvania period coal swamp, describe the climatic and biological conditions associated with this unique environment. Next, examine the accompanying diagram that illustrates the geographic position of North America during the period of coal formation. Where, relative to the equator, was North America located during the time of coal formation? Why is it unlikely that a similar coal-forming environment will repeat itself in North America in the near future? (You may find it helpful to visit the University of California Time Machine Exhibit at www.ucmp.berkeley.edu/carboniferous/carboniferous.html.)

MasteringGeology™

Looking for additional review and test prep materials? Visit the Self Study area in **www.masteringgeology.com** to find practice quizzes, study tools, and multimedia that will aid in your understanding of this chapter's content. In **MasteringGeology™** you will find:

- GEODe: Earth Science: An interactive visual walkthrough of key concepts
- Geoscience Animation Library: More than 100 animations illuminating many difficult-to-understand Earth science concepts

- In The News RSS Feeds: Current Earth science events and news articles are pulled into the site with assessment
- Pearson eText
- Optional Self Study Quizzes
- Web Links
- Glossary
- Flashcards

13

CHAPTER 13
The Evolution of Life

MARINE IGUANAS swim through seawater with their long, flattened tails. Flies taste food with the hairs on their feet. Bats catch insects in midair. Cactuses grow sharp spines that protect them from animals. These adaptations, and the countless other ways in which organisms are structured to survive and reproduce, make up the incredible story of evolution. How do living things change over time in response to their environments? After all, a giraffe can't grow a long neck just because it *wants* to. So, how do adaptations (such as a giraffe's long neck) actually come about? Does the same process explain how new types of living things—new species— originate? Also, if all organisms today evolved from earlier organisms, then how did life get started in the first place? Read on to discover these secrets of life.

13.1 The Origin of Life

EXPLAIN THIS Why do scientists think the first living things had genes made of RNA rather than DNA?

LEARNING OBJECTIVE
Explain how scientists think life originated, and describe the evidence that supports these ideas.

How did life originate? For thousands of years, the answer to this question was thought to be *spontaneous generation*, the sudden emergence of living organisms from nonliving materials. For "simple" life forms, spontaneous generation was believed to occur regularly, and evidence for it was everywhere—frogs leaped out of the mud when rain fell, mice appeared in grain stores, maggots squirmed suddenly in rotting meat. More complex organisms such as walruses or human beings were thought to have sprung into existence through spontaneous generation as well, though not as often.

The idea that larger organisms appeared through spontaneous generation lost favor in the 1600s, when experiments with maggots—lowly creatures universally considered to originate that way—showed that they did not appear when rotting meat was kept isolated from flies. However, many people saw spontaneous generation at work in the way microscopic organisms appeared in huge numbers, as if from nowhere, in places like meat broths. It wasn't until 1862, with the experiments of Louis Pasteur, that spontaneous generation was dealt a fatal blow. Pasteur designed a flask that kept out dust and other airborne particles, filled the flask with sterile meat broth, let it sit, and waited for life to emerge (Figure 13.1). It never did, and Pasteur concluded that life did not arise from nonlife.

So, how did life originate? We know from fossils that life has existed for at least 3.5 billion years. This means that the Earth on which life evolved was very different from the Earth of today. It contained vast, lifeless oceans, violent volcanoes, and a turbulent atmosphere filled with lightning storms (see Figure 7.40). The atmosphere of the early Earth included no oxygen, which, we will see, was produced by the activity of living things. Although this environment seems a hostile place for life today, it may have been appropriate for producing the first life. Why do we think that the early Earth environment could produce life from nonliving materials? A famous experiment suggests exactly this.

In 1953, Stanley Miller and Harold Urey built a model of the early Earth in a chemistry lab (Figure 13.2). A flask containing a mixture of simple compounds—including water vapor, ammonia, methane, and hydrogen gas—simulated Earth's early atmosphere. Liquid water was added to represent Earth's oceans. Electric sparks sent through the gases simulated lightning. When this model of early Earth was assembled, an amazing thing happened. Many complex organic molecules were formed, including amino acids, the building blocks of proteins. Not only had these molecules formed quickly, they formed in huge numbers. Further experiments showed that all the important organic molecules that make up life—not just amino acids but also sugars, lipids, and the nitrogenous bases found in RNA and DNA—can be generated in a similar way.

However, some scientists today question the importance of the Miller–Urey experiment. They think that Earth's early atmosphere was actually quite different from the model atmosphere Miller and Urey used, and that organic molecules may not have been so easy to generate. They have proposed two other hypotheses for how Earth got its first organic building blocks. One

FIGURE 13.1
Louis Pasteur demonstrated that life did not arise from nonlife.

UNIFYING CONCEPT

● *The Scientific Method*
Section 1.3

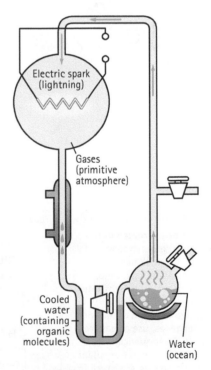

Electric spark (lightning)

Gases (primitive atmosphere)

Cooled water (containing organic molecules)

Water (ocean)

FIGURE 13.2
Stanley Miller and Harold Urey built a model of the early Earth and showed that complex organic molecules could be formed during lightning storms.

UNIFYING CONCEPT

● *The Scientific Method*
Section 1.3

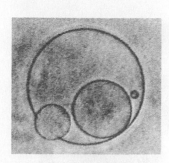

FIGURE 13.3
Liposomes show some cell-like behaviors. Here, a large liposome produces smaller "offspring."

A lipid sphere with captured nucleic acids—the ultimate ancestor of all life today?

FIGURE 13.4
This 3.5-billion-year-old fossil shows a chain of microscopic prokaryotes.

Has life ever been created in the lab? In 2010, a research team led by Craig Venter, who helped to sequence the human genome, claimed to have built a "synthetic cell." What Venter's group did, however, was choose a collection of bacterial genes, use a yeast cell to assemble the sequences into a chromosome, and then transplant the chromosome into a bacterium. It was not a case of creating a new life form or of creating a living organism from scratch.

hypothesis is that organic molecules were brought to Earth by meteorites. Earth was steadily bombarded by meteorites during its early history, and some of the meteorites recovered here do in fact contain a wide variety of complex organic molecules, presumably formed in outer space. For example, a meteorite found in Australia in 1969 contained nearly one hundred different amino acids. A second hypothesis is that large numbers of organic molecules were formed in deep-sea environments on Earth, similar to the hydrothermal vent habitats of today (see Chapter 8).

The next question is how these many separate organic molecules advance to become living cells. Scientists do not know the entire story, but they have discovered some clues. For example, when certain lipids are added to water, they spontaneously form tiny hollow spheres called liposomes. Liposomes have double membranes similar to cell membranes. Although they are not alive, liposomes sometimes behave like living cells—they grow, shrink, and divide (Figure 13.3). Liposomes also run chemical reactions inside their membranes and control what molecules move into and out of them, two key features of living cells.

Some liposomes may have eventually captured nucleic acids—that is, primitive genes. These early genes were probably made of RNA, not DNA. This is because, even in the absence of cells and enzymes, short strands of RNA can spontaneously assemble from individual nucleotides and even reproduce themselves. With a few more changes, RNA-containing liposomes may have become the very first cells—the first organisms on Earth. However it occurred, the transition to living cells was complete by 3.5 billion years ago, the time of the earliest known fossil organisms (Figure 13.4).

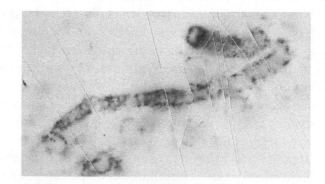

CHECK YOURSELF
Miller and Urey found that organic molecules are easily formed in large quantities from non-organic materials. But Pasteur had already shown that life does not come from nonlife. Why aren't these results contradictory?

CHECK YOUR ANSWER
Pasteur's experiment took place under conditions on Earth today, whereas life originated on a very different, younger Earth. Miller and Urey modeled conditions that may have been present on this early Earth. Also, it is a long way from organic molecules of the sort that Miller and Urey obtained to the microscopic organisms Pasteur was looking for.

Integrated Science 17A
ASTRONOMY

Did Life on Earth Originate on Mars?

EXPLAIN THIS If Mars once had life, how could that life have moved from Mars to Earth?

Is that bacteria?! In 1996, National Aeronautics and Space Administration (NASA) scientists found what looked like fossils of tiny bacteria in a Martian meteorite (Figure 13.5). The potential fossils were found very close to complex organic molecules and carbonate minerals that, on Earth, are associated with living organisms. The fossil-like structures are tube-shaped and measure 20 to 100 nanometers across, or less than 1/100th the width of a human hair. The meteorite is about 3.6 billion years old, so it dates from a time when Mars was a much warmer and wetter planet.

This discovery fueled tremendous speculation about whether life on Earth could possibly have originated on Mars. Some scientists suggested that life may have found its way to Earth in Martian dust that was set adrift in space when a comet collided with Mars. Skeptics were quick to point out, however, that the proposed fossils are much smaller than the tiniest bacteria on Earth and that they are likely to be too small to contain all the DNA, proteins, and other molecules a bacterium needs to function. Since the original report, no further evidence has been uncovered. However, ongoing NASA missions to Mars continue to collect data from the Red Planet, so eventually the mystery may be solved.

LEARNING OBJECTIVE
Describe the two sides of the debate over whether a meteorite from Mars contains fossil bacteria.

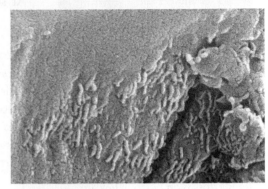

FIGURE 13.5
A startling possibility, or just science fiction? Could the tubelike structures on this Martian meteorite be fossilized bacteria?

CHECK YOURSELF

1. What evidence is there that life on Earth could have originated on Mars?
2. What is the primary objection to this hypothesis?

CHECK YOUR ANSWERS

1. A meteorite from Mars contains structures that could be the fossils of very small bacteria-like creatures. That these potential fossils were found very close to complex organic molecules and carbonate minerals associated with living organisms on Earth is particularly intriguing.
2. The primary objection is the supposed fossils' small size—they are smaller than any bacteria found on Earth and perhaps too small to contain all the molecules necessary for a living organism to function.

13.2 Early Life on Earth

EXPLAIN THIS What role did prokaryotes play in the origin of the eukaryotes?

LEARNING OBJECTIVE
Describe some of the key events in the early history of life on Earth.

We now know how life on Earth may have originated. In this section, we will look at some key events in the early history of life on Earth.

The Origin of Autotrophs

The earliest living organisms were marine prokaryotes living in a world with no free oxygen. They were **heterotrophs**, organisms that obtain energy and organic molecules from outside sources, as humans and other animals do today. Earth's early heterotrophs found a ready supply of food in the organic molecules that had accumulated in the oceans. As the number of heterotrophs increased through reproduction, however, the supply of organic molecules dwindled.

At some point, **autotrophs**, organisms able to convert inorganic molecules into food and organic molecules, evolved. The origin of autotrophic organisms was a crucial event in Earth history—without autotrophs, heterotrophs would have eaten through their food supply and died out. Plants are present-day examples of autotrophs: Plants use light energy from the Sun, water, and carbon dioxide to build organic molecules during photosynthesis. Some of Earth's early autotrophs also used energy from the Sun to build organic molecules. Others were *chemoautotrophs* that used energy from certain inorganic chemicals. Today, the large majority of autotrophs photosynthesize. However, some living prokaryotes are chemoautotrophs.

The Oxygenation of the Atmosphere

Oxygen is essential to life as we know it. Specifically, oxygen is essential for cellular respiration, a process used by most living things today to obtain energy. As we saw, though, Earth's early atmosphere contained no oxygen. This changed with the rise of the cyanobacteria, a group of photosynthetic bacteria, about 2.7 billion years ago. Cyanobacteria release oxygen as a by-product of photosynthesis, and it was their incredible success that first introduced oxygen into Earth's atmosphere. Evidence of an oxygenated atmosphere comes from the presence of banded iron formations in old sedimentary rocks. These formations are produced when atmospheric oxygen combines with iron dissolved in Earth's oceans. Fossilized cyanobacteria, called stromatolites, are shown in Figure 13.6.

The First Eukaryotes

The living organisms we are most familiar with—animals, plants, and fungi—are all eukaryotes. Unlike the prokaryotes, which are at least 3.5 billion years old, eukaryotes first appeared on Earth only about 2 billion years ago.

Eukaryotes differ from prokaryotes in many ways. Most important, eukaryotic cells contain a nucleus and many organelles. The nucleus and most eukaryotic organelles probably originated from inward foldings of the cell membrane. Mitochondria and chloroplasts, however, appear to have a different origin. (Remember that mitochondria, which are found in most eukaryotic cells, function in cellular respiration. Chloroplasts are found in plant cells and are responsible for photosynthesis.) Scientists believe that mitochondria and chloroplasts evolved from prokaryotes that started to live inside the earliest eukaryotic cells (Figure 13.7). This *endosymbiotic theory* (*endo* means "in" and *symbiotic* means "to live with") is supported by several observations. First, mitochondria and chloroplasts have their own membranes and their own DNA. Furthermore, this DNA is in the form of a circular chromosome, just like prokaryotic DNA. Finally, both mitochondria and chloroplasts make their own proteins, using ribosomes that resemble those of prokaryotes. So, which prokaryotes did mitochondria and chloroplasts evolve from? By studying their structures, scientists

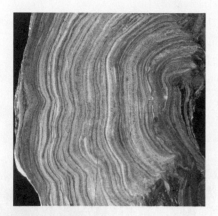

FIGURE 13.6
Stromatolites are among the oldest known fossils on Earth. They are formed by mats of photosynthetic cyanobacteria, the prokaryotes that changed the history of life on Earth by creating an atmosphere rich in oxygen.

Oxygen is essential to life as we know it in more ways than one. Atmospheric ozone, another form of oxygen, shields the Earth from dangerous mutation-causing ultraviolet radiation. Without this protective ozone layer, life might never have been able to move onto land.

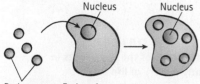

FIGURE 13.7
The mitochondria and chloroplasts in eukaryotic cells evolved from prokaryotes that started living inside early eukaryotes.

have concluded that mitochondria are most likely descended from a group of oxygen-breathing bacteria and that chloroplasts most likely originated from photosynthesizing cyanobacteria. This makes sense given the functions of mitochondria and chloroplasts today.

13.3 Charles Darwin and *The Origin of Species*

EXPLAIN THIS How did the Galápagos finches contribute to Darwin's ideas about evolution?

H ow has life on Earth changed over time? For example, how did we get from tiny, primitive cells to humans, hippos, redwoods, and all the amazing diversity of life on Earth today?

For thousands of years, people believed that life on Earth did not change. They believed that Earth had always had the same species, and always would. Then fossils were discovered in Earth's rocks, and people began to wonder. Fossils suggested that the kinds of species living on Earth changed over time—old species disappeared, and new species appeared. Also interesting was that fossil organisms sometimes showed a distinct resemblance to modern species (Figure 13.8). Could some fossils actually be the ancestors of modern species?

French naturalist Jean-Baptiste Lamarck (1744–1829) was one of the first to argue that this was the case. Lamarck believed that modern species were descended from ancestors that had evolved—changed over time—to become better adapted to the environments they lived in. According to Lamarck, organisms acquired new characteristics during their lifetimes and then passed these characteristics to their offspring. For example, ancestral giraffes stretched their necks to grab the high leaves on a tree, and their necks became longer. They then passed these longer necks to their offspring. The offspring reached for even higher leaves, stretching their necks even further, and so on (Figure 13.9a). Lamarck's theory for how change occurs, called the *inheritance of acquired characteristics*, proved to be incorrect: Organisms cannot pass characteristics acquired during their lifetimes to their offspring because these acquired characteristics are not genetic. However, Lamarck's fierce support for the idea that organisms evolve set the stage for Charles Darwin.

LEARNING OBJECTIVE
Describe some of the influences and events that brought Darwin to his theory of evolution through natural selection.

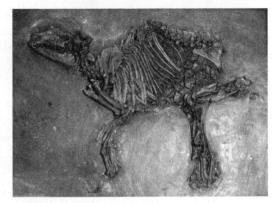

FIGURE 13.8
Could fossils be the ancestors of modern species? This fossil, found in Germany, is about 50 million years old. It has a clear resemblance to a horse, yet is only the size of a fox.

UNIFYING CONCEPT

● *The Scientific Method*
  Section 1.3

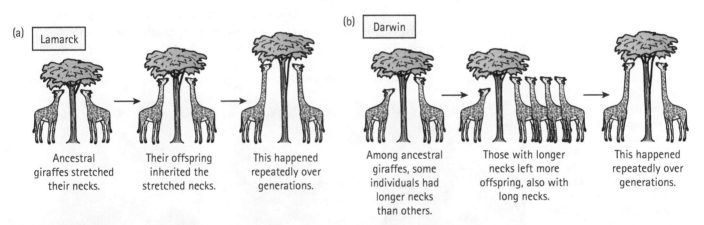

FIGURE 13.9
(a) Lamarck believed that organisms acquired new characteristics during their lifetimes and passed these characteristics to their offspring. (b) In his theory of evolution by natural selection, Darwin argued that organisms with advantageous traits left more offspring than organisms with other traits. As a result, advantageous traits became more common in a population.

FIGURE 13.10
Charles Darwin developed the theory of evolution by natural selection.

There's an expression: Genius is 1% inspiration and 99% perspiration. Darwin's genius reflects a lot of perspiration. While on the *Beagle*, Darwin collected 1529 alcohol-preserved specimens and 3907 skins, bones, and dried specimens. He also took 2000 pages of notes on plants, animals, and geology. It's no wonder that when he wrote down his theory, he was able to support it with a wide variety of well-considered examples.

English naturalist Charles Darwin (1809–1882), shown in Figure 13.10, set forth the theory of evolution in his book *The Origin of Species by Means of Natural Selection*, published in 1859. Darwin proposed that **evolution**—inherited changes in populations of organisms over time—had produced all the living forms on Earth.

Darwin's theory of evolution grew out of the observations he made as the official naturalist aboard the H.M.S. *Beagle*, which sailed around South America from 1831 to 1836. During these years, Darwin studied South American species, collecting large numbers of plants, animals, and fossils. Darwin became increasingly intrigued by the question of how species got to be the way they were. He was particularly struck by the living things he encountered on the Galápagos Islands, 950 kilometers from the South American continent. Darwin took particular note of the 13 species of Galápagos finches—now known as Darwin's finches. Darwin's finches showed remarkable variation in the size and shape of their beaks, with each beak being suited to, and used for, a different diet (Figure 13.11). How had the beaks of these finches come to differ in this way? Darwin wrote, "Seeing this gradation and diversity of structure in one small, intimately related group of birds, one might really fancy that from an original paucity of birds in this archipelago, one species had been taken and modified for different ends."*

Darwin was also inspired by the work of two of his contemporaries, Charles Lyell and Thomas Malthus. Lyell, a geologist, argued that Earth's geological features were created not by major catastrophic events—the favored theory of the time—but by gradual processes that produced their effects over long time periods. For example, the formation of a deep canyon did not require a cataclysmic flood, but could result from a river's slow erosion of rock over millennia. Darwin realized this could be true for organisms as well: The accumulation of gradual changes over long periods could produce all the diversity of living organisms as well as all their remarkable features.

The economist Thomas Malthus was a second important influence for Darwin, and the one who led Darwin to his great idea on the cause of evolutionary change. Malthus observed that human populations grow much faster than available food supplies, and he concluded, with despair, that famine was an inevitable feature of human existence. Darwin applied Malthus's idea to the natural world and argued that, because there are not enough resources for all organisms to survive and to reproduce as much as they can, living organisms are involved in an intense "struggle for existence." As a result, organisms with advantageous traits leave more offspring than organisms with other traits, causing populations to change over time. To go back to the giraffe's long neck: Darwin argued that

---

*Charles Darwin, *The Voyage of the Beagle*, 1909.

FIGURE 13.11
The finches Darwin saw on the Galápagos Islands—now called Darwin's finches—show remarkable variation in the size and shape of their beaks. Each is suited to a different diet. (a) The cactus finch has a pointy beak that it uses to eat cactus pulp and flowers. (b) The large ground finch has a blunt, powerful beak that it uses to crack seeds. (c) The woodpecker finch has a woodpecker-like beak that it uses to drill holes in wood. It then uses a cactus spine to pry out insects.

(a)   (b)   (c)

ancestral giraffes with longer necks were better at reaching the high leaves on trees. Because longer-necked giraffes got more food, they were able to survive and leave more offspring than ancestral giraffes with shorter necks. This happened repeatedly over generations. Over time, there were more longer-necked giraffes in the giraffe population (Figure 13.9b). This process, which Darwin called **natural selection**, is the major driving force behind evolution.

MasteringPhysics®

TUTORIAL: Darwin and the Galapagos Islands
VIDEO: Galapagos Islands Overview
VIDEO: Galapagos Marine Iguana

CHECK YOURSELF

1. If Lamarck had been correct and evolutionary change occurred through the inheritance of acquired characteristics, what trait might a bodybuilder pass to his offspring?
2. Many animals that live in the Arctic, such as Arctic hares, have white fur. How could natural selection explain the evolution of their white fur color?

CHECK YOUR ANSWERS

1. If Lamarck were correct, the bodybuilder's children would inherit the increased muscle mass that the bodybuilder had acquired over a lifetime of weightlifting. Because Lamarck's theory turned out to be incorrect, however, the children will have to do their own bodybuilding.
2. Animals that were harder to see in their snowy environments had an advantageous trait—predators were less likely to spot them. Arctic hares with whiter fur were more likely to survive to adulthood, reproduce, and leave offspring. These offspring would also have inherited whiter fur. As a result, whiter fur became more common in the Arctic hare population. Over many generations, natural selection produced a white coat that matches the Arctic snow.

13.4 How Natural Selection Works

EXPLAIN THIS What does it mean to say that one rabbit has greater fitness than another?

> **LEARNING OBJECTIVE**
> Explain how natural selection results in populations becoming adapted to their environments.

Rabbits were introduced into Australia in 1859, when a man named Thomas Austin released 24 individuals onto his property in the southeastern part of the continent. The rabbits quickly became pests, devastating farmlands and natural habitats (Figure 13.12). Breeding "like rabbits," they spread across the continent in such large numbers that they were described as a "gray blanket" that covered the land. Many attempts were made to control the rabbit population, including the construction of an 1822-kilometer-long "rabbit-proof" fence—still the longest fence in the world. Unfortunately, by the time the fence was completed in 1907, the rabbits had already passed through. (The fence wouldn't have worked anyway—even after it was completed, rabbits would pile up so thickly behind it that some were eventually able to walk right over their companions' backs to the other side.)

In the early 1950s, the government decided to try to control the rabbit population by releasing myxoma virus, a virus deadly to rabbits. Initially, the virus was a wonder, killing more than 99.9% of infected rabbits. Within a few years, however, fewer rabbits were dying. What had happened? Within the original rabbit population, a small number of individuals happened to be resistant to the

MasteringPhysics®

TUTORIAL: Causes of Microevolution

(a)

(b)

FIGURE 13.12
(a) Rabbits introduced into Australia caused widespread destruction, including here on Phillip Island. (b) This photo shows the same area after rabbits were eradicated. The vegetation has grown back.

myxoma virus. These resistant individuals survived the disease and reproduced, producing more disease-resistant offspring (Figure 13.13). Over time, the number of disease-resistant rabbits increased, and the virus became less and less effective. The rabbit population had evolved resistance to the myxoma virus through natural selection.

Natural selection occurs when organisms with advantageous traits leave more offspring than organisms with other traits, causing populations to change over time. Let's look more carefully at the process of natural selection.

1. *Variation.* In any population of organisms, individuals have many traits that show **variation**—that is, they vary from individual to individual. In humans, some variable traits are height, hair color, hairstyle, foot size, and blood type.

2. *Heritability.* Many traits are determined at least partly by genes and so are **heritable**—that is, they are passed from parents to offspring. Which of the human traits listed above are heritable? All of them are heritable except hairstyle. Hairstyle is not heritable because it is not genetically determined.

3. *Natural selection.* Some variable heritable traits are advantageous. The organisms that possess these advantageous traits are able to leave more offspring than organisms without the advantageous traits. The **fitness** of an organism describes the number of offspring it leaves over its lifetime compared to other individuals in the population. An organism that leaves more offspring than other individuals in the population is said to have greater fitness.

4. *Adaptation.* Because organisms with advantageous traits leave more offspring, advantageous traits are "selected for" and become more common in a population. What is the result? The population evolves to become better adapted to its environment.

Figure 13.14 summarizes the process of natural selection. Note that, although natural selection acts on individuals within a population, allowing some individuals to leave more offspring than others, it is the population as a whole that evolves and becomes adapted to its environment.

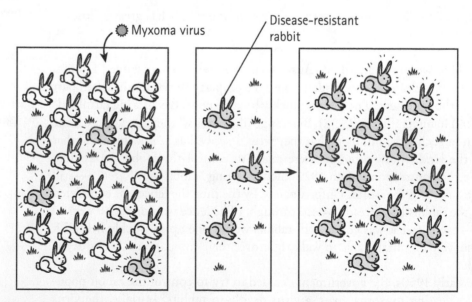

FIGURE 13.13
At first, the myxoma virus killed 99.9% of infected rabbits. However, a small number of naturally disease-resistant rabbits (blue) survived and reproduced, passing their myxoma-resistant genes to their offspring. The population became more resistant, and the virus became less effective.

(1) VARIATION

Organisms have lots of traits,
many of which show variation.

(2) HERITABILITY

Some traits are heritable. They are
determined by genes and so are
passed from parents to offspring.

(3) NATURAL SELECTION

Variation in heritable traits can result in
some organisms leaving more offspring
than others. This is called natural selection.

(4) ADAPTATION

Natural selection causes advantageous
traits to become more common in a
population. In this way, entire populations
become adapted to their environments.

FIGURE 13.14
How natural selection works.

CHECK YOURSELF

1. (a) Which of these traits are variable in cats: fur color, tail length, number of eyes? (b) Which of the traits are heritable?

2. The cheetah is the fastest land animal on Earth. It can run 112 kilometers/hour (70 miles/hour)! Cheetahs prey on Thomson's gazelles that can run almost as fast, 80 kilometers/hour (50 miles/hour). How might natural selection have produced the cheetah's fast running speed?

CHECK YOUR ANSWERS

1. (a) Fur color varies among cats—there are tabby cats, black cats, gray cats, and so on. Tail length also varies—not all cats' tails are exactly the same length. But there is no variation in the number of eyes—all cats have two eyes. (b) All three traits are heritable because all are determined genetically.

2. Faster cheetahs were better at catching Thomson's gazelles. Being better at catching food made faster cheetahs better at surviving and reproducing. As a result, faster cheetahs left more offspring, which were also fast. This resulted in a cheetah population with faster individuals. Over many generations, natural selection produced the remarkably fast cheetah we know today.

HISTORY OF SCIENCE

The Peppered Moth

During the Industrial Revolution, coal was the primary fuel in England. Burning coal slathered dark soot on trees, rocks, and ground. And then a startling thing happened to the moths.

Peppered moths in England had always been light in color, with the scattering of dark peppery flecks that gave them their name. Their coloration made them hard to see in a habitat of lichen-covered trees and rocks. (Lichens are fungi that grow with photosynthetic algae or bacteria; they form crustlike growths on rocks, trees, and other surfaces.) It was believed that this camouflage protected the moths from birds, their main predators.

As the Industrial Revolution progressed, pollution killed the lichens, leaving the trees first bare and then darkened with soot. In 1848, the first dark peppered moth was found in the industrial center of Manchester, England. Dark moths had probably always existed in the population, but they had been extremely rare. Over the next decades, as more coal burned and the environment became increasingly sooty, more and more dark moths were seen. By 1895, 98% of peppered moths in industrialized areas were dark. Then, in the second half of the 20th century, antipollution laws were passed and soot disappeared. Light moths increased in number, and today the dark moths have all but disappeared.

Did natural selection cause the coloration shifts in the peppered moth? Biologists hypothesized that in lichen-covered habitats, natural selection favored light moths because they were better camouflaged. In sooty habitats, natural selection favored dark moths. A series of experiments by Bernard Kettlewell tested this hypothesis. Kettlewell released equal numbers of marked dark and light moths in polluted and unpolluted areas. After a while, he tried to recapture the moths. In polluted areas, Kettlewell recaptured more dark moths than light moths, which suggested that dark moths had survived better. The opposite was true in unpolluted habitats, where he

Can you find the moths? Light peppered moths are well camouflaged on lichen-covered trees.

recaptured more light moths. Kettlewell also placed moths on tree trunks and filmed birds eating the moths. He found that birds ate what they could see: Birds ate more light moths in polluted habitats and more dark moths in unpolluted habitats.

Kettlewell's work became a classic example of natural selection. Eventually, however, certain aspects of his experiments were challenged. For example, moth experts pointed out that peppered moths don't usually sit on tree trunks, where Kettlewell had placed them. Instead, they usually rest on the undersides of branches. In addition, Kettlewell released the normally nocturnal moths during the daytime. This may have affected the moths' ability to find resting spots. Finally, Kettlewell used a mix of lab-raised and wild-caught moths, which could differ in their behavior. These doubts led Michael Majerus of Cambridge University to conduct a new set of experiments between 2001 and 2007. Majerus's work confirmed that bird predation was the key factor affecting the relative numbers of light and dark peppered moths. It is also interesting that a shift from light to dark forms in polluted areas (and back again, as pollution is cleaned up) has been reported in more than 70 other moth species in England and the United States alone.

LEARNING OBJECTIVE
Use examples to describe different kinds of adaptations found in living organisms.

13.5 Adaptation

EXPLAIN THIS Why do some birds have bright feathers despite the fact that the vivid colors make them more visible to predators?

Natural selection leads to the evolution of **adaptations**—traits that make organisms well suited to living and reproducing in their environments. The Check Yourself question in the preceding section gave an example of an adaptation—the cheetah's speed. The cheetah's speed helps it catch the food it needs to survive and reproduce.

Adaptations can relate to various aspects of an organism's life. Some adaptations help organisms survive. Survival is, after all, usually an important first step in successful reproduction. Survival requires that organisms be able to acquire food and other necessary resources. It also requires that organisms avoid becoming food for someone else (Figure 13.15). Anti-predator adaptations include camouflage, toxicity, or just the ability to hide or run away.

(a)   (b)

FIGURE 13.15
Almost every organism has adaptations that help prevent it from becoming food for someone else. (a) The spines of this cactus prevent most animals from eating it. (b) When threatened, this octopus releases a cloud of dark ink that may confuse a predator long enough for the octopus to escape.

The peacock may be the organism with the most famous adaptation for attracting mates. The male peacock's great fan of colorful tail feathers not only is admired by people but, more important, impresses peahens.

Other adaptations have evolved to help organisms acquire mates. These include the beautiful feathers of male peacocks and birds of paradise (Figure 13.16a), the sexy "rib-bits" of male frogs, and the enchanting songs of many male birds. Males have evolved these "sexy" traits because females of the species find them attractive. In other species, females don't choose their mates based on attractive traits. Instead, males fight with other males to obtain mates. The adaptations of these males may include large size, great strength, or fighting structures such as antlers (Figure 13.16b). Natural selection that favors individuals best able to acquire mates is also called *sexual selection*.

And speaking of bright colors— the bold colors of organisms such as wasps, coral snakes, and poison dart frogs evolved to warn potential predators that they are dangerous.

(a)   (b)

FIGURE 13.16
Some adaptations for acquiring mates. (a) The beautiful feathers of this male bird of paradise (shown here displaying his wings) help attract female mates. (b) These male deer are fighting for control of territory as well as mates.

Finally, some adaptations relate to bearing and raising young. Figure 13.17 shows one such adaptation—parental care. Parental care evolved because natural selection favored organisms that were able to help their offspring survive and thrive. Parental care is found in many animals, including humans.

Natural selection has produced remarkable adaptations over time. Nature does not plan ahead—it does not plan to make a falcon or a polar bear. Instead, adaptations are built step by step, through the never-ending selection of the most successful forms.

FIGURE 13.17
Parental care occurs in many species. This male poison dart frog is carrying his tadpoles on his back.

When a male praying mantis (the smaller insect on top) mates with a female, he is in danger of having his head bitten off.

CHECK YOURSELF

Mating is very dangerous for a male praying mantis. Quite often, the female will eat him as he mates with her.

1. **What advantage does the female get from eating the male?**
2. **Would it be more advantageous ("adaptive") for the male not to mate at all?**

CHECK YOUR ANSWERS

1. The female gets nutrients when she eats the male.
2. A male praying mantis that never mates is more likely to survive to old age. But, if he doesn't mate, he won't leave any offspring. Remember

SCIENCE AND SOCIETY

Antibiotic-Resistant Bacteria

A patient is ill with pneumonia and gets a prescription for penicillin. After three days, he feels better and stops taking his pills. A few days later, his symptoms return. He quickly finds his pills and starts taking them again, but this time they have no effect. What happened? This frightening phenomenon is called *antibiotic resistance*. Antibiotic resistance is caused by natural selection: Penicillin killed most of the pneumonia bacteria, but a few penicillin-resistant bacteria survived. These bacteria multiplied, and the patient's infection came back—only this time, the bacteria are resistant to penicillin.

Antibiotics are wonder drugs. When penicillin, the first antibiotic, appeared, it dramatically cut the number of illnesses and deaths resulting from bacterial infections. After only a decade of use, however, the first penicillin-resistant bacterial strains appeared. Since then, antibiotic resistance has spread, with more and more bacterial populations becoming resistant to more and more different antibiotics. Diseases once easy to treat—tuberculosis, pneumonia, even common childhood ailments such as ear infections—are now often resistant to multiple antibiotics. In 2011 the World Health Organization reported that about 440,000 new cases of multi-drug-resistant tuberculosis appear each year, resulting in at least 150,000 deaths.

Some of the most dangerous antibiotic-resistant bacteria are found in hospitals, where the use of many different types of antibiotics allows widely resistant strains to evolve. The Centers for Disease Control reported that in 2005, methicillin-resistant *Staphylococcus aureus* (MRSA), a bacterial strain that is resistant to most of the antibiotics currently available, was responsible for more than 94,000 life-threatening infections and 18,650 deaths in the United States alone. And, some MRSA strains are beginning to show resistance to the antibiotic vancomycin, often considered "the drug of last resort." Another worrisome development is the emergence of MRSA in the wider community. Community-based MRSA infections usually start as skin infections and spread through skin-to-skin contact. Some of these cases turn into "flesh-eating" disease, and others are halted only by drastic measures such as amputation. Environments with a higher

risk for community-based MRSA infections include athletic facilities, dorms, prisons, and day-care centers. Compared to people whose infections respond to antibiotics, people who have antibiotic-resistant infections require longer hospital stays and are more likely to die from their infections.

All antibiotic use has the potential of contributing to resistance. However, resistance has been greatly accelerated by the overuse of antibiotics. Under pressure from patients, physicians may prescribe antibiotics for illnesses that are not caused by bacteria. (Many common illnesses, such as colds, flus, and most sore throats, are caused by viruses.) These antibiotics select for resistance in the normal (non–disease-causing) bacterial populations in our bodies, making it possible for resistant genes to be transferred to disease-causing bacteria that later invade the body. The fact that patients sometimes stop taking their medications too soon contributes to the problem; this selects for antibiotic-resistant strains without providing the sustained dose that would actually kill all the bacteria. Antibiotics are also used heavily in the livestock industry, where animals are given antibiotics regularly—even when they are healthy—to promote growth. Unfortunately, this practice greatly promotes the evolution of antibiotic resistance. In recent years, reports of food-borne illnesses caused by antibiotic-resistant bacteria have become regular items in the news. For example, in August 2011, an outbreak of antibiotic-resistant salmonella in ground turkey caused at least 79 illnesses and one death.

What can be done about antibiotic resistance? First, humans must learn to use antibiotics wisely, taking them only when they are needed—that is, for bacterial infections—and then taking the entire course of treatment. Second, physicians and veterinarians can promote a socially responsible approach to antibiotics by educating patients and agriculturalists on the proper application of these drugs. Third, antibiotics should not be used to promote growth in livestock. In 2012, steps were finally taken to ban the agricultural use of certain antibiotics. Finally, since many antibiotics are less effective now because of resistance, scientists must search for new antibiotics to take the place of those that no longer do the job.

that adaptations are traits that make organisms good at living *and repro-ducing* in their environments. It's not enough to survive—you also have to reproduce! This male praying mantis may not have long to live, but at least he has a good chance of leaving offspring.

Integrated Science 17B
PHYSICS

Staying Warm and Keeping Cool

EXPLAIN THIS Why do Arctic mammals have relatively big bodies, short legs, and small ears?

In this section, we will see how being the right size and shape can be an adaptation. Most mammals maintain a fairly constant body temperature. We humans, for example, have a body temperature that always stays around 37°C (98.6°F). Animals that live in extremely hot or extremely cold habitats need to be able to maintain appropriate body temperatures in those environments—to *thermoregulate*. In deserts, animals have to be able to lose heat to avoid overheating. In cold habitats, animals have to be able to retain heat.

A key factor in thermoregulation is an animal's surface-area-to-volume ratio. The heat an animal produces depends on its volume. The heat it loses to its environment depends on its surface area because heat is lost through the body's surface. As a result, animals are better able to *lose* heat if they have a high surface-area-to-volume ratio, and they are better able to *retain* heat if they have a low surface-area-to-volume ratio. This has consequences for both the size and shape of animals that live in extreme habitats.

A large animal tends to have a *lower* surface-area-to-volume ratio because volume increases more quickly than surface area as organisms get bigger. For this reason, animals that live in cold habitats are often larger than related species that live in warm habitats. For example, the smallest bear in the world is the sun bear, found in the tropical forests of Southeast Asia (Figure 13.19). Adult sun bears weigh between 27 and 65 kilograms (60 to 140 pounds). The largest bear in the world is the polar

LEARNING OBJECTIVE
Explain how the need to thermo-regulate affects the size and shape of animals that live in very cold and very hot habitats.

FIGURE 13.18
The amount of *caramel* on this caramel-covered apple is determined by its surface area. The amount of *apple* in this caramel-covered apple is determined by its volume. The surface-area-to-volume ratio is the amount of caramel divided by the amount of apple. A small caramel-covered apple has a high surface-area-to-volume ratio. A big caramel-covered apple has a low surface-area-to-volume ratio.

Good cooks know that there are a lot more peelings from several small potatoes than from one large potato of the same volume. This is because little things have more skin per volume than big things!

FIGURE 13.19
(a) The small sun bear is found in tropical forests in Southeast Asia. A small animal is better able to lose heat because of its high surface-area-to-volume ratio. (b) The polar bear, the largest terrestrial carnivore in the world, is found throughout the Arctic. A large animal is better able to retain heat because of its low surface-area-to-volume ratio.

(a)

(b)

(a)   (b)

FIGURE 13.20
(a) This black-tailed jackrabbit lives in a California desert. Extensive blood vessels in its ears help it dissipate heat. It also has long legs. (b) This arctic hare is a relative of the black-tailed jackrabbit. Its ears are much smaller.

bear, which ranges throughout the Arctic. Adult polar bears weigh between 200 and 800 kilograms (440 to 1760 pounds).

Animals adapted to hot versus cold climates also vary in shape. Desert species often have long legs and large ears that increase the surface area available for heat dissipation. Their legs and ears are also covered with extensive blood vessels that carry heat from the core of the body to the skin, where convection, the transfer of heat by moving air, cools the animal. Arctic species often have short appendages and small ears that help conserve heat. An example is the rabbits shown in Figure 13.20.

UNIFYING CONCEPT

● *Convection*
Section 6.9

CHECK YOURSELF
On cold days, people often bundle up babies and small children carefully. Are babies more likely to need the extra bundling than adults? Why or why not?

CHECK YOUR ANSWER
Babies have higher surface-area-to-volume ratios than adult humans because they are smaller. So, yes, they are likely to appreciate the extra bundling.

LEARNING OBJECTIVE
Explain how an understanding of genetics produced insights about the mechanisms of evolution and the origin of genetic diversity.

13.6 Evolution and Genetics

EXPLAIN THIS Can chance cause a population to evolve?

So far, we've seen how natural selection acts on organisms' traits—giraffe neck length, cheetah speed, peppered moth color, and so on. Traits are only part of the story, though, because what gets passed from parents to offspring are not traits, but genes. The incorporation of modern genetics into Darwin's theory of evolution took place in the middle of the twentieth century and produced many new insights about how populations evolve.

The focus on genes led to a description of evolution as *changes in the allele frequencies of genes over time. Allele frequencies* describe how common different alleles are in a population. For example, the peppered moths we discussed earlier have a light allele (*a*) and a dark allele (*A*) for color. A population with many light moths and few dark moths might have allele frequencies of 92% *a* and 8% *A*. As the habitat becomes more polluted, dark moths become more common, and the dark allele increases in frequency. In a polluted area, the allele frequencies might change to 5% *a* and 95% *A*.

We can describe natural selection in terms of allele frequencies as well: (1) There is variation in a gene when multiple alleles for that gene exist within a population. For example, in peppered moths there are two alleles for color, *A* and *a*. (2) A specific allele may give an organism an advantage that allows it to reproduce more than other organisms in the population. In a polluted habitat, for example, the *A* allele is advantageous. (3) As a result, more copies of the advantageous allele are passed to the next generation, and the frequency of the advantageous allele increases in the population. In a polluted habitat, the frequency of the *A* allele increases.

Notice that, although natural selection *affects* genes and allele frequencies, natural selection does not act *directly* on genes. Another way to say this is: Natural selection acts on an organism's phenotype (traits), not on its genotype (genes). To see why, let's go back to the peppered moth. In peppered moths, the dark allele (*A*) is dominant and the light allele (*a*) is recessive. This means that both *AA* moths and *Aa* moths have dark wings (Figure 13.21). Whether a bird is likely to eat the moth depends on the moth's phenotype (whether it is dark or light), not its genotype. A bird is equally likely to eat a dark moth whether it has genotype *AA* or *Aa*.

AA   Aa

FIGURE 13.21
Natural selection acts on phenotype, not genotype. In the case of these two dark moths, it's the phenotype (dark color) that matters, not the genotype (*AA* versus *Aa*).

Mechanisms of Evolution

Natural selection is the driving force behind evolution, and it causes populations to become adapted to their environments. However, natural selection is not the only mechanism that causes populations to evolve. Populations also change over time because of mutation pressure, genetic drift, and gene flow. In order to understand these processes, let's consider peppered moths again.

Mutation pressure exists if the alleles responsible for peppered moth color are more likely to mutate in one direction than the other. For example, a genetic mutation may be more likely to turn a dark allele into a light allele than vice versa. If so, then over time, the frequency of the light allele will increase.

Genetic drift is the evolution of populations due to chance. Imagine a half-polluted town where light moths and dark moths are equally successful—neither allele is advantageous. Now suppose a sudden storm wiped out part of the town's peppered moth population. It *just might happen*—just by chance—that more dark moths survive. If so, then the frequency of the dark allele will increase. Notice that genetic drift produces evolution (heritable changes in a population over time) but that this evolution is not the result of natural selection—the dark allele was not advantageous. Genetic drift can also occur when, just by chance, more alleles of one type are transmitted to the next generation than alleles of the other type. For example, even if light and dark moths have equal fitness, light

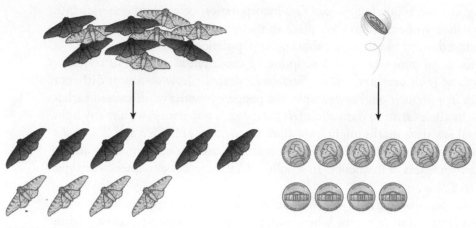

FIGURE 13.22
If light and dark moths have equal fitness, we would expect them to leave the same number of offspring. However, just by chance, one group could leave more offspring than the other, resulting in genetic drift. This is true for the same reason that, even though you expect the same number of heads and tails when you flip a coin 10 times, you might get more heads or more tails.

moths might just happen to leave more offspring (and therefore more light alleles) one year. Genetic drift works a lot like a coin flip (Figure 13.22). In our imaginary town, light and dark moths are equally likely to survive and reproduce the same way you are equally likely to get heads or tails when you flip a coin. But, if you flip a coin 100 times, you won't always get *exactly* 50 heads and 50 tails. Similarly, of 100 moths born in the next generation, there won't necessarily be *exactly* 50 light ones and 50 dark ones.

Genetic drift is particularly important in small populations because chance is more likely to change allele frequencies significantly in a small population. To see why, consider flipping a coin 10 times (a small population) versus 1000 times (a large population). With 10 flips, it is not at all unlikely that you'll get heads 60% of the time—that is, 6 heads and 4 tails. On the other hand, a similar result with 1000 flips—600 heads and 400 tails—is practically impossible.

Gene flow describes changes in allele frequencies that result from a net movement of alleles into or out of a population. For example, our half-polluted town may be next to a clean woodland that is home to a population of light moths. If a few of these light moths migrate from the woodland into town, the frequency of the light allele in the town will increase.

Where Variation Comes From

Natural selection cannot happen without variation. Furthermore, populations with more variation have a better chance of adapting to a changing environment. This is because with more variation, it is more likely that somewhere in the population there are alleles that will allow some individuals to survive under the new conditions. For instance, what would have happened to peppered moths during the Industrial Revolution if all the moths had been light and none were dark? In polluted areas, populations with only light moths might have died out. (We'll see that having many kinds of *species* in a habitat also increases the chance that at least some organisms will survive major changes in the environment.)

But where does variation come from? An understanding of genetics enabled biologists to answer this question. Genetic mutations constantly create new variations within populations. For example, when a genetic mutation changes the amino acids in a protein, it may produce a new allele for a given gene. Sexual reproduction also contributes to variation by bringing together alleles for different traits in new combinations.

CHECK YOURSELF

1. **In a peppered moth population, genetic drift causes the frequency of the dark allele to increase one year. Will genetic drift have the same effect the following year?**
2. **Twenty dark moths migrate into a peppered moth population, and 30 light moths migrate out. What effect does gene flow have on this population?**

CHECK YOUR ANSWERS

1. Genetic drift is evolution due to chance, and there is no guarantee that chance will have the same effect the following year. The situation is the same as flipping coins—when you flip a coin 100 times and then do it again, you may get more heads the first time and more tails the second time.
2. Gene flow causes the frequency of the dark allele to increase in this population.

13.7 How Species Form

LEARNING OBJECTIVE
Explain how new species arise.

EXPLAIN THIS Why is speciation often associated with the introduction of a geographic barrier?

We have seen how evolution through natural selection and other mechanisms causes populations to change over time. Can evolution also explain how different kinds of living things came to live on Earth? How does evolution produce new species?

A **species** is a group of organisms whose members can breed with one another but not with members of other species. (Notice that this definition works only for organisms that reproduce sexually. For asexually reproducing organisms, species are usually recognized by their similar characteristics and ways of life.) This means that the key to **speciation**—the formation of new species—is the evolution of *reproductive barriers* that prevent two groups of organisms from interbreeding.

There are two kinds of reproductive barriers: prezygotic and postzygotic. (A *zygote* is a fertilized egg, so *prezygotic* means "before fertilization" and *postzygotic* means "after fertilization.") *Prezygotic reproductive barriers* prevent individuals of different species from mating in the first place or prevent fertilization from occurring if they do mate. There are many types of prezygotic barriers—organisms may differ in when they breed, where they breed, or in the details of their courtship rituals. Their sex organs may not fit together properly, preventing successful sperm transfer, or other factors may prevent fertilization if sperm is transferred. Figure 13.23 shows an example of a prezygotic reproductive barrier. *Postzygotic reproductive barriers* act after fertilization has taken place. Postzygotic barriers

Humans may vary in significant ways from one part of the world to another, but we all belong to the same species—all humans are able to interbreed!

FIGURE 13.23
During courtship in red-crowned cranes, the birds dance around each other, bob their heads, stretch their necks, extend their wings, and leap straight into the air, singing in unison. Unless you can perform all these behaviors just right, you have little hope of convincing a red-crowned crane to mate with you.

MasteringPhysics®
VIDEO: Albatross Courtship
VIDEO: Blue-Footed Booby Courtship

FIGURE 13.24
A postzygotic reproductive barrier—the liger, a lion–tiger hybrid, is sterile.

occur when mating produces hybrids that either don't survive or are sterile—unable to breed themselves. The mule, the offspring of a horse and a donkey, is sterile and cannot reproduce. Likewise, a liger (Figure 13.24), the product of the mating of a lion and a tiger, is sterile.

Now let's consider how reproductive barriers—and therefore new species—evolve. In **allopatric speciation**, new species are formed after a geographic barrier divides a single population into two isolated populations (Figure 13.25). A geographic barrier could be a mountain range, a river, an ocean, a canyon, or—for aquatic organisms—a piece of land. Once two populations are geographically isolated from each other, they evolve independently. Over time, natural selection and genetic drift may contribute to the evolution of key differences that prevent interbreeding. If a reproductive barrier evolves, the different populations become separate species.

Numerous instances of allopatric speciation have been recorded. The rise of the Isthmus of Panama, 3 million years ago, divided the Caribbean Sea from the Pacific Ocean, splitting hundreds of types of marine organisms into separate Caribbean and Pacific populations. Most of these populations subsequently

FIGURE 13.25
Geographic barriers isolate populations and allow them to evolve independently. Sometimes, a reproductive barrier will evolve, resulting in allopatric speciation. In this example, the courtship song of birds divided by a mountain range diverges, resulting in a prezygotic reproductive barrier.

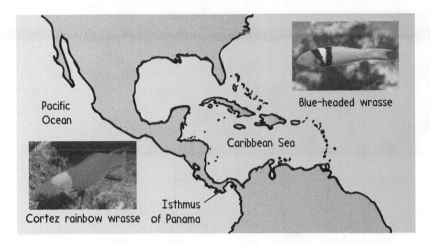

FIGURE 13.26
The formation of the Isthmus of Panama 3 million years ago isolated Pacific and Caribbean marine populations, producing numerous instances of allopatric speciation. The blue-headed wrasse (Caribbean) and the Cortez rainbow wrasse (Pacific) are descended from a single ancestral species that formerly spanned Pacific and Caribbean waters.

speciated by evolving reproductive barriers, including the wrasses in Figure 13.26. *Adaptive radiations* are spectacular examples of allopatric speciation where many new species, each adapted to a distinct way of life, evolve from a single ancestor. Many adaptive radiations have occurred on island archipelagos, which have abundant opportunities for geographic isolation. Adaptive radiations often occur after a new habitat is colonized. Examples of adaptive radiations include Darwin's finches, representing 13 species on the Galápagos Islands, and the Hawaiian honeycreepers, which include more than 30 species that differ in plumage, beak shape and size, and diet (Figure 13.27).

Sympatric speciation occurs without geographic isolation. Sympatric speciation is less common than allopatric speciation and often results from a sudden chromosomal change. One such chromosomal change is *polyploidy*, which occurs when organisms inherit more than the usual two sets of chromosomes, usually as a result of improper meiosis. Figure 13.28a shows a species of anemone that arose through polyploidy—it has four copies of each chromosome instead of two copies. Sympatric speciation can also result from hybridization. *Hybridization* occurs when two species interbreed and produce fertile offspring (Figure 13.28b). In both polyploidy and hybridization, chromosomal differences between the new species and the parent species prevent interbreeding. These types of speciation are more common in plants than in animals.

MasteringPhysics®
TUTORIAL: Polyploid Plants

FIGURE 13.27
The Hawaiian honeycreepers represent an adaptive radiation consisting of more than 30 bird species. The honeycreepers differ in plumage, beak shape and size, and diet. Unfortunately, many species are extinct or endangered because of habitat destruction and the introduction of nonnative species such as rats, pigs, mongooses, cats, and mosquitoes. (Mosquitoes are harmful because some carry avian malaria.)

FIGURE 13.28
Sympatric speciation often occurs through an abrupt chromosomal change. (a) A new species of anemone (right) was produced through polyploidy. The parental species is shown on the left. Note the doubling of chromosomes. (b) The sunflower *Helianthus anomalus* (right) originated through the hybridization of two other sunflower species (left and center).

(a)

H. annuus (parent)   H. petiolarus (parent)   H. anomalus (hybrid)

(b)

CHECK YOURSELF

1. A small river forms, dividing a group of moles into two isolated populations. After many years, a biologist puts moles from opposite sides of the river together and finds that they will not mate. Has speciation occurred? If so, what type of speciation was it?
2. Do you think the same river would cause a population of birds to become two separate species?
3. Two species of frogs do not interbreed because one species breeds in the spring and the other breeds in the fall. Is this a prezygotic or postzygotic reproductive barrier?

CHECK YOUR ANSWERS

1. The moles on the two sides of the river now represent two different species because they don't interbreed. This was allopatric speciation because it occurred after a geographic barrier (the river) separated the populations.
2. Probably not, since a small river is not much of a geographic barrier for flying animals.
3. Prezygotic because it prevents mating.

13.8 Evidence of Evolution

EXPLAIN THIS How do corn on the cob, a dog's dewclaw, and the human hand provide evidence for evolution?

LEARNING OBJECTIVE
List and provide examples of the main kinds of evidence that support the theory of evolution.

All scientific theories make predictions about what we should observe in nature (see Chapter 1). If these predictions are confirmed, the theory is supported. The theory of evolution has been tested repeatedly against observations of the natural world, and the evidence for evolution is overwhelming. Eight main kinds of evidence support the idea that evolution produced the diversity of life on Earth: (1) observations of natural selection in action, (2) artificial selection, (3) similarities in body structures, (4) vestigial organs, (5) DNA and molecular evidence, (6) patterns of development, (7) hierarchical organization of living things, (8) biogeography, and (9) fossils. We will look at the first eight topics here, and then consider fossils in Integrated Science 17C.

UNIFYING CONCEPT

● *The Scientific Method*
Section 1.3

1. *Observations of natural selection in action.* In many cases, scientists have seen natural selection produce evolutionary changes in populations; they have observed and measured the actual changes in populations. Examples include some of the cases we have looked at: Australian rabbits evolved resistance to the myxoma virus, so that over time a smaller and smaller fraction of individuals died from the disease. Peppered moths evolved to become better camouflaged in their environments—dark moths became more and more common as habitats became polluted, and then became less and less common as pollution was cleaned up. Bacteria evolved resistance to certain antibiotics, so that these antibiotics no longer controlled infections. Scientists have also studied how the beaks of Darwin's finches evolve after a drought, how insects evolve resistance to pesticides, and natural selection in a wide variety of other populations.

2. *Artificial selection.* **Artificial selection** is the selective breeding of organisms with desirable traits in order to obtain organisms with similar traits. Humans artificially select for desirable traits in domesticated animals and crops all the time: We breed fast racehorses to try to get faster racehorses; different types of dogs to produce superior hunters, herders, or sled-pullers (Figure 13.29); and varieties of strawberries to grow the largest and sweetest fruit. In artificial selection, humans control the reproductive success of different organisms and bring about distinct evolutionary changes in populations over time. These changes can be dramatic—think how much a Chihuahua differs from the animal it is descended from, the wolf. Or look at Figure 13.30 to see the difference between the corn we eat today and teosinte, the plant from which corn was bred. Artificial selection has produced countless forms of domestic animals and crops, all with traits valued by humans.

3. *Similarities in body structures.* We see evidence of the evolutionary histories of species in the structures of their bodies. Consider, for example, the limbs of different mammals. Different mammals use their front limbs for different purposes: Humans use theirs as arms and hands for manipulating tools, cats use theirs to walk on, whales use theirs as flippers, and bats use theirs as wings. If each of these animals had originated independently, we would expect their limbs to look completely different. Each limb would have been designed from scratch to best perform its function. But, despite the different functions of human hands, cat legs, whale flippers, and bat wings, all these limbs show the same arrangement of bones (Figure 13.31). This suggests that the limbs were inherited from a common ancestor and then modified through natural selection for different functions.

FIGURE 13.29
Artificial selection has produced great diversity in dogs.

FIGURE 13.30
Corn (*below*), one of the most important agricultural crops in the world, was laboriously bred through artificial selection from teosinte (*above*). Teosinte has tiny cobs, only a few rows of kernels, and inedible hard coverings on its seeds.

A mouse and a whale are about as different as two mammals can be. Yet just about every bone in a mouse corresponds to a specific bone in a whale. These similarities suggest that mice and whales had a common ancestor and that their skeletons were modified over time by natural selection to fit different environments and ways of life.

MasteringPhysics®
TUTORIAL: Reconstructing Forelimbs

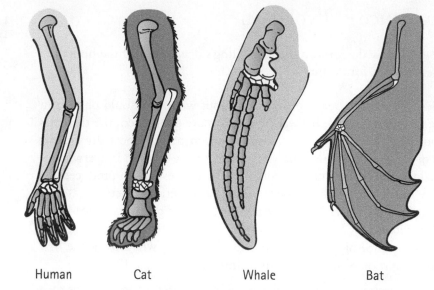

Human   Cat   Whale   Bat

FIGURE 13.31
Although these mammalian limbs are used for different activities, they are composed of the same set of bones, evidence that they were inherited from a common ancestor.

FIGURE 13.32
The Texas blind salamander lives in lightless caves. It has tiny vestigial eyes (dark dots in the photo) that are covered by skin.

A dog's dewclaw is a vestigial organ. The dewclaw is a digit that appears on the inside of the front paws. It does not reach the ground and has no function. It is just what remains of a formerly functional toe.

4. *Vestigial organs.* An organism's evolutionary history often leaves traces in its body. Some organisms have vestigial organs. *Vestigial organs* are not functional—they are just the remains of an organ found in the organism's ancestor. For example, we think of snakes as legless. But did you know that certain snakes actually have tiny, partial hind legs? The tiny stubs have no purpose—they are just the remains of what once were bigger limbs. A snake's vestigial hind legs provide evidence that snakes evolved from animals with legs. In the same way, many blind cave species lack functional eyes in their lightless habitats but retain vestigial eyes (Figure 13.32). These vestigial organs suggest that cave species evolved from animals with eyes.

5. *DNA and molecular evidence.* The DNA of related species have similar nucleotide (ACGT) sequences. In fact, the more closely related two species are, the more similar their DNA sequences tend to be. This is true not only for DNA sequences that code for proteins, but even for sequences that have no known function. If each species on Earth had originated independently, would we expect to see similar noncoding DNA in related species? DNA similarity suggests that DNA did not originate independently in each species but was inherited from a common ancestor and then modified during evolution.

6. *Patterns of development.* Related species develop in similar ways. If each species on Earth had originated independently, we wouldn't expect these similarities in development. For example, even though humans have no tails, we go through a tailed stage, just like other vertebrates (Figure 13.33).

7. *Hierarchical organization of living things.* Darwin's theory of evolution explains Earth's diversity of species as originating through numerous speciation events. If this is the case, then we expect living things to be organized into hierarchical sets of "nested groups"—that is, "groups within groups." Each living species should have fewer traits in common with more distant relatives, and more traits in common with species that it split off from more recently. This is in fact how living things on Earth are organized. Humans, for example, share a backbone with other vertebrates such as fishes, amphibians, reptiles, and mammals; they share four limbs with terrestrial vertebrates such as amphibians, reptiles, and mammals but not with fish, which are more distantly related; they share a waterproof skin with reptiles and mammals

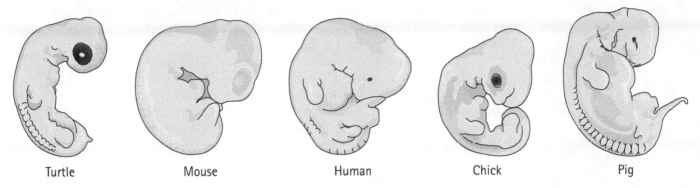

Turtle   Mouse   Human   Chick   Pig

FIGURE 13.33
Related species go through similar stages in their development. The human embryo goes through a tailed stage just like the other vertebrates, even though humans don't have tails.

but not with amphibians, which are more distantly related; and they share the trait of nursing their young with milk with other mammals but not with the more distantly related reptiles. Living things fit into a hierarchical organization, as predicted by evolution. We do not see traits scattered across living things. For example, we do not see a backbone in vertebrates plus some worms and some insects and some snails. The characteristics that organisms have make sense based on their evolutionary history and relationships.

8. *Biogeography. Biogeography* is the study of how species are distributed on Earth. Biogeography is consistent with evolution: It supports the idea that organisms evolved in a certain place and then left descendants in the places where they were able to spread. Biogeography does not support the idea that organisms were specially designed to fit into a specific type of habitat and then distributed where these habitats occur on Earth. For example, even though the Arctic and Antarctic have similar environments, they are occupied by entirely different species (Figure 13.34). The same is true for New World tropical forests and Old World tropical forests.

What biogeography does show is that the ranges of many species are bounded by geographic barriers such as oceans or mountain ranges. For example, many organisms are restricted to a single continent. In addition, closely related species tend to be found close together, suggesting that they evolved in one place and then spread. For example, all of Darwin's finches

FIGURE 13.34
The Arctic and Antarctic, which have similar habitats, are occupied by very different species. Polar bears are found in the Arctic but not the Antarctic. Penguins are found in the Antarctic but not the Arctic.

FIGURE 13.35
Why are terrestrial vertebrates rare or absent from islands, whereas flying species are common? This is the Hawaiian hoary bat, the only mammal found on Hawaii prior to human colonization of the islands.

are found in or near the Galápagos, and all the honeycreepers are found in Hawaii. Similarly, island species are usually most closely related to species found on the closest mainland. Islands also tend to have fewer species than an equally sized area of the mainland, and many island species are *endemic*, meaning they are found nowhere else on Earth. Finally, islands tend to be occupied by many flying animals but few terrestrial ones (Figure 13.35). All these points suggest that organisms were not dispersed purposefully around Earth, but instead evolved in one place and then left descendants where they were able to spread.

CHECK YOURSELF
Why is the fact that many species found on islands resemble species found on the nearest mainland evidence for evolution?

CHECK YOUR ANSWER
This pattern suggests that island species evolved when some mainland individuals colonized the island and then evolved in isolation, rather than that species were distributed purposefully around the Earth.

LEARNING OBJECTIVE
Explain how fossils provide evidence of evolution.

Integrated Science 17C
EARTH SCIENCE

Fossils: Earth's Tangible Evidence of Evolution

EXPLAIN THIS Why do fossil whales have legs?

Evolution has left a record in Earth's rocks—fossils. Because we can date fossils from the age of the rock formations they belong to, we can follow the evolution of certain groups of organisms over time. For example, fossil whales show that whales are descended from hoofed mammals. Fossil whales also tell us how many key whale traits evolved. In Figure 13.36a, we can see how, over time, whale nostrils moved from the front of the skull to the top of the skull, forming a blowhole. Fossil whales also show how whales lost their hind legs as they became more and more adapted to an aquatic existence. The oldest whale fossils, such as the 50-million-year-old *Ambulocetus*, have large hind legs that were used both on land and for swimming (Figure 13.36b). *Ambulocetus* also has small hooves on its front legs, providing clear evidence that whales are descended from hoofed mammals. *Rhodocetus*, a 46-million-year-old fossil whale, shows reduced hind legs—these are not attached to the backbone and so could not have supported much weight. *Rhodocetus* also shows prominent tail muscles that would have been effective for swimming. In the 40-million-year-old *Dorudon*, hind limbs are present, but they are tiny: *Dorudon* was clearly a fully aquatic species. In modern whales, there is no evidence of hind limbs on the outside of the body, although tiny remnants of the pelvis and sometimes femurs remain inside the body.

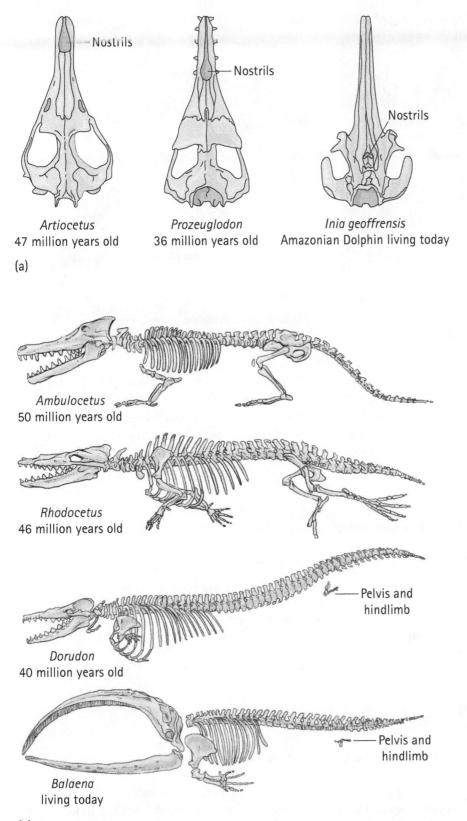

FIGURE 13.36

Fossil whales show how key features of these marine creatures evolved over time. (a) These fossil skulls show that the location of the nostrils shifted over time, from a position in front of the skull to a position on top of the skull—the "blowhole" seen in modern species. (b) Fossil whales also show the reduction and loss of hind legs over time.

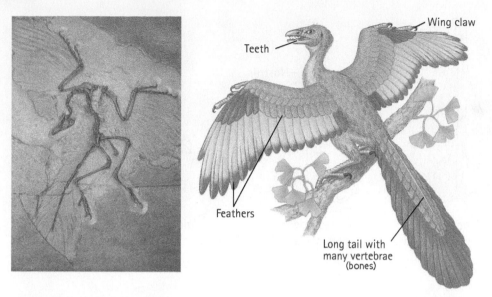

FIGURE 13.37
Archaeopteryx, an early bird, has features of both the dinosaurs it evolved from and modern birds.

You just learned that *Archaeopteryx*, the ancient bird, had clawed wings. Most birds today do not have claws on their wings, but there are a few exceptions—the most famous may be the hoatzin, which lives in tropical forests in the Amazon. Hoatzin chicks use their claws to move along branches. In addition, when threatened, they may drop from one tree, swim or move to another tree trunk, and then climb back up using their claws.

Archaeopteryx, the famous 150-million-year-old fossil bird (Figure 13.37), also shows intermediate traits in the evolution of birds from their dinosaur ancestors. *Archaeopteryx* has many birdlike features, such as feathers, wings, and a wishbone. However, it also has dinosaur-like features absent in modern birds, including claws on its wings, bones in its tail, and teeth.

CHECK YOURSELF
How do fossil whales provide evidence for evolution?

CHECK YOUR ANSWER
Fossils show how key traits evolved in whales. For example, the whale fossils that have been found show traits that are intermediate between the features of the ancestors (nostrils in front of the skull and large functional hind legs) and present-day whales (a blowhole on top of the skull and tiny vestigial hind limbs).

LEARNING OBJECTIVE
Describe some fossil hominids and what they reveal about the evolution of humans.

13.9 The Evolution of Humans

EXPLAIN THIS Is there a little bit of Neanderthal in you?

Humans are *primates*, a group of mammals that also includes the monkeys and apes. This does not mean we are descended from any modern species of monkey or ape, just that we share a common ancestor with these species more recently than we do with a dog, or a lizard, or a plant. Humans are also *hominids*, the group within the primates that includes modern *Homo sapiens* (our species) as well as some of our extinct relatives. Although humans are the only hominids in existence today, fossil hominids provide clues as to how humans evolved. A timeline of human evolution is shown in Figure 13.38.

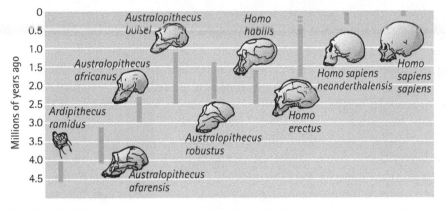

FIGURE 13.38
This timeline shows when certain hominid species existed on Earth. The skulls are all drawn to the same scale to show relative brain sizes.

Humans are not descended from any species of monkey or ape that is living today. However, we are more closely related to monkeys and apes than we are to other animals. *Descended from* and *related to* are entirely different.

Every creature alive now is equally evolved. Every creature alive today is the product of at least 3.5 billion years of evolution. Humans are not "more evolved" than any other species.

Some of the earliest hominids known belong to the group *Australopithecus*. Fossil *Australopithecus* have been found at multiple sites in Africa, where hominids are believed to have originated. "Lucy," the famous *Australopithecus afarensis* fossil shown in Figure 13.39, dates from 3.2 million years ago. When she was alive, Lucy stood 3 feet 8 inches tall and had a brain about the size of a chimpanzee's. However, the bones of Lucy's pelvis make it clear that she walked upright on two legs. In fact, older *Australopithecus* fossils show that an upright posture dates to at least 4 million years ago and therefore evolved long before increased brain size and intelligence.

Homo habilis is the earliest known species that belongs to the group *Homo*, which includes the species most closely related to modern humans. Some *Homo habilis* fossils are 2.2 million years old. *Homo habilis* had a larger brain than *Australopithecus*. *Homo habilis* also made stone tools—in fact, its scientific name means "handy man." Male *Homo habilis* were much larger than females. This is interesting because in other primates, such as gorillas and baboons, a big size difference between males and females is a sign that males fight each other for female mates.

Homo erectus lived from about 2 million years ago to about 400,000 years ago. *Homo erectus* had an even larger brain than *Homo habilis*. In fact, the brain of *Homo erectus* was not much smaller than that of modern humans. *Homo erectus* was a skilled toolmaker as well as the first hominid species to migrate out of Africa and spread into much of what is now Europe and Asia. Like *Homo habilis*, older *Homo erectus* fossils show that males were much larger than females. However, later fossils of the same species show a male–female size difference closer to that present in modern humans, suggesting the development of a more humanlike social system.

The Neanderthals—*Homo sapiens neanderthalensis*—are closely related to modern humans (Figure 13.40). They lived from about 200,000 years ago to about 30,000 years ago. Neanderthals had very thick arms and legs, and their brains were as large as those of modern humans. Archaeological finds show that Neanderthals were effective hunters, had complex burial rituals, and made use of medicinal plants. One question that remains unanswered is whether the Neanderthals had language. For thousands of years, modern humans coexisted with Neanderthals. However, Neanderthal populations disappeared as modern humans spread. Scientists are not sure why, although it seems likely that modern

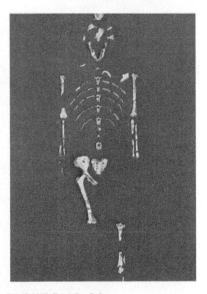

FIGURE 13.39
"Lucy," a fossil *Australopithecus afarensis*, stood upright and walked on two feet.

In one of the most spectacular archaeological finds in centuries, skeletons of a tiny human relative were discovered on a remote Indonesian island in 2004. Nicknamed "hobbits," *Homo floresiensis* adults had skulls the size of grapefruits and were no bigger than 3-year-old modern children. *Homo floresiensis* lived alongside pygmy elephants, giant rodents, and Komodo dragons. Most amazing is the fact that they still occupied the island only 13,000 years ago, which means that they coexisted with our own species.

humans outcompeted the Neanderthals and drove them to extinction. The development of modern genetic techniques has allowed scientists to collect information about the Neanderthals from a new source—DNA. Scientists are now attempting to sequence the Neanderthal genome from fossil remains. Genetic studies have already revealed that modern humans interbred with Neanderthals at some point in time; Neanderthal DNA accounts for at least 1%–4% of the genome of most humans.

The earliest fossils of modern humans, *Homo sapiens sapiens*, were found in Ethiopia and are 195,000 years old. Although anatomically modern humans are quite old, the cultural traits we associate with humans—things like art, music, and religion—are more recent, appearing only about 50,000 years ago. The reason for this gap between modern anatomy and modern behavior is the subject of continued debate.

FIGURE 13.40
Neanderthals coexisted with modern humans and interbred with them. These reconstructions appear at the Neanderthal Museum in Mettmann, Germany.

CHECK YOURSELF

1. Have multiple species of hominids ever coexisted on Earth? Do any hominids other than humans survive to this day?
2. What is the significance of the transition from a large male–female size difference in early *Homo erectus* fossils to a size difference closer to that of modern humans in later fossils of the same species?
3. What is the result of trillions and trillions of living things passing genetic traits to their offspring, here and there making an adaptive change, and surviving to today?

CHECK YOUR ANSWERS

1. The timeline of hominid evolution shows that multiple species of hominids coexisted during much of hominid history. Today, however, humans are the only species of hominids in existence. The others have all died out.
2. A large size difference between males and females is a sign that males fought each other for female mates. This may have been true in early *Homo erectus*. More equal body sizes in later *Homo erectus* suggests that males and females had longer-term bonds, perhaps as they raised offspring together.
3. We and Earth's other living things are the result of this long and astounding journey!

For instructor-assigned homework, go to www.masteringphysics.com **MP**

SUMMARY OF TERMS (KNOWLEDGE)

Adaptations Evolved traits that make organisms well suited to living and reproducing in their environments.

Allopatric speciation Speciation that occurs after a geographic barrier divides a group of organisms into two isolated populations.

Artificial selection The selective breeding of organisms with desirable traits in order to produce offspring with the same traits.

Autotrophs Living organisms that convert inorganic molecules into food and organic molecules.

Evolution Inherited changes in populations of organisms over time.

Fitness The number of offspring an organism produces in its lifetime compared to other organisms in the population.

Gene flow The evolution of a population due to the movement of alleles into or out of the population.

Genetic drift The evolution of a population due to chance.

Heritable Description of traits that are passed from parents to offspring because they are at least partially determined by genes.

Heterotrophs Living organisms that obtain energy and organic molecules from other living organisms or other organic materials.

Natural selection The process in which organisms with heritable, advantageous traits leave more offspring than organisms with other traits, causing these advantageous traits to become more common in a population over time.

Speciation The formation of new species.

Species A group of organisms whose members can breed with one another but not with members of other species.

Sympatric speciation Speciation that occurs without geographic isolation.

Variation Differences in a trait from one individual to another.

READING CHECK (COMPREHENSION)

13.1 The Origin of Life

1. How did Pasteur disprove the idea of spontaneous generation?
2. What experiment did Miller and Urey perform? What were their results?
3. How do liposomes resemble real cells?
4. Why is RNA, rather than DNA, believed to be the first genetic material?

13.2 Early Life on Earth

5. Why was the evolution of autotrophs an important event in the history of life on Earth?
6. What fundamental change in Earth's environment is attributed to the cyanobacteria?
7. How did the mitochondria and chloroplasts of eukaryotic cells originate?

13.3 Charles Darwin and *The Origin of Species*

8. What was Lamarck's theory about how evolutionary change occurred?
9. What impressed Darwin about the finches on the Galápagos Islands?
10. How did the work of Thomas Malthus influence Darwin?
11. How did Charles Lyell's work influence Darwin?

13.4 How Natural Selection Works

12. What is variation?
13. What is a heritable trait?
14. Describe how natural selection occurs.

13.5 Adaptation

15. From the point of view of natural selection, why is it important for an organism to survive?
16. Define sexual selection, and provide some examples of adaptations that evolved as a result of sexual selection.
17. Why is parental care adaptive in certain species?

13.6 Evolution and Genetics

18. Does natural selection act on genotype or phenotype?
19. Define genetic drift, and provide an example of how genetic drift can cause a population to evolve.
20. What is gene flow? Use an example to explain how gene flow can cause a population to evolve.
21. Why are genetic mutations and sexual reproduction important to creating and maintaining variation in populations?

13.7 How Species Form

22. What is a species?
23. What is the difference between a prezygotic reproductive barrier and a postzygotic reproductive barrier? Give an example of each.
24. Explain the difference between allopatric speciation and sympatric speciation. Which is more common?
25. What is an adaptive radiation, and when does it most commonly occur?

13.8 Evidence of Evolution

26. What is artificial selection? Why does artificial selection provide evidence for evolution?
27. Why does the similarity of the mammalian limb in all different species of mammals provide evidence for evolution?
28. How does biogeography provide evidence for evolution?

13.9 The Evolution of Humans

29. What important feature of modern humans can already be seen in 4-million-year-old *Australopithecus* fossils?
30. What was the first species of hominid to leave Africa and spread throughout Europe and Asia?
31. How old is our species, the modern humans known as *Homo sapiens sapiens*?

THINK INTEGRATED SCIENCE

17A—Did Life on Earth Originate on Mars?

32. Why do some NASA scientists think that life on Earth could originally have come from Mars?

33. If life on Earth did originate on Mars, how did it get here?

34. Why are some people skeptical that the supposed Martian fossils are of bacteria?

17B—Staying Warm and Keeping Cool

35. Why is the surface-area-to-volume ratio important in thermoregulation?

36. Recall that the amount of caramel on a caramel-covered apple is determined by the apple's surface area, and the amount of apple is determined by the apple's volume. If you like to eat a lot more caramel than apple, should you choose one large caramel apple or two smaller caramel apples with the same total volume? Defend your answer.

37. You are studying a species of tropical goat and comparing it with a related Arctic species. Based on your knowledge of thermoregulation in mammals and its effect on the size and shape of organisms, predict some of the differences you might see between the tropical and Arctic species.

17C—Fossils: Earth's Tangible Evidence of Evolution

38. Explain how the fossil whales that have been discovered support Darwin's theory of evolution.

39. What does the fossil *Archaeopteryx* tell us about bird evolution?

THINK AND DO (HANDS-ON APPLICATION)

40. Look at these photos, taken from Kettlewell's original publication on peppered moths. If *you* were the primary predator of peppered moths, would there be natural selection for color? Why or why not? (How many moths do you see in each photo? Which one did you see first?)

41. Take a hike or a walk in your neighborhood, and examine some of the plants, insects, birds, and other organisms that you come across. For each organism, note one or two traits that make it adapted to its environment. Did you notice any adaptations that keep organisms from being eaten by potential predators? What types of adaptations were these—ones that allowed them to flee or ones that allow them to remain camouflaged? Did you notice any adaptations related to finding mates? What about adaptations related to raising offspring?

42. Here's one more thing to think about during your walk. The species you see (whether they are pigeons, squirrels, mice, robins, sow bugs, or others) all share the ability to coexist with humans in a human-created environment. What adaptations allow these species to thrive in human communities?

THINK AND COMPARE (ANALYSIS)

43. Three bears are shown. Rank the bears according to how well suited they are to living (and thermoregulating) in a cold climate, from best suited to least suited.

44. Peppered moths collected from three different areas are shown. Rank the habitats the moths live in, from most sooty to least sooty.

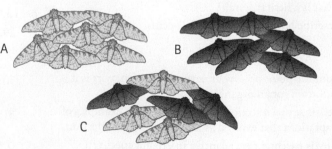

THINK AND SOLVE (MATHEMATICAL APPLICATION)

45. Let's look at how natural selection causes advantageous traits to become more common in populations. Suppose there is a population of bugs in which some individuals are green and some individuals are brown. Suppose that, because brown bugs are better camouflaged against predators, each brown bug leaves two brown offspring per generation (on average) and each green bug leaves one green offspring per generation (on average). (Is this natural selection? Why?) You start with two brown bugs and two green bugs in generation 1. How many brown and green bugs are there in generation 2? Calculate the number of brown and green bugs there are in generations 1 to 10. Show that 50% of the bugs in generation 1 are brown, 94% in generation 5 are brown, and more than 99% in generation 10 are brown. What is happening?

46. Let's consider a very small population of snapdragons, one with only two individuals. One snapdragon has two red alleles for flower color—it is *RR*. The other snapdragon has a red allele and a white allele for flower color—it is *RW*. (You may wish to review the inheritance of snapdragon flower color.) Show that the frequency of the red allele *R* in the population is 0.75 and the frequency of the white allele *W* is 0.25.

47. Now let's assume that the two snapdragons in our tiny population mate and produce a single offspring with genotype *RR*. We now have a snapdragon population with only one individual. Calculate the allele frequencies of the red and white alleles in the population. Is this an example of genetic drift?

THINK AND EXPLAIN (SYNTHESIS)

48. What types of experiments showed that living organisms are not spontaneously generated in nonliving matter? Why do you think the idea of spontaneous generation survived so long—that is, why was spontaneous generation so difficult to disprove?

49. Why do scientists consider Miller and Urey's experiment important?

50. How are liposomes similar to cells? How are they different from real cells?

51. What are some human traits that do not show variation? What are some that do show variation? What are some heritable human traits? Some nonheritable human traits?

52. How would you determine whether a trait you were interested in studying is heritable?

53. How is the story of the myxoma virus and Australian rabbits similar to the story of antibiotic resistance in bacteria?

54. Nancy Burley of the University of California, Irvine, ran the following experiment: She placed red color bands on the feet of some male birds and green color bands on the feet of other male birds. Females preferred to mate with males that had red color bands. Is this an example of natural selection? Why or why not?

55. In recent decades, average human height has increased in many parts of the world. Do you think this is an example of evolution?

56. On islands, many large animals—such as elephants—evolve to become miniaturized. On the other hand, many small animals—including some rodents—evolve to be exceptionally large. Why might natural selection produce these results? Do you think this phenomenon sheds light on *Homo floresiensis*, the miniature relative of humans?

57. Male birds of many species have brighter feathers than females. Bright colors on males are often adaptations for winning mates, as in the case of birds of paradise and

peacocks, discussed in this chapter. Is being less colorful adaptive for female birds? Defend your answer.

58. Two species of foxes are shown here. One is a kit fox in Arizona. The other is an Arctic fox. Which is which? How can you tell? Describe at least two traits that make each animal well adapted to its environment.

59. You are studying a population of beetles that includes some red individuals and some yellow individuals. You know that color is a heritable trait in the population. By counting the number of red and yellow beetles over a period of 5 years, you notice that the proportion of red individuals is increasing over time while the proportion of yellow individuals is decreasing over time. How could you determine whether this is a result of natural selection? Are there other potential explanations?

60. In a population of mice that you are studying, tail length appears to be increasing over time. However, you find no evidence that natural selection is acting on tail length. What are two alternative explanations for your observation?

61. Individuals of two different fish species sometimes mate, but their offspring die soon after hatching. Is this an example of a prezygotic or postzygotic reproductive barrier?

62. Finches on two closely situated islands look different; on one island, they have brown tail feathers, and on the other island, they have black tail feathers. Can you conclude that these are two different species? How could you determine whether they are in fact distinct species?

63. At your field site, there are butterflies with yellow wings and butterflies with orange wings. After observing them carefully, you notice that the yellow butterflies always mate in shady areas under trees, whereas the orange butterflies always mate in sunny meadows. Can you conclude that they are different species?

64. Many of the living organisms in Hawaii are found nowhere else on Earth. Hawaii has numerous unique species of plants, birds, insects, mammals, mushrooms, and other living things. Why?

65. What are some examples of artificial selection? How are artificial selection and natural selection similar? How are they different?

66. Islands tend to have fewer species than the mainlands they resemble. Furthermore, island species often include many flying organisms and few terrestrial ones. Do these biogeographic patterns support evolution or the purposeful distribution of organisms? Why?

67. Laura says she doesn't believe that humans were at one time chimpanzees or gorillas. Jeff says he doesn't believe it either. Explain why biologists also don't believe that humans are descended from chimps or gorillas.

68. Write a letter to Grandma telling her about drug resistance in living organisms. Explain to her why drug resistance is such a common phenomenon—including why insects become more resistant to pesticides over time, and why diseases such as tuberculosis and malaria have become harder to treat in recent years.

THINK AND DISCUSS (EVALUATION)

69. During a drought, the supply of seeds available to a finch population decreases. The smaller, softer seeds, which are easier to crack, are quickly eaten up. Finches with larger, stronger beaks are better able to crack the larger seeds that remain. What evolutionary changes do you expect to see in this finch population?

70. Caterpillars of the Monarch butterfly eat plants that are toxic to other animals so that their tissues become toxic. Birds that try to eat Monarchs vomit and then avoid the striking orange-and-black pattern in the future. The viceroy is another species of butterfly. Viceroys resemble monarchs, but they are not toxic. Is the appearance of the viceroy adaptive? How could you test this hypothesis?

Can you tell which is the Monarch and which is the Viceroy? Viceroys have a black stripe in the hind wing that goes across the other stripes. Monarchs do not.

71. You are eating a salad when you almost bite down on a green insect hidden among the lettuce leaves. The friend who is eating with you says, "That would have been gross, but I don't think it would have poisoned you." Do you agree?

72. Bird eggs vary tremendously in color. Do you think the color of a bird's eggs is adaptive? What factors may have shaped the evolution of egg color in different species?

73. A population of beetles that includes both sandy and green individuals is introduced into a grassy environment. How do you expect the population to evolve due to natural selection? Now suppose that another beetle population lives in a nearby sandbank. Most of the individuals in this population are sandy colored. If beetles regularly migrate from one population to the other, what will be the effect on each population? Does gene flow make it easier or harder for these beetle populations to adapt to their environments?

74. Islands tend to have fewer species than an equally sized area of the mainland. Is this consistent with the idea that species were spread around Earth purposefully? Is it consistent with evolution?

75. Scientific theories must be falsifiable. Is evolution falsifiable? For example, can you imagine some biogeographic evidence that would not be consistent with evolution? Has any evidence of this sort been found?

76. Scientists who are searching for new fossils of early hominids usually look in Africa. Does this make sense, or should they expand their search?

77. Broad-spectrum antibiotics are effective against a wide variety of bacteria. Narrow-spectrum antibiotics are effective against only certain types of bacteria. Public health officials have suggested that one way to combat antibiotic resistance is to use narrow-spectrum antibiotics whenever possible. Do you agree? Explain how the use of narrow-spectrum antibiotics instead of broad-spectrum antibiotics could slow the evolution of resistance in bacteria.

READINESS ASSURANCE TEST (RAT)

If you have a good handle on this chapter, if you really do, then you should be able to score 7 out of 10 on this RAT. If you score less than 7, you need to study further before moving on.

Choose the BEST answer to each of the following:

1. Which of these statements regarding the origin of life is false?
   (a) Life originated on an Earth whose atmosphere contained high levels of oxygen.
   (b) Miller and Urey obtained amino acids and other organic molecules when they sent electric sparks through a model of Earth's early atmosphere.
   (c) The first genes were probably made of RNA.
   (d) When certain lipids are added to water, they spontaneously form structures that resemble cell membranes.

2. The primary problem with the hypothesis that life on Earth originated on Mars is that
   (a) Mars has never had water.
   (b) the proposed Martian fossils are much smaller than the tiniest bacteria on Earth.
   (c) life on Mars would have had no way to get to Earth.
   (d) life has never been found on Mars.

3. Photosynthesizing plants are
   (a) heterotrophs.
   (b) autotrophs.
   (c) chemoautotrophs.
   (d) archaeans.

4. Organisms with heritable, advantageous traits leave more offspring than organisms with other traits, which causes these advantageous traits to become more common in a population over time. This describes
   (a) the inheritance of acquired characteristics.
   (b) speciation.
   (c) natural selection.
   (d) genetic drift.

5. Which of these adaptations is the result of sexual selection?
   (a) the spines on cactus plants
   (b) parental care in male poison dart frogs
   (c) the songs of male birds
   (d) dark wings in peppered moths

6. If we compare related rabbit species in desert and Arctic environments, we would expect
   (a) the desert species to have shorter legs.
   (b) the Arctic species to be smaller.
   (c) the desert species to have larger ears.
   (d) the Arctic species to be the same size as the desert species.

7. Which of the following mechanisms of evolution consistently causes populations to become more adapted to their environments?
   (a) natural selection
   (b) mutation pressure
   (c) genetic drift
   (d) gene flow

8. When a lion mates with a tiger, the offspring are sterile. This is an example of
   (a) allopatric speciation.
   (b) sympatric speciation.
   (c) speciation by hybridization.
   (d) a postzygotic reproductive barrier.

9. Which of the following provides evidence for evolution?
   (a) changes in the coloration of peppered moth populations over time
   (b) the presence of vestigial eyes in cave salamanders
   (c) the fact that island species tend to most closely resemble species found on the nearest mainland
   (d) all of these

10. Which statement about human evolution is true?
    (a) The earliest fossils of modern humans are almost 200,000 years old.
    (b) Humans are descended from chimpanzees.
    (c) Modern humans are the only hominids that used tools.
    (d) During human evolution, large brains evolved before upright posture.

Answers to RAT

1. a, 2. b, 3. b, 4. c, 5. c, 6. c, 7. a, 8. d, 9. d, 10. a

14

Crowded street in Shanghai, one of China's largest cities

Human Population

Upon completing this chapter, you will be able to:

- Perceive the scope of human population growth

- Assess divergent views on population growth

- Evaluate how human population, affluence, and technology affect the environment

- Explain and apply the fundamentals of demography

- Outline and assess the concept of demographic transition

- Describe how family planning, the status of women, and wealth and poverty affect population growth

- Characterize the dimensions of the HIV/AIDS epidemic

China's One-Child Policy

"The population problem concerns us, but it will concern our children and grandchildren even more. How we respond to the population threat may do more to shape the world in which they will live than anything else we do."

—Lester Brown, President, Earth Policy Institute

"As you improve health in a society, population growth goes down. . . . Before I learned about it, I thought it was paradoxical."

—Bill Gates, Chair, Microsoft Corporation

The People's Republic of China is the world's most populous nation, home to one-fifth of the 7 billion people living on Earth today.

When Mao Zedong founded the country's current regime six decades ago roughly 540 million people lived in a mostly rural, war-torn, impoverished nation. Mao believed population growth was desirable, and under his rule China grew and changed. By 1970, improvements in food production, food distribution, and public health allowed China's population to swell to 790 million people. At that time, the average Chinese woman gave birth to 5.8 children in her lifetime.

However, the country's burgeoning population and its industrial and agricultural development were eroding the nation's soils, depleting its water, leveling its forests, and polluting its air. Chinese leaders realized that the nation might not be able to feed its people if their numbers grew much larger. They saw that continued population growth could exhaust resources and threaten the stability and progress of Chinese society. The government decided to institute a population control program that prohibited most Chinese couples from having more than one child.

The program began with education and outreach efforts encouraging people to marry later and have fewer children (**FIGURE 14.1**). Along with these efforts, the Chinese government increased the availability of contraceptives and abortion. By 1975, China's annual population growth rate had dropped from 2.8% to 1.8%.

To further decrease the birth rate, in 1979 the government took the more drastic step of instituting a system of rewards and punishments to enforce a one-child limit. One-child families received better access to schools, medical care, housing, and government jobs, and mothers with only one child were given longer maternity leaves. In contrast, families with more than one child were subjected to monetary fines, employment discrimination, and social scorn and ridicule. In some cases, the fines exceeded half of a couple's annual income.

Population growth rates dropped still further, but public resistance to the policy was simmering. Beginning in 1984, the one-child policy was loosened, strengthened, and then loosened again as government leaders explored ways to maximize population control while minimizing public opposition. Today the one-child program is less strict than in past years and applies mostly to families in urban areas. Many farmers and ethnic minorities in rural areas are exempted, because success on the farm often depends on having multiple children.

In enforcing its policies, China has been conducting one of the largest and most controversial social experiments in history. In purely quantitative terms, the experiment has been a major success: The nation's growth rate is now down to 0.5%, making it easier for the country to deal with its many social, economic, and environmental challenges.

However, the one-child policy has also produced unintended consequences. Traditionally, Chinese culture has valued sons because they carry on the family name, assist with

控制人口数量 提高人口素质
Control the growth of the Population   Improve the qualities of the Population

FIGURE 14.1 Billboards and murals like this one in the Chinese city of Chengdu promote the national "one-child" policy.

farm labor in rural areas, and care for aging parents. Daughters, in contrast, will most likely marry and leave their parents, as the culture dictates. As a result, they cannot provide the same benefits to their parents as will sons. Thus, faced with being limited to just one child, many Chinese couples prefer a son to a daughter. Tragically, this has led to selective abortion, killing of female infants, an unbalanced sex ratio, and a black-market trade in teenaged girls for young men who cannot find wives.

Further problems are expected in the near future, including an aging population and a shrinking workforce. Moreover, China's policies have elicited criticism worldwide from people who oppose government intrusion into personal reproductive choices.

As other nations become more and more crowded, might their governments also feel forced to turn to drastic policies that restrict individual freedoms? In this chapter, we examine human population dynamics worldwide, consider their causes, and assess their consequences for the environment and our society. ●

Our World at Seven Billion

China receives a great deal of attention on population issues because of its unique reproductive policies and its status as the world's most populous nation. But China is not alone in dealing with population issues. India, China's neighbor, is also a population powerhouse, and is only slightly less populous than China. India lacks China's stringent reproductive policies, though, and soon will overtake China and possess the world's largest population (FIGURE 14.2).

Like India, many of the world's poorer nations continue to experience substantial population growth. Many of these nations are ill-equipped to handle such growth, and this leads to stresses on society, the environment, and people's well-being. In our world of now 7 *billion* people, one of our greatest challenges in this century is finding ways to slow the growth of the human population without the requirement of measures

such as those used in China, but by establishing the conditions for all people that lead them to desire to have fewer children.

The human population is growing rapidly

Our global population is now over 7 billion and grows by more than 70 million people each year. This is the equivalent of adding all the people of California, Texas, and New Jersey to the world annually—and it means that we add more than 2 people to the planet *every second*. Take a look at FIGURE 14.3 and note just how recent and sudden our

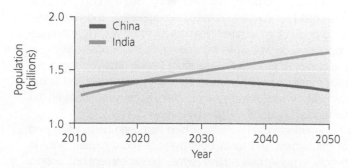

FIGURE 14.2 China and India will likely soon switch places as the most populous and second-most populous nations. China's rate of growth is now lower than India's as a result of China's aggressive population policies. *Data from Population Division of the Department of Economic and Social Affairs of the United Nations Secretariat, 2011. World population prospects: The 2010 revision, http://esa. un.org/wpp. © United Nations, 2011.*

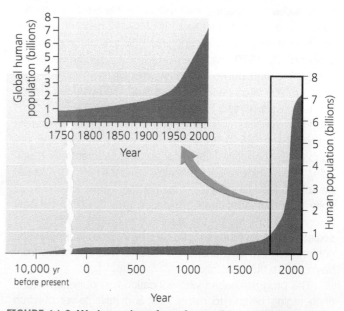

FIGURE 14.3 We have risen from fewer than 1 billion in 1800 to 7 billion today. Viewing global human population size over a long time scale (**bottom graph**) and growth since the industrial revolution (**inset top graph**) shows that nearly all growth has occurred in just the past 200 years. *Data from U.S. Bureau of Census.*

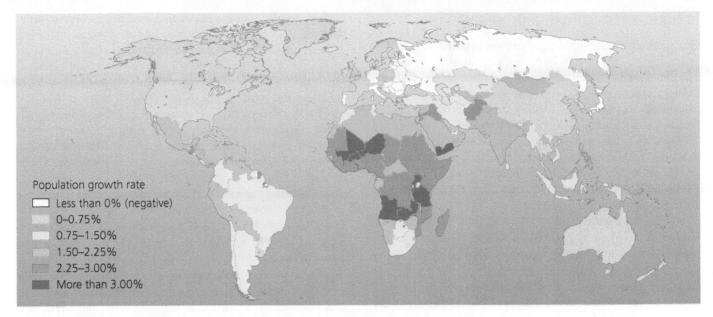

FIGURE 14.4 Population growth rates vary greatly from place to place. Population is growing fastest in poorer nations of the tropics and subtropics but is now beginning to decrease in some northern industrialized nations. Shown are rates of natural increase as of 2012. *Data from Population Reference Bureau, 2012. 2012 World population data sheet.*

 Which world region has the highest population growth rate? What are the geographic patterns in growth rate within this region?

Population growth rate
- ☐ Less than 0% (negative)
- 0–0.75%
- 0.75–1.50%
- 1.50–2.25%
- 2.25–3.00%
- More than 3.00%

rapid increase has been. It took until after 1800, virtually all of human history, for our population to reach 1 billion. Yet we reached 2 billion by 1930, and 3 billion in just 30 more years. Our population added its next billion in just 15 years, and it has taken only 12 years to add each of the next three installments of a billion people. Consider when you were born, and estimate the number of people added to the planet just since that time. No previous generations have *ever* lived amid so many other people.

You may not feel particularly crowded, but consider that we in the United States are not experiencing as much population growth and density as people in most other nations. In today's world, rates of annual growth vary greatly from region to region (**FIGURE 14.4**) and are highest in developing nations.

What accounts for our unprecedented growth? As you may recall, exponential growth—the increase in a quantity by a fixed percentage per unit time—accelerates increase in population size, just as compound interest accrues in a savings account. The reason for this pattern is that a fixed percentage of a small number makes for a small increase, but that the same percentage of a large number produces a large increase. Thus, even if the growth *rate* remains steady, population *size* will increase by greater increments with each successive generation.

For much of the 20th century, the growth rate of the human population rose from year to year. This rate peaked at 2.1% during the 1960s and has declined to 1.2% since then. Although 1.2% may sound small, exponential growth endows small numbers with large consequences. A hypothetical population starting with one man and one woman that grows at

1.2% gives rise to a population of 2939 after 40 generations and 112,695 after 60 generations.

At a 1.2% annual growth rate, a population doubles in size in just 58 years. We can roughly estimate doubling times with a handy rule of thumb. Just take the number 70 (which is 100 times 0.7, the natural logarithm of 2) and divide it by the annual percentage growth rate: 70/1.2 = 58.3. Had China not instituted its one-child policy, and had its growth rate remained at 2.8%, it would have taken only 25 years to double in size.

FAQ How big is a billion?

Human beings have trouble conceptualizing huge numbers. As a result, we often fail to recognize the true magnitude of a number such as 7 billion. Although we know that a billion is bigger than a million, we tend to view both numbers as impossibly large and therefore similar in size. For example, guess (without calculating) how long it would take a banker to count out $1 million if she did it at a rate of a dollar a second for 8 hours a day, 7 days a week. Now guess how long it would take to count $1 billion at the same rate. The difference between your estimate and the answer may surprise you. Counting $1 million would take a mere 35 days, whereas counting $1 billion would take 95 years! Living 1 million seconds takes only 12 days, while living for 1 billion seconds requires more than 31 years. You couldn't live for 7 billion seconds if you tried, because that would take 221 years. Examples like these can help us appreciate the *b* in *billion*.

Is population growth a problem?

Our spectacular growth in numbers has resulted largely from technological innovations, improved sanitation, better medical care, increased agricultural output, and other factors that have brought down death rates. These improvements have been particularly successful in reducing **infant mortality rates,** the frequency of children dying in infancy. Birth rates have not declined as much, so births have outpaced deaths for many years now. Thus, our population explosion has arisen from a very good thing—our ability to keep more of our fellow human beings alive longer! Why then do so many people view population growth as a problem?

Let's start with a bit of history. At the outset of the industrial revolution, population growth was universally regarded as a good thing. For parents, high birth rates meant more children to support them in old age. For society, it meant a greater pool of labor for factory work. However, British economist **Thomas Malthus** (1766–1834) had a different view. Malthus (FIGURE 14.5a) argued that unless population growth were controlled by laws or other social strictures, the number of people would eventually outgrow the available food supply. Malthus's most influential work, *An Essay on the Principle of Population,* published in 1798, argued that if society did not limit births (through abstinence and contraception, for instance), then rising death rates would reduce the population through war, disease, and starvation.

In our day, biologists Paul and Anne Ehrlich of Stanford University have been called "neo-Malthusians" because they too have warned that our population may grow faster than our ability to produce and distribute food. In his best-selling 1968 book, *The Population Bomb,* Paul Ehrlich (FIGURE 14.5b) predicted that population growth would unleash famine and conflict that would consume civilization by the end of the 20th century.

Although human population quadrupled in the past 100 years—the fastest it has ever grown (see Figure 14.3)—Ehrlich's forecasts have not fully materialized. This is due, in part, to the way we have intensified food production in recent decades. Population growth has indeed contributed to famine, disease, and conflict—but as we shall see, enhanced prosperity, education, and gender equality have also helped to reduce birth rates.

Does this mean we can disregard the concerns of Malthus and Ehrlich? Some Cornucopians say yes. Under the Cornucopian view that many economists hold, population growth poses no problem if new resources can be found or created to replace depleted ones. In contrast, environmental scientists recognize that not all resources can be replaced. Once a species has gone extinct, for example, we cannot replicate its exact functions in an ecosystem or know what benefits it might have provided us. Land, too, is irreplaceable; we cannot expand Earth like a balloon to increase the space we have in which to live.

Even if resource substitution could hypothetically enable our population to grow indefinitely, could we maintain the quality of life that we desire for ourselves and our descendants? Unless the availability and quality of all resources keeps pace forever with population growth, the average person in the future will have less space in which to live, less food to eat, and less material wealth than the average person does today. Thus, population growth is indeed a problem if it depletes resources, stresses social systems, and degrades the natural environment, such that our quality of life declines (FIGURE 14.6).

Some national governments now fear falling populations

Despite these considerations, many policymakers find it difficult to let go of the notion that population growth increases a nation's economic, political, and military strength. This notion has held sway despite the clear fact that in today's world, population growth is correlated with poverty, not wealth: Strong and wealthy nations tend to have slow population growth, whereas nations with fast population growth tend to be weak and poor. While China and India struggle to get their population growth under control, many other national governments are offering financial and social incentives that encourage their own citizens to produce more children.

Much of the concern is that when birth rates decline, a population grows older. In aging populations, larger numbers of elderly people will need social services, but fewer workers will be available to pay taxes to fund these services. Such concerns about the sustainability of the Social Security program in the United States, for example, led some in the media to call for an emphasis on increased fertility when it was reported that the U.S. birthrate in 2011 had reached its lowest level in recorded history.

Moreover, in nations with declining birth rates that are also accepting large numbers of foreign immigrants, some native-born citizens may worry that their country's culture is at risk of being diluted or lost. For both these reasons, governments of nations now experiencing population declines (such as many in Europe) feel uneasy. According to the Population Reference Bureau, two of every three European governments

(a) Thomas Malthus　　　　**(b) Paul Ehrlich**

FIGURE 14.5 **Thomas Malthus and Paul Ehrlich each argued that runaway population growth would surpass food supply and lead to disaster.**

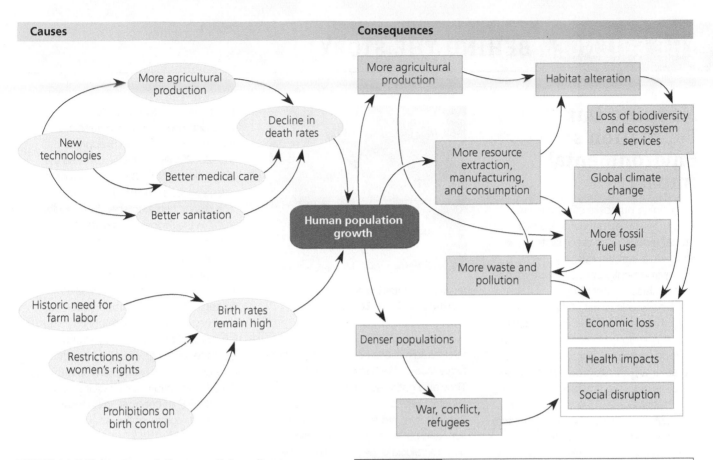

| Causes | | Consequences |

FIGURE 14.6 **Human population growth has diverse causes and consequences.** The consequences of rapid population growth are generally negative for society and the environment. Arrows in this concept map lead from causes to consequences. Note that items grouped within outlined boxes do not necessarily share any special relationship; the outlined boxes are merely to streamline the figure.

Solutions

As you progress through this chapter, try to identify as many solutions to human population growth as you can. What could you personally do to help address this issue? Consider how each action or solution might affect items in the concept map above.

now feel their birth rates are too low, and none states that its country's birth rate is too high. However, outside Europe, 49% of national governments still feel their birth rates are too high, and only 12% feel they are too low.

Population is one of several factors that affect the environment

One widely used formula gives us a handy way to think about population and other factors that affect environmental quality. Nicknamed the **IPAT model**, it is a variation of a formula proposed in 1974 by Paul Ehrlich and John Holdren, a Harvard University environmental scientist who today is President Obama's science advisor. The IPAT model represents how our total impact (I) on the environment results from the interaction among population (P), affluence (A), and technology (T):

$$I = P \times A \times T$$

Increased population intensifies impact on the environment as more individuals take up space, use resources, and

generate waste. Increased affluence magnifies environmental impact through the greater per capita resource consumption that generally has accompanied enhanced wealth. Technology that enhances our abilities to exploit minerals, fossil fuels, old-growth forests, or fisheries generally increases impact, but technology to reduce smokestack emissions, harness renewable energy, or improve manufacturing efficiency can decrease impact.

We might also add a sensitivity factor (S) to the equation to denote how sensitive a given environment is to human pressures:

$$I = P \times A \times T \times S$$

For instance, the arid lands of western China are more sensitive to human disturbance than the moist regions of southeastern China. Plants grow more slowly in the arid west, making the land more vulnerable to deforestation and soil degradation. Thus, adding an additional person to western China has more environmental impact than adding one to southeastern China.

We could refine the IPAT equation further by adding terms for the effects of social institutions such as education, laws and their enforcement, stable and cohesive societies,

Mapping Our Population's Environmental Impact

Burgeoning numbers of people are making heavy demands on Earth's natural resources and ecosystem services. How can we quantify and map the environmental impacts our expanding population is exerting?

One way is to ask. Of all the biomass that Earth's plants can produce, what proportion do human beings use (for food, clothing, shelter, etc.) or otherwise prevent from growing? This was the question asked by nine environmental scientists led by Helmut Haberl of the Institute of Social Ecology in Austria. They teamed up to measure our consumption of net primary production (NPP; p. 25), the net amount of energy stored in plant matter as a result of photosynthesis. Human overuse of NPP diminishes resources for other species; alters habitats, communities, and ecosystems; and threatens our future ability to derive ecosystem services.

Haberl's team began with a well-established model that maps how vegetation varies with climate across the globe and used it to produce a detailed world map of "potential NPP"—vegetation that would exist if there were no human influence. The team then gathered data for the year 2000 on crop harvests, timber harvests, grazing pressure, and other human uses of vegetation from various global databases from

Dr. Helmut Haberl of Austria's Institute for Social Ecology

the United Nations Food and Agriculture Organization (FAO) and other sources. They also gathered data on how people affect vegetation indirectly, such as through fires, erosion and soil degradation, and other changes due to land use. To calculate the proportion of NPP that people appropriate, the researchers divided the amounts used up in these impacts by the total "potential" amount.

When all the data crunching was done, Haberl's group concluded that people harvest 12.5% of global NPP and that land use reduces it 9.6% further and fires 1.7% further (FIGURE 1). This makes us responsible for using up fully 23.8% of the planet's NPP—a staggeringly large amount for just a single species! Half of this use occurred on cropland, where 83.5% of NPP was used. In urban areas, 73.0% of NPP was consumed; on grazing land, 19.4%; and in forests, 6.6%.

To determine how human use of NPP varies across regions of the world,

Haberl's group layered the data sets atop one another in a geographic information systems (GIS) approach (pp. 28–29). Again, they calculated the proportion of NPP that we appropriate and produced a global map (FIGURE 2). The researchers published their results in 2007 in the *Proceedings of the National Academy of Sciences of the USA*.

In their global map of NPP consumption, densely populated and heavily farmed regions such as India, eastern China, and Europe show the greatest proportional use of NPP. The influence of population is clear. For instance, although people in southern Asia consume very little per capita, dense populations here result in a 63% use of NPP. In contrast, in sparsely inhabited regions of the world (such

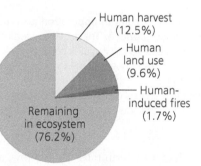

FIGURE 1 Humanity uses or causes Earth to lose 23.8% of the planet's net primary production. Direct harvesting (of crops, timber, etc.) accounts for most of this, and land use impacts and fire also contribute. *Data from Haberl, H., et al., 2007. Quantifying and mapping the human appropriation of net primary production in Earth's terrestrial ecosystems. Proc. Natl. Acad. Sci. 104:12942–12947.*

and ethical standards that promote environmental well-being. Such factors all affect how population, affluence, and technology translate into environmental impact.

Impact can be thought of in various ways, but we can generally boil it down either to pollution or resource consumption. The depletion of resources by larger and hungrier populations has been a focus of scientists and philosophers since Malthus's time. Today, researchers calculate that humanity is appropriating for its own use nearly one-quarter of Earth's terrestrial net primary production (see THE SCIENCE BEHIND THE STORY, above).

One reason our population has kept growing, despite limited resources, is that we have developed technology—the *T* in the IPAT equation—time and again to increase efficiency, alleviate our strain on resources, and allow us to expand further. For instance, we have employed technological advances to increase global agricultural production faster than our population has risen.

Modern-day China shows how all elements of the IPAT formula can combine to cause tremendous environmental impact in little time. The world's fastest-growing economy over the past two decades, China is "demonstrating what

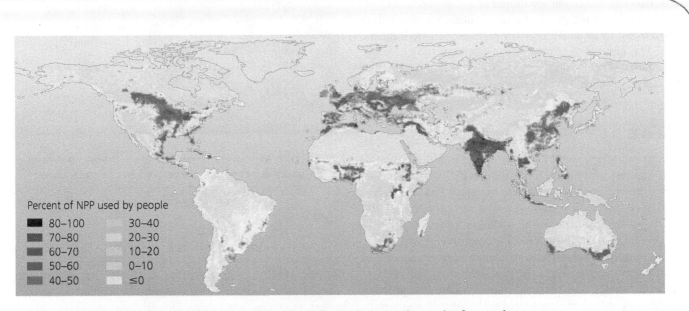

FIGURE 2 The proportion of Earth's net primary production that people appropriate varies from region to region. Regions that are densely populated or intensively farmed exert the heaviest impact. *Source: Haberl, H., et al., 2007. Quantifying and mapping the human appropriation of net primary production in Earth's terrestrial ecosystems.* Proc. Natl. Acad. Sci. *104:12942–12947, Fig 1b. © 2007 National Academy of Sciences, U.S.A. By permission.*

as the boreal forest, Arctic tundra, Himalayas, and Sahara Desert), humans consume almost no NPP. In North America, NPP use is heaviest in the East, Midwest, and Great Plains. In general, the map shows heavy appropriation of NPP in areas where population is dense relative to the area's vegetative production.

The map does not fully show the effects of resource consumption due to affluence. Wealthy societies tend to import food, fiber, energy, and products from other places, and this consumption can drive environmental degradation in poorer regions. For instance, North Americans and Europeans import timber logged from the Amazon basin, as well as soybeans and beef grown in areas where Amazonian forest was cleared. Through global trade, we redistribute the products we gain from the planet's NPP. As a result, the environmental impacts of our consumption are often felt far from where we consume products.

By showing areas of high and low impact, maps like the one produced in this project can help us to make better decisions and minimize our impacts on ecosystems and ecosystem services. Haberl's team also says its data show that we are using a great deal of Earth's plant matter already, so that schemes to expand biomass energy production may not be wise.

Environmental scientists who have commented on the paper agree and say the team's data should give us pause. As Jonathan Foley of the University of Wisconsin and his colleagues put it, "Ultimately, we need to question how much of the biosphere's productivity we can appropriate before planetary systems begin to break down. 30%? 40%? 50%? More? . . . Or have we already crossed that threshold?" ●

happens when large numbers of poor people rapidly become more affluent," in the words of Earth Policy Institute president Lester Brown. While millions of Chinese are increasing their material wealth and their resource consumption, the country is battling unprecedented environmental challenges brought about by its rapid economic development. Intensive agriculture has expanded westward out of the country's moist rice-growing areas, causing farmland to erode and literally blow away, much like the Dust Bowl tragedy that befell the U.S. heartland in the 1930s. China has overpumped aquifers and has drawn so much water for irrigation from the Yellow River that the once-mighty waterway now dries up in many stretches. Although China is reducing its air pollution from industry and charcoal-burning homes, the country faces new urban pollution and congestion threats from rapidly rising numbers of automobiles. In August 2010, for example, a 100-km (60-mi) traffic jam formed on the outskirts of the capital city of Beijing and persisted for more than 10 days! Such issues are not unique to China. As the world's other industrializing countries strive to attain the material prosperity that industrialized nations enjoy, they too may soon face many of the same challenges as China.

Demography

It is a fallacy to think of people as being somehow outside nature. We exist within our environment as one species out of many. As such, all the principles of population ecology that apply to birds, frogs, and passenger pigeons apply to humans as well. The application of principles from population ecology to the study of statistical change in human populations is the focus of **demography.**

Earth has a carrying capacity for us

Environmental factors set limits on our population growth, and the environment has a carrying capacity for our species, just as it does for every other. We happen to be a particularly successful species, however, and we have repeatedly raised this carrying capacity by developing technology to overcome the natural limits on our population growth.

Environmental scientists who have tried to pin a number to the human carrying capacity have come up with wildly differing estimates. The most rigorous estimates range from 1–2 billion people living prosperously in a healthy environment to 33 billion living in extreme poverty in a degraded world of intensive cultivation without natural areas. As our population climbs beyond 7 billion, we may yet continue to find ways to raise our carrying capacity. Given our knowledge of population ecology and logistic growth, however, we have no reason to presume that human numbers can go on growing indefinitely.

Demography is the study of human population

Demographers study population size, density, distribution, age structure, sex ratio, and rates of birth, death, immigration, and emigration of people, just as population ecologists study these characteristics in other organisms. Each of these characteristics is useful for predicting population dynamics and environmental impacts.

Population size Our global human population of over 7 billion is spread among 200 nations with populations ranging up to China's 1.35 billion, India's 1.26 billion, and the 314 million of the United States (FIGURE 14.7). The United Nations Population Division estimates that by the year 2050, the global population will surpass 9 billion (FIGURE 14.8). However, population size alone—the absolute number of individuals—doesn't tell the whole story. Rather, a population's environmental impact depends on its density, distribution, and composition (as well as on affluence, technology, and other factors outlined earlier).

Population density and distribution People are distributed unevenly over our planet. In ecological terms, our distribution is clumped at all spatial scales. At the global scale (FIGURE 14.9), population density is highest in regions with temperate, subtropical, and tropical climates, such as China,

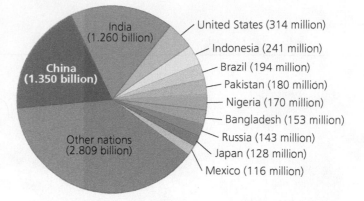

FIGURE 14.7 Almost one in five people in the world lives in China, and more than one of every six live in India. Three of every five people live in one of the 11 nations that have populations above 100 million. *Data from Population Reference Bureau, 2012. 2012 World population data sheet.*

Europe, Mexico, southern Africa, and India. Population density is lowest in regions with extreme-climate biomes, such as desert, rainforest, and tundra. Dense along seacoasts and rivers, human population is less dense away from water. At more local scales, we cluster together in cities and towns.

This uneven distribution means that certain areas bear more environmental impact than others. Just as the Yellow River experiences pressure from Chinese cities and farms,

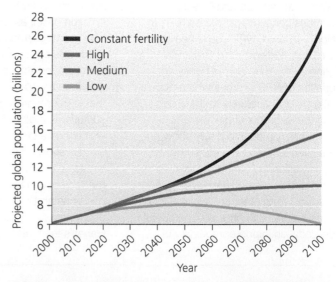

FIGURE 14.8 The United Nations predicts world population growth. In the latest projection (made in 2010), population is estimated to reach 11.0 billion in the year 2050 if fertility rates remain constant at 2005–2010 levels (top line in graph). However, U.N. demographers expect fertility rates to continue falling, so they arrived at a best guess (medium scenario) of 9.3 billion for 2050. In the high scenario, if women on average have 0.5 child more than in the medium scenario, population will reach 10.6 billion in 2050. In the low scenario, if women have 0.5 child fewer than in the medium scenario, the world will contain 8.1 billion people in 2050. *Adapted by permission from Population Division of the Department of Economic and Social Affairs of the United Nations Secretariat, 2011. World population prospects: The 2010 revision. http://esa.un.org/wpp, Fig 1. © United Nations, 2011.*

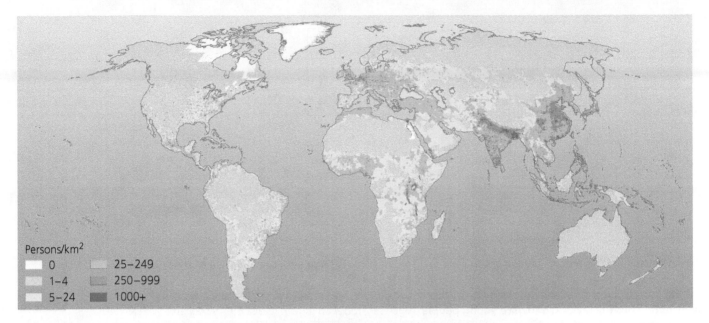

FIGURE 14.9 **Human population density varies significantly from one region to another.** Arctic and desert regions have the lowest population densities, whereas areas of India, Bangladesh, and eastern China have the densest populations. *Source:* The world: Population density, 2000. *Center for International Earth Science Information Network (CIESIN), Columbia University; and Centro Internacional de Agricultura Tropical (CIAT). 2005. Gridded Population of the World Version 3 (GPWv3). Palisades, NY: Socioeconomic Data and Applications Center (SEDAC), Columbia University.*

the world's other major rivers, from the Nile to the Danube to the Ganges to the Mississippi, all receive more than their share of human impact. At the same time, some areas with low population density are sensitive (a high *S* value in our revised IPAT model) and thus vulnerable to impact. Deserts and arid grasslands, for instance, are easily degraded by development that commandeers too much water.

Age structure Age structure, describes the relative numbers of individuals of each age class within a population. Data on age structure are especially valuable to demographers trying to predict future dynamics of human populations. A population made up mostly of individuals past reproductive age will tend to decline over time. In contrast, a population with many individuals of reproductive age or pre-reproductive age is likely to increase. A population with an even age distribution will likely remain stable as births keep pace with deaths.

Age structure diagrams, often called population pyramids, are visual tools scientists use to illustrate age structure (**FIGURE 14.10**). The width of each horizontal bar represents the number of people in each age class. A pyramid with a wide base denotes a large proportion of people who have not yet reached reproductive age—and this indicates a population soon capable of rapid growth. In this respect, a wide base of a population pyramid is like an oversized engine on a rocket—the bigger the booster, the faster the increase.

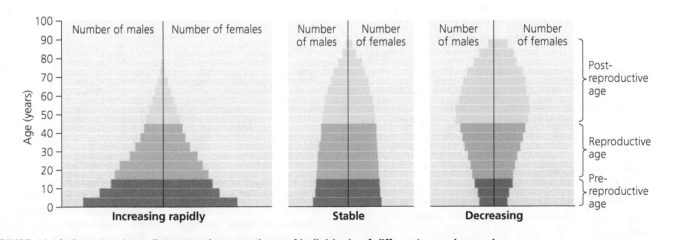

FIGURE 14.10 **Age structure diagrams show numbers of individuals of different age classes in a population.** A diagram like that on the left is weighted toward young age classes, indicating a population that will grow quickly. A diagram like that on the right is weighted toward old age classes, indicating a population that will decline. Populations with balanced age structures, like the one shown in the middle diagram, will remain relatively stable in size.

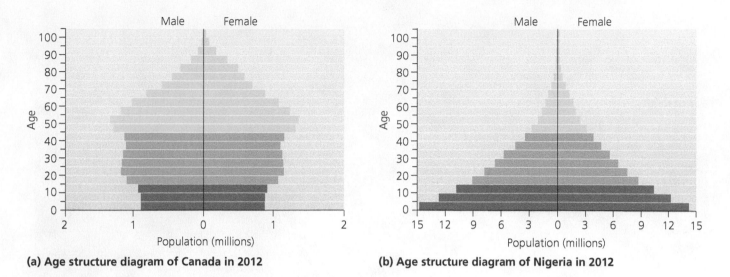

(a) Age structure diagram of Canada in 2012

(b) Age structure diagram of Nigeria in 2012

FIGURE 14.11 Canada (a) shows a fairly balanced age structure, whereas Nigeria (b) shows an age distribution heavily weighted toward young people. Nigeria's population growth rate (2.6%) is over six times greater than Canada's (0.4%). *Data from United States Census Bureau International Database. http://www.census.gov/ population/international/data/idb/.*

As an example, compare age structures for the nations of Canada and Nigeria (**FIGURE 14.11**). Nigeria's large concentration of individuals in young age groups portends a great deal of reproduction. Not surprisingly, Nigeria's population growth rate is much greater than Canada's.

Today, populations are aging in many nations (**FIGURE 14.12**). The global median age today is 28, but it will be 38 in the year 2050. Population aging is pronounced in the United States, where the "baby boom" generation is now approaching retirement age. In coming years you will likely be required to pay more taxes to support Social Security and Medicare benefits for your elders.

By causing dramatic reductions in the number of children born since 1970, China's one-child policy virtually guaranteed that the nation's population age structure would change. Indeed, in 1970 the median age in China was 20; by 2050 it will be 45. In 1970 there were more children under age 5 than people over 60 in China, but by 2050 there will be 12 times more people over 60 than under 5! Today there are 121 million Chinese people older than 65, but that number will triple by 2050 (**FIGURE 14.13**). This dramatic shift in age structure will challenge China's economy, health care system, families, and military forces because fewer working-age people will be available to support social programs to assist the rising number of older people. In response, China has recently taken small steps to loosen its reproductive policies to increase its proportion of young people. For example, if both the man and the woman in an urban couple are single children, then they are permitted to have a second child.

On the one hand, older populations will present new challenges for many nations as increasing numbers of elderly will require the care and assistance of relatively fewer working-age citizens.

On the other hand, a shift in age structure toward an older population reduces the proportion of dependent children. Fewer young adults may mean a decrease in crime rates. Moreover, older people are often productive members of society, contributing volunteer activities and services to their children and grandchildren. In many ways both good and bad, "graying" populations will affect societies in China, the United States, Europe, and other nations throughout our lifetimes.

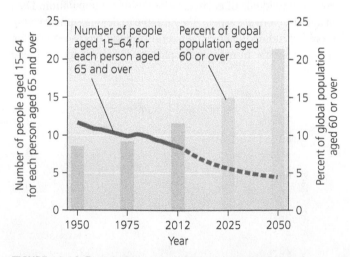

FIGURE 14.12 Populations are aging worldwide as people of "baby boom" generations grow older and as birth rates decline. As the percentage of the global population that is over 60 increases, fewer working-age people are available to support the elderly. *Data from Population Division of the Department of Economic and Social Affairs of the United Nations Secretariat, 2009. World population prospects: The 2008 revision. http://esa.un.org/wpp. © United Nations, 2009. By permission. 2012 update from United States Census Bureau International Database. http://www.census.gov/population/international/data/idb/.*

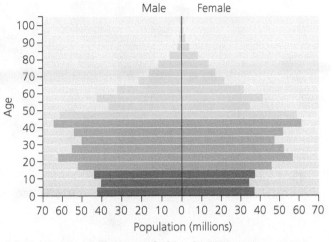

(a) Age structure diagram of China in 2012

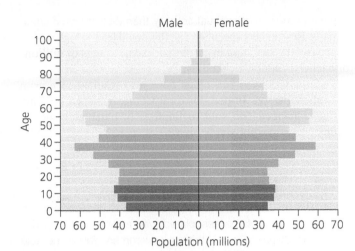

(b) Projected age structure diagram of China in 2025

(c) Young female factory workers in Hong Kong

(d) Elderly Chinese

FIGURE 14.13 As China's population ages, older people will outnumber the young. Population pyramids show the predicted graying of the Chinese population from 2012 **(a)** to 2025 **(b)**. Today's children may, as working-age adults **(c)**, face pressures to support greater numbers of elderly citizens **(d)** than has any previous generation. *Data in (a) and (b) from United States Census Bureau International Database. http://www.census.gov/population/international/data/idb.*

Sex ratios The ratio of males to females also can affect population dynamics. Note that population pyramids give data on sex ratios by representing numbers of males and females on opposite sides of each diagram. To understand the consequences of sex ratio variation, imagine two islands, one populated by 99 men and 1 woman and the other by 50 men and 50 women. Where would we be likely to see the greatest population increase over time? Of course, the island with an equal number of men and women would have a greater number of potential mothers and thus a greater potential for population growth.

The naturally occurring sex ratio at birth in human populations features a slight preponderance of males; for every 100 female infants born, about 106 male infants are born. This phenomenon is an evolutionary adaptation to the fact that males are slightly more prone to death during any given year of life. It tends to ensure that the ratio of men to women will be approximately equal when people reach reproductive age. Thus, a slightly uneven sex ratio at birth may be beneficial. However, a greatly distorted ratio can lead to problems.

In recent years, demographers have witnessed an unsettling trend in China: The ratio of newborn boys to girls has become strongly skewed. Today, roughly 120 boys are born for every 100 girls. Some provinces have reported sex ratios as high as 138 boys for every 100 girls. The leading hypothesis for these unusual sex ratios is that many parents, having learned the sex of their fetuses by ultrasound, are selectively aborting female fetuses.

Recall that Chinese culture has traditionally valued sons over daughters. Sociologists maintain that this cultural gender preference, combined with the government's one-child policy, has led some couples to selectively abort female fetuses or to abandon or kill female infants. The Chinese government reinforced this gender discrimination when in 1984 it exempted rural peasants from the one-child policy if their first child was a girl, but not if the first child was a boy.

China's skewed sex ratio may further lower population growth rates. However, it has the undesirable social consequence of leaving large numbers of Chinese men single. Many of these men find employment as migrant workers and tend to engage in more risky sexual activity than their married counterparts. Researchers speculate that this could lead to higher incidence of HIV in China in coming decades, as tens of millions of bachelors adopt such a lifestyle.

China's skewed sex ratios have also resulted in a grim new phenomenon. In parts of rural China, teenaged girls are being kidnapped and sold to families in other parts of the country as brides for single men.

WEIGHING THE ISSUES

CHINA'S REPRODUCTIVE POLICY Consider the benefits as well as the problems associated with a reproductive policy such as China's. Do you think a government should be able to enforce strict penalties for citizens who fail to abide by such a policy? If you disagree with China's policy, what alternatives can you suggest for dealing with the resource demands of a rapidly growing population?

Population change results from birth, death, immigration, and emigration

Rates of birth, death, immigration, and emigration determine whether a population grows, shrinks, or remains stable. The formula for measuring population growth also pertains to people: Birth and immigration add individuals to a population, whereas death and emigration remove individuals. Technological advances have led to a dramatic decline in human death rates, widening the gap between birth rates and death rates and resulting in the global human population expansion.

In today's ever more crowded world, immigration and emigration play increasingly important roles. Refugees, people forced to flee their home country or region, have become more numerous as a result of war, civil strife, and environmental degradation. The United Nations puts the number of refugees who flee to escape poor environmental conditions at 25 million per year and possibly many more. Often the movement of refugees causes environmental problems in the receiving region as these desperate victims try to eke out an existence with no livelihood and no cultural or economic attachment to the land or incentive to conserve its resources. The millions who fled Rwanda following the genocide there in the 1990s, for example, inadvertently destroyed large areas of forest while trying to obtain fuelwood, food, and shelter to stay alive in the Democratic Republic of Congo (FIGURE 14.14).

For most of the past 2000 years, China's population was relatively stable. The first significant increases resulted from enhanced agricultural production and a powerful government during the Qing Dynasty in the 1800s. Population growth began to outstrip food supplies by the 1850s, and quality of life for the average Chinese peasant began to decline. Over the next 100 years, China's population grew slowly, at about 0.3% per year, amid food shortages and political instability. Population growth rates rose again following Mao's establishment of the People's Republic in

FIGURE 14.14 Immigration, including movements of refugees, can affect a nation's demographics. The flight of refugees from Rwanda into the Democratic Republic of Congo in 1994 following the Rwandan genocide caused unimaginable hardship for the refugees and tremendous stress on the environment into which they moved.

1949, and they have declined since the advent of the one-child policy (TABLE 14.1).

In recent decades, falling growth rates in many countries have led to an overall decline in the global growth rate (FIGURE 14.15). This decline has come about, in part, from a steep drop in birth rates. Note, however, that although the rate of growth is slowing, the absolute size of the population continues to increase. Even though our percentage increases are getting smaller year by year, these are percentages of ever-larger numbers, so we continue to add over 70 million people to the planet each year.

Total fertility rate influences population growth

One key statistic demographers calculate to examine a population's potential for growth is the **total fertility rate (TFR)**, the average number of children born per woman during her lifetime. **Replacement fertility** is the TFR that keeps the size of a population stable. For humans, replacement fertility roughly

TABLE 14.1 Trends in China's Population Growth				
MEASURE	**1950**	**1970**	**1990**	**2012**
Total fertility rate	5.8	5.8	2.2	1.5
Rate of natural increase (% per year)	1.9	2.6	1.4	0.5
Doubling time (years)	37	27	49	140
Population (billions)	0.56	0.83	1.15	1.35

Data from China Population Information and Research Center; and Population Reference Bureau, 2012. 2012 World population data sheet.

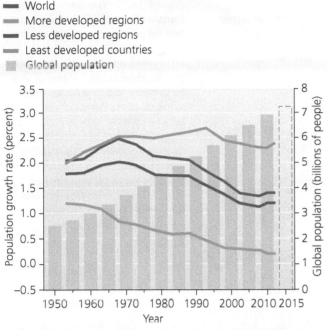

World
More developed regions
Less developed regions
Least developed countries
Global population

FIGURE 14.15 The annual growth rate of the global human population peaked in the late 1960s and has declined since then. Growth rates of developed nations have fallen since 1950, whereas those of developing nations have fallen since the global peak in the late 1960s. For the world's least developed nations, growth rates began to fall in the 1990s. Although growth rates are declining, global population size is still growing about the same amount each year, because smaller percentage increases of ever-larger numbers produce roughly equivalent additional amounts. *Data from Population Division of the Department of Economic and Social Affairs of the United Nations Secretariat, 2011.* World population prospects: The 2010 revision. *http://esa.un.org/wpp. © United Nations, 2011. Data updates for 2011–2012 from Population Reference Bureau, 2011 and 2012* World population data sheets. *Global population in 2015 is projected.*

REGION	TOTAL FERTILITY RATE (TFR)
Africa	4.7
Australia and South Pacific	2.5
Latin America and Caribbean	2.2
Asia	2.2
North America	1.9
Europe	1.6

TABLE 14.2 Total Fertility Rates for Major Continental Regions

Data from Population Reference Bureau, 2012. 2012 World population data sheet.

equals a TFR of 2.1. (Two children replace the mother and father, and the extra 0.1 accounts for the risk of a child dying before reaching reproductive age.) If the TFR drops below 2.1, population size (in the absence of immigration) will shrink.

Factors such as industrialization, improved women's rights, and quality health care have driven TFR downward in many nations in recent years. All these factors have come together in Europe, where TFR has dropped from 2.6 to 1.6 in the past half-century. Nearly every European nation now has a fertility rate below the replacement level, and populations are declining in 16 of 45 European nations. In 2012, Europe's overall annual **rate of natural increase** (also called the *natural rate of population change*)—change due to birth and death rates alone, excluding migration—was between 0.0% and 0.1%. Worldwide by 2012, 92 countries had fallen below the replacement fertility of 2.1. These countries make up roughly half of the world's population and include China (with a TFR of 1.5). **TABLE 14.2** shows TFRs of major continental regions.

Many nations are experiencing the demographic transition

Many nations with lowered birth rates and TFRs are experiencing a common set of interrelated changes. In countries

with good sanitation, effective health care, and reliable food supplies, more people than ever before are living long lives. As a result, over the past 50 years the life expectancy for the average person has increased from 46 to 70 years as the global death rate has dropped from 20 deaths per 1000 people to 8 deaths per 1000 people. Strictly speaking, **life expectancy** is the average number of years that an individual in a particular age group is likely to continue to live, but often people use this term to refer to the average number of years a person can expect to live from birth. Much of the increase in life expectancy is due to reduced rates of infant mortality. Societies going through these changes are generally those that have undergone urbanization and industrialization and have generated personal wealth for their citizens.

To make sense of these trends, demographers developed a concept called the **demographic transition.** This is a model of economic and cultural change first proposed in the 1940s and 1950s by demographer Frank Notestein to explain the declining death rates and birth rates that have occurred in Western nations as they industrialized. Notestein believed nations move from a stable pre-industrial state of high birth and death rates to a stable post-industrial state of low birth and death rates (**FIGURE 14.16**). Industrialization, he proposed, causes these rates to fall by first decreasing mortality and then lessening the need for large families. Parents thereafter choose to invest in quality of life rather than quantity of children. Because death rates fall before birth rates fall, a period of net population growth results. Thus, under the demographic transition model, population growth is seen as a temporary phenomenon that occurs as societies move from one stage of development to another.

WEIGHING THE ISSUES

CONSEQUENCES OF LOW FERTILITY? In the United States, Canada, and almost every European nation, the total fertility rate is now at or below the replacement fertility rate (although some of these nations are still growing because of immigration). What economic or social consequences do you think might result from below-replacement fertility rates? Would you rather live in a society with a growing population, a shrinking population, or a stable population? Why?

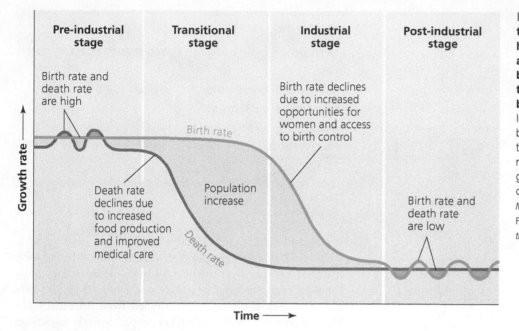

FIGURE 14.16 The demographic transition models a process that has taken some populations from a pre-industrial stage of high birth rates and high death rates to a post-industrial stage of low birth rates and low death rates. In this diagram, the wide green area between the two curves illustrates the gap between birth and death rates that causes rapid population growth during the middle portion of this process. *Adapted from Kent, M. and K. Crews, 1990.* World population: Fundamentals of growth. *By permission of the Population Reference Bureau.*

The pre-industrial stage   The first stage of the demographic transition model is the **pre-industrial stage**, characterized by conditions that have defined most of human history. In pre-industrial societies, both death rates and birth rates are high. Death rates are high because disease is widespread, medical care rudimentary, and food supplies unreliable and difficult to obtain. Birth rates are high because people must compensate for infant mortality by having several children. In this stage, children are valuable as workers who can help meet a family's basic needs. Populations within the pre-industrial stage are not likely to experience much growth, which is why the human population grew relatively slowly until the industrial revolution.

Industrialization and falling death rates   Industrialization initiates the second stage of the demographic transition, known as the **transitional stage.** This transition from the pre-industrial stage to the industrial stage is generally characterized by declining death rates due to increased food production and improved medical care. Birth rates in the transitional stage remain high, however, because people have not yet grown used to the new economic and social conditions. As a result, population growth surges.

The industrial stage and falling birth rates   The third stage in the demographic transition is the **industrial stage.** Industrialization increases opportunities for employment outside the home, particularly for women. Children become less valuable, in economic terms, because they do not help meet family food needs as they did in the pre-industrial stage. If couples are aware of this, and if they have access to birth control, they may choose to have fewer children. Birth rates fall, closing the gap with death rates and reducing population growth.

The post-industrial stage   In the final stage, the **post-industrial stage,** both birth and death rates have fallen to low and stable levels. Population sizes stabilize or decline slightly. The society enjoys the fruits of industrialization without the threat of runaway population growth. The United States is an example of a nation in this stage, although the U.S. population is growing faster than most other post-industrial nations because of a relatively high immigration rate.

Is the demographic transition a universal process?

The demographic transition has occurred in many European countries, the United States, Canada, Japan, and several other developed nations over the past 200 to 300 years. It is a model that may or may not apply to all developing nations as they industrialize now and in the future. On the one hand, note in Figure 14.15 (p. 413) how growth rates fell first for industrialized nations, then for less developed nations, and finally for least developed nations, suggesting that it may merely be a matter of time before all nations experience the transition. On the other hand, some developing nations may already be suffering too much from the impacts of large populations to replicate the developed world's transition. And some demographers assert that the transition will fail in cultures that place greater value on childbirth or grant women fewer freedoms.

Moreover, natural scientists estimate that for people of all nations to attain the material standard of living that North Americans now enjoy, we would need the natural resources of four-and-a-half more planet Earths. Whether developing nations (which include the vast majority of the planet's people) pass through the demographic transition is one of the most important and far-reaching questions for the future of our civilization and Earth's environment.

Population and Society

Demographic transition theory links the quantitative study of how populations change with the societal factors that influence (and are influenced by) population dynamics. There are many factors that affect fertility in a given society. They include public health issues, such as people's access to contraceptives and the rate of infant mortality. They also include cultural factors—such as the level of women's rights, the relative acceptance of contraceptive use, and even television programs (see THE SCIENCE BEHIND THE STORY, pp. 416–417). There are also effects from economic factors, such as the society's level of affluence, the importance of child labor, and the availability of governmental support for retirees. Let's now examine a few of these societal influences on fertility more closely.

Family planning is a key approach for controlling population growth

Perhaps the greatest single factor enabling a society to slow its population growth is the ability of women and couples to engage in **family planning,** the effort to plan the number and spacing of one's children. Family-planning programs and clinics offer information and counseling to potential mothers and fathers on reproductive issues. An important component of family planning is **birth control,** the effort to control the number of children a woman bears by reducing the frequency of pregnancy. Birth control relies on **contraception,** the deliberate attempt to prevent pregnancy despite engaging in sexual intercourse. Common methods of modern contraception in use today include condoms, spermicide, hormonal treatments (birth control pill/hormone injection), intrauterine devices (IUDs), and permanent sterilization through tubal ligation or vasectomy. Many family-planning organizations aid clients by offering free or discounted contraceptives.

Worldwide in 2012, 56% of women (aged 15–49) reported using contraceptives, with rates of use varying widely among nations. China, at 84%, had the highest rate of contraceptive use of any nation. Eight European nations showed rates of contraceptive use of 70% or more, as did Australia, Brazil, Canada, Colombia, Costa Rica, Cuba, Dominican Republic, Micronesia, New Zealand, Paraguay, Puerto Rico, South Korea, Thailand, the United States, and Uruguay. At the other end of the spectrum, 14 African nations had rates below 10%.

Low usage rates for contraceptives in some societies are caused by limited availability, especially in rural areas. In others, low usage may be due to religious doctrine or cultural influences that hinder family planning, denying counseling and contraceptives to people who might otherwise use them. This can result in family sizes that are larger than the parents desire and to elevated rates of population growth.

In a physiological sense, access to family planning (and the civil rights to demand its use) gives women control over their **reproductive window,** the period of their life, beginning with sexual maturity and ending with menopause, in which they may become pregnant. A woman can bear up to 25 children within this window (FIGURE 14.17a), but she may choose to delay the birth of her first child to pursue education and employment. She may also use contraception to delay her first child, space births within the window, and "close" her reproductive window after achieving her desired family size (FIGURE 14.17b).

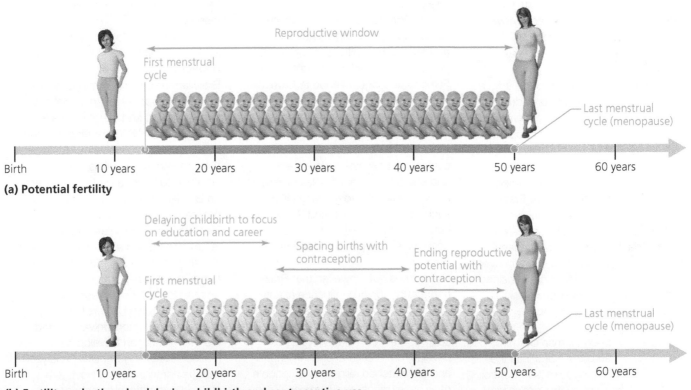

(a) Potential fertility

(b) Fertility reductions by delaying childbirth and contraceptive use

FIGURE 14.17 Women can potentially have very high fertility within their "reproductive window" but can choose to reduce the number of children they bear. They may do this by delaying the birth of their first child, or by using contraception to space pregnancies or to end their reproductive window at the time of their choosing.

Did Soap Operas Reduce Fertility in Brazil?

Over the past 50 years, the South American nation of Brazil experienced the second-largest drop in fertility among developing nations with large populations—second only to China. In the 1960s, the average woman in Brazil had six children. Today, Brazil's total fertility rate is 1.9 children per woman, which is lower than that of the United States. Brazil's drastic decrease in fertility is interesting because, unlike China, it occurred without governmental policies that advocated controls on its citizens' reproduction.

So how did Brazil accomplish this? A major factor was change in society's view of women. It began with a civil rights movement in the 1960s, which gave females equal access to education and the opportunity to pursue careers outside the home. These efforts have been highly successful. Women now comprise 40% of the workforce in Brazil and graduate from college in greater numbers than men. And in 2010, Brazilians elected a woman, Dilma Rousseff, as their nation's president.

Although the Brazilian government does not put restrictions on people's reproduction, it provides family planning and contraception to all its citizens free of charge. Eighty percent of married women of childbearing age in Brazil currently utilize contraception, a rate higher than that in the United States or Canada. Universal access to family planning has given women control over their desired family size and has helped reduce fertility across all economic groups, from the very rich to the very poor.

Brazil is largely Roman Catholic, and Roman Catholicism prohibits the use of artificial methods of birth control, so the high rates of contraceptive use in modern Brazil represent a significant shift from traditional values. Induced abortion is not utilized in Brazil as it is in

Brazilian soap operas, called *telenovelas*, are a surprising cultural force for promoting lower fertility. Here, residents gather outside a cafe in Rio de Janeiro to watch the popular program *Avenida Brasil*.

China; the procedure is illegal except in rare circumstances.

As Brazil's economy grew with industrialization, people's nutrition and access to health care improved, greatly reducing infant mortality rates. Families no longer needed to have more children than they desired for fear one or more would die at a young age. Increasing personal wealth promoted materialism and greater emphasis on career and possessions over family and children. The nation also urbanized as people flocked to growing cities such as Río de Janeiro and São Paolo, conveying the fertility reductions that occur when people leave the farm for the city.

It turns out, however, that Brazil had a rather unique influence affecting its fertility rates over the past several decades—"soap operas." Brazilian soap operas, called *telenovelas* or *novelas*, are a cultural phenomenon and are watched religiously by people of all ages, races, and incomes. Each *novela* follows the activities of several fictional families, and these TV shows are wildly popular because they have

characters, settings, and plot lines with which everyday Brazilians can identify.

Telenovelas do not overtly address fertility issues, but they do promote a vision of the "ideal" Brazilian family. This family is typically middle or upper class, materialistic, individualistic, and full of empowered women. By challenging existing cultural and religious values through their characters, *novelas* had, and continue to have, a profound impact on Brazilian society. In essence, these programs provided a model family for Brazilians to emulate—with small family sizes being a key characteristic.

In a 2012 paper in the *American Economic Journal: Applied Economics*, a team of researchers from Bocconi University in Italy, George Washington University, and the Inter-American Development Bank (based in Washington, D.C.) analyzed various parameters to investigate statistical relationships between *telenovelas* and fertility patterns in Brazil from 1965 to 2000. Rede Globo, the network that has a virtual monopoly

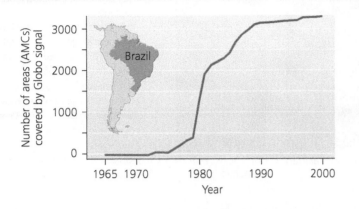

FIGURE 1 The Globo television network expanded over time and now reaches nearly all households in Brazil. Fertility declines across minimally comparable areas (AMCs) were correlated with the availability of Globo, and its *novelas*, over the time periods in the study. *Source: La Ferrara, E., et al., 2012.* Soap operas and fertility: Evidence from Brazil. *Am. Econ. J. Appl. Econ. 4: 1-31.*

on the most popular *novelas*, increased the number of areas that received its signal in Brazil over those 35 years (**FIGURE 1**), and currently it reaches 98% of Brazilian households. By combining data on Rede Globo broadcast range with demographic data, the researchers were able to compare changes in fertility patterns over time in areas of Brazil that received access to *novelas* with areas in Brazil that did not.

The team found that women in areas that received the Globo signal had significantly lower fertility than those in areas not served by Rede Globo, and they also found that fertility declines were related to the timing of receiving access to *novelas*. Diving deeper into census data, the researchers concluded that the greatest reductions in fertility occurred in women aged 25–34 and 35–44, but not in younger women (**FIGURE 2**). The

authors hypothesized that this effect was likely due to the fact that women between 25 and 44 were closer in age to the main female characters in *novelas*, who typically had no children or only a single child. The depressive effect on fertility among women in areas served by Globo was therefore attributed to wider spacing of births and earlier ending of reproduction, not to delaying the birth of their first child.

Further evidence for the influence of *novelas* on fertility was found in school records. The researchers found that fifth graders living in areas reached by the Globo network were four times more likely to be named after the lead characters in *novelas* in the year they were born than were children in areas not served by Globo. These results were particularly compelling because most *novela* characters have relatively unusual names.

The researchers determined that access to television alone did not depress fertility. For example, comparisons of fertility rate in areas with access to a different television network, Sistema Brasileiro de Televisão, found no relationship. The study authors concluded that this was likely due to the network's reliance on programming imported from other nations, with which everyday Brazilians did not connect as they did with *novelas*.

Television's ability to change cultural attitudes is not limited to Brazil. A 2007 study found that access to cable television in rural villages in India correlated with lower fertility, reduced acceptance of violence against women, decreased preference for sons over daughters, and increases in attitudes about female autonomy.

The factors that affect human fertility can be complex and vary greatly from one society to another. The influence of *novelas* on fertility in Brazil also shows that the factors influencing fertility can sometimes come from unexpected sources. ●

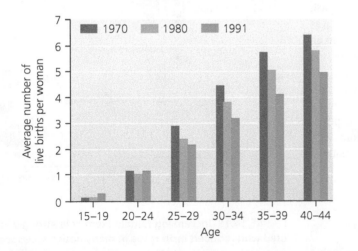

FIGURE 2 Fertility declines among Brazilian women between 1970 and 1991 were most pronounced in later age classes. The authors attribute some of this decline to women in those age classes emulating the low fertility of lead female characters in *novelas*. *Source: La Ferrara, E., et al., 2012.* Soap operas and fertility: Evidence from Brazil. *Am. Econ. J. Appl. Econ. 4: 1-31.*

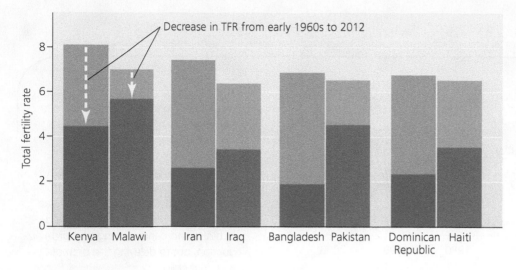

FIGURE 14.18 **Four pairs of neighboring countries demonstrate the results of family planning initiatives.** In each case, the nation that invested in family planning and established societal conditions that promoted low fertility (**blue bars**) reduced its total fertility rate (TFR) more than its neighbor (**red bars**) from 1960–1965 to 2012. *Data from from Population Reference Bureau, 2012* World population data sheet *and Population Division of the Department of Economic and Social Affairs of the United Nations Secretariat, 2011.* World population prospects: The 2010 revision, *http://esa.un .org/wpp. © United Nations, 2011.*

Family-planning programs are working around the world

Data show that funding and policies that encourage family planning can lower population growth rates in all types of nations, even those that are least industrialized. No nation has pursued a sustained population control program as intrusive as China's, but other rapidly growing nations have implemented programs that are less restrictive.

India was the first nation to implement population control policies. However, when some policymakers introduced forced sterilization in the 1970s, the resulting outcry brought down the government. Since then, India's efforts have been more modest and far less coercive, focusing on family planning and reproductive health care. This has greatly reduced rates of growth in India, but India will nonetheless likely overtake China and become the world's most populous nation in several decades because of China's more aggressive population initiatives.

The government of Thailand has reduced birth rates and slowed population growth. In the 1960s, Thailand's growth rate was 2.3%, but in 2012 it was 0.5%. This decline was achieved without a one-child policy, resulting instead from an education-based approach to family planning and the increased availability of contraceptives. Brazil, Cuba, Iran, Mexico, and many other developing countries have instituted active programs to reduce their population growth; these entail setting targets and providing incentives, education, contraception, and reproductive health care. Studies show that nations with such programs have lower fertility rates than similar nations without them (**FIGURE 14.18**).

Empowering women reduces fertility rates

Today, many social scientists and policymakers recognize that for population growth to slow and stabilize, women should be granted equal power to men in societies worldwide. This would have many benefits: Studies show that where women are freer to decide whether and when to have children, fertility rates fall, and children are better cared for, healthier, and better educated.

One benefit of equal rights for women is the ability to make reproductive decisions. In many societies, men restrict women's decision-making abilities, including decisions about how many children a woman will bear. Fertility rates have dropped most noticeably in nations where women have gained improved access to contraceptives and to family planning.

Equality for women also involves expanding educational opportunities for them. In many nations girls are discouraged from pursuing an education or are kept out of school altogether. Worldwide, over two-thirds of people who cannot read are women. And data clearly show that as women receive educational opportunities, fertility rates decline (**FIGURE 14.19**). Education helps more women delay childbirth as they pursue careers and gives them a greater say in reproductive decisions.

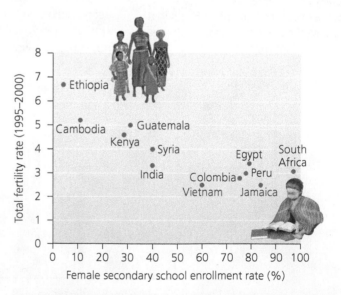

FIGURE 14.19 **Increasing female literacy is strongly associated with reduced birth rates in many nations.** *Data from McDonald, M., and D. Nierenberg, 2003.* Linking population, women, and biodiversity. *State of the world 2003. Washington, D.C.: Worldwatch Institute.*

DATA Q Is the relationship between total fertility rate and the rate of enrollment of girls in secondary school positive (as variable 1 increases, so does variable 2), negative (as variable 1 increases, variable 2 decreases), or is there no obvious relationship (increases in variable 1 are not correlated with changes in variable 2)?

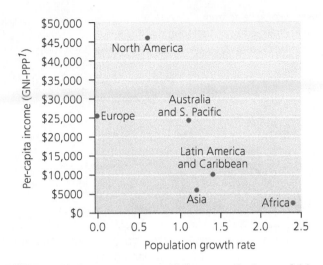

FIGURE 14.20 Poverty and population growth show a fairly strong correlation, despite the influence of many other factors. Per capita income is here measured in GNI PPP, or "gross national income in purchasing power parity." GNI PPP is a measure that standardizes income among nations by converting it to "international" dollars, which indicate the amount of goods and services one could buy in the United States with a given amount of money. *Data from Population Reference Bureau, 2010.* 2010 World population data sheet.

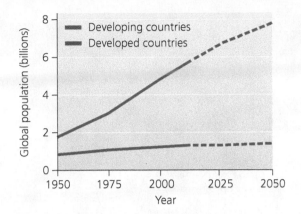

FIGURE 14.21 Over 99% of the next 1 billion people added to Earth's population will be born into developing countries. Dashed portions of the lines indicate projected future trends. *Data from Population Division of the Department of Economic and Social Affairs of the United Nations Secretariat, 2011.* World population prospects: The 2010 revision. *http://esa.un.org/wpp. © United Nations, 2011. Data updates for 2011–2012 from Population Reference Bureau, 2011 and 2012* World population data sheets.

Increasing affluence lowers fertility

Poorer societies tend to show higher population growth rates than do wealthier societies (**FIGURE 14.20**), as one would expect given the demographic transition model. There are many ways that growing affluence and reducing poverty lead to lower rates of population growth.

Historically, people tended to conceive many children, which helped ensure that at least some would survive. Today's improved medical care in wealthy nations has reduced infant mortality rates, making it less necessary to bear multiple children. Increasing urbanization has also driven TFR down; whereas rural families need children to contribute to farm labor, in urban areas children are usually excluded from the labor market, are required to go to school, and impose economic costs on their families. Moreover, if a government provides some form of social security, as most do these days, parents need fewer children to support them in their old age. Finally, with greater educational opportunities and changing roles in society, women tend to shift into the labor force, putting less emphasis on child rearing.

Economic factors are tied closely to population growth. Poverty exacerbates population growth, and rapid population growth worsens poverty. This connection is important because 99% of the next billion people to be added to the global population will be born into nations in the developing world (**FIGURE 14.21**). This is unfortunate from a social standpoint, because in some cases these people will be born into nations that are unable to provide for them. It is also unfortunate from an environmental standpoint, because poverty often results in environmental degradation. People who depend on agriculture and live in areas of poor farmland, for instance, may need to farm even if doing so degrades the soil and is not sustainable. This is largely why Africa's Sahel region—like many arid areas of western China—turns to desert during climatically dry periods (**FIGURE 14.22**). Poverty also drives people to cut forests and to deplete biodiversity. For example, impoverished settlers and miners hunt large mammals for "bush meat" in Africa's forests, including the great apes that are now heading toward extinction.

WEIGHING THE ISSUES

ABSTAINING FROM INTERNATIONAL FAMILY PLANNING? Over the years, the United States has joined 180 other nations in providing millions of dollars to the United Nations Population Fund (UNFPA), which advises governments on family planning, sustainable development, poverty reduction, reproductive health, and AIDS prevention in many nations, including China. Starting in 2001, the George W. Bush administration withheld funds from UNFPA, saying that U.S. law prohibits funding any organization that "supports or participates in the management of a program of coercive abortion or involuntary sterilization," and maintaining that the Chinese government has been implicated in both. Many nations criticized the U.S. decision, and the European Union offered UNFPA additional funding to offset the loss of U.S. contributions. Once President Obama came to office, he reinstated funding to the program. What do you think U.S. policy should be? Should the United States fund family-planning efforts in other nations? What conditions, if any, should it place on the use of such funds?

Expanding wealth can increase the environmental impact per person

Poverty can lead people into environmentally destructive behavior, but wealth can produce even more severe and far-reaching environmental impacts. The affluence of a society such as the United States, Japan, or France is built on levels of resource consumption unprecedented in human history. Much

FIGURE 14.22 **In the semi-arid Sahel region of Africa, population may be increasing beyond the land's ability to handle it.** Here, drought and dependence on grazing agriculture have led to environmental degradation.

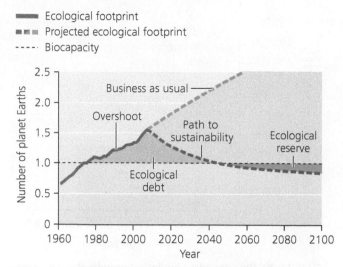

FIGURE 14.23 **The global ecological footprint of the human population is estimated to be 50% greater than what Earth can bear.** If population and consumption continue to rise (orange dashed line), we will increase our ecological deficit, or degree of overshoot, until systems give out and populations crash. If, instead, we pursue a path to sustainability (red dashed line), we can eventually repay our ecological debt and sustain our civilization. *Adapted from WWF International. 2010. Living planet report 2010. Published by WWF-World Wide Fund for Nature. © 2010 WWF (panda.org), Zoological Society of London, and Global Footprint Network.*

of this chapter has dealt with numbers of people rather than with the amount of resources each member of the population consumes or the amount of waste each member produces. The environmental impact of human activities, however, depends not only on the number of people involved but also on the way those people live. Recall the *A* (for affluence) in the IPAT equation. Affluence and consumption are spread unevenly across the world, and wealthy societies generally consume resources from regions far beyond their own.

We have explored the concept of the ecological footprint, the cumulative amount of Earth's surface area required to provide the raw materials a person or population consumes and to dispose of or recycle the waste produced. Individuals from affluent societies leave considerably larger per capita ecological footprints. In this sense, the addition of one American to the world has as much environmental impact as the addition of 3.4 Chinese, 8 Indians, or 14 Afghans. This fact reminds us that the "population problem" does not lie solely with the developing world, but is relevant to people everywhere.

Indeed, just as population is rising, so is consumption, and some environmental scientists have calculated that we are already living beyond the planet's means to support us sustainably. One recent analysis concludes that humanity's global ecological footprint surpassed Earth's capacity to support us in 1971 and that our species is now living 50% beyond its means (FIGURE 14.23). This is our overshoot. In this analysis, our ecological footprint can be compared to the amount of biologically productive land and sea available to us—an amount termed **biocapacity.** For any given area, if the footprint is greater than the biocapacity, there is an "ecological deficit." If the footprint is less than the biocapacity, there is an "ecological reserve." Because our footprint exceeds our biocapacity by 50% worldwide, we are running a global ecological deficit, gradually draining our planet of its natural capital and its long-term ability to support our civilization.

The richest one-fifth of the world's people possesses over 80 times the income of the poorest one-fifth (FIGURE 14.24). The richest one-fifth also uses 86% of the world's resources.

That leaves only 14% of global resources—energy, food, water, and other essentials—for the remaining four-fifths of the world's people to share. It is therefore imperative that we continue and accelerate efforts to promote renewable energy (Chapter 16), "smart" urban design, and other forms of sustainable development. This way, the rapid industrialization of China, India, and other populous nations can occur with far less environmental impact than that which accompanied the industrialization of developed nations.

HIV/AIDS is exerting major impacts on African populations

The rising material wealth and falling fertility rates of many developed nations today is slowing population growth in accord with the demographic transition model. However, nations where the human immunodeficiency virus (HIV) and acquired immunodeficiency syndrome (AIDS) has taken hold are not following Notestein's script. Instead, in these countries death rates have increased, presenting a scenario more akin to Malthus's fears.

The AIDS epidemic (FIGURE 14.25) is having the greatest impact on human populations of any communicable disease since the Black Death killed roughly one-third of Europe's population in the 14th century and since smallpox and other diseases brought by Europeans to the New World wiped out likely millions of Native Americans.

Africa is being hit hardest. Of the world's 34 million people infected with HIV/AIDS as of 2012, two-thirds live in sub-Saharan Africa. Because HIV is spread by the exchange of bodily fluids during sexual contact, the low rate of contraceptive use that contributes to this region's high TFR also

Average per U.S. resident:
• $47,310 annual income
• 30,300 m² of land
• 17.3 metric tons of CO_2 emitted per year

(a) A family living in the United States

Average per resident of India:
• $3400 annual income
• 2600 m² of land
• 1.6 metric tons of CO_2 emitted per year

(b) A family living in India

FIGURE 14.24 Material wealth varies widely across countries. A typical U.S. family **(a)** may own a large house with a wealth of material possessions. A typical family in a developing nation such as India **(b)** may live in a small, sparsely furnished dwelling with few material possessions and little money or time for luxuries. Compared with the average resident of India, the average U.S. resident enjoys 14 times more income, uses 11 times more land, and emits 11 times more carbon dioxide emissions. *Data from Population Reference Bureau, 2012. 2012 World population data sheet and 2012, World Bank, http://data.worldbank.org/.*

fuels the spread of HIV. One in every 20 adults in sub-Saharan Africa is infected with HIV, and for southern African nations, the figure is 1 in 5. As AIDS takes roughly 3800 lives in sub-Saharan Africa every day, the epidemic unleashes a variety of demographic changes. Infant mortality here has risen to 7 deaths out of 100 live births—14 times the rate in the developed world. Infant mortality and the premature deaths of young adults have caused life expectancy in parts of southern Africa to fall from almost 60 years in the early 1990s back

down to 40–50 years, where it stood decades earlier. AIDS also leaves behind millions of orphans.

Africa is not the only region with reason to worry. HIV is well established in the Caribbean and in Southeast Asia, and it is spreading in eastern Europe and central Asia. In China, the government has historically been reluctant to monitor or publicize the status of the disease because of the social stigma that the culture attaches to it. The government has admitted to fewer than 1 million cases, although some international experts fear the number of actual cases is 10 times higher and that vigilance is needed to keep the number from rising, especially with distorted sex ratios in China leaving many men unmarried.

Demographic change has social and economic repercussions

Because it removes young and productive members of society, AIDS undermines the ability of poorer nations to develop. Nations lose billions of dollars in productivity when large numbers of its citizens are battling the disease, and treatment puts a huge burden on health care systems. Children orphaned by AIDS further strain social safety nets, requiring interventions to prevent the cycle of poverty and disease from claiming yet another generation.

These problems are hitting many African countries at a time when their governments are already experiencing **demographic fatigue.** Demographically fatigued governments face overwhelming challenges related to population growth, including educating and employing swelling ranks of young people. With the added stress of HIV/AIDS, these governments face so many demands that they are stretched beyond their capacity to address problems. As a result, the problems grow worse, and citizens lose faith in their governments' abilities to help them. This constellation of challenges is making it difficult for some African nations to advance through the demographic transition.

There is good news, however. Improved public health efforts (including sex education, contraceptives, and intravenous drug abuse policies) across the world have slowed HIV transmission rates, and improved medical treatments are lengthening the lives of people who are infected. Note in Figure 14.25 that the number of AIDS deaths began to decrease in 2006, following a drop in new HIV infections since the late 1990s. We may finally be turning the corner on this challenge, thanks to government policy, international collaboration, medical research, nonprofit aid groups, and the grassroots efforts of patients and their advocates. With continued work, we can venture to hope that the multipronged effort to combat HIV/AIDS might eventually become a success story in humanity's timeless battle against disease.

Population goals support sustainable development

The factors that influence fertility are complex and interacting, so initiatives to slow population growth must be diverse, flexible, and culturally specific. This approach was echoed at the milestone 1994 United Nations conference on population and development in Cairo, Egypt. The conference marked a turn away from older notions of top-down command-and-control

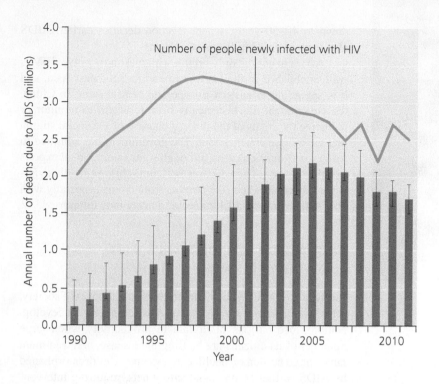

FIGURE 14.25 **Nearly 2 million people die from AIDS worldwide each year, and even more are newly infected with HIV each year.** However, extensive efforts to combat the disease are beginning to bear fruit; infections have been decreasing since 1998, and deaths began decreasing in 2006. The error bars indicate the range of the number of deaths attributable to AIDS, as not all deaths caused by the disease are reported. *Data from UNAIDS and WHO, 2012.* UNAIDS Report on the global AIDS epidemic. *Geneva, Switzerland.*

FAQ Why hasn't HIV/AIDS drastically lowered Africa's fertility rates?

As shown in Table 14.2, Africa's TFR remains the highest, by a wide margin, of all world regions despite high rates of HIV/AIDS infection. This seems contradictory, but it is related to the mode of transmission of HIV/AIDS and the time it takes for the disease to affect its victims' health. Because the disease is typically spread in Africa through sexual behavior, it afflicts individuals who are already in the reproductive age group. Hence, many people already have children by the time they contract the disease and continue having children even after becoming HIV-positive as infected people often live for several years before succumbing to AIDS. As a result, nations with high rates of HIV infection still have extremely high fertility. The southern African nation of Swaziland in 2012, for example, had one of Africa's highest HIV infection rates (21% of females and 30% of males infected) but also one of the region's highest total fertility rates (3.5 children per woman).

population policy geared toward pushing contraception and lowering populations to preset targets. Instead, it urged governments to offer better education and health care and to address social needs that affect population from the bottom up (such as alleviating poverty, disease, and sexism).

The connections we have discussed in this chapter should show that to achieve sustainable development, both population growth and resource consumption levels will need to be addressed. If humanity's overarching goal is to generate a high standard of living and quality of life for all of the world's people, then developing nations must find ways to slow their population growth. However, those of us living in the developed world must also be willing to reduce our consumption. Earth does not hold enough resources to sustain all 7 billion

of us at the current North American standard of living, nor can we venture out and bring home extra planets. We must make the best of the one place that supports us all.

Conclusion

Today's human population is larger than at any time in the past. Our growing population and our growing consumption affect the environment and our ability to meet the needs of all the world's people.

However, there are at least two major reasons to be encouraged. First, although global population is still rising, the rate of growth has decreased nearly everywhere, and some countries are even seeing population declines. Most developed nations have passed through the demographic transition, showing that it is possible to lower death rates while stabilizing population and creating more prosperous societies. Second, progress has been made in expanding rights for women worldwide. Although there is still a long way to go, women are obtaining better education, more economic independence, and more ability to control their reproductive decisions. Aside from the clear ethical progress these developments entail, they are helping to slow population growth.

Human population cannot continue to rise forever. The question is how it will stop rising: Will it be through the gentle and benign process of the demographic transition, through restrictive governmental intervention such as China's one-child policy, or through the miserable Malthusian checks of disease and social conflict caused by overcrowding and competition for scarce resources? How we answer this question today will determine not only the quality of the world in which we live, but also the quality of the world we leave to our children and grandchildren.

Reviewing Objectives

You should now be able to:

Perceive the scope of human population growth

- Our global population of nearly 7 billion people adds over 70 million people per year (>2 people every second). (p. 402)

- The global population growth rate peaked at 2.1% in the 1960s and now stands at 1.2%. Growth rates vary among regions. (p. 403)

Assess divergent views on population growth

- Thomas Malthus and Paul Ehrlich warned that overpopulation would deplete resources and harm humanity, whereas Cornucopians see little to fear in population growth (p. 404)

- Rising population can deplete resources, intensify pollution, stress social systems, and degrade ecosystems, such that environmental quality and our quality of life decline. (p. 404)

- Population decline and population aging in some nations have given rise to fears of economic decline. (pp. 404–405)

Evaluate how human population, affluence, and technology affect the environment

- The IPAT model summarizes how environmental impact (*I*) results from interactions among population size (*P*), affluence (*A*), and technology (*T*). (p. 405)

- Rising population and rising affluence may each increase consumption and environmental impact. Technology has frequently worsened environmental degradation, but it can also help mitigate our impacts. (pp. 405–407)

Explain and apply the fundamentals of demography

- Demography applies principles of population ecology to the statistical study of human populations. (p. 408)

- Demographers study size, density, distribution, age structure, and sex ratios of populations, as well as rates of birth, death, immigration, and emigration. (pp. 408–412)

- Total fertility rate (TFR) contributes greatly to change in population size. (pp. 412–413)

Outline and assess the concept of demographic transition

- The demographic transition model explains why population growth has slowed in industrialized nations. Industrialization and urbanization reduce the economic need for children, and education and the empowerment of women decrease unwanted pregnancies. Parents in developed nations choose to invest in quality of life rather than quantity of children. (pp. 413–414)

- The demographic transition may or may not proceed to completion in all of today's developing nations. Whether it does is of immense importance in the quest for sustainability. (p. 414)

Describe how family planning, the status of women, and wealth and poverty affect population growth

- Many birth control methods serve to reduce unwanted pregnancies. (p. 415)

- Family-planning programs and reproductive education have reduced population growth in many nations. (p. 418)

- When women are empowered and achieve equality with men, fertility rates fall, and children tend to be better cared for, healthier, and better educated. (p. 418)

- Poorer societies tend to show faster population growth than do wealthier societies. (p. 419)

- The intensive consumption of affluent societies often makes their ecological impact greater than that of poorer nations with larger populations. (pp. 419–420)

Characterize the dimensions of the HIV/AIDS epidemic

- About 34 million people worldwide are infected with HIV, and 2 million die from AIDS each year. Most live in sub-Saharan Africa. (pp. 420–421)

- Epidemics that claim many young and productive members of society influence population dynamics and can have severe social and economic ramifications. (p. 421)

- We may at last be turning the corner on HIV/AIDS, thanks to a multifaceted effort. (p. 421)

Testing Your Comprehension

1. What is the approximate current human global population? How many people are being added to the population each day?

2. Why has the human population continued to grow despite environmental limitations? Do you think this growth is sustainable? Why or why not?

3. Contrast the views of environmental scientists with those of Cornucopian economists and policymakers regarding whether population growth is a problem. Name several reasons why population growth is commonly viewed as a problem.

4. Explain the IPAT model. How can technology either increase or decrease environmental impact? Provide at least two examples.

5. Describe how demographers use size, density, distribution, age structure, and sex ratio of a population to estimate how it may change. How does each of these factors help determine the impact of human populations on the environment?

6. What is the total fertility rate (TFR)? Why is the replacement fertility for humans approximately 2.1? How is Europe's TFR affecting its rate of natural increase?

7. How does the demographic transition model explain the increase in population growth rates in recent centuries? How does it explain the recent decrease in population growth rates in many countries?

8. Why have fertility rates fallen in many countries?

9. Why are the empowerment of women and the pursuit of gender equality viewed as important to controlling population growth? Describe the aim of family-planning programs.

10. Why do poorer societies have higher population growth rates than wealthier societies? How does poverty affect the environment? How does affluence affect the environment?

Seeking Solutions

1. China's reduction in birth rates is leading to significant change in the nation's age structure. Review Figure 14.12, which shows that the population is growing older, leading to the top-heavy population pyramid for the year 2050. What effects might this ultimately have on Chinese society? What steps could be taken in response?

2. The World Bank estimates that half the world's people survive on less than $2 per day. How do you think this situation affects the political stability of the world? Explain your answer.

3. Apply the IPAT model to the example of China provided in the chapter. How do population, affluence, technology, and ecological sensitivity affect China's environment? Now consider your own country or your own state. How do population, affluence, technology, and ecological sensitivity affect your environment? How can we minimize the environmental impacts of growth in the human population?

4. Do you think that all of today's developing nations will complete the demographic transition and come to enjoy a permanent state of low birth and death rates? Why or why not? What steps might we as a global society take to help ensure that they do? Now think about developed nations such as the United States and Canada. Do you think these nations will continue to lower and stabilize their birth and death rates in a state of prosperity? What factors might affect whether they do so?

5. **THINK IT THROUGH** India's prime minister puts you in charge of that nation's population policy. India has a population growth rate of 1.5% per year, a TFR of 2.5, a 47% rate of contraceptive use, and a population that is 69% rural. What policy steps would you recommend, and why?

6. **THINK IT THROUGH** Now suppose that you have been tapped to design population policy for Germany. Germany is losing population at an annual rate of 0.2%, has a TFR of 1.4, a 66% rate of contraceptive use, and a population that is 73% urban. What policy steps would you recommend, and why?

Calculating Ecological Footprints

A nation's population size and the affluence of its citizens each influence its resource consumption and environmental impact. As of 2012, the world's population passed 7 billion. Average per capita income was $10,030 per year, and the latest estimate for the world's average ecological footprint was 2.7 hectares (ha) per person. The sampling of data in the table will allow you to explore patterns in how population, affluence, and environmental impact are related.

Nation	Population (millions of people)	Affluence (per capita income)[1]	Personal impact (per capita footprint, in ha/person)	Total impact (national footprint, in millions of ha)
Belgium	11.1	$34,760	8.0	89
Brazil	194.3	$10,070	2.9	
China	1350.4	$6,020	2.2	
Ethiopia	87.0	$870	1.1	
India	1259.7	$2,960	0.9	
Japan	127.6	$35,220	4.7	
Mexico	116.1	$14,270	3.0	
Russia	143.2	$15,630	4.4	
United States	313.9	$46,970	8.0	2511

[1]Measured in GNI PPP (gross national income in purchasing power parity), a measure that standardizes income among nations by converting it to "international" dollars, which indicate the amount of goods and services one could buy in the United States with a given amount of money.

Data: Population and affluence data are from Population Reference Bureau, 2012. World population data sheet 2012. Footprint data are for 2007, from WWF International, Zoological Society of London, and Global Footprint Network. Living planet report 2010.

1. Calculate the total impact (national ecological footprint) for each country.

2. Draw a graph illustrating per capita impact (on the y axis) vs. affluence (on the x axis). What do the results show? Explain why the data look the way they do.

3. Draw a graph illustrating total impact (on the y axis) in relation to population (on the x axis). What do the results suggest to you?

4. Draw a graph illustrating total impact (on the y axis) in relation to affluence (on the x axis). What do the results suggest to you?

5. You have just used three of the four variables in the IPAT equation. Now give one example of how the T (technology) variable could potentially increase the total impact of the United States, and one example of how it could potentially decrease the U.S. impact.

Mastering ENVIRONMENTALSCIENCE™

STUDENTS
Go to **MasteringEnvironmentalScience** for assignments, the etext, and the Study Area with practice tests, videos, current events, and activities.

INSTRUCTORS
Go to **MasteringEnvironmentalScience** for automatically graded activities, current events, videos, and reading questions that you can assign to your students, plus Instructor Resources.

Extraction of oil sands at a mine in Alberta

15

Fossil Fuels, Their Impacts, and Energy Conservation

Upon completing this chapter, you will be able to:

- Identify the energy sources we use

- Describe the origin and nature of major types of fossil fuels

- Explain how we extract and use fossil fuels

- Evaluate peak oil and the challenges it may pose

- Examine how we are reaching further for fossil fuels

- Outline and assess environmental impacts of fossil fuel use, and explore solutions

- Evaluate political, social, and economic aspects of fossil fuel use

- Specify strategies for conserving energy and enhancing efficiency

CENTRAL CASE STUDY

Alberta's Oil Sands and the Keystone XL Pipeline

Fort McMurray○ — **Oil sands**
Alberta
Hardisty○ *Saskatchewan*
Manitoba
Montana *North Dakota*
South Dakota
Sandhills
Nebraska
— Existing Keystone pipeline
▪▪▪ Proposed Keystone XL extension
Kansas
Ogallala Aquifer
Oklahoma
○Steele City
Illinois
○Patoka
Missouri
○Cushing
Texas
Houston○ ○
Port Arthur

"It's good for our country, and it's good for our economy, and it's good for the American people, especially those who are looking for work."

—House Speaker John Boehner (R-Ohio)

"It will be game over for the climate."

—Climate scientist James Hansen

Everything about Canada's oil sands is huge. These fossil fuel deposits cover a region the size of Illinois, within boreal forests that span the width of the continent. The open pit mines dug to extract the fuel are miles wide; the vehicles moving inside them like ants are million-pound haul trucks with 14-foot tires and shovels that are five stories high. The economic value of the extracted oil is astounding. Last but not least, burning all this fuel will alter the very climate of our planet.

Oil sands, also called **tar sands,** are layers of sand or clay saturated with a viscous, tarry type of petroleum called *bitumen*. Huge areas of these wet blackish deposits underlie a thinly populated region of northern Alberta, and the implications of mining them for oil are momentous. To some people the oil sands represent wealth and security, a key to maintaining our fossil-fuel-based lifestyle far into the future. To others they are a source of appalling pollution and threaten to radically alter Earth's climate.

To extract oil from oil sands, companies clear the boreal forest and then strip-mine the land, peeling back layers of peat and creating open pits 215 m (400 ft) deep. The gooey deposits are mixed with hot water and chemicals to separate the bitumen from the sand, and the bitumen is removed and processed, while wastewater is dumped into toxic tailings lakes that are even larger than the mines. In locations where oil sands are more deeply buried, hot water is injected down deep shafts to liquefy, separate, and extract the bitumen *in situ*.

Mining for oil sands began in Alberta in 1967, but for many years it was hard to make money extracting these low-quality deposits. Rising oil prices in recent years have now turned it into a profitable venture, and today dozens of companies are mining here. Canadian oil sands are producing 1.7 million barrels of oil per day, more than half of Canada's petroleum production. Thanks to the oil sands, Canada boasts the world's third-largest proven reserves of oil, after Saudi Arabia and Venezuela. Each truckload of oil sands that leaves a mine carries oil worth close to $20,000 at 2013 prices.

Canada looked for buyers south of its border first, seeking to capitalize on the United States' insatiable appetite for oil. TransCanada Corporation built the Keystone Pipeline to ship diluted bitumen into the United States. This pipeline system began operating in 2010, bringing oil from Alberta nearly 3500 km (2200 mi) to Illinois and Oklahoma. At the Oklahoma terminus in the town of Cushing, a bottleneck created a glut of oil that was unable to reach refineries on the Texas coast fast enough to meet demand. TransCanada proposed the Keystone XL extension, a two-part project consisting of (1) a southern leg to connect Cushing to the Texas refineries and (2) a northern leg that would cut across the Great Plains to shave off distance and add capacity to the existing line.

The Keystone XL pipeline proposal soon met opposition from people living along the proposed route who were concerned about health, environmental protection, and property rights. It also faced nationwide opposition from advocates of action to address global climate change.

Pipeline proponents feel the Keystone XL project will create jobs for workers in the U.S. heartland and will guarantee a dependable oil supply for decades to come. They stress that buying oil from Canada—a stable, friendly, democratic neighbor—could help end U.S. reliance on oil-producing nations such as Saudi Arabia and Venezuela that have had authoritarian governments and poor human rights records.

Opponents of the pipeline extension express dismay at the destruction of boreal forest and anxiety about transporting oil over the continent's largest aquifer, where spills could contaminate drinking water for millions of people and irrigation water for America's breadbasket. They also seek to avoid extracting a vast new source of fossil fuels whose combustion would release immense amounts of greenhouse gases that will intensify climate change. By buying a source of oil that is energy-intensive to extract and that burns less cleanly than conventional fuels, they maintain, the United States would be prolonging fossil fuel dependence and worsening climate change when it should instead be transitioning to clean renewable energy.

Under pressure from all sides, the administration of U.S. President Barack Obama walked a fine line. Because the northern leg of the Keystone XL extension crosses an international border, it requires a presidential permit from the U.S. Department of State—which TransCanada applied for in 2008. After three years of review, the State Department hesitated to approve the project because of concerns about damage to the ecologically sensitive Sandhills area of Nebraska and potential contamination of the Ogallala Aquifer. Facing street protests at the White House (**FIGURE 15.1**), Obama in November 2011 postponed the permit decision.

Republicans in Congress reacted by demanding a decision in 60 days and attaching this mandate to legislation for a payroll tax cut. Obama responded by announcing that the application would be denied because of insufficient time to review the pipeline's impact. However, Obama encouraged TransCanada to renew its application with a revised route avoiding the areas of concern in Nebraska and to proceed with the southern leg of the pipeline, which requires no permit. TransCanada did both. Meanwhile, Canadian officials grew irritated and began considering building a pipeline west to British Columbia and selling the oil to China instead.

In March 2013 the State Department released a draft environmental impact statement for the new route. The draft EIS gave little indication that it would stand in the way of pipeline development. The State Department planned to issue a final

FIGURE 15.1 Many Americans have opposed the Keystone XL pipeline extension. Tens of thousands of activists protested in front of the U.S. White House in increasingly large rallies in 2011, 2012, and 2013.

EIS after receiving public comment, after which Obama would decide whether to approve the pipeline.

Throughout 2013 the debate intensified. In February, tens of thousands of Americans protested against the pipeline in front of the White House. These protestors viewed the decision on Keystone XL as a test of Obama's vow to deal with climate change, made in his inauguration speech a month earlier. Pipeline proponents countered that Canada would find a way to extract and sell its oil in any case, so the United States might as well take advantage of the trade benefits of buying it and reselling it on the world market.

Later that year, Obama announced that he would approve the pipeline only if it "does not significantly exacerbate the problem of carbon pollution." What this signaled was unclear, however: The draft EIS suggested the pipeline would not do so, but the Environmental Protection Agency had judged the EIS to be inadequate.

As this book went to press, a decision to approve or deny the Keystone XL pipeline had not yet been made. We will leave it to you and your instructor to flesh out the rest of this story!

The divergent views on Canada's oil sands reflect our confounding relationship with fossil fuels. These energy sources power our civilization and have enabled our modern standard of living—yet as climate change worsens, we face the need to wean ourselves from them and shift to clean renewable energy sources. The way in which we handle this complex transition will determine a great deal about the quality of our lives and the future of our society and our planet. ●

Sources of Energy

Humanity has devised many ways to harness the renewable and nonrenewable forms of energy available on our planet (TABLE 15.1). We use these energy sources to heat and light our homes; power our machinery; fuel our vehicles; produce plastics, pharmaceuticals, and synthetic fibers; and provide the comforts and conveniences to which we've grown accustomed in the industrial age.

Nature offers us a variety of energy sources

Most of Earth's energy comes from the sun. We can harness energy from the sun's radiation directly by using solar power technologies. Solar radiation also helps drive wind and the water cycle, enabling us to harness wind power and hydroelectric power. And of course, sunlight drives photosynthesis and the growth of plants, from which we take wood and other biomass as a fuel source. When plants and other organisms die and are buried in sediments under particular conditions, their stored chemical energy may eventually be transferred to **fossil fuels,** highly combustible substances formed from the remains of organisms from past geologic ages. Today we rely on three main fossil fuels, in the form of a solid (coal), liquid (oil), and gas (natural gas).

In addition, a great deal of energy emanates from Earth's core, making geothermal power available for our use. Energy also results from the gravitational pull of the moon and sun, and we are just beginning to harness power from the ocean tides that these forces generate. Finally, an immense amount of energy resides within the bonds among protons and neutrons in atoms, and this energy provides us with nuclear power. We explore all these energy sources as alternatives to fossil fuels in Chapter 16.

Energy sources such as sunlight, geothermal energy, and tidal energy are considered perpetually renewable because they are readily replenished, so we can keep using them without depleting them. In contrast, energy sources such as coal, oil, and natural gas are considered nonrenewable. These nonrenewable fuels result from ongoing natural processes, but it takes so long for fossil fuels to form that, once depleted, they cannot be replaced within any time span useful to our civilization. It takes a thousand years for the biosphere to generate the amount of organic matter that must be buried to produce a single day's worth of fossil fuels for our society. To replenish the fossil fuels we have depleted so far would take many millions of years. At our

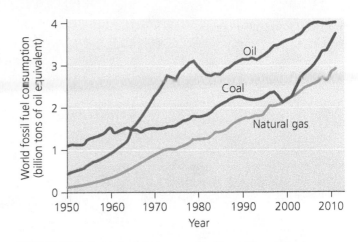

FIGURE 15.2 Annual global consumption of fossil fuels has risen greatly over the past half-century. Oil remains our leading energy source. *Data from U.S. Energy Information Administration; International Energy Agency; and BP p.l.c., 2012,* Statistical review of world energy 2012.

DATA Q By roughly what percentage has the annual consumption of oil risen since the year you were born?

accelerating rate of consumption, we will use up Earth's easily accessible store of conventional fossil fuels in just decades. For this reason, and because fossil fuels exert severe environmental impacts, renewable energy sources increasingly are being developed as alternatives to fossil fuels (Chapter 16).

Fossil fuels dominate our energy use

Since the industrial revolution, fossil fuels have replaced biomass as our society's dominant source of energy. Global consumption of coal, oil, and natural gas has risen for years and is now at its highest level ever (FIGURE 15.2). The high energy content of fossil fuels makes them efficient to burn, ship, and store. We use these fuels for transportation, manufacturing, heating, and cooking and also to generate **electricity,** a secondary form of energy that is convenient to transfer over long distances and apply to a variety of uses. Each type of fuel has its own mix of uses, and each contributes in different ways to our economies and our daily needs. For instance, oil is used mostly for transportation, whereas coal is used mostly to generate electricity.

Societies differ in how they use energy. Industrialized nations apportion roughly one-third of their energy to transportation, one-third to industry, and one-third to all other uses. In contrast, industrializing nations devote a greater proportion of energy to subsistence activities such as agriculture, food preparation, and home heating, and much less to transportation. Moreover, people in developing countries often rely on manual or animal energy sources instead of automated ones. For instance, most rice farmers in Southeast Asia plant rice by hand, but industrial rice growers in California use airplanes. Because industrialized nations rely more on equipment and technology, they use more fossil fuels. In the United States, oil, coal, and natural gas together supply 82% of energy demand (FIGURE 15.3).

TABLE 15.1	Energy Sources We Use	
ENERGY SOURCE	**DESCRIPTION**	**TYPE OF ENERGY**
Crude oil	Fossil fuel extracted from ground (liquid)	Nonrenewable
Natural gas	Fossil fuel extracted from ground (gas)	Nonrenewable
Coal	Fossil fuel extracted from ground (solid)	Nonrenewable
Nuclear energy	Energy from atomic nuclei of uranium	Nonrenewable
Biomass energy	Energy stored in plant matter from photosynthesis	Renewable
Hydropower	Energy from running water	Renewable
Solar energy	Energy from sunlight directly	Renewable
Wind energy	Energy from wind	Renewable
Geothermal energy	Earth's internal heat rising from core	Renewable
Tidal and wave energy	Energy from tides and ocean waves	Renewable

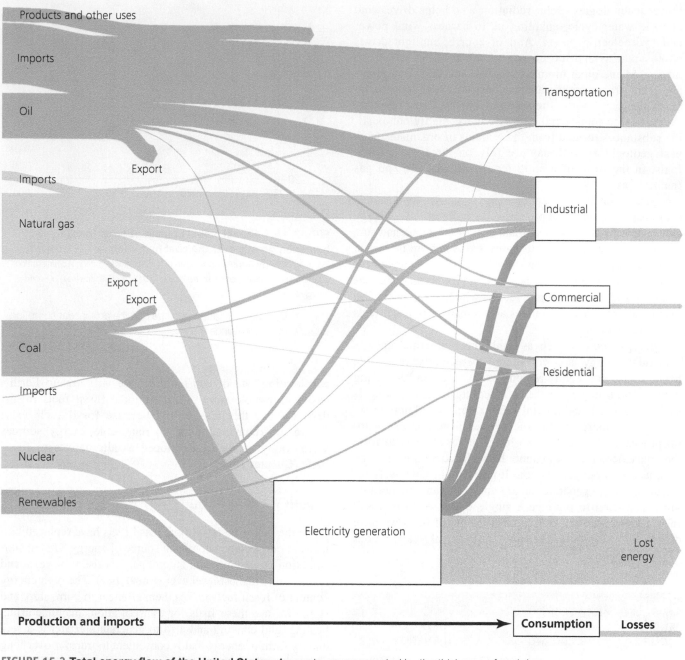

Products and other uses

Imports

Oil

Imports

Natural gas

Export

Export

Export

Coal

Imports

Nuclear

Renewables

Electricity generation

Transportation

Industrial

Commercial

Residential

Lost energy

Production and imports → **Consumption** **Losses**

FIGURE 15.3 Total energy flow of the United States. Amounts are represented by the thickness of each bar. Domestic production and imports are shown on the left, and destinations of the energy are shown on the right. Portions of each energy source are used directly in the residential, commercial, industrial, and transportation sectors. Other portions are used to generate electricity, which in turn powers these sectors. The large amounts of energy lost as waste heat are shown on the right. *Data are for 2012, from U.S. Energy Information Administration and Lawrence Livermore National Laboratory.*

Energy sources and consumption are unevenly distributed

A world map of per capita consumption rates shows that citizens of developed regions generally consume far more energy than do those of developing regions (**FIGURE 15.4**). Per person, the most industrialized nations use up to 100 times more energy than do the least industrialized nations. The United States has only 4.4% of the world's population, but it consumes nearly 19% of the world's energy.

The origins of most energy sources also are unevenly distributed over Earth's surface. Some regions have substantial reserves of oil, coal, or natural gas, whereas others have very few. Half the world's proven reserves of crude oil lie in the Middle East. The Middle East is also rich in natural gas, but Russia holds more natural gas than any other country. Russia is also rich in coal, as is China, but the United States possesses the most coal of any nation (**TABLE 15.2**).

It takes energy to make energy

We do not simply get energy for free. To harness, extract, process, and deliver the energy we use, we need to invest

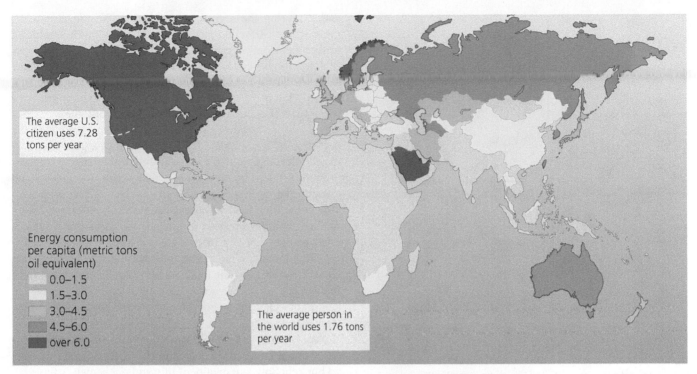

FIGURE 15.4 People in wealthy industrialized nations tend to consume the most energy per person. This map combines all types of energy, standardized to metric tons of "oil equivalent," that is, the amount of fuel needed to produce the energy gained from combusting one metric ton of crude oil. *Data from BP p.l.c., 2012. Statistical review of world energy 2012.*

DATA Q How many times more energy does the average U.S. citizen use than the average person in the world?

substantial inputs of energy. For instance, mining oil sands in Alberta requires extensive use of powerful vehicles and heavy machinery, as well as construction of an immense infrastructure of roads, pipelines, waste ponds, storage tanks, water intakes, processing facilities, housing for workers, and more—all requiring the use of energy. Natural gas must be burned to heat the water that is used to separate the bitumen from the sand. Processing and piping the oil away from the extraction site, and then refining it into products we can use, requires further energy inputs. Thus, when evaluating an energy source, it is important to take energy inputs into consideration by subtracting costs in energy invested from the benefits in energy received. **Net energy** expresses the difference between energy returned and energy invested:

Net energy = Energy returned − Energy invested

When assessing energy sources, it is useful to use a ratio often denoted as **EROI—energy returned on investment.** EROI ratios are calculated as follows:

EROI = Energy returned/ Energy invested

Higher EROI ratios mean that we receive more energy from each unit of energy that we invest. Fossil fuels are widely used because their EROI ratios have historically been high. However, EROI ratios can change over time. Ratios rise as the technology to extract and process fossil fuels improves, and they fall as resources are depleted and remaining resources become harder to extract.

EROI ratios for producing conventional oil and natural gas in the United States declined from roughly 30:1 in the 1950s to about 20:1 in the 1970s, and today they hover around 11:1

TABLE 15.2 Nations with the Largest Proven Reserves of Fossil Fuels					
OIL (% world reserves)		**NATURAL GAS** (% world reserves)		**COAL** (% world reserves)	
Venezuela*	17.9	Russia	21.4	United States	27.6
Saudi Arabia	16.1	Iran	15.9	Russia	18.2
Canada*	10.6	Qatar	12.0	China	13.3
Iran	9.1	Turkmenistan	11.7	Australia	8.9
Iraq	8.7	United States	4.1	India	7.0

*Most reserves in Venezuela and Canada consist of oil sands, which are included in these figures.
Data from BP p.l.c., 2012. Statistical review of world energy 2012.

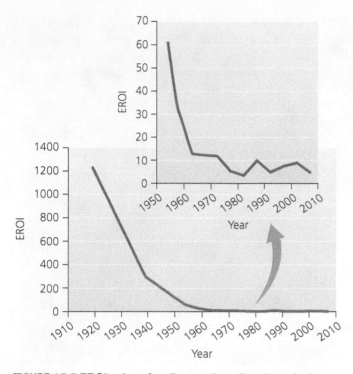

FIGURE 15.5 EROI values for discovering oil and gas in the United States have declined over the past century. *Data from Guilford, M., et al., 2011. A new long term assessment of energy return on investment (EROI) for U.S. oil and gas discovery and production. Pp. 115–136 in Sustainability, Special Issue, 2011, eds. C. Hall and D. Hansen, New studies in EROI (Energy return on investment).*

(FIGURE 15.5). This means that we used to be able to gain 30 units of energy for every unit of energy expended, but now we can gain only 11. EROI ratios for oil and gas declined because we extracted the easiest deposits first and now must work harder and harder to extract the remaining amounts. For the Alberta oil sands, EROI ratios are still lower, because oil sands are a low-quality fuel that requires a great deal of energy to extract and process. EROI estimates for oil sands from studies so far range from 1.5:1 to 9:1, with most estimates around 3:1 to 5:1.

Where will we turn in the future for energy?

Throughout the 20th century, abundant and inexpensive coal, oil, and natural gas powered the astonishing advances of our civilization. These extraordinarily rich sources of energy helped to bring us a standard of living our ancestors could scarcely have imagined.

We began by extracting the fossil fuel deposits that were readily located and accessed, and we took advantage of boundless energy at cheap prices. Yet because fossil fuel deposits are finite and nonrenewable, we gradually began depleting them. As easily accessible supplies of the three main fossil fuels became depleted, EROI ratios rose, and fuels became more expensive.

In response, we have developed technology to reach deeper and farther, expending more money and energy in order to continue obtaining fossil fuel energy. We have returned to sites that were already extracted, bringing powerful new machinery and approaches to squeeze more fuels from known locations. We are now reaching into formerly inaccessible places by drilling deeper, moving further offshore,

and exploring the seabed of the Arctic. We are also using more potent extraction methods, such as hydraulic fracturing to free gas from rock layers. And we are pursuing new types of fossil fuels, including oil sands, shale oil, and methane hydrates. These fuels are more expensive and lower in quality, but they are increasingly being extracted as market prices of fossil fuels rise and make their extraction profitable.

There is, however, another way we can respond to the depletion of conventional fossil fuel resources. This is to hasten the development of clean and renewable energy sources to replace them. By transitioning away from fossil fuels and toward renewable sources, we can gain energy that is sustainable in the long term while greatly reducing pollution, health impacts, and the emission of greenhouse gases that drive climate change (Chapter 16).

This transition has begun to occur, but it is apparent that we will continue to gain much of our future energy from fossil fuels. Alas, so far our ability to control pollution has lagged behind our capacity to consume energy. Many scientists now warn that if we do not immediately step up energy conservation and accelerate our shift to renewables, we will drive our planet's climate into unprecedented territory, threatening impacts on our economy, our quality of life, and our society's future.

Fossil Fuels and Their Extraction

The three conventional fossil fuels on which our modern industrial society was built, and on which we rely today, are coal, natural gas, and oil. Additional fossil fuels we are beginning to extract or considering for the future include oil sands, shale oil, and methane hydrates. We will first consider how each of these fossil fuels is formed, how we locate deposits, how we extract these resources, and how our society puts them to use. We will then examine some of their environmental and social impacts.

Fossil fuels are formed from ancient organic matter

The fossil fuels we burn today in our vehicles, homes, industries, and power plants were formed from the tissues of organisms that lived 100–500 million years ago. The energy these fuels contain came originally from the sun and was converted to chemical-bond energy by photosynthesis. The chemical energy in these organisms' tissues then became concentrated as these tissues decomposed and their hydrocarbon compounds were altered and compressed (FIGURE 15.6).

Most organisms, after death, do not end up as part of a coal, gas, or oil deposit. A tree that falls and decays as a rotting log on the forest floor undergoes mostly **aerobic** decomposition; in the presence of air, bacteria and other organisms that use oxygen break down plant and animal remains into simpler carbon molecules that are recycled through the ecosystem. Fossil fuels are produced only when organic material is broken down in an **anaerobic** environment, one that has little or no oxygen. Such environments include the bottoms of lakes, swamps, and shallow seas. Over millions of years, organic matter that accumulates at the bottoms of such water bodies may be converted into crude oil, natural gas, or coal, depending on (1) the

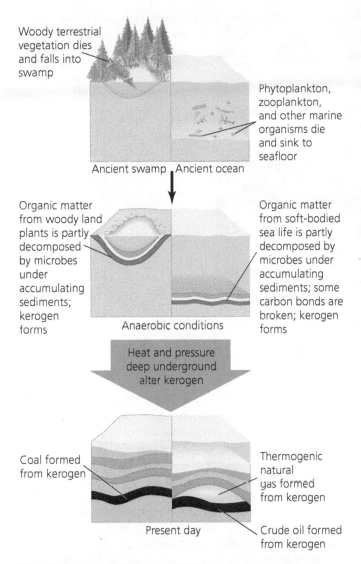

Woody terrestrial vegetation dies and falls into swamp

Phytoplankton, zooplankton, and other marine organisms die and sink to seafloor

Ancient swamp | Ancient ocean

Organic matter from woody land plants is partly decomposed by microbes under accumulating sediments; kerogen forms

Organic matter from soft-bodied sea life is partly decomposed by microbes under accumulating sediments; some carbon bonds are broken; kerogen forms

Anaerobic conditions

Heat and pressure deep underground alter kerogen

Coal formed from kerogen

Thermogenic natural gas formed from kerogen

Present day

Crude oil formed from kerogen

FIGURE 15.6 Fossil fuels begin to form when organisms die and end up in oxygen-poor conditions. This can occur when trees fall into lakes and are buried by sediment, or when phytoplankton and zooplankton drift to the seafloor and are buried (**top diagram**). Organic matter that undergoes slow anaerobic decomposition deep under sediments forms kerogen (**middle diagram**). Coal results when plant matter is compacted so tightly that there is little decomposition (**bottom left diagram**). The action of geothermal heating on kerogen may create crude oil and natural gas (**bottom right diagram**), which come to reside in porous rock layers beneath dense, impervious layers.

chemical composition of the material, (2) the temperatures and pressures to which it is subjected, (3) the presence or absence of anaerobic decomposers, and (4) the passage of time.

Coal The world's most abundant fossil fuel is **coal**, a hard blackish substance formed from organic matter (generally woody plant material) that was compressed under very high pressure, creating dense, solid carbon structures (**FIGURE 15.7**). Coal typically results when little decomposition takes place because the material cannot be digested or appropriate decomposers are not present. The proliferation 300–400 million years ago of swampy environments where organic material was buried has created coal deposits throughout the world.

Coal varies from deposit to deposit in the amount of water, carbon, and potential energy it contains. Organic material that is broken down anaerobically but remains wet, near the surface, and not well compressed is called *peat*. As peat decomposes further, as it is buried under sediments, as heat and pressure increase, and as time passes, water is squeezed out and carbon compounds are packed more tightly together, forming coal. Scientists classify coal into four types (see Figure 15.7). The more coal is compressed, the greater is its carbon content and the greater is the energy content per unit volume.

Oil and natural gas The sludgelike liquid we know as **oil**, or **crude oil**, contains a mixture of hundreds of different types of hydrocarbon molecules. **Natural gas** is a gas consisting primarily of methane (CH_4) and including varying amounts of other volatile hydrocarbons. Oil is also known as **petroleum**, although this term is commonly used to refer to oil and natural gas collectively.

Both oil and natural gas are formed from organic material (especially dead plankton) that drifted down through coastal marine waters millions of years ago and was buried in sediments on the ocean floor. As organic matter is buried more deeply, the pressure exerted by overlying sediments grows, and temperatures increase. Carbon bonds in the organic matter begin breaking, and the organic matter turns to a substance called *kerogen*, which acts as a source material for both natural gas and crude oil. Further heat and pressure act on the kerogen to degrade complex organic molecules into simpler hydrocarbon molecules. Oil tends to form under temperature and pressure conditions often found 1.5–3 km (1–2 mi) below the surface. At depths below 3 km (1.9 mi), the high temperatures and pressures tend to form natural gas.

Natural gas that forms in this way from compression and heat deep underground is called *thermogenic* gas. Thermogenic gas may be formed directly, or from coal or oil that is altered by heating. Most gas extracted commercially is thermogenic and is found above deposits of crude oil or seams of coal, so its extraction often accompanies the extraction of those fossil fuels.

Natural gas is also formed by a second process; *biogenic* gas is created at shallow depths by the anaerobic decomposition of organic matter by bacteria. An example is the "swamp gas" you may smell when stepping into the muck of a swamp. One source of biogenic natural gas is the decay process in landfills, and many landfill operators are now capturing this gas to sell as fuel. Biogenic gas is nearly pure methane, whereas thermogenic gas contains small amounts of other gases as well as methane.

Oil sands As we've seen, oil sands (also called tar sands) consist of moist sand and clay containing 1–20% bitumen, a thick and heavy form of petroleum that is rich in carbon and poor in hydrogen. Oil sands represent crude oil deposits that have been degraded and chemically altered by water erosion and bacterial decomposition. The leading scientific hypothesis to explain Alberta's oil sands is that geological changes tens of millions of years ago as the Rocky Mountains were uplifted allowed crude oil deposits to migrate northeastward and upward until they saturated rock and soil in what is now

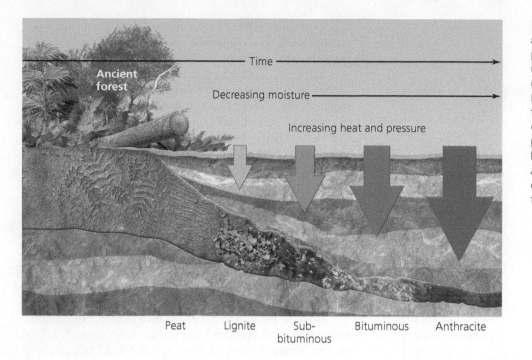

FIGURE 15.7 **Coal forms as ancient plant matter turns to peat and then is compressed underground.** Of the four classes of coal, lignite coal forms under the least pressure and heat and retains the most moisture. Anthracite coal is formed under the greatest pressure, where temperatures are high and moisture content is low. Anthracite coal has the densest carbon content and so contains the most potential energy.

northeast Alberta. Microorganisms (which are abundant near the surface but absent at depth) began to consume the oil, particularly the lighter components, leaving degraded heavy bitumen.

Oil shale
Oil shale is sedimentary rock filled with kerogen that can be processed to produce a liquid form of petroleum called **shale oil.** Oil shale is formed by the same processes that form crude oil but occurs when kerogen was not buried deeply enough or subjected to enough heat and pressure to form oil.

Methane hydrate
Methane hydrate occurs in sediments in the Arctic and on the ocean floor. Also called *methane clathrate* or *methane ice*, this fossil fuel is an ice-like solid consisting of molecules of methane embedded in a crystal lattice of water molecules. Methane hydrate is stable at temperature and pressure conditions found in many sediments in the Arctic and on the seafloor. Most methane in these gas hydrates formed from bacterial decomposition in anaerobic environments, but some resulted from thermogenic formation deeper below the surface.

We mine and drill for fossil fuels

Because fossil fuels of each type form only under certain conditions, they occur in isolated deposits. For instance, oil and natural gas tend to rise upward through cracks and fissures in porous rock until meeting a dense impermeable rock layer that traps them. As a result, geologists search for fossil fuels by drilling cores and conducting ground, air, and seismic surveys to map underground rock formations. With knowledge of underground geology, they can predict where fossil fuel deposits might lie (see THE SCIENCE BEHIND THE STORY, pp. 438–439).

Once geologists have identified a promising location for a deposit of oil or natural gas, a company will typically conduct *exploratory drilling*, drilling small holes that descend to great depths. If enough oil or gas is encountered, extraction begins. Just as you would squeeze a sponge to remove its liquid, pressure is required to extract oil from porous rock. Oil is typically already under pressure—from above by rock or trapped gas, from below by groundwater, and at times internally from natural gas dissolved in the oil. All these forces are held in check by surrounding rock until drilling reaches the deposit, whereupon oil will often rise to the surface of its own accord. Once pressure is relieved and some oil or gas has risen to the surface, however, the remainder becomes more difficult to extract and needs to be pumped out.

Coal is a solid, and so we mine it rather than drilling for it. For coal deposits near the surface, we use *strip mining*, in which heavy machinery scrapes away huge amounts of earth to expose the coal. For deposits deep underground, we use *subsurface mining*, digging vertical shafts and blasting out networks of horizontal tunnels to follow seams, or layers, of coal. We are also now mining coal on immense scales in the Appalachian Mountains, essentially scraping off entire mountaintops in a process called *mountaintop removal mining.*

Oil from oil sands is extracted by two main methods. For deposits near the surface (FIGURE 15.8a), a process akin to strip mining for coal or open-pit mining for minerals is used. Shovel-trucks peel back layers of peat and soil and then dig out vast quantities of bitumen-soaked sand or clay. This is mixed with hot water and piped to an extraction facility, where sand sinks to the bottom of tanks while bitumen floats to the top. The bitumen is skimmed off, solvent is added, and the mixture is spun in a centrifuge to further purify the bitumen, which is then processed into crude oil. Three barrels of water are required to extract each barrel of oil, and the resulting toxic wastewater is discharged into vast tailings lakes.

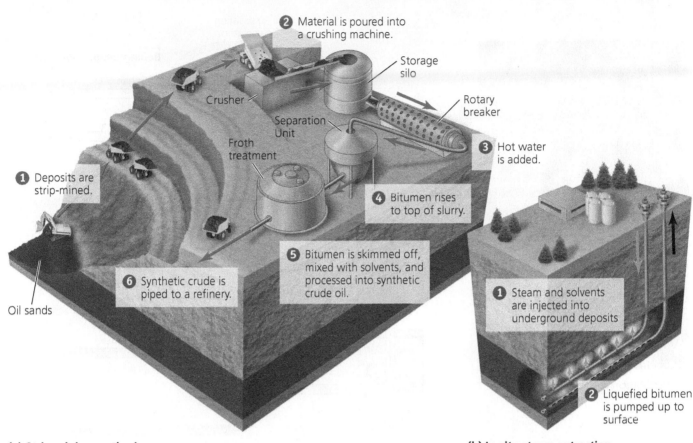

(a) Strip-mining method

(b) In-situ steam extraction

FIGURE 15.8 Oil sands are extracted by two processes. Near-surface deposits of oil sands **(a)** are strip-mined. The deposits are first dug out **1** with gigantic shovels and trucks and then poured into a crushing machine **2**. The material is then mixed with hot water **3**, and the slurry is piped to a facility where the bitumen floats in a froth atop water in a tank **4**, while sand and clay settle out. The bitumen froth is skimmed off, mixed with chemical solvents, and processed into synthetic crude oil **5**; it is then sent in a pipeline **6** to a refinery. Deeper deposits of oil sands **(b)** are extracted through well shafts. Pressurized steam is injected down the well **1** into the oil sand formation, liquefying the bitumen and allowing it to be pumped **2** to the surface.

Oil sands that are deeper underground (**FIGURE 15.8b**) are extracted by drilling shafts down to the deposit and injecting steam and solvents down to liquefy and isolate the bitumen in place, then pump it out. After extraction, the bitumen must be refined using chemical reactions that add hydrogen or remove carbon, thus upgrading it into more valuable synthetic crude oil (called *syncrude*).

We mine oil shale using strip mines or subsurface mines. Once mined, oil shale can be burned directly like coal, or it can be baked in the presence of hydrogen and in the absence of air to extract liquid petroleum (a process called *pyrolysis*).

Economics determines how much will be extracted

As we develop more powerful technologies for locating and extracting fossil fuels, the amounts of these fuels that are physically accessible to us—the "technically recoverable" amounts—tend to increase. However, whereas technology determines how much of a fossil fuel *can* be extracted, economics determines how much *will* be extracted. This is because extraction becomes increasingly costly as a resource is removed, so companies will not find it profitable to extract the entire amount. Instead, a company will consider the costs of extraction (and other expenses), and balance these against the income it expects from sale of the fuel. Because market prices of fuel fluctuate, the portion of fuel from a given deposit that is "economically recoverable" fluctuates as well. As market prices rise, economically recoverable amounts approach technically recoverable amounts.

The amount of a fossil fuel that is technologically and economically feasible to remove under current conditions is termed its **proven recoverable reserve.** Proven reserves increase as extraction technology improves or as market prices of the fuel rise. Proven reserves decrease as fuel deposits are depleted by extraction or as market prices fall (making extraction uneconomical).

Refining produces a diversity of fuels

Once we extract oil or gas, it must be processed and refined before we can use it. Let's examine what happens when crude

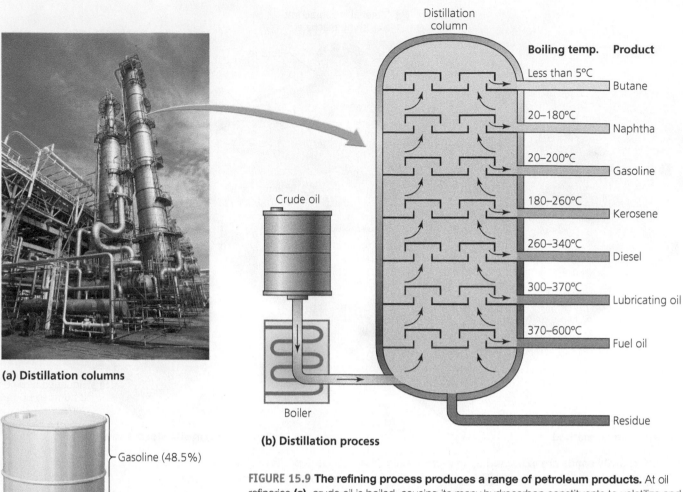

(a) Distillation columns

Crude oil

Distillation column

Boiling temp.	Product
Less than 5°C	Butane
20–180°C	Naphtha
20–200°C	Gasoline
180–260°C	Kerosene
260–340°C	Diesel
300–370°C	Lubricating oil
370–600°C	Fuel oil
	Residue

Boiler

(b) Distillation process

Gasoline (48.5%)

Diesel fuel and heating oil (24.1%)

Jet fuel (7.8%)

Liquefied petroleum gases (3.3%)

Heavy fuel oil (2.9%)

Other (13.4%)

(c) Typical composition of refined oil

FIGURE 15.9 The refining process produces a range of petroleum products. At oil refineries **(a)**, crude oil is boiled, causing its many hydrocarbon constituents to volatilize and proceed upward **(b)** through a distillation column. Constituents that boil at the hottest temperatures and condense readily once the temperature cools will condense at low levels in the column. Constituents that volatilize at cooler temperatures will continue rising through the column and condense at higher levels, where temperatures are cooler. In this way, heavy oils (generally those with hydrocarbon molecules with long carbon chains) are separated from lighter oils (generally those with short-chain hydrocarbon molecules). Shown in **(c)** are percentages of each major category of product typically generated from a barrel of crude oil. *Data (c) from U.S. Energy Information Administration, 2012. Annual energy review 2011.*

oil is shipped to a refinery (**FIGURE 15.9**). Because crude oil is a complex mix of hydrocarbons, we can create many types of petroleum products by separating its various components. The many types of hydrocarbon molecules in crude oil have carbon chains of different lengths. A chain's length affects its chemical properties, and this has consequences for our use, such as whether a given fuel burns cleanly in a car engine. Through the process of **refining,** hydrocarbon molecules are separated into different size classes and are chemically transformed to create specialized fuels for heating, cooking, and transportation, and to create lubricating oils, asphalts, and the precursors of plastics and other petrochemical products.

Fossil fuels have many uses

As we saw in Figure 15.3, each major type of fossil fuel has its own mix of uses. Let's survey how coal, oil, and natural gas each are used in our society today.

Coal People have burned coal to cook food, heat homes, and fire pottery for thousands of years and in many cultures, from ancient China to the Roman Empire to the Hopi Nation. Coal-fired steam engines helped drive the industrial revolution by powering factories, agriculture, trains, and ships, and by fueling the furnaces of the steel industry. Today we burn coal largely to generate electricity. In coal-fired power plants, coal combustion converts water to steam, which turns a turbine to create electricity (**FIGURE 15.10**). Coal provides 40% of the electrical generating capacity of the United States, and it powers China's surging economy. China is now the world's primary producer and consumer of coal (**TABLE 15.3**).

Natural gas Versatile and clean-burning, natural gas emits just half as much carbon dioxide per unit of energy produced as coal and two-thirds as much as oil. We use natural gas to generate electricity in power plants, to heat and cook in our homes, and for much else. Converted to a liquid

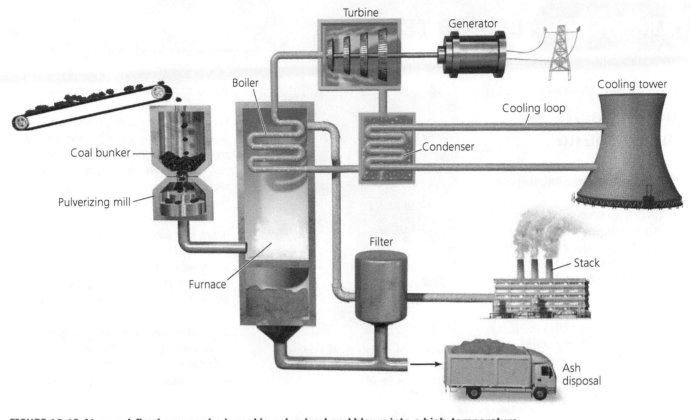

FIGURE 15.10 At a coal-fired power plant, coal is pulverized and blown into a high-temperature furnace. Heat from the combustion boils water, and the resulting steam turns a turbine, generating electricity by passing magnets past copper coils. The steam is then cooled and condensed in a cooling loop and returned to the furnace. "Clean coal" technologies (p. 445) help filter pollutants from the combustion process, and toxic ash residue is taken to hazardous waste disposal sites.

TABLE 15.3 Top Producers and Consumers of Fossil Fuels			
PRODUCTION (% world production)		**CONSUMPTION** (% world consumption)	
COAL			
China	49.5	China	49.4
United States	14.1	United States	13.5
Australia	5.8	India	7.9
India	5.6	Japan	3.2
Indonesia	5.1	South Africa	2.5
OIL			
Saudi Arabia	13.2	United States	20.5
Russia	12.8	China	11.4
United States	8.8	Japan	5.0
Iran	5.2	India	4.0
China	5.1	Russia	3.4
NATURAL GAS			
United States	20.0	United States	21.5
Russia	18.5	Russia	13.2
Canada	4.9	Iran	4.7
Iran	4.6	China	4.0
Qatar	4.5	Japan	3.3

Data from BP p.l.c., 2012. Statistical review of world energy 2012.

at low temperatures (*liquefied natural gas*, or *LNG*), it can be shipped long distances in refrigerated tankers. When we replace coal with natural gas to generate electricity, this cuts carbon emissions in half. For this reason, many energy experts view natural gas as a "bridge fuel"—a bridge leading from today's polluting fossil-fuel economy toward a clean renewable energy economy for the future. The United States and Russia lead the world in gas production and gas consumption (see Table 15.3).

Oil The modern use of oil for energy began after 1859, when the world's first oil well was drilled in Titusville, Pennsylvania. Over the next 40 years, Pennsylvania's oil fields produced half the world's oil supply and helped establish a fossil-fuel-based economy that would hold sway for decades to come.

Today our global society produces and consumes nearly 750 L (200 gal) of oil each year for every man, woman, and child. The majority is used as fuel for vehicles, including gasoline for cars, diesel for trucks, and jet fuel for airplanes. Fewer homes burn oil for heating these days, but industry and manufacturing still account for a great deal of oil use.

Over the past several decades, refining techniques and chemical manufacturing have greatly expanded our uses of petroleum to include a wide array of products and applications, from plastics to lubricants to fabrics to pharmaceuticals. In today's world, petroleum-based products are all around us

Locating Fossil Fuel Deposits Underground

Drilling for oil or gas is risky business: Most wells are unproductive, and a company that doesn't pick its spots effectively could soon go bankrupt. So oil and gas companies turn to scientists to help them figure out where to drill.

The industry employs petroleum geologists who study underground rock formations to predict where deposits of oil and natural gas might lie. Because the organic matter that gave rise to fossil fuels was buried in sediments, geologists know to look for sedimentary rock that may act as a source. They also know that oil and gas tends to seep upward through porous rock until being trapped by impermeable layers.

To map subsurface rock layers, petroleum geologists first survey the landscape on the ground and from airplanes, studying rocks on the surface. Because rock layers often become tilted over geologic time, these strata may protrude at the surface, giving geologists an informative "side-on" view.

But to really understand what's deep beneath the surface, scientists need to conduct seismic surveys. In seismic surveying, a base station creates powerful vibrations at the surface by exploding dynamite, thumping the ground with a large weight, or using an electric vibrating machine (FIGURE 1). This sends seismic waves down and outward in all directions through the ground, just as ripples spread when a pebble is dropped into a pond.

As they travel, the waves encounter layers of different types of rock. The waves travel more quickly through

Petroleum geologists study mapped seismic data to determine where oil or gas might be found.

denser rock. Each time a seismic wave encounters a new type of rock with a different density, some of the wave's energy is reflected off the boundary, and the rest passes through the boundary into the new layer. Some wave energy may be refracted, or bent, along the edge of the layer, sending refraction waves upward.

As reflected and refracted waves return to the surface, devices called seismometers (also used to measure earthquakes) record data on their strength and precise timing. Scientists collect data from seismometers at multiple surface locations and run the data through computer programs for analysis. By analyzing how long it takes all the reflected and refracted seismic waves to reach the various

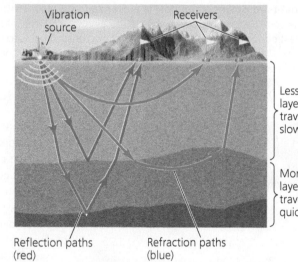

Reflection paths (red)

Refraction paths (blue)

FIGURE 1 Seismic surveying provides clues to the location and size of fossil fuel deposits. Powerful vibrations are created, and receivers measure how long it takes seismic waves to reach other locations. Waves travel more quickly through denser layers, and density differences cause waves to reflect or refract. Scientists interpret the patterns of wave reception to infer the densities, thicknesses, and locations of underlying rock layers.

---

in our everyday lives (FIGURE 15.11). The fact that petroleum is used to create so many items and materials we have come to rely on makes it vital that we take care to conserve our remaining oil reserves.

The United States consumes one-fifth of the world's oil, but rapidly industrializing populous nations such as China and India are increasingly driving world demand (see Table 15.3).

We are gradually depleting fossil fuel reserves

Because fossil fuels are nonrenewable, the total amount available on Earth declines as we use them. Many scientists and oil industry analysts calculate that we have already extracted half the world's conventional oil reserves. So far we have used up about 1.1 trillion barrels of oil, and most estimates hold that receiving stations, and how strong the waves are at each site, researchers can triangulate and infer the densities, thicknesses, and locations of underlying geologic layers.

Seismic surveying is similar to how we use sonar in water or how bats use echolocation as they fly. It is also used for finding coal deposits, salt and mineral deposits, and geothermal energy hotspots, as well as for studying faults, aquifers, and engineering sites.

Still, even with good survey data, oil companies may have only a 10% success rate in finding oil or gas. They need to conduct exploratory drilling to confirm whether oil or gas actually exists in any given location.

Using data from such techniques, geologists with the U.S. Geological Survey (USGS) in 1998 assessed the subsurface geology of the Arctic National Wildlife Refuge on Alaska's North Slope to predict how much oil it may hold (FIGURE 2). Over three years, dozens of scientists conducted fieldwork and combined their results with a reanalysis of 2300 km (1400 mi) of seismic survey data that industry had collected in the 1980s.

After studying their resulting subsurface maps, USGS scientists concluded, with 95% certainty, that between 11.6 and 31.5 billion barrels of oil lay underneath the region of the refuge that Congress has debated opening for drilling. The mean estimate of 20.7 billion barrels is enough to supply the United States for 3 years at its current rate of consumption.

However, some portion of oil from any deposit is impossible to extract using current technology, so geologists estimate "technically recoverable" amounts of fuels. In its estimate for

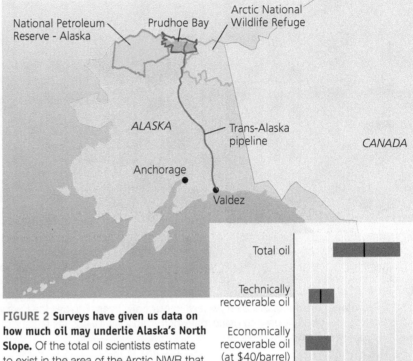

FIGURE 2 **Surveys have given us data on how much oil may underlie Alaska's North Slope.** Of the total oil scientists estimate to exist in the area of the Arctic NWR that may someday be opened to drilling, only some is technically recoverable, and less is economically recoverable. *Data from U.S. Geological Survey.*

the Arctic Refuge, the USGS calculated technically recoverable oil to total 4.3–11.8 billion barrels, with a mean estimate of 7.7 billion barrels (just over 1 year of U.S. consumption).

The portion of this oil that is "economically recoverable" depends on the costs of extracting it and the price of oil on the world market. USGS scientists calculated that at a price of $40 per barrel, 3.4–10.8 billion barrels would be economically worthwhile to recover. At today's much higher prices, the economically recoverable amount would be closer to the technically recoverable amount.

In 2002, the USGS conducted similar analyses for the National Petroleum Reserve–Alaska, a vast parcel of tundra to the west of the Arctic Refuge and Prudhoe Bay that the U.S. government set aside 90 years ago as an emergency reserve of petroleum. USGS scientists estimated that this region contained 9.3 billion barrels of technically recoverable oil.

Across the world, petroleum geologists are using similar methods to try to determine how much oil remains to extract. Their work is of vital importance as the world's nations struggle to pursue well-informed energy policies. ●

slightly more than 1 trillion barrels of proven reserves remain. Adding proven reserves of oil sands from Canada and Venezuela brings the total remaining to just over 1.6 trillion barrels.

To estimate how long this remaining oil will last, analysts calculate the **reserves-to-production ratio,** or **R/P ratio,** by dividing the amount of total remaining reserves by the annual rate of production (i.e., extraction and processing). At current levels of production (30 billion barrels globally per year),

1.6 trillion barrels would last about 54 more years. Applying the R/P ratio to natural gas, we find that the world's proven reserves of this resource would last 64 more years. For coal, the latest R/P ratio estimate is 112 years.

The true number of years remaining for these fuels may be less than these figures suggest, however, because our demand and production have been increasing, not constant. Yet at the same time, the true number of years may be *more*

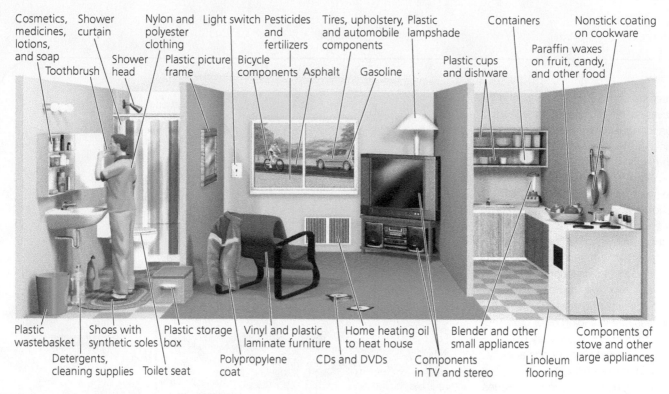

Cosmetics, medicines, lotions, and soap Shower curtain Toothbrush Shower head Nylon and polyester clothing Plastic picture frame Light switch Pesticides and fertilizers Bicycle components Asphalt Tires, upholstery, and automobile components Plastic lampshade Gasoline Plastic cups and dishware Containers Paraffin waxes on fruit, candy, and other food Nonstick coating on cookware

Plastic wastebasket Shoes with synthetic soles Detergents, cleaning supplies Plastic storage box Toilet seat Vinyl and plastic laminate furniture Polypropylene coat Home heating oil to heat house CDs and DVDs Blender and other small appliances Components in TV and stereo Linoleum flooring Components of stove and other large appliances

FIGURE 15.11 Petroleum products are everywhere in our daily lives. Besides the fuels we use for transportation and heating, petroleum is used to make many of the fabrics we wear, the materials we consume, and the plastics in countless items we use every day.

than these figures suggest, because proven reserves tend to increase as technology becomes more powerful and as market prices rise. Indeed, mining for oil sands and hydraulic fracturing for natural gas in recent years have increased the proven reserves of these fuels in North America substantially. In fact, advances in oil and gas extraction in the United States in the past several years have been so great that the International Energy Agency in 2012 predicted a resurgence would make the United States the world's biggest oil producer into the 2020s.

Regardless of how many years' worth of a resource we might calculate to be left, a society dependent on that resource will face a crisis not when the last bit of it is extracted from the ground, but rather once the rate of its production comes to a peak and begins to decline. In general, production of a resource tends to decline once reserves are depleted halfway. Past this production peak, if demand for the resource holds steady or continues to increase while production declines, a shortage will result. Many scientists and economists have been anxious about this phenomenon with oil, and the scenario has come to be nicknamed **peak oil.** Because we have already used roughly half of Earth's conventional oil reserves, many experts calculate that a peak oil crisis may well begin in the very near future.

Peak oil will pose challenges

To understand concerns about peak oil, we need to turn back the clock to 1956. In that year, Shell Oil geologist M. King Hubbert calculated that U.S. oil production would peak around 1970. His prediction was ridiculed at the time, but it proved to

be accurate; U.S. production peaked in that very year and has fallen since then (FIGURE 15.12a). The peak in production came to be known as **Hubbert's peak.**

In 1974, Hubbert analyzed data on technology, economics, and geology, and predicted that global oil production would peak in 1995. It grew past 1995, but many scientists using newer data today predict that at some point in the coming decade, production will begin to decline (FIGURE 15.12b). Discoveries of new oil fields peaked 30 years ago, and since then we have been extracting and consuming more oil than we have been discovering.

FAQ Why should I worry about "peak oil" if there are still years of oil left?

Bear in mind that the term *peak oil* doesn't refer to running out of oil. It refers to the point at which our production of oil comes to a peak. Once we pass this peak and production begins to decline, the economics of supply and demand take over. Supply will fall, with some estimates putting the decline at 5% per year. Demand, meanwhile, is forecast to continue rising, especially as China, India, and other industrializing nations put millions of new vehicles on the road. The resulting divergence of supply and demand would drive up oil prices, causing substantial economic ripple effects. Although high oil prices will provide financial incentive to develop alternative energy sources and better conservation measures, we may be challenged in a depressed economy to find adequate time and resources to develop new renewable sources.

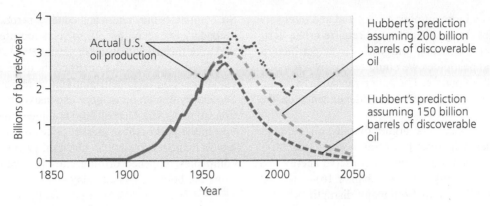

(a) Hubbert's prediction of peak in U.S. oil production, with actual data

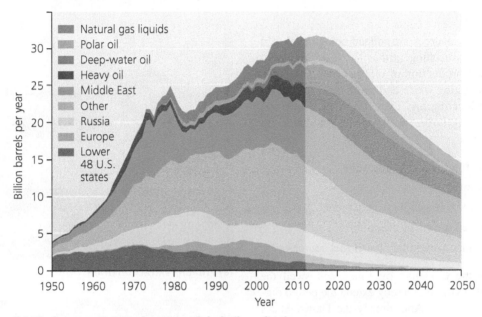

(b) Modern prediction of peak in global oil production

FIGURE 15.12 Peak oil describes a peak in production. U.S. oil production peaked in 1970 **(a)**, just as geologist M. King Hubbert had predicted. Since then, success in Alaska, in the Gulf of Mexico, and with secondary extraction has enhanced production during the decline. (Note that curves shift to the right and peaks increase in height as more oil is discovered.) Today U.S. oil production is spiking upward as deep offshore drilling and hydraulic fracturing make new deposits accessible. Still, some analysts believe global oil production will soon peak. Shown in **(b)** is one recent projection, from a 2011 analysis by scientists at the Association for the Study of Peak Oil. *Data from (a) Hubbert, M.K., 1956.* Nuclear energy and the fossil fuels. *Shell Development Co. Publ. No. 95, Houston, TX; and U.S. Energy Information Administration; and (b) Campbell, C.J., and Association for the Study of Peak Oil. By permission of Dr. Colin Campbell.*

Discovery or development of wholly new sources of oil can delay the peak by boosting our overall proven reserves. This is what is happening as we exploit Canada's oil sands. People counting on a series of new sources in the future tend to believe we can continue relying on oil for a long time, and this may indeed turn out to be the case. However, at some point we will reach peak oil—and peak gas and peak coal. The question is when—and whether we will be prepared to deal with the resulting challenges.

Predicting an exact date for peak oil is difficult. Many companies and governments do not reveal their true data on oil reserves, and estimates differ as to how much oil we can extract secondarily from existing deposits. Indeed, a recent

U.S. Geological Survey report estimated 2 trillion barrels of conventional oil remaining in the world, rather than 1 trillion, and some estimates predict still greater amounts. A 2007 report by the U.S. General Accounting Office reviewed 21 studies and found that most estimates for the timing of the oil production peak ranged from now through 2040.

Whenever it occurs, the divergence of supply and demand could have momentous economic, social, and political consequences that will profoundly affect our lives. One prophet of peak oil, writer James Howard Kunstler, has sketched a frightening scenario of our post-peak world during what he calls "the long emergency": Lacking cheap oil with which to transport goods long distances, today's globalized economy would collapse into a large number of isolated and intensely localized economies. Large cities would require urban agriculture to feed their residents, and with fewer petroleum-based fertilizers and pesticides we could feed only a fraction of the world's 7 billion people. The American suburbs would be hit particularly hard because of their dependence on the automobile.

More optimistic observers argue that as oil supplies dwindle, rising prices will create powerful incentives for businesses, governments, and individuals to conserve energy and to develop alternative energy sources (Chapter 16)—and that these developments will save us from major disruptions.

Or might we end up with "too much" fossil fuel energy?

Today renewable energy sources are indeed being developed faster—but we are also reaching farther for fossil fuels. To stave off the day when production of oil, gas, and coal begin to decline, we are investing more and more money, energy, and technology into locating and extracting new fossil fuel deposits. We are reaching further for fossil fuels by pursuing several main approaches:

- Secondary extraction from existing wells
- Hydraulic fracturing for oil and shale gas
- Offshore drilling in increasingly deep waters
- Moving into ice-free waters of the Arctic
- Exploiting new "unconventional" fossil fuel sources

Development of the Canadian oil sands will swell the amount of oil available to us and thereby extend the period during which we can rely on oil. And already the United States is seeing increased production from deep offshore drilling, hydraulic fracturing, and secondary extraction—so much so that energy experts now project that within a decade the United States may be exporting more oil than Saudi Arabia! As we extend our reach into less-accessible places to obtain fuel that is harder to extract, we expand our proven reserves and postpone the threat of peak production. However, we also reduce the EROI ratios of our fuels, drive up fuel prices for consumers, and intensify pollution and climate change. Indeed, the threat of climate change is serious enough that some scientists are beginning to wonder if we should plan to intentionally leave most oil, gas, and coal in the ground.

In the long term, to achieve a sustainable society we will need to switch to renewable energy sources. Investments in energy efficiency and conservation (pp. 454–456) are vital because they extend the time we have to make this transition.

Secondary extraction produces more fuel

One way we are reaching further for fossil fuels is by returning to sites where we have already removed easily accessible oil or gas and applying new technology or approaches to extract the remaining amounts. At a typical oil or gas well, as much as two-thirds of a deposit may remain in the ground after **primary extraction,** the initial drilling and pumping of oil or gas (FIGURE 15.13a).

So, companies may return and conduct **secondary extraction.** In secondary extraction for oil, solvents are used or underground rocks are flushed with water or steam (FIGURE 15.13b).

Even after secondary extraction, quite a bit of oil or gas can remain; we lack the technology to remove every last drop. Secondary extraction is more expensive than primary extraction, so many U.S. deposits did not undergo secondary extraction in the past because market prices of oil and gas were too low to make it economical. Once oil prices rose in the 1970s, companies reopened drilling sites for secondary extraction. More are being reopened today.

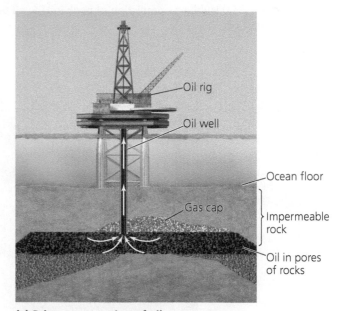

(a) Primary extraction of oil

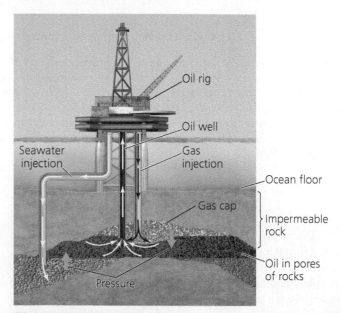

(b) Secondary extraction of oil

FIGURE 15.13 Secondary extraction removes oil not removed by primary extraction. In primary extraction **(a)**, oil is drawn up through a well by keeping pressure at the top lower than pressure at the bottom. Once pressure in the deposit drops, however, material must be injected to increase the pressure. Secondary extraction **(b)** involves injecting seawater beneath the oil and/or injecting gases just above the oil to force more oil up and out of the deposit.

Hydraulic fracturing expands our access to oil and gas

For oil and for natural gas trapped tightly in impermeable shale deposits, we are now using **hydraulic fracturing** to break into rock formations and pump the oil or gas to the surface. Hydraulic fracturing (also called *hydrofracking*, or *fracking*) is being used for secondary extraction and also to tap into new deposits. This technique involves pumping chemically treated water under high pressure into deep layers of shale to crack them. Sand or small glass beads are inserted to hold the cracks open as the water is withdrawn. Gas or oil then travels upward, with pressure and pumping, through the newly created system of fractures.

Hydraulic fracturing allows us to extract gas and oil that is so dispersed through shale formations that it cannot be pumped out by standard drilling. By making formerly inaccessible deposits accessible, hydrofracking has raised proven reserves and has ignited a boom in natural gas extraction in the United States. Natural gas prices have fallen, and gas usage in the United States has risen.

Fracking has engendered debate among people living in each area where it has occurred (FIGURE 15.14). For example, hydrofracking of the massive Marcellus Shale deposit is affecting the landscapes, economies, politics, and everyday lives of people in Pennsylvania, New York, and neighboring states. The choices people face between financial gain and impacts to their health, drinking water, and environment have been dramatized in popular films such as *Promised Land* and *Gasland*. As with Alberta's oil sands, and like all energy booms before it, today's natural gas rush brings jobs and money to small towns but can also spark social upheaval and leave communities with a legacy of pollution.

We are drilling farther and farther offshore

Today we drill for oil and natural gas not only on land but also below the seafloor on the continental shelves. Offshore drilling platforms must withstand wind, waves, and ocean currents. Some are fixed, standing platforms built with unusual strength. Others are resilient floating platforms anchored in place above the drilling site. Roughly 35% of the oil and 10% of the natural gas extracted in the United States today comes from offshore sites, primarily in the Gulf of Mexico and secondarily off southern California. The Gulf today is home to 90 drilling rigs and 3500 production platforms. Geologists estimate that most U.S. gas and oil remaining to be extracted occurs offshore and that deepwater sites in the Gulf of Mexico alone may hold 59 billion barrels of oil.

We have been drilling in shallow water for several decades, but as oil and gas are depleted at shallow-water sites and as drilling technology improves, the industry is moving into deeper and deeper water. This poses risks; the *Deepwater Horizon* oil spill of 2010 (pp. 446–449) occurred at a deepwater site. In that event, faulty equipment allowed natural gas accompanying the oil deposit to shoot up the well shaft. It ignited atop the platform, killing 11 workers and leading to

FIGURE 15.14 Hydraulic fracturing is expanding U.S. production of oil and natural gas, but it is sparking debates within communities where it is taking place. This drill rig is hydrofracking a shale formation on private land among homes in the rural Hopewell Township of Pennsylvania. Here, some residents support drilling and hope for financial benefits whereas others oppose drilling and fear contamination of their drinking water and damage to their quality of life.

the largest accidental oil spill in history. British Petroleum's Macondo well, where the accident took place, lay beneath 1500 m (5000 ft) of water. The deepest wells in the Gulf of Mexico are now twice that depth.

Globally, recent discoveries off the coasts of Brazil, Angola, Nigeria, and other nations suggest that a great deal of oil and gas could lie well offshore, and companies are racing one another to get there. Unfortunately, our ability to drill in deep water has outpaced our capacity to deal with accidents there. The fact that it took 86 days for BP to plug the leak at its Macondo well demonstrates the challenge of addressing an emergency situation a mile or more beneath the surface of the sea.

Today all eyes are on the Arctic. As global climate change melts the sea ice that covers the Arctic Ocean new shipping lanes are opening and nations and companies are scrambling to lay claim to patches of ocean that could hold fossil fuels and other resources. The oil and gas industry plans to drill offshore in deep water—something that has environmental advocates very worried. The Arctic's frigid temperatures, ice floes, winds, waves, and brutal storms make conditions harsh and challenging and make accidents more likely.

In 2008, responding to rising gasoline prices and a desire to lessen dependence on foreign oil, the U.S. Congress lifted a long-standing moratorium on offshore drilling along much of the nation's coastline. The Obama administration in 2010 followed through by designating vast areas open for drilling that had formerly been closed. These included most waters along the Atlantic coast from Delaware south to central Florida, a region of the eastern Gulf of Mexico, and most waters off Alaska's North Slope. However, just weeks after this announcement, the *Deepwater Horizon* spill occurred. Public reaction forced the Obama administration to backtrack, canceling offshore drilling projects it had approved and putting a hold on further approvals until new safety measures could be devised.

In 2011, after weighing economic and environmental concerns, the administration issued a five-year plan that opened access to 75% of technically recoverable offshore oil and gas reserves while banning drilling offshore from states that did not want it. Drilling leases were expanded off Alaska and in the Gulf of Mexico, but areas along the East and West Coasts were not opened to drilling.

The risks from expansion into Arctic waters were highlighted in 2012–2013, when Royal Dutch Shell's *Kulluk* drilling rig ran aground while being towed south from Alaska during a winter storm. Damage to the rig and examination by public officials and the media raised fresh questions as to whether Arctic Ocean drilling can be conducted safely.

We are exploiting new fossil fuel sources

As sources of conventional fossil fuels decline and as prices rise, we will turn increasingly to newer alternatives. These include at least three further sources of fossil fuels that exist in large amounts: oil sands, oil shale, and methane hydrate. The oil sands of Alberta—and those in Venezuela, which likely hold even more oil—are already significantly increasing the amount of oil available to our society. Oil from shale is not yet economical to extract. Gas from methane hydrate is only now becoming technically feasible to extract.

The world's known deposits of oil shale may contain as much as 3 trillion barrels of oil (more than all the conventional crude oil in the world), but most of this will not easily be extracted. About 40% of global oil shale reserves are in the United States, mostly on federally owned land in Colorado, Wyoming, and Utah. Shale oil is costly to extract, and its EROI is very low, with the best estimates ranging from just 1.1:1 to 4:1. Historically, low prices for crude oil have kept investors away from shale oil, but every time crude oil prices rise, shale oil again attracts attention.

As for methane hydrate, scientists believe there are immense amounts of this substance on Earth, holding perhaps twice as much carbon as all known deposits of oil, coal, and natural gas combined. Japan recently showed that it could extract methane hydrate from the seafloor by sending down a pipe and lowering pressure within it so that the methane turned to gas and rose to the surface. However, we do not yet know whether such extraction is safe and reliable. Destabilizing a methane hydrate deposit on the seafloor during extraction could lead to a catastrophic release of gas. This could cause a massive landslide and tsunami and would release huge amounts of methane, a potent greenhouse gas, into the atmosphere, worsening global climate change.

Oil sands, oil shale, and methane hydrate are abundant, but they are no panacea for our energy challenges. For one thing, their net energy values are low, because they are expensive to extract and process. Thus, their EROI ratios are low. Moreover, these fuels exert severe environmental impacts. We will now turn to some of the impacts of our fossil fuel use—environmental, economic, social, and political—and examine potential solutions to these impacts.

Addressing Impacts of Fossil Fuel Use

Our society's love affair with fossil fuels and the many petrochemical products we develop from them has helped to ease constraints on travel, lengthen our life spans, and boost our material standard of living beyond what our ancestors could have dreamed. However, it also causes harm to the environment and human health, and can lead to political and economic instability. Concern over these impacts is a prime reason many scientists, environmental advocates, businesspeople, and policymakers are increasingly looking toward clean and renewable sources of energy.

Fossil fuel emissions pollute air and drive climate change

When we burn fossil fuels, we alter fluxes in Earth's carbon cycle (pp.35–37). We essentially take carbon that has been retired into a long-term reservoir underground and release it into the air. This occurs as carbon from the hydrocarbon molecules of fossil fuels unites with oxygen from the atmosphere during combustion, producing carbon dioxide (CO_2). Carbon dioxide is a greenhouse gas, and CO_2 released from fossil fuel combustion warms our planet and drives changes in global climate.

Because global climate change is beginning to have diverse, severe, and widespread ecological and socioeconomic impacts, carbon dioxide pollution (FIGURE 15.15) is becoming recognized as the greatest environmental impact of fossil fuel use. Moreover, methane is a potent greenhouse gas that drives climate warming. Switching to new fossil fuel sources may

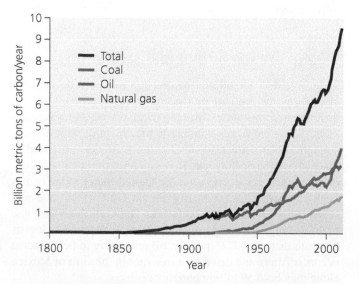

FIGURE 15.15 **Emissions from fossil fuel combustion have risen dramatically as nations have industrialized and as population and consumption have grown.** Here, global emissions of carbon from carbon dioxide are subdivided by source (oil, coal, or natural gas). *Data from Carbon Dioxide Information Analysis Center, Oak Ridge National Laboratory, U.S. Department of Energy, Oak Ridge, TN.*

DATA Q By what percentage have carbon emissions risen since the year your mother or father was born?

only make emissions worse; oil sands are estimated to generate 14–20% more greenhouse gas emissions than conventional oil, and shale oil is still more polluting.

Besides modifying our climate, fossil fuel emissions affect human health. Combusting coal high in mercury content emits mercury that can bioaccumulate in organisms' tissues, poisoning animals as it moves up food chains and presenting health risks to people. Gasoline combustion in automobiles releases pollutants that irritate the nose, throat, and lungs. Some hydrocarbons, such as benzene and toluene, cause cancer in laboratory animals and likely in people. Gases such as hydrogen sulfide can evaporate from crude oil, irritate the eyes and throat, and cause asphyxiation. Crude oil also often contains trace amounts of known poisons such as lead and arsenic. As a result, workers at drilling operations, refineries, and in other jobs that entail frequent exposure to oil or its products can develop serious health problems, including cancer.

The combustion of oil in our vehicles and coal in our power plants releases sulfur dioxide and nitrogen oxides, which contribute to industrial and photochemical smog and to acid deposition. Fossil fuel pollution is intensifying in developing nations that are industrializing rapidly as they grow in population. In contrast, air pollution from fossil fuel combustion has been reduced in developed nations in recent decades as a result of laws such as the U.S. Clean Air Act and government regulations to protect public health. In these nations, public policy has encouraged industry to develop and install technologies that reduce pollution, such as catalytic converters that cleanse vehicle exhaust. Wider adoption of such technologies in the developing world would reduce pollution there considerably.

Clean coal technologies aim to reduce air pollution from coal

Burning coal emits a variety of pollutants unless effective pollution control measures are in place. The composition of emissions from coal combustion depends on chemical impurities in the coal, and coal deposits vary in the impurities they contain, including sulfur, mercury, arsenic, and other trace metals. Coal from the eastern United States tends to be high in sulfur because it was formed in marine sediments, and sulfur is present in seawater. Most coal in China is even more sulfur-rich.

At coal-fired power plants, scientists and engineers are seeking ways to cleanse coal of sulfur, mercury, and other impurities. **Clean coal technologies** refer to an array of techniques, equipment, and approaches that aim to remove chemical contaminants during the process of generating electricity from coal. Among these technologies are various types of scrubbers, devices that chemically convert or physically remove pollutants. Some scrubbers use minerals such as magnesium, sodium, or calcium in reactions to remove sulfur dioxide (SO_2) from smokestack emissions. Others use chemical reactions to strip away nitrogen oxides (NO_x), breaking them down into elemental nitrogen and water. Multilayered filtering devices are used to capture tiny ash particles.

Another clean coal approach is to dry coal that has high water content in order to make it cleaner-burning. We can also gain more power from coal with less pollution through a process called *gasification*, in which coal is converted into a cleaner synthesis gas, or *syngas*, by reacting it with oxygen and steam at a high temperature. In an "integrated gasification combined cycle" process, syngas from coal is used to turn a gas turbine and also to heat water to turn a steam turbine.

The U.S. government and the coal industry have each invested billions of dollars in clean coal technologies for new power plants, and these have helped to reduce air pollution from sulfates, nitrogen oxides, mercury, and particulate matter. If these technologies were applied to the many older plants that still pollute our air, they could help even more. At the same time, the coal industry spends a great deal of money fighting regulations and mandates on its practices. As a result, many power plants are built with few clean coal technologies, and these plants will continue polluting our air for decades. Moreover, many energy analysts emphasize that these technologies may make for "cleaner" coal but will never result in energy production that is completely clean. Some argue that coal is an inherently dirty way of generating power and should be replaced outright with cleaner energy sources.

Can we capture and store carbon?

Even if clean coal technologies were able to remove every last chemical contaminant from power plant emissions, coal combustion would still pump huge amounts of carbon dioxide (CO_2) into the air, intensifying the greenhouse effect and worsening global climate change. This is why many current efforts focus on **carbon capture** followed by **carbon storage** or **carbon sequestration**. This approach consists of capturing carbon dioxide emissions, converting the gas to a liquid form, and then sequestering (storing) it in the ocean or underground in a geologically stable rock formation (FIGURE 15.16).

Carbon capture and storage (abbreviated as CCS) is being attempted at a variety of new and retrofitted facilities. The world's first coal-fired power plant to approach zero emissions opened in 2008 in Germany. This Swedish-built plant removes its sulfate pollutants and captures its carbon dioxide, then compresses the CO_2 into liquid form, trucks it 160 km (100 mi) away, and injects it 900 m (3000 ft) underground into a depleted natural gas field.

In North Dakota, the Great Plains Synfuels Plant gasifies its coal, then sends half the CO_2 through a pipeline into Canada, where a Canadian oil company buys the gas to inject into an oilfield to help it pump out the remaining oil. The North Dakota plant also captures, isolates, and sells seven other types of gases for various purposes.

Currently the U.S. Department of Energy is teaming up with seven energy companies to build a prototype of a near-zero-emissions coal-fired power plant. The $1.3-billion *FutureGen* project aims to design, construct, and operate a power plant that burns coal, produces electricity, captures 90% of its carbon dioxide emissions, and sequesters the CO_2 underground. The project, located in Meredosia, Illinois, will pump CO_2 more than 1200 m (three-quarters of a mile) underground beneath layers of impermeable rock. If this showcase project succeeds, it could be a model for a new generation of power plants across the world.

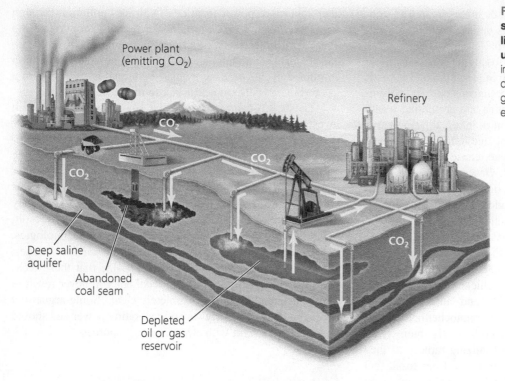

Power plant (emitting CO_2)

Refinery

CO_2

CO_2

CO_2

CO_2

Deep saline aquifer

Abandoned coal seam

Depleted oil or gas reservoir

At this point, however, carbon capture and storage is too unproven to be the central focus of a clean energy strategy. We do not know whether we can ensure that carbon dioxide will stay underground once injected there or whether these attempts might trigger earthquakes. Injection might in some cases contaminate groundwater supplies, and injecting carbon dioxide into the ocean would further acidify its waters. Moreover, CCS is energy-intensive and decreases the EROI of coal, adding to its cost and the amount we consume. Finally, many renewable energy advocates fear that the CCS approach takes the burden off emitters and prolongs our dependence on fossil fuels rather than facilitating a shift to renewables.

WEIGHING THE ISSUES

CLEAN COAL AND CARBON CAPTURE Do you think we should be spending billions of dollars to try to find ways to burn coal cleanly and to sequester carbon emissions from fossil fuels? Or is our money better spent on developing new clean and renewable energy sources that don't yet have enough infrastructure to produce power at the scale that coal can? What pros and cons do you see in each approach?

Oil spills pollute oceans and coasts

Of the many ways that our fossil fuel use pollutes water, what comes to mind most readily for people is the pollution that occurs when oil from tanker ships or drilling platforms fouls coastal waters and beaches. In 2010, BP's *Deepwater Horizon* offshore drilling platform exploded and sank off the coast of Louisiana (FIGURE 15.17). Eleven workers were killed, and oil gushed out of a broken pipe on the ocean floor a mile beneath the surface at a rate of 62,000 barrels per day. Emergency

shut-off systems had failed, and BP engineers tried one solution after another to stop the flow of oil and gas, which continued for three months, spilling roughly 4.9 million barrels (206 million gallons) of oil.

The crisis proved difficult to control because we had never had to deal with a spill so deep underwater. It revealed that offshore drilling presents serious risks of environmental impact that may be difficult to address, even with our best engineering.

As the oil spread through the Gulf of Mexico and washed ashore, the region suffered a wide array of impacts (FIGURE 15.18). Of the countless animals killed, most conspicuous were birds, which cannot regulate their body temperature once their feathers become coated with oil. However, the underwater nature of the BP spill meant that unknown numbers of fish, shrimp, corals,

FIGURE 15.17 **The explosion on BP's *Deepwater Horizon* drilling platform in 2010 unleashed the world's biggest-ever accidental oil spill.** Here vessels try to put out the blaze.

(a) Brown pelican coated in oil

(b) Beach cleanup

FIGURE 15.18 Impacts of the *Deepwater Horizon* spill were numerous and severe. This brown pelican, coated in oil **(a)**, was one of countless animals killed. For months, volunteers and workers paid by BP labored **(b)** to clean oil from the Gulf's beaches.

and other marine animals were also killed, affecting coastal and ocean ecosystems in complex ways. Plants in coastal marshes died, and the resulting erosion of marshes put New Orleans and other coastal cities at greater risk from storm surges and flooding. Gulf Coast fisheries, which supply much of the nation's seafood, were hit hard by the spill, with thousands of fishermen and shrimpers put out of work. Beach tourism suffered, and indirect economic and social impacts were expected to last for years. Throughout this process, scientists have been studying aspects of the spill and its impact on the region's people and natural systems (see THE SCIENCE BEHIND THE STORY, pp. 448–449).

The *Deepwater Horizon* spill was the largest accidental oil spill in world history, far eclipsing the spill from the *Exxon Valdez* tanker in 1989. In that event, oil from Alaska's North Slope, piped to the port of Valdez through the trans-Alaska pipeline, caused long-term damage to ecosystems and economies in Alaska's Prince William Sound when the tanker ran aground. Two-and-a-half decades later, a layer of oil remains just inches beneath the sand of the region's beaches.

Today as climate change melts sea ice in the Arctic, opening new shipping lanes, nations are jockeying for position, hoping to stake claim to oil and gas deposits that lie beneath the seafloor. Offshore drilling in Arctic waters, however, poses severe pollution risks, because if a spill were to occur, icebergs, pack ice, storms, cold temperatures, and wintertime darkness would hamper response efforts, while frigid water temperatures would slow the natural breakdown of oil. In U.S. Arctic waters that are now open to oil and gas leasing, some sites are 1000 miles away from the nearest Coast Guard station. The Obama administration approved these leases despite admitting that infrastructure to respond to a major spill there does not exist. Natural Resources Defense Council president Frances Beinecke, a member of the commission Obama set up to draw lessons from the BP spill, called such Arctic leases a "reckless gamble" and lamented that neither the

administration, Congress, nor industry had improved safety measures in any meaningful way since the BP spill.

Fortunately, pollution from large spills has decreased greatly in recent decades thanks to government regulations (such as requirements for double-hulled ships) and improved spill response efforts. And although large catastrophic oil spills have significant impacts on the marine environment, it is important to recognize that most water pollution from oil results from countless small non-point sources to which all of our actions contribute. Oil from automobiles, homes, industries, gas stations, and businesses runs off roadways and enters rivers and wastewater facilities, being discharged eventually into the ocean. Oil can also contaminate groundwater supplies when pipelines rupture or when underground storage tanks containing petroleum products leak. In addition, atmospheric deposition of pollutants from the combustion of fossil fuels exerts many impacts on freshwater ecosystems. Water pollution from industrial point sources has been greatly reduced in the United States following the Clean Water Act, and many solutions exist to address non-point-source pollution.

Hydrofracking poses new concerns

Extracting oil or natural gas by hydraulic fracturing (in which chemicals are mixed with the pressurized water and sand that is injected deep underground) presents risks of water pollution that are not yet completely understood. One risk is that the chemicals (often called fracking fluids) may leak out of the drilling shafts and into aquifers that people use for drinking water. Another concern is that methane may contaminate groundwater used for drinking if it travels up the fractures or leaks through the shaft.

Fracking sites also create air pollution as methane and volatile toxic components of fracking fluids seep up from drilling locations. In fact, some of the unhealthiest air pollution in

Discovering Impacts of the Gulf Oil Spill

President Barack Obama echoed the perceptions of many Americans when he called the *Deepwater Horizon* oil spill "the worst environmental disaster America has ever faced." But what has scientific research told us about the actual impacts of the Gulf oil spill?

We don't yet have all the answers, because the deep waters affected by the spill have been difficult for scientists to study. A great deal will remain unknown. Yet the intense and focused scientific response to the spill demonstrates the dynamic way in which science can assist society.

As the spill took place, government agencies called on scientists to help determine how much oil was leaking. Researchers eventually determined the rate reached 62,000 barrels per day. Using underwater imaging, aerial surveys, and shipboard water samples, researchers tracked the movement of oil up through the water column and across the Gulf. These data helped predict when and where oil might reach shore, thereby helping to direct prevention and cleanup efforts.

Meanwhile, as engineers struggled to seal off the well using remotely operated submersibles, researchers helped government agencies assess the fate of the oil (**FIGURE 1**). This data would help inform studies of the oil's impacts on marine life and human communities.

Tracking movement of the oil underwater was challenging. University of Georgia biochemist Mandy Joye, who had studied natural seeps in the Gulf for years, documented that the leaking wellhead was creating a plume of oil the size of Manhattan. She also found evidence of low oxygen concentrations, or hypoxia (pp. 19), because some bacteria consume oil and gas, depleting oxygen from the water and making it uninhabitable for fish and other creatures.

Joye and other researchers feared that the thinly dispersed oil might prove devastating to plankton (the base of the marine food chain) and to the tiny larvae of shrimp, fish, and oysters (the pillars of the fishing industry). Scientists taking water samples documented sharp drops in plankton during the spill, but it will take several years to

A scientist rescues an oiled Kemp's ridley sea turtle.

learn whether the impact on larvae will diminish populations of adult fish and shellfish. Studies on the condition of living fish in the region are now being published, some of which show gill damage, tail rot, lesions, and reproductive problems at much higher levels than is typical.

What was happening to life on the seafloor was a mystery, because there are only a handful of submersible vehicles in the world able to travel to the crushing pressures of the deep sea. Luckily, a team of researchers led by Charles Fisher of Penn State University was scheduled to embark on a regular survey of deepwater coral across the Gulf of Mexico in late 2010. Using the three-person submersible *Alvin* and the robotic vehicles *Jason* and *Sentry*, the team found healthy coral communities at sites far away from the Macondo well but found dying corals and brittlestars covered in a brown material at a site 11 km from the Macondo well.

Eager to determine whether this community was contaminated by the BP oil spill, the research team added chemist Helen White of Haverford College and returned a month later, thanks to a National Science Foundation program that funds rapid response research. On this trip, chemical analysis of the brown material showed it to match oil from the BP spill, rather than from any other known source.

Other questions revolve around impacts of the chemical dispersant that BP used to break up the oil, a compound called Corexit 9500. Work by biologist Philippe Bodin following

FIGURE 1 Scientists helped track oil from the *Deepwater Horizon* spill. The map **(a)** shows areas polluted by oil. The pie chart **(b)** gives a breakdown of the oil's fate. *Source (a): National Geographic and NOAA; (b) NOAA.*

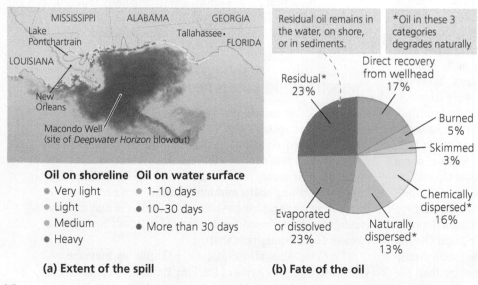

Oil on shoreline
- Very light
- Light
- Medium
- Heavy

Oil on water surface
- 1–10 days
- 10–30 days
- More than 30 days

(a) Extent of the spill

Residual oil remains in the water, on shore, or in sediments.

*Oil in these 3 categories degrades naturally

- Residual* 23%
- Direct recovery from wellhead 17%
- Burned 5%
- Skimmed 3%
- Chemically dispersed* 16%
- Naturally dispersed* 13%
- Evaporated or dissolved 23%

(b) Fate of the oil

the *Amoco Cadiz* oil spill in France in 1978 had found that Corexit 9500 appeared more toxic to marine life than the oil itself. BP threw an unprecedented amount of the chemical at the *Deepwater Horizon* spill, injecting a great deal directly into the path of the oil at the wellhead. This caused the oil to dissociate into trillions of tiny droplets that dispersed across large regions. Many scientists worried that this expanded the oil's reach, affecting more plankton, larvae, and fish.

Impacts of the oil on birds, sea turtles, and marine mammals were easier to assess. Officially confirmed deaths numbered 6104 birds, 605 turtles, and 97 mammals—and hundreds more animals were cleaned and saved by wildlife rescue teams—but a much larger, unknown, number succumbed to the oil. What impacts this mortality may have on populations in coming years is unclear. (After the *Exxon Valdez* spill in Alaska in 1989, populations of some species rebounded, but populations of others have never come back.) Researchers are following the movements of marine animals in the Gulf with radio transmitters to try to learn what effects the oil may have had.

As images of oil-coated marshes saturated the media, researchers worried that widespread death of marsh grass would leave the shoreline vulnerable to severe erosion by waves. Louisiana has already lost many coastal wetlands to subsidence, dredging, sea level rise, and silt capture by dams on the Mississippi River. Fortunately, researchers found that oil did not penetrate to the roots of most plants and that oiled grasses were sending up new growth. Indeed, Louisiana State University researcher Eugene Turner said that loss of marshland from the oil "pales in comparison" with marshland lost each year due to other factors.

The ecological impacts of the spill had measurable impacts on people. The region's mighty fisheries were shut down, forcing thousands of fishermen out of work. The government tested fish and shellfish for contamination and reopened fishing once they were found to be safe, but consumers balked at buying Gulf seafood. Beach tourism remained low all summer as visitors avoided the region. Together, losses in fishing and tourism totaled billions of dollars.

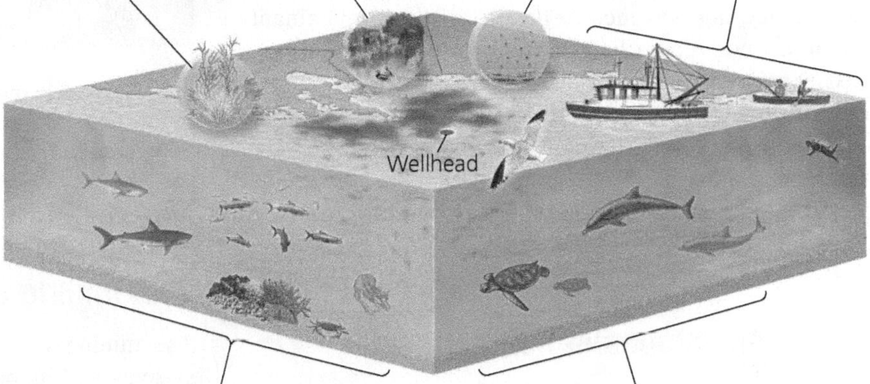

Scientists expect some impacts from the Gulf spill to be long-lasting. Oil from the similar *Ixtoc* blowout off Mexico's coast in 1979 still lies in sediments near dead coral reefs, and fishermen there say it took 15–20 years for catches to return to normal. After the *Amoco Cadiz* spill, it took seven years for oysters and other marine species to recover. In Alaska, oil from the *Exxon Valdez* spill remains embedded in beach sand today.

However, many researchers are hopeful about the Gulf of Mexico's recovery from the *Deepwater Horizon* spill. The Gulf's warm waters and sunny climate speed the natural breakdown of oil. In hot sunlight, volatile components of oil evaporate from the surface and degrade in the water, so that fewer toxic compounds such as benzene, naphthalene, and toluene reach marine life.

In addition, bacteria that consume hydrocarbons thrive in the Gulf because some oil has always seeped naturally from the seafloor and because leakage from platforms, tankers, and pipelines is common. These microbes give the region a natural self-cleaning capacity.

Researchers continue to conduct a wide range of scientific studies (FIGURE 2). A consortium of federal and state agencies is coordinating research and restoration efforts in the largest ever Natural Resource Damage Assessment, a process mandated under the Oil Pollution Act of 1990. Answers to questions will come in gradually as long-term impacts become clear. ●

SHORELINES
- Air and ground surveys
- Habitat assessment
- Measurements of subsurface oil

WATER COLUMN AND SEDIMENTS
- Water quality surveys
- Sediment sampling
- Transect surveys to detect oil
- Oil plume modeling

AQUATIC VEGETATION
- Air and coastal surveys

HUMAN USE
- Air and ground surveys

Wellhead

FISH, SHELLFISH, AND CORALS
- Population monitoring of adults and larvae
- Surveys of food supply (plankton and invertebrates)
- Tissue collection and sediment sampling
- Testing for contaminants

BIRDS, TURTLES, MARINE MAMMALS
- Air, land, and boat surveys
- Radiotelemetry, satellite tagging, and acoustic monitoring
- Tissue sampling
- Habitat assessment

FIGURE 2 Thousands of researchers continue to help assess damage to natural resources from the *Deepwater Horizon* oil spill. They are surveying habitats, collecting samples and testing them in the lab, tracking wildlife, monitoring populations, and more.

the United States was found to be far away from the nearest city, in a little-populated region of Wyoming home to extensive fracking operations.

Many residents of areas near hydraulic fracturing sites have experienced polluted air and fouled drinking water but more research is needed to assess the extent of such pollution and to quantify the health risks.

Hydrofracking also produces immense volumes of wastewater. Injected water often returns to the surface laced with salts, radioactive elements such as radium, and toxic chemicals such as benzene that come from deep underground. This wastewater is often sent to sewage treatment plants that are not designed to handle all the contaminants and that do not regularly test for radioactivity. This has caused concern in Pennsylvania, where a boom in natural gas extraction from the vast Marcellus Shale deposit continues to send millions of gallons of drilling waste to treatment plants, which then release their water into rivers that supply drinking water for people in Pittsburgh, Harrisburg, and other cities.

Oil sands development pollutes water

Similar concerns are being voiced about the extraction and transport of oil from oil sands. People living along the route of the Keystone XL pipeline worry that if oil were to spill from a leak in the pipeline, it would sink into the area's porous ground and quickly reach the region's shallow water table, contaminating the Ogallala Aquifer. This aquifer provides 2 million Americans with drinking water and irrigates a large portion of U.S. agriculture. The pipeline was originally slated to cross the Sandhills region of Nebraska, an ecologically valuable area that hosts most of the world's Sandhill cranes as well as other migratory birds. At the behest of government regulators, TransCanada agreed to move the proposed route eastward to skirt around the edge of the Sandhills region and the Ogallala Aquifer.

Pipeline leaks are a legitimate concern, as oil from oil sands is more corrosive than conventional crude oil. Recent leaks along the Kalamazoo River in Michigan, in a residential neighborhood of Mayflower, Arkansas, and in other locations have caused severe contamination.

In Alberta where the oil sands are mined, the process uses immense amounts of water, and the polluted wastewater that results is left to sit in gigantic reservoirs. The Syncrude company's massive tailings pond near Fort McMurray, Alberta, is so large that it is held back by the world's second-largest dam. Migratory waterfowl land on water bodies like this and are killed as the oily water gums up their feathers and impairs their ability to insulate themselves. These water pollution impacts come on top of the deforestation required to mine the fuels in the first place.

Industry representatives counter that the area deforested so far amounts to just 0.1% of Canada's vast boreal forest. They also point out they are mandated to attempt restoration afterwards. However, effective reclamation has not yet been demonstrated, and regions denuded by the very first oil sand mine in Alberta 30 years ago have still not recovered.

FIGURE 15.19 In mountaintop removal mining for coal, entire mountain peaks are leveled and fill is dumped into adjacent valleys, as shown here over many square miles in West Virginia. This can cause erosion and acid drainage into waterways that flow into surrounding valleys, affecting ecosystems and people over large areas.

Coal mining devastates natural systems

The mining of coal exerts substantial impacts on natural systems and human well-being. Strip mining destroys large swaths of habitat and causes extensive soil erosion. It also can cause chemical runoff into waterways through the process of **acid drainage**. This occurs when sulfide minerals in newly exposed rock surfaces react with oxygen and rainwater to produce sulfuric acid. As the sulfuric acid runs off, it leaches metals from the rocks, many of which are toxic. Acid drainage is a natural phenomenon, but mining greatly accelerates the rate at which it occurs by exposing many new rock surfaces at once. Regulations in the United States require mining companies to restore strip-mined land following mining, but complete restoration is impossible, and ecological modifications are severe and long-lasting. Most other nations exercise less oversight.

Mountaintop removal mining (FIGURE 15.19 and has impacts that exceed even conventional strip mining. When countless tons of rock and soil are removed from the top of a mountain, material slides downhill, where immense areas of habitat can be degraded or destroyed and creek beds can be clogged and polluted. Loosening of U.S. government regulations in 2002 enabled mining companies to legally dump mountaintop rock and soil into valleys and rivers below, regardless of the consequences for ecosystems, wildlife, and local residents.

Oil and gas extraction modify the environment

To drill for conventional oil or gas on land, road networks must be constructed and many sites may be explored in the course of prospecting. The extensive infrastructure needed to support a full-scale drilling operation typically includes housing for workers, access roads, transport pipelines, and waste piles for removed soil. Ponds may be constructed to collect the toxic sludge that remains after the useful components of oil have been removed. These activities can pollute the soil, air, and water, fragment habitats, and disturb wildlife. All these impacts have been documented on the tundra of Alaska's North Slope, where policymakers continue to debate whether to open the Arctic National Wildlife Refuge to drilling.

Fortunately, drilling technology is more environmentally sensitive than in the past. **Directional drilling** allows drillers to bore down vertically and then curve to drill horizontally. This enables extraction companies to follow the course of horizontal layered deposits to extract the most they can from them. It allows drilling to reach a large underground area (up to several thousand meters in radius) around a drill pad. As a result, fewer drill pads are needed, and the surface footprint of drilling is smaller.

We all pay external costs

The costs of alleviating the many health and environmental impacts of fossil fuel extraction and use are generally not internalized in the market prices of fossil fuels. Instead, we all pay these external costs through medical expenses, costs of environmental cleanup, and impacts on our quality of life. Moreover, the prices we pay at the gas pump or on our monthly utility bill do not even cover the financial costs of fossil fuel production. Rather, fossil fuel prices have been kept inexpensive as a result of government subsidies to extraction companies. The profitable and well-established fossil fuel industries still receive far more financial support from taxpayers than do the young and struggling renewable energy sources Figure 16.6, p. 465). Thus, we all pay extra for our fossil fuel energy through our taxes, generally without even realizing it.

Fossil fuel extraction has mixed consequences for local people

Across the world today, people living in fossil-fuel-bearing regions must weigh the environmental, health, and social drawbacks of fossil fuel development against the financial benefits that they and their families may gain. Communities where fossil fuel extraction is taking place generally experience a flush of high-paying jobs and economic activity, and for many people these economic benefits far outweigh other concerns. Perceptions may change with time, however. Economic booms often prove temporary, and residents may be left with the legacy of a polluted environment for generations to come.

Fort McMurray is the hub of Alberta's oil sands boom. Fort McMurray's population has skyrocketed from 2000 in the 1960s to over 100,000 today as people have flocked here looking for jobs. Most residents are men, averaging 32 years of age, and the city boasts the highest birthrate in Canada. Salaries are high, but so are rents and home prices. A well-disciplined worker can become wealthy, but others fall behind, victims of drug abuse, alcoholism, or gambling. Like all boomtowns, Fort McMurray is outgrowing its infrastructure, and it is likely to experience a bust when the price of its principal resource falls.

Along the route the oil would take out of Alberta, the Keystone XL pipeline extension would create 20,000 "job-years," TransCanada estimates—6500 construction jobs for two years plus 7000 one-year jobs for manufacturers of supplies. For landowners, the pipeline project has mixed consequences. TransCanada has had to negotiate with thousands of landowners along the Keystone XL route, offering them money for the right to install the pipeline across their land. Many were happy to accept payments, but landowners who declined TransCanada's offers found their land rights taken away by **eminent domain**—the policy by which courts set aside private property rights to make way for projects judged to be for the public good. Following a 2005 U.S. Supreme Court ruling, even private companies can usurp land rights. The landowner is paid an amount determined by a court to be fair and cannot appeal the decision. As John Harter, a South Dakota rancher along the pipeline route, put it, "I found out that they have more rights to my property than I do. It makes me very angry when I paid for it . . . and take care of it."

In Alaska, to gain support for oil drilling among state residents, the oil industry pays the Alaskan government a portion of its revenues. Since the 1970s, the state of Alaska has received over $65 billion in oil revenues. Alaska's state constitution requires that one-quarter of state oil revenues be placed in the Permanent Fund, which pays yearly dividends to all residents. Since 1982, each Alaska resident has received annual payouts ranging from $331 to $2069.

Such distribution of revenue among citizens is unusual; in most parts of the world where fossil fuels are extracted, local residents suffer pollution without compensation. Even when multinational gas or oil corporations pay developing nations for access to extract oil or gas, the money generally does not trickle down from the government to the people who live where the extraction takes place. Moreover, oil-rich developing nations such as Ecuador, Venezuela, and Nigeria tend to have few environmental regulations, and governments may not enforce regulations if there is risk of losing the large sums of money associated with oil development.

In Nigeria, the Shell Oil Company extracted $30 billion of oil from land of the native Ogoni people, yet the Ogoni still live in poverty, with no running water or electricity. Profits from the oil extraction went to Shell and to the military dictatorships of Nigeria. The development resulted in oil spills, noise, and constantly burning gas flares—all of which caused illness among people living nearby. Starting in 1962, Ogoni activist and leader Ken Saro-Wiwa worked for fair compensation to the Ogoni. After years of persecution by the Nigerian government, Saro-Wiwa was arrested in 1994, given a trial universally regarded as a sham, and put to death by military tribunal.

Wherever in the world fossil fuel extraction comes to communities, people seem to find themselves divided over whether the short-term economic benefits are worth the long-term health and environmental impacts. Today this debate is occurring in North Dakota and parts of the West in response to oil and gas drilling, and in Pennsylvania, New York, and other states above the Marcellus Shale where the petroleum industry is hydrofracking for gas. The debate has gone on for years in Appalachia over mountaintop removal mining. There are no easy answers, but impacts would be lessened if extraction industries were to put more health and environmental safeguards in place for workers and residents.

Dependence on foreign energy affects the economies of nations

Putting all your eggs in one basket is always a risky strategy. Because virtually all our modern technologies and

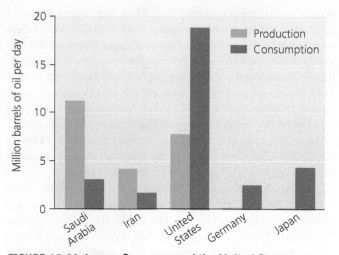

FIGURE 15.20 Japan, Germany, and the United States are among nations that consume far more oil than they produce. Iran and Saudi Arabia produce more oil than they consume and are able to export oil to high-consumption countries. *Data from BP p.l.c., 2012.* Statistical review of world energy 2012.

DATA Q For every barrel of oil produced in the United States, how many barrels are consumed in the United States?

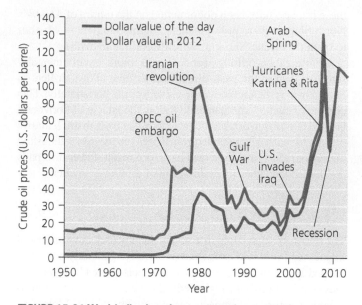

FIGURE 15.21 World oil prices have gyrated over the decades. Often this has resulted from political and economic events in oil-producing countries, particularly in the Middle East. *Data from U.S. Energy Information Administration and BP p.l.c., 2012,* Statistical review of world energy 2012.

services depend in some way on fossil fuels, we are vulnerable to supplies becoming costly or unavailable. Nations that lack adequate fossil fuel reserves of their own are especially vulnerable. For instance, Germany, France, South Korea, and Japan consume far more energy than they produce and thus rely almost entirely on imports (**FIGURE 15.20**). Since its 1970 oil production peak, the United States has relied more on foreign energy, and today imports nearly half of its oil.

Such reliance means that seller nations can control energy prices, forcing buyer nations to pay more as supplies dwindle. This became clear in 1973, when the *Organization of Petroleum Exporting Countries (OPEC)* resolved to stop selling oil to the United States. The predominantly Arab nations of OPEC opposed U.S. support of Israel in the Arab–Israeli Yom Kippur War and sought to raise prices by restricting supply. The embargo created panic in the West and caused oil prices to skyrocket (**FIGURE 15.21**), spurring inflation. Fear of oil shortages drove American consumers to wait in long lines at gas pumps. A similar supply shock followed in 1979 in response to the Iranian revolution.

With the majority of world oil reserves located in the politically volatile Middle East, crises in this region are a constant concern for U.S. policymakers. The democratic street uprisings of the "Arab Spring" that began in 2011 in Tunisia and Egypt and spread elsewhere in the region put leaders of the United States and other Western nations in an awkward position, because they had long supported many of the region's autocratic rulers. These rulers had facilitated Western access to oil, even as they suppressed democracy in their own societies. The Arab Spring uprisings were only the most recent in a long history of events that have affected oil prices and global access to oil, stretching back through the U.S.–led wars in Iraq and the Iran–Iraq war of the 1980s to the 1973 OPEC embargo.

From this perspective, turning to Canada's oil sands as a primary source of oil represents a perfect solution for the United States. Canada is a stable, friendly, democratic neighboring country that is already the United States' biggest

trading partner. Trading with Canada for petroleum from the oil sands would lessen U.S. reliance on Middle Eastern oil, and this is a major reason that many American policymakers and citizens favor building the Keystone XL pipeline. Indeed, in recent years the United States has already diversified its sources of imported petroleum considerably and now receives most from non–Middle Eastern nations, including Canada, Mexico, Venezuela, and Nigeria (**FIGURE 15.22**).

Diversifying sources of foreign oil was one way in which the U.S. government responded to the 1973 embargo. The United States also enacted conservation measures, capped the price that domestic producers could charge for oil, funded research into renewable energy sources, and urged oil companies to pursue secondary extraction at old wells. It established an emergency

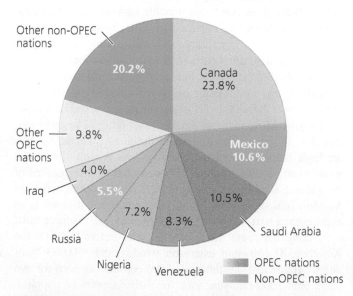

FIGURE 15.22 The United States now imports most oil from non-OPEC nations and from non-Middle-Eastern nations. *Data from U.S. Energy Information Administration, 2012.* Annual energy review 2011.

stockpile (which today stores one month of oil) deep underground in salt caverns in Louisiana, called the Strategic Petroleum Reserve. And it called for developing additional domestic sources, including offshore oil from the Gulf of Mexico.

Since then, the desire to reduce reliance on foreign oil by boosting domestic production has driven the expansion of offshore drilling into deeper and deeper water. It has repeatedly driven a proposal to open the Arctic National Wildlife Refuge on Alaska's North Slope to oil extraction, despite critics' charges that drilling there would spoil America's last true wilderness while adding little to the nation's oil supply. Today it is driving the push to drill for oil offshore in the waters of the Arctic, despite the environmental risks. As domestic U.S. production of oil and gas increase due to enhanced drilling

WEIGHING THE ISSUES

DRILL, BABY, DRILL? Do you think the United States should open more of its offshore waters to oil and gas extraction? Would the benefits exceed the potential costs? What factors should the government consider when deciding which areas to lease for drilling? How strongly should government regulate oil and gas extraction once drilling begins? Give reasons for your answers.

efforts, the United States becomes freer to make geopolitical decisions without being hamstrung by dependence on foreign energy imports. As pressure for increased drilling intensifies in coming years, our society will be debating the complex mix of social, political, economic, and environmental costs and benefits.

How will we convert to renewable energy?

Fossil fuels are limited in supply, and their use has health, environmental, political, and socioeconomic consequences (FIGURE 15.23). For these reasons, many scientists, environmental advocates, businesspeople, and policymakers have concluded that fossil fuels are not a sustainable long-term solution to our energy needs. They further conclude that we need to shift to clean and renewable sources of energy that exert less impact on natural systems and human health. Many nations are moving far faster than the United States. France relies on nuclear power for its energy needs, Germany is investing in solar power (pp. 461–462), and China is forging ahead and developing multiple renewable energy technologies.

As we make the transition to renewable energy sources, it will benefit us to extend the availability of fossil fuels. We can prolong our access to fossil fuels by instituting measures to

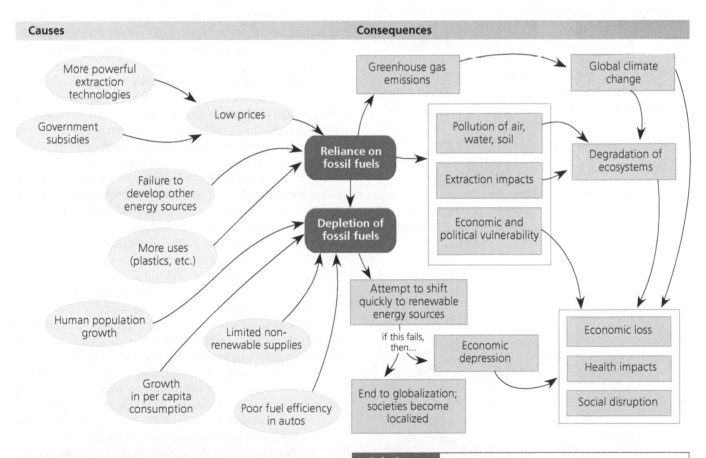

FIGURE 15.23 Our reliance on and depletion of fossil fuels have many causes (ovals on left) and consequences (boxes on right). Arrows in this concept map lead from causes to consequences. Note that items grouped within outlined boxes do not necessarily share any special relationship; the outlined boxes are merely intended to streamline the figure.

Solutions

As you progress through this chapter, try to identify as many solutions to our reliance on and depletion of fossil fuels as you can. What could you personally do to help address this issue? Consider how each action or solution might affect items in the concept map above.

Energy Efficiency and Conservation

Until our society makes the transition to renewable energy sources, we will need to find ways to minimize and extend the use of our precious fossil fuel resources. **Energy efficiency** describes the ability to obtain a given result or amount of output while using less energy input. **Energy conservation** describes the practice of reducing wasteful or unnecessary energy use. In general, efficiency results from technological improvements, whereas conservation stems from behavioral choices. Because greater efficiency allows us to reduce energy use, efficiency is one primary means of conservation.

Efficiency and conservation allow us to be less wasteful and to reduce our environmental impact. Moreover, by enabling us to extend the lifetimes of our nonrenewable energy supplies, efficiency and conservation help to alleviate many of the difficult individual choices and divisive societal debates related to fossil fuels, from oil sands development and the Keystone XL pipeline to Arctic drilling to hydraulic fracturing.

The United States burns through twice as much energy per dollar of Gross Domestic Product (GDP) as do most other industrialized nations. However, there is good news: Per-person energy consumption has declined slightly in the United States over the past four decades. During this time the United States has reduced its energy use per dollar of GDP by about 50% (FIGURE 15.24). Americans have achieved tremendous gains in efficiency already, and should be able to make still-greater progress in the future.

Personal choice and efficient technologies are two routes to conservation

As individuals, we can make conscious choices to reduce our own energy consumption by driving less, turning off lights when rooms are not being used, dialing down thermostats, and

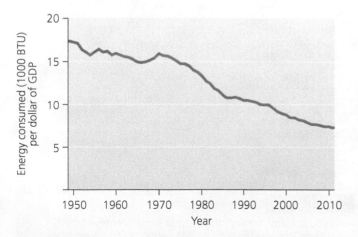

FIGURE 15.24 The United States has been producing more economic output per energy input. This graph shows how energy consumption per inflation-adjusted dollar of GDP has fallen. *Data from U.S. Energy Information Administration, 2012.* Annual energy review 2011.

FIGURE 15.25 A thermogram reveals heat loss from buildings by recording energy in the infrared portion of the electromagnetic spectrum. In this image, one house is uninsulated; its red color signifies warm temperatures where heat is escaping, whereas green shades signify cool temperatures where heat is being conserved. Also note that in all houses, more heat is escaping from windows than from walls.

cutting back on the use of energy-intensive machines and appliances. Many European nations use far less energy per capita than the United States yet enjoy equivalent standards of living. This indicates that Americans could reduce their energy consumption considerably without diminishing their quality of life. Moreover, for any given individual or business, reducing energy consumption saves money while helping to conserve resources.

As a society, we can conserve energy by developing technologies and strategies to make our energy-consuming devices and processes more efficient. Currently, more than two-thirds of the fossil fuel energy we use is simply lost, as waste heat, in automobiles and power plants (see Figure 15.3).

We can improve the efficiency of our power plants through **cogeneration,** in which excess heat produced during the generation of electricity is captured and used to heat nearby workplaces and homes and to produce other kinds of power. Cogeneration can almost double the efficiency of a power plant. The same is true of coal gasification and combined cycle generation (p. 445). In this process, coal is treated to create hot gases that turn a gas turbine, while the hot exhaust of this turbine heats water to drive a conventional steam turbine.

In homes, offices, and public buildings, a significant amount of heat is needlessly lost in winter and gained in summer because of poor design and inadequate insulation (FIGURE 15.25). Improvements in design can reduce the energy required to heat and cool buildings. Such improvements may involve passive solar design (p. 468), better insulation, a building's location, the vegetation around it, and even the color of its roof (lighter colors keep buildings cooler by reflecting the sun's rays).

Many consumer products, from lightbulbs to appliances, have been reengineered through the years to enhance efficiency. Energy-efficient lighting, for example, can reduce energy use by 80%. Compact fluorescent bulbs are much more efficient than incandescent light bulbs, and many governments are phasing out incandescent bulbs for this reason; the U.S. phaseout is scheduled to be complete in 2014.

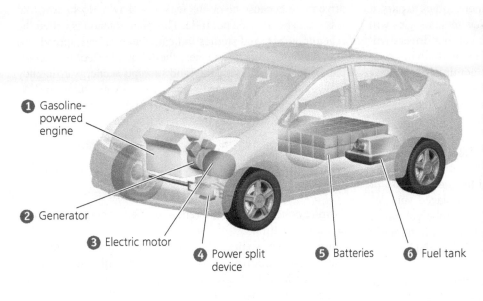

FIGURE 15.26 **Hybrid cars have high fuel efficiencies.** The Toyota Prius diagrammed here uses a small, clean, and efficient gasoline-powered engine ❶ to produce power that the generator ❷ can convert to electricity to drive the electric motor ❸. The power split device ❹ integrates the engine, generator, and motor, serving as a continuously variable transmission. The car automatically switches among all-electrical power, all-gas power, and a mix of the two, depending on the demands being placed on the engine. Typically, the motor provides power for low-speed city driving and adds extra power on hills. The motor and generator charge a pack of nickel-metal-hydride batteries ❺, which can in turn supply power to the motor. Energy for the engine comes from gasoline carried in a typical fuel tank ❻.

❶ Gasoline-powered engine

❷ Generator

❸ Electric motor

❹ Power split device

❺ Batteries

❻ Fuel tank

Federal standards for energy-efficient appliances have already reduced per-person home electricity use below what it was in the 1970s. The Energy Star program labels refrigerators, dishwashers, and other appliances for their energy efficiency, enabling consumers to take energy use into account when shopping for these items. For the consumer, studies show that the slightly higher cost of buying energy-efficient washing machines is rapidly offset by savings on water and electricity bills. The U.S. Environmental Protection Agency (EPA) estimates that if all U.S. households purchased energy-efficient appliances, the national annual energy expenditure would be reduced by $200 billion.

Automotive technology represents perhaps our best opportunity to conserve large amounts of fossil fuels fairly easily. We can accomplish this with alternative-technology vehicles such as electric cars, electric/gasoline hybrids (FIGURE 15.26), or vehicles that use hydrogen fuel cells (pp. 482–484). Among electric/gasoline hybrids, current U.S. models of the Toyota Prius and the Chevrolet Volt average fuel-economy ratings of 50 miles per gallon (mpg) and 60 mpg, respectively—two to three times better than the average American car. Even without alternative vehicles, we already possess the means to enhance fuel efficiency for gasoline-powered vehicles by using lightweight materials, continuously variable transmissions, and more efficient gasoline engines.

Automobile fuel efficiency is a key to conservation

Among the measures enacted by the U.S. government in response to the OPEC embargo of 1973–1974 were a mandated increase in the mile-per-gallon (mpg) fuel efficiency of automobiles and a reduction in the national speed limit to 55 miles per hour. These measures notably reduced U.S. dependence on Middle Eastern oil and held down greenhouse gas emissions. Over the next three decades, however, many of the conservation initiatives of this time were abandoned. Without high market prices and an immediate threat of shortages, people lacked economic motivation to conserve. Government funding for research into alternative energy

sources dwindled, speed limits rose, and U.S. policymakers repeatedly failed to raise the *corporate average fuel efficiency (CAFE) standards*, which set benchmarks for auto manufacturers to meet. The average fuel efficiency of new vehicles fell from 22.0 mpg in 1987 to 19.3 mpg in 2004, as sales of sport-utility vehicles increased relative to sales of cars.

Since then, fuel economy climbed to 22.8 mpg in 2011 (FIGURE 15.27) after Congress passed legislation in 2007 mandating that automakers raise average fuel efficiency to 35 mpg by the year 2020. This was a substantial advance, yet even after this boost, American automobiles would still have lagged well behind the efficiency of the vehicles of most other developed nations. As a result, when automakers required a government bailout during the recent recession, President Obama negotiated with them, forcing a series of agreements that ended with automakers agreeing to boost average fuel economies to

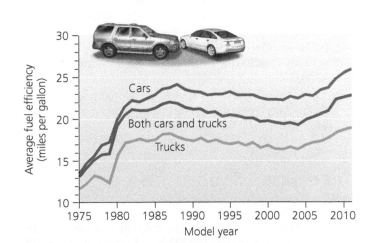

FIGURE 15.27 **Automotive fuel efficiencies have responded to public policy.** Fuel efficiency for automobiles in the United States rose dramatically in the late 1970s as a result of legislative mandates but then stagnated once no further laws were enacted to improve fuel economy. Recent legislation is now improving it again. *Data from U.S. Environmental Protection Agency, 2012. Light-duty automotive technology, carbon dioxide emissions, and fuel economy trends: 1975 through 2011.*

54.5 mpg by 2025. If this strong improvement comes to pass, it will enable a huge reduction in oil use. New technologies will add over $2000 to the average price of a car, but drivers will save perhaps $6000 in fuel costs over the car's lifetime.

In 2009, Congress and the Obama administration took another major step to improve automobile fuel efficiency while stimulating economic activity and saving jobs during a severe recession. The popular "Cash for Clunkers" program—formally named the Consumer Assistance to Recycle and Save (CARS) Act—paid Americans $3500 or $4500 each to turn in old vehicles and purchase newer, more fuel-efficient ones. The $3-billion program subsidized the sale or lease of 678,000 vehicles averaging 24.9 mpg that replaced vehicles averaging 15.8 mpg. It is estimated that 824 million gallons of gasoline will be saved as a result, preventing 9 million metric tons of greenhouse gas emissions and creating social benefits worth $278 million.

U.S. policymakers could do still more to encourage oil conservation. So far the United States has kept its taxes on gasoline extremely low, relative to most other nations. Americans pay two to three times *less* per gallon of gas than drivers in many European countries. In fact, gasoline in the United States is sold more cheaply than bottled water! As a result, U.S. gasoline prices do not account for the substantial external costs that oil production and consumption impose on society. Some experts have estimated that if all costs to society were taken into account, the price of gasoline would exceed $13/gallon. Instead, our artificially low gas prices diminish our economic incentives to conserve.

WEIGHING THE ISSUES

MORE MILES, LESS GAS If you drive an automobile, what gas mileage does it get? How does it compare to the vehicle averages in Figure 15.27? If your vehicle's fuel efficiency were 10 mpg greater, and if you drove the same amount, how many gallons of gasoline would you no longer need to purchase each year? How much money would you save?

Do you think the U.S. government should mandate further increases in the CAFE standards? Should the government raise taxes on gasoline sales as an incentive for consumers to conserve energy? What effects (on economics, on health, and on environmental quality, for instance) might each of these steps have?

The rebound effect cuts into efficiency gains

Energy efficiency is a vital pursuit, but it may not always save as much energy as we expect. This is because gains in efficiency from better technology can be partly offset if people engage in more energy-consuming behavior as a result. For instance, a person who buys a fuel-efficient car may choose to drive more because he or she feels it's okay to do so now that less gas is being used per mile. This phenomenon is called the **rebound effect,** and studies indicate that it is widespread and significant. In some instances, the rebound effect may completely erase efficiency gains, and attempts at energy efficiency may end up actually causing greater energy consumption! As our society pursues energy efficiency in more and more ways, this will be an important factor to consider.

We need both conservation and renewable energy

Despite concerns over the rebound effect, energy efficiency and conservation efforts are vital to creating a sustainable future for our society. It is often said that reducing our energy use is equivalent to finding a new oil reserve. Some estimates hold that effective energy conservation and efficiency in the United States could save 6 million barrels of oil a day—nearly the amount gained from all offshore drilling, and considerably more than would be gained from Canada's oil sands. In fact, conserving energy is *better* than finding a new reserve because it alleviates health and environmental impacts while at the same time extending our future access to fossil fuels.

Yet regardless of how effectively we conserve, we will still need energy to power our civilization, and it will need to come from somewhere. Most energy experts feel that the only sustainable way of guaranteeing ourselves a reliable long-term supply of energy is to ensure sufficiently rapid development of renewable energy sources (Chapter 16).

Conclusion

Over the past two centuries, fossil fuels have helped us build the complex industrialized societies we enjoy today. Yet sometime soon our production of conventional fossil fuels will begin to decline. We can respond to this challenge by seeking out new sources of fossil fuels and continuing our way of life but paying ever-higher economic, health, and environmental costs. Or, we can encourage conservation and efficiency while aggressively developing alternative clean and renewable energy sources. The path we choose will have far-reaching consequences for human health and well-being, for Earth's climate, and for the stability and progress of our civilization.

The debate over the Canadian oil sands and the Keystone XL pipeline is a microcosm of this debate over our energy future. Fortunately, we are not caught in a simple trade-off between fossil fuels' economic benefits and their impacts on the environment, climate, and health. Instead, as renewable energy sources become increasingly feasible and economical, it becomes easier to envision freeing ourselves from a reliance on fossil fuels and charting a bright future for humanity and the planet with renewable energy.

Reviewing Objectives

You should now be able to:

Identify the energy sources we use

- Many renewable and nonrenewable energy sources are available to us. (pp. 428–429)

- Since the industrial revolution, nonrenewable fossil fuels—including coal, natural gas, and oil—have become our primary sources of energy. (p. 429)

- Energy sources and energy consumption are each unevenly distributed across the world. (pp. 430–431)

- The concepts of net energy and EROI allow us to compare the amount of energy obtained from a source with the amount invested in its extraction and production. (pp. 430–432)

- We face a choice in whether to pursue new low-quality fossil fuel sources such as oil sands or whether to develop alternative sources of clean renewable energy. (p. 432)

Describe the origin and nature of major types of fossil fuels

- Fossil fuels are formed very slowly as buried organic matter is chemically transformed by heat, pressure, and/or anaerobic decomposition. (pp. 432–433)

- Coal, our most abundant fossil fuel, results from organic matter that undergoes compression but little decomposition. (pp. 433–434)

- Crude oil is a thick, liquid mixture of hydrocarbons that is formed underground under high temperature and pressure. (p. 433)

- Natural gas consists mostly of methane and can be formed in two ways. (p. 433)

- Oil sands contain bitumen, a tarry substance formed from oil that was degraded by bacteria. This can be processed into synthetic crude oil. (p. 433)

- Shale oil and methane hydrate are fossil fuel sources with potential for future use (p. 434)

Explain how we extract and use fossil fuels

- Scientists locate fossil fuel deposits by analyzing subterranean geology. We then estimate the technically and economically recoverable portions of those reserves. (pp. 434–435, 438–439)

- Coal is mined underground and strip-mined from the land surface, whereas we drill wells to pump out oil and gas. Oil sands may be strip-mined or dissolved underground and extracted through well shafts. (pp. 434–435)

- Components of crude oil are separated in refineries to produce a wide variety of fuel types. (pp. 435–436)

- Coal is used today principally to generate electricity. (pp. 436–437)

- Natural gas is cleaner-burning than coal or oil. (pp. 436–437)

- Oil powers transportation and also is used to create a diversity of petroleum-based products that are everywhere in our daily lives. (pp. 437, 440)

Evaluate peak oil and the challenges it may pose

- R/P ratios help indicate how long a resource may last, but they tell only part of the story. (pp. 439–440)

- Any nonrenewable resource can be depleted, and we have depleted nearly half the world's conventional oil. (pp. 438–441)

- Once we pass the peak of oil production, the gap between rising demand and falling supply may pose immense economic and social challenges for our society. (pp. 440–442)

Examine how we are reaching further for fossil fuels

- Primary extraction may be followed by secondary extraction, in which gas or liquid is injected into the ground to help force up additional oil or gas. (p. 442)

- Hydraulic fracturing is producing natural gas from shale deposits. (p. 443)

- We are drilling for oil and gas further offshore, in deeper water, and are moving into the Arctic. (pp. 443–444)

- New types of fossil fuels we may exploit include oil sands, shale oil, and methane hydrate (p. 444)

Outline and assess environmental impacts of fossil fuel use, and explore solutions

- Emissions from fossil fuel combustion pollute air, pose human health risks, and drive global climate change. (pp. 444–445)

- Public policy and advances in pollution control technology have reduced many of these emissions, but much more remains to be done. (p. 445)

- Clean coal technologies aim to reduce pollution from coal combustion. (p. 445)

- If we could safely and effectively capture carbon dioxide and sequester it underground, this would mitigate a primary drawback of fossil fuels. Carbon capture and storage remain unproven so far, however. (pp. 445–446)

- Oil is a major contributor to water pollution. (pp. 446–447)

- Hydrofracking poses pollution concerns. (pp. 447, 450)

- Oil sands mining and transport cause deforestation, water pollution, and other impacts. (p. 450)

- Coal mining can devastate ecosystems and pollute waterways. (p. 450)

- Oil and gas extraction exert various impacts, but directional drilling has eased them. (pp. 450–451)

■ **Evaluate political, social, and economic aspects of fossil fuel use**

- Fossil fuels impose external costs. (p. 451)

- Fossil fuel extraction creates jobs but leaves pollution. People living in areas of fossil fuel extraction experience a range of consequences. (p. 451)

- Today's societies are so reliant on fossil fuel energy that sudden restrictions in oil supplies can have major economic consequences. (pp. 451–453)

- Nations that consume far more fossil fuels than they produce are especially vulnerable to supply restrictions. (p. 452)

■ **Specify strategies for conserving energy and enhancing efficiency**

- Energy conservation involves both personal choices and efficient technologies. (p. 454)

- Efficiency in power plant combustion, lighting, and consumer appliances, as well as changes in public policy, can help us conserve. (pp. 454–455)

- Automotive fuel efficiency plays a key role in conserving energy. (pp. 455–456)

- The rebound effect can partly negate our conservation efforts. (p. 456)

- Conservation lengthens our access to fossil fuels and reduces environmental impact, but to build a sustainable society we will also need to shift to renewable energy sources. (p. 456)

Testing Your Comprehension

1. Why are fossil fuels our most prevalent source of energy today? Why are they considered nonrenewable sources of energy?

2. Describe how net energy differs from energy returned on investment (EROI). Why are these concepts important in the evaluation of energy sources?

3. How are fossil fuels formed? How do environmental conditions determine which type of fossil fuel is formed in a given location? Why are fossil fuels often concentrated in localized deposits?

4. How do geologists find oil and gas deposits and estimate amounts of oil or gas available? How do "technically recoverable" and "economically recoverable" amounts of a resource differ?

5. Describe how coal is used to generate electricity.

6. How do we create petroleum products? Provide examples of several of these products.

7. What is meant by *peak oil*? Why do many experts think we are about to pass the global production peak for conventional oil? What consequences could there be for our society?

8. Describe three environmental impacts of fossil fuel production and consumption. Compare contrasting views regarding the impacts of extracting oil from Alberta's oil sands and shipping it by pipeline to the U.S. Gulf Coast.

9. Give an example of a clean coal technology. Now describe how carbon capture and storage is intended to work.

10. Describe one specific example of how technological advances can improve energy efficiency. Now describe one specific action you could take to conserve energy.

Seeking Solutions

1. Summarize the main arguments for and against the Keystone XL pipeline extension. What problems might it help solve? What problems might it create? Do you personally think Canada should continue to develop Alberta's oil sands? Should the United States have approved construction of the Keystone XL pipeline extension? Give reasons for your answers.

2. What impacts might you expect on your lifestyle once our society arrives at peak oil? What lessons do you think we can take from the conservation methods adopted by the United States in response to the "energy crisis" of 1973–1974? What steps do you think we should take to avoid energy shortages in a post-peak-oil future?

3. Compare the health and environmental effects of coal extraction and consumption with those of oil and gas extraction and consumption. What steps could governments, industries, and individuals take to alleviate some of these impacts?

4. Contrast the experiences of the Ogoni people of Nigeria with those of the citizens of Alaska. How have they been similar and different? Do you think businesses or governments should take steps to ensure that local people benefit from oil drilling operations? How could they do so?

5. **THINK IT THROUGH** You have been elected governor of the state of Florida as the federal government is debating opening new waters to offshore drilling for oil and

natural gas. Drilling in Florida waters would create jobs for Florida citizens as well as revenue for the state in the form of royalty payments from oil and gas companies. However, there is always the risk of a catastrophic oil spill, with its ecological, social, and economic impacts. Would you support or oppose offshore drilling off the Florida coastline? Why? What, if any, regulations would you insist be imposed on such development? What questions would you ask of scientists before making your decision? What factors would you consider in making your decision?

6. **THINK IT THROUGH** You are the mayor of a rural Nebraska town along the route of the proposed Keystone XL pipeline extension. Some of your town's residents are eager to have jobs they believe the pipeline will bring. Others are fearful that oil leaks from the pipeline could contaminate the water supply. Some of your town's landowners are looking forward to receiving payments from TransCanada for use of their land, whereas others dread the prospect of noise, pollution, and trees being cut on their property. If the company receives too much local opposition it says it may move the pipeline route away from your town. What information would you seek from TransCanada, from your state regulators, and from scientists and engineers before deciding whether support for the pipeline is in the best interest of your town? How would you make your decision? How might you try to address the diverse preferences of your town's residents?

Calculating Ecological Footprints

Scientists at the Global Footprint Network calculate the energy component of our ecological footprint by estimating the amount of ecologically productive land and sea required to absorb the carbon released from fossil fuel combustion. This translates into 4.9 ha of the average American's 7.2-ha ecological footprint. Another way to think about our footprint, however, is to estimate how much land would be needed to grow biomass with an energy content equal to that of the fossil fuel we burn.

Assume that you are an average American who burns about 6.3 metric tons of oil-equivalent in fossil fuels each year and that average terrestrial net primary productivity (p. 25) can be expressed as 0.0037 metric tons/ha/year. Calculate how many hectares of land it would take to supply our fuel use by present-day photosynthetic production.

	Hectares of land for fuel production
You	1703
Your class	
Your state	
United States	

1. Compare the energy component of your ecological footprint calculated in this way with the 4.9 ha calculated using the method of the Global Footprint Network. Explain why results from the two methods may differ.

2. Earth's total land area is approximately 15 billion hectares. Compare this to the hectares of land for fuel production from the table.

3. In the absence of stored energy from fossil fuels, how large a human population could Earth support at the level of consumption of the average American, if all of Earth's area were devoted to fuel production? Do you consider this realistic? Provide two reasons why or why not.

Mastering**ENVIRONMENTALSCIENCE**™

STUDENTS

Go to **MasteringEnvironmentalScience** for assignments, the etext, and the Study Area with practice tests, videos, current events, and activities.

INSTRUCTORS

Go to **MasteringEnvironmentalScience** for automatically graded activities, current events, videos, and reading questions that you can assign to your students, plus Instructor Resources.

Homes in Freiburg, Germany, which produce excess solar power and sell it to the grid

16

New Renewable Energy Alternatives

Upon completing this chapter, you will be able to:

- Outline the major sources of renewable energy, summarize their benefits, and assess their potential for growth

- Describe solar energy and the ways it is harnessed, and evaluate its advantages and disadvantages

- Describe wind power and how we harness it, and evaluate its benefits and drawbacks

- Describe geothermal energy and the ways we make use of it, and assess its advantages and disadvantages

- Describe ocean energy sources and how we can harness them

- Explain hydrogen fuel cells and weigh options for energy storage and transportation

Germany Goes Solar

RUSSIA

GERMANY

Atlantic Ocean

EUROPE

AFRICA

"Someday we will harness the rise and fall of the tides and imprison the rays of the sun."

—Thomas A. Edison, 1921

"[Renewable energy] will provide millions of new jobs. It will halt global warming. It will create a more fair and just world. It will clean our environment and make our lives healthier."

—Hermann Scheer, energy expert and member of the German parliament, 2009

When we think of solar energy, most of us envision a warm sunny place like Arizona or southern California. Yet the country that produces the most solar power in the world is Germany, a northern European nation that receives less sun than Alaska! Germany is the world's top generator of photovoltaic (PV) solar power, a technology that produces electricity from sunshine. In recent years Germany has installed nearly half the world's total of this technology. Germany now obtains more of its energy from solar power than any other nation, and the amount is growing each year.

How is this happening in such a cool and cloudy country? A bold federal policy is using economic incentives to promote solar power and other forms of renewable energy. Germany has a **feed-in tariff** system whereby utilities are required to buy power from anyone who can generate power from renewable energy sources and feed it into the electric grid. Under this system, utilities must pay guaranteed premium prices for this power under long-term contract. As a result, German homeowners and businesses have rushed to install PV panels and are selling their excess solar power to the utilities at a profit.

The feed-in tariffs apply to all forms of renewable energy. As a result of these incentives, Germany established itself as the world leader in wind power in the 1990s, until being overtaken by the United States and China. It ranks third in the world in using power from biomass, and second in solar water heating. Overall, Germany ranks third in the world in electrical power capacity from renewable sources, trailing only China and the United States, which have far more people and businesses. In renewable energy generated per person, Germany is number one in the world.

Germany's push for renewable energy goes back to 1990. In the wake of the Chernobyl nuclear disaster, Germany decided to phase out its nuclear power plants. However, by shutting these down, the nation would lose virtually all its clean energy and would become utterly dependent on oil, gas, and coal imported from Russia and the Middle East.

Enter Hermann Scheer, a German parliament member and an expert on renewable energy. While everyone else assumed that technologies for harnessing solar, wind, and geothermal energy were costly, risky, and underdeveloped, Scheer saw them as a great economic opportunity—and as the only long-term answer. In 1990, Scheer helped push through a landmark law establishing feed-in tariffs. Ten years later, the law was revised and strengthened: The Renewable Energy Sources Act of 2000 aimed to promote renewable energy production and use, enhance the security of the energy supply, reduce carbon emissions, and lessen the many external costs of fossil fuel use.

Under this landmark law, each renewable energy source is assigned its own payment rate according to market considerations, and most rates are reduced year by year in order to encourage increasingly efficient means of producing power. In 2004 and in 2009, the government adjusted the amounts utilities were required to pay homeowners and businesses for their energy production.

In recent years, the feed-in-tariffs were adding about 2 cents per kilowatt-hour onto the average German citizen's electric bill, amounting to an annual cost of about $60 per person. To reduce the cost of these subsidies, the German government in 2010 slashed PV solar tariff rates by 16%. The new lower rates eased the burden on ratepayers, while homeowners still had economic incentive to invest in solar panels because the feed-in-tariffs had already helped to cut PV market prices in half.

In response to the prospect of lower tariffs, sales of PV modules skyrocketed as Germans rushed to lock in the old rates. Since then, a series of reductions in the payment rates have each spurred rushes to install more PV systems. In 2010, 2011, and 2012, Germans installed over 7 gigawatts of PV solar capacity each year—an amount equal to the total cumulative capacity of the United States. In 2012 the government proposed to end subsidies once the nation reaches 52 gigawatts of cumulative capacity, roughly twice its total as of 2011.

By reducing the subsidies gradually, the government aims to create a stronger solar industry that can sustain growth over the long term and can compete with foreign companies for international business. Indeed, boosted by domestic demand, German industries have become global leaders in "green tech," designing and selling renewable energy technologies around the world. Germany is second in PV production behind China, leads the world in production of biodiesel, and has developed several cellulosic ethanol facilities. Renewable energy industries in Germany today employ nearly 400,000 citizens.

By 2020, Germany aims to obtain 35% of its electricity from renewable sources, and plans to increase this percentage to 50% by 2030, 65% by 2040, and 80% by 2050. To make this happen, the government has been allotting more public money to renewable energy than any other nation—over $25 billion annually in recent years. Following the Fukushima nuclear disaster in Japan in 2011, the German government responded to anti-nuclear demonstrations by shutting down 7 of its 15 nuclear power plants and promising to phase out the rest by 2022. This dramatic reduction in electricity supply from nuclear power is causing rates to rise and puts added pressure on Germany to develop alternative energy sources quickly.

By developing renewable energy to replace some of its fossil fuel use, Germany has decreased its emissions of carbon dioxide by 140 million tons per year—equal to taking 24 million cars off the road. Since 1990, carbon dioxide emissions from German energy sources have fallen by 24%, and emissions of seven other major pollutants (CH_4, N_2O, SO_2, NO_x, CO, VOCs, and dust) have been reduced by 12–95%. At least half of these reductions are thought to be due to renewable energy paid for under the feed-in tariff system.

Germany's success is serving as a model for other countries in Europe and around the world. As of 2013, more than 90 nations had implemented some sort of feed-in tariff. Spain and Italy ignited their wind and solar development as a result. In North America, Vermont and Ontario established feed-in tariff systems similar to Germany's, while California, Hawaii, Oregon, Washington, and New York conduct more-limited programs. In 2010, Gainesville, Florida, became the first U.S. city to establish feed-in tariffs, and solar power is growing quickly there as a result. Moreover, utilities in 46 U.S. states now offer net metering, in which utilities credit customers who produce renewable power and feed it into the grid. As more nations, states, and cities encourage renewable energy, we may soon experience a historic transition in the way we meet our energy demands.

"New" Renewable Energy Sources

Germany's bold federal policy is just one facet of a global shift toward renewable energy. Across the world, nations are searching for ways to move away from fossil fuels while ensuring a reliable and affordable supply of energy for their economies. This is because the economic and social costs, security risks, and health and environmental impacts of fossil fuel dependence (Chapter 15) are all continuing to intensify.

The two renewable energy sources that are most developed and widely used are bioenergy, the energy from combustion of biomass (wood and other plant matter), and hydropower, the energy from running water. These conventional alternatives to fossil fuels are renewable, but they can be depleted with overuse and exert some undesirable environmental impacts.

In this chapter we explore a group of alternative energy sources that are often called "new renewables." These diverse sources include energy from the sun, from wind, from Earth's geothermal heat, and from ocean water. These energy sources are not truly new. In fact, they are as old as our planet, and people have used them for millennia. We commonly refer to them as "new" because (1) they are just beginning to be used on a wide scale in our modern industrial society, (2) they are harnessed using technologies still in a rapid phase of development, and (3) they will likely play much larger roles in the future.

New renewable sources are growing fast

As with other energy sources, the new renewables provide energy for three types of applications: (1) to generate electricity, (2) to heat air or water, and (3) to fuel vehicles. Their potential is enormous, yet so far their contribution to our society's overall energy budget remains small. Today we obtain just 1% of our global energy from the new renewable energy sources. Fossil fuels provide 81% of the world's energy and nuclear power provides 6%, while biomass and hydropower supply nearly all of the 13% that renewable energy sources provide.

The new renewables make a similarly small contribution to our global generation of electricity thus far. Only 20% of our electricity comes from renewable energy, and hydropower accounts for four-fifths of this amount.

Nations and regions vary in the renewable sources they use. In the United States, most renewable energy comes from biomass and hydropower. As of 2012, wind power accounted for 15%, solar energy for 3%, and geothermal energy for 3% (FIGURE 16.1a). Of electricity generated in the United States from renewables, hydropower accounts for most, while as of 2012 wind power accounted for 29%, geothermal for 3%, and solar for just 1% (FIGURE 16.1b).

Although they comprise a small proportion of our energy budget, the new renewable energy sources are growing quickly. Over the past four decades, solar, wind, and geothermal energy sources have grown far faster than has

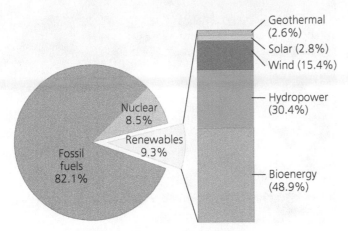

(a) U.S. consumption of renewable energy, by source

Geothermal (2.6%)
Solar (2.8%)
Wind (15.4%)
Hydropower (30.4%)
Bioenergy (48.9%)

Nuclear 8.5%
Renewables 9.3%
Fossil fuels 82.1%

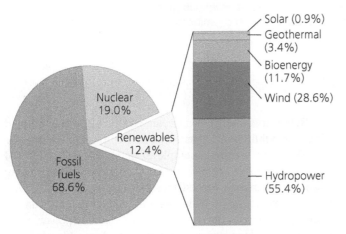

(b) U.S. electricity generation from renewable sources

Solar (0.9%)
Geothermal (3.4%)
Bioenergy (11.7%)
Wind (28.6%)
Hydropower (55.4%)

Nuclear 19.0%
Renewables 12.4%
Fossil fuels 68.6%

FIGURE 16.1 Nine percent of the energy consumed in the United States each year comes from renewable sources. Of this amount **(a)**, most derives from bioenergy and hydropower. Wind power, solar energy, and geothermal energy together account for just 21% of this amount. Similarly, just 12% of electricity generated in the United States **(b)** comes from renewable energy sources, predominantly hydropower. *Data are for 2012, from Energy Information Administration, U.S. Department of Energy, 2013.*

the overall energy supply. The long-term leader in growth is wind power, which has expanded by nearly 50% *each year* since the 1970s. In recent years, solar power has grown faster than wind (**FIGURE 16.2**). Because these sources started from such low levels of use, however, it will take them

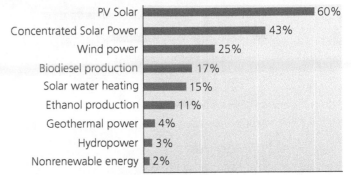

PV Solar — 60%
Concentrated Solar Power — 43%
Wind power — 25%
Biodiesel production — 17%
Solar water heating — 15%
Ethanol production — 11%
Geothermal power — 4%
Hydropower — 3%
Nonrenewable energy — 2%

FIGURE 16.2 The "new renewable" energy sources are growing far faster than conventional energy sources. Shown are average rates of growth each year between 2007 and 2012. *Data from REN21, 2013. Renewables 2013: Global status report. REN21, UNEP, Paris.*

DATA Q At the yearly growth rate shown, if you began with 10 units of PV solar capacity, how much would there be after 5 years?

some time to catch up to conventional sources. The absolute amount of energy added by a 50% increase in wind power today is less than the amount added by just a 1% increase in fossil fuels.

The new renewables offer advantages

Use of new renewables has been expanding because of growing concerns over diminishing fossil fuel supplies and because of the many environmental and health impacts of fossil fuel combustion (Chapter 15). Advances in technology are also making it easier and less expensive to harness renewable energy sources.

The new renewables promise several benefits over fossil fuels. They help alleviate many types of air pollution. In particular, they help reduce the greenhouse gas emissions that drive global climate change (**FIGURE 16.3**). Unlike fossil fuels, renewable sources are inexhaustible on time scales relevant to our society. Renewables also can diversify an economy's energy mix, helping to reduce price volatility and buffer us against restrictions in supply of imported fuels. Moreover, novel energy sources can generate income and property tax for communities, especially in rural areas passed over by other economic development.

Shifting to renewable energy also creates new employment opportunities. The design, installation, maintenance, and

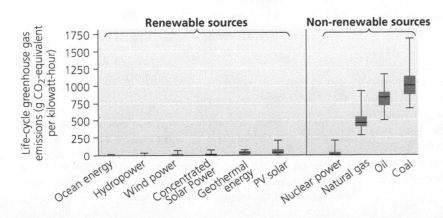

FIGURE 16.3 Renewable energy sources release far fewer greenhouse gas emissions than fossil fuels. Shown are ranges of estimates from scientific studies of each source when used to generate electricity. *Data from Intergovernmental Panel on Climate Change, 2012. Renewable energy sources and climate change mitigation. Special report. Cambridge Univ. Press, New York.*

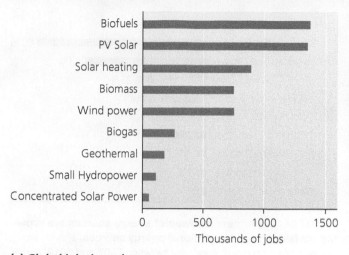

(a) Global jobs in each sector

(b) A wind power technician in Texas

FIGURE 16.4 **Renewable energy creates new green-collar jobs.** Nearly 6 million people worldwide were employed in renewable energy jobs as of 2012, with more than half of these in solar, wind, and geothermal energy. *Data from REN21, 2013. Renewables 2013: Global status report. REN21, UNEP, Paris.*

management required to develop technologies and rebuild and operate our society's energy infrastructure promise to be major sources of employment for young people today, through **green-collar jobs.** Nearly 6 million people work in renewable energy jobs around the world already, and the number is rising (FIGURE 16.4).

As renewable energy technologies evolve and as novel energy sources are harnessed and developed, we can better assess the particular benefits and drawbacks of each approach. As we learn more about the contributions and impacts of each source and technique, we can better judge how to prioritize our energy choices (see THE SCIENCE BEHIND THE STORY, pp. 466–467).

Policy and investment can accelerate our transition

Rapid growth in renewable energy seems likely to continue as global population and consumption rise, easily accessible fossil fuel supplies decline, and people demand cleaner environments. Yet we cannot wholly convert to renewable energy sources overnight, because we lack the infrastructure needed to transfer huge volumes of power from renewable sources inexpensively on a continent-wide scale. Advances in recent years, though, suggest that we can overcome these technological and economic barriers if renewables are lent political support.

Renewable energy efforts received support when some national governments responded to the global financial downturn of 2008–2009 by enacting stimulus packages and boosting spending on green energy programs to help create jobs. As more governments, utilities, corporations, and consumers promote and use renewable energy, market prices of renewables should continue to fall, further hastening their adoption. At this point, most renewable energy is priced more highly than fossil fuel energy, but some sources have become cost-competitive (FIGURE 16.5).

Renewable energy has expanded quickly whenever and wherever public policy has supported it. Feed-in-tariffs like Germany's are a prime example of an economic policy tool that can hasten the spread of renewable energy by creating financial incentives for businesses and individuals. There are other policy approaches as well. Governments can set goals and mandate that certain percentages of power come from renewable sources by a certain date. As of 2013,

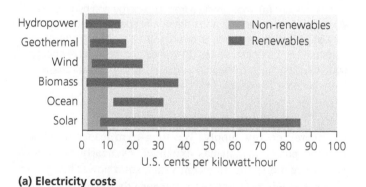

(a) Electricity costs

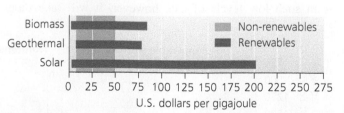

(b) Heating costs

FIGURE 16.5 **Most renewable energy sources have market prices greater than those for nonrenewable sources, but some are competitive.** Shown are price ranges for each source used for **(a)** electricity and **(b)** heating. *Data from Intergovernmental Panel on Climate Change, 2012. Renewable energy sources and climate change mitigation. Special report. Cambridge Univ. Press, New York.*

120 nations and 36 U.S. states had set official targets for renewable energy use. Governments also invest in research and development of technologies, lend money to businesses as they start up, and offer tax credits and tax rebates to companies and individuals who produce or buy renewable energy.

When a government boosts an industry with such policies, the private sector often responds by investing in the industry as private investors recognize an enhanced chance of success and profit. As a result, throughout the world in recent years, advances in renewable energy have been tightly linked to national, state, or local policies that encourage them and to the investment funding that flows more freely as a result. Global investment (public plus private) in renewable energy rose to $244 billion in 2012—nearly six times the amount just seven years earlier. In a feedback process, investment breeds success, and success breeds further investment.

Yet the economics of renewable energy has been erratic. Technologies evolve quickly, and policies vary from place to place and can change unpredictably. As a result, the industry has been volatile, experiencing steep price fluctuations, bankruptcies of promising companies, and bursts of rapid growth. Moreover, we are still learning how to apply policies wisely. In 2007 Spain adopted feed-in tariffs that were so generous (58 cents per kilowatt-hour) that thousands of people rushed to set up solar facilities. Within a year, Spain increased its solar capacity fivefold, accounting for half the solar power installed worldwide that year. However, the generous payments attracted a flood of unqualified contractors and speculators; as a result, many solar plants were hastily built, poorly designed, or badly located. The government realized that many of these new plants would never be economically self-sufficient, so it abruptly slashed the tariff rates.

Critics of government subsidies for renewable energy complain that funneling taxpayer money to particular energy sources is inefficient and skews the market. Instead, they propose, we should let energy sources compete in a free market. Proponents of renewable energy point out that governments have long subsidized fossil fuels and nuclear power far more than they are now subsidizing renewable energy. As a result, there has never been a level playing field, nor a truly free market.

A 2011 study by venture capitalist Nancy Pfund and Yale University graduate student Ben Healey dug deep into data on the U.S. government's many subsidies and tax breaks for all energy sources, from the early days of oil and gas in 1918 through to the present. Their report revealed three main findings:

1. In total, oil and gas have received 75 times more subsidies than new renewable energy sources (FIGURE 16.6a). Nuclear power has received 31 times more subsidies than new renewable energy. This alone is not terribly surprising, because oil, gas, and nuclear power have been major contributors to the U.S. energy supply for a longer time period than solar, wind, and geothermal sources.

2. Per year, oil and gas have received 13 times more subsidies than new renewable energy sources, and nuclear power has received over 9 times more support than new renewable energy (FIGURE 16.6b). This is notable, because

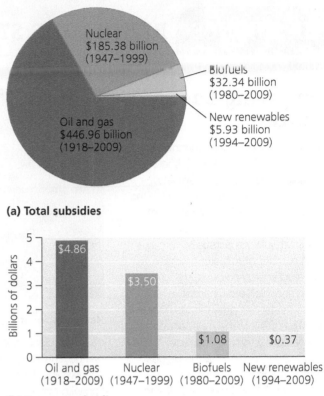

(a) Total subsidies

(b) Per-year subsidies

FIGURE 16.6 Fossil fuels and nuclear power have received far more in U.S. government subsidies than have renewable energy sources. This is true both for **(a)** total amounts over the past century and for **(b)** average amounts per year. *Data are in 2010 dollars, from Pfund, N., and B. Healey, 2011. What would Jefferson do? The historical role of federal subsidies in shaping America's energy future. DBL Investors.*

this per-year comparison controls for the amount of time each source has been used and thereby shows that oil, gas, and nuclear power have received far more support than solar, wind, and geothermal power.

3. Even in the earliest years of each energy source (when subsidies are most useful), oil, gas, and nuclear power received far more in subsidy support than the new renewables have received. In fact, only in one single year have solar, wind, and geothermal combined *ever* received as much support as the *lowest* amount ever offered to oil, gas, or nuclear power.

These findings corroborate the notion that renewable energy sources have not received nearly the amount of support in subsidies and tax breaks that our long-established nonrenewable energy sources continue to enjoy.

Many feel that the subsidies showered on fossil fuels have helped to enhance America's economy, national security, and international influence by establishing thriving global energy industries dominated by U.S. firms. By this logic, if America wants to be a global leader in the transition to clean and renewable energy, then political and financial support will likely need to be redirected toward these new energy sources. In his 2010 State of the Union speech, U.S. President Barack Obama declared: "The nation that leads the clean energy economy will be the nation that leads the global economy." Whether the United States will be that nation remains to be seen.

Comparing Energy Sources

In a world facing climate change, air pollution, and risks to energy security, the choices we make as a society about energy are far-reaching. With the stakes so high, and with a variety of energy sources to choose from, which sources should we pursue?

A number of researchers have compared energy sources, trying to determine which are cleanest, which release the fewest greenhouse gases, and which provide the most economic stability. Let's examine one recent study that sought to analyze all the biggest issues in a comprehensive way.

In 2009 Mark Jacobson, director of the Atmosphere/Energy Program at Stanford University, undertook a broad review of renewable energy sources, digging deep into the published literature to calculate impacts of different energy sources across their entire life cycles (including their materials, construction, operation, and so on). Reviewing over 100 existing studies, his life-cycle analysis was published in the journal *Energy and Environmental Science*.

It is difficult to compare energy sources because some are used primarily to generate electricity whereas others are used mostly for heating and cooling, while still others provide fuel for transportation. To make an apples-to-apples comparison, Jacobson calculated impacts for each source as if it alone were being used to power all the vehicles in the United States. For example, for electricity-producing sources such as wind or PV solar, he calculated how much was needed to power electric vehicles for the entire nation, and he compared the impacts to those from powering the same number of combustion-engine vehicles with liquid fuels.

Mark Jacobson of Stanford University

In all, Jacobson evaluated and ranked nine electric power sources and two liquid fuel sources, in conjunction with three vehicle types: battery-electric vehicles, hydrogen-fuel-cell vehicles (p. 484), and E85 flex-fuel vehicles.

He first examined carbon dioxide emissions. His analysis showed that wind power was lowest in CO_2 emissions but that nearly all renewable options eliminated the vast majority of emissions from vehicles, thus reducing total U.S. emissions by close to 30%. The exceptions were corn-based ethanol and cellulosic ethanol, both of which, he found, would be likely to *increase* emissions.

Next, Jacobson analyzed air pollution from seven major pollutants. Using data on U.S. deaths attributed to fossil fuel pollution each year, he calculated the number of deaths expected to result from using each energy source to fuel vehicles. The number of deaths was close to zero for all renewable sources except for biofuels. Deaths from ethanol emissions were equivalent in number to those currently attributed to gasoline. Nuclear power was equivalent to most renewables in having a low death rate, but Jacobson also calculated impacts from potential nuclear proliferation and weapons use

by a government or by terrorists. When these factors were included, nuclear power emerged as the least safe option.

Jacobson next looked at the footprint in land area that each energy source takes up. He calculated area taken up by energy infrastructure directly, as well as area influenced by the spacing of infrastructure. All electricity-generating renewables were very modest in their land demand, with hydropower and wind power taking up greater areas than the rest. Again, biofuels were high-impact; both corn ethanol and cellulosic ethanol required land areas greater than the size of California.

Jacobson continued by assessing water consumption, effects on wildlife, thermal pollution, chemical pollution of water, radioactive waste, operating reliability, and energy supply disruption.

With regard to supply disruption, he concluded that although many renewables are intermittent in their supply, they are least prone to major disruptions because they are less centralized than coal-fired plants, nuclear plants, or oil and ethanol refineries. Moreover, he argued that intermittency could be overcome by integrating sources over large geographic areas and by combining them strategically through the day, taking advantage of peaks in power from solar and wind and balancing the troughs with geothermal, pumped-storage hydropower, batteries, hydrogen fuel, and other means (FIGURE 1).

When Jacobson at last went to assess overall results and rank the energy sources by a weighted average of all the above issues, he found that wind power was most desirable, followed by concentrated solar power, geothermal power, tidal power, and

PV solar (**FIGURE 2**). Worst were corn ethanol and cellulosic ethanol.

Is it realistic to think we could power all our vehicles with wind power? Jacobson says yes. He calculated that to power all U.S. vehicles would require between 73,000 and 144,000 5-megawatt wind turbines. This sounds like a lot, yet it is fewer than the 300,000 airplanes that the United States built during World War II, and fewer than the number of (mostly smaller) turbines already erected worldwide. One reason so few turbines are needed is that battery-electric vehicles make use of power much more efficiently than gasoline-powered vehicles, so that far less energy is required.

As his research paper was being published, Jacobson also co-authored an article in the popular magazine *Scientific American* with Mark Delucchi of the University of California–Davis, analyzing how the world could meet all its energy needs from renewable energy.

The pair concluded that our needs could be met with a combination of:

- 490,000 tidal turbines
- 5350 geothermal plants
- 900 hydroelectric plants
- 3.8 million wind turbines
- 720,000 wave converters
- 1.7 billion rooftop PV systems
- 49,000 concentrated solar power plants
- 40,000 PV power plants

These researchers judged that our main potential barrier was not the scale of development but rather the availability of a handful of rare-earth metals in limited supply (e.g., silver, platinum, lithium, indium, tellurium, and neodymium).

Critics of Jacobson's work have pointed to such articles in popular magazines, and to public speaking events, to question Jacobson's objectivity and paint him as an advocate. Critics who objected to his inclusion of impacts from a nuclear weapons

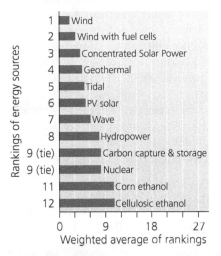

FIGURE 2 **Jacobson found wind power to be the most desirable renewable energy source overall, and ethanol to be least desirable.** *Data from Jacobson, M., 2009. Review of solutions to global warming, air pollution, and energy security.* Energy & Environmental Science *2009 (2): 148–173.*

disaster in his comparison of energy sources pointed out that he has spoken out against nuclear power in public forums.

Any scientist who steps out of the lab, field, or office and advocates publicly for particular solutions is liable to be criticized by those who disagree with his or her positions. Whether such criticisms are fair—and whether they are in society's best interest—are complicated questions. On one hand, remaining objective and free of advocacy gives science its strength and credibility. On the other hand, don't we want our advocates to be the people who have studied the issues themselves and are the best informed about them?

Regardless of how one views the recent research by Jacobson and his colleagues, the number of such energy comparisons is increasing, and policymakers today have a better and better array of information to draw on to help chart our energy future. ●

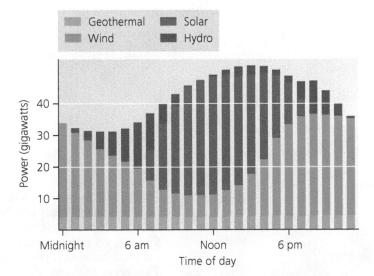

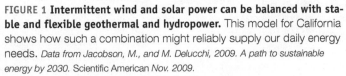

FIGURE 1 **Intermittent wind and solar power can be balanced with stable and flexible geothermal and hydropower.** This model for California shows how such a combination might reliably supply our daily energy needs. *Data from Jacobson, M., and M. Delucchi, 2009. A path to sustainable energy by 2030.* Scientific American *Nov. 2009.*

Solar Energy

The sun releases astounding amounts of energy by converting hydrogen to helium through nuclear fusion. The tiny proportion of this energy that reaches Earth is enough to drive most processes in the biosphere, helping to make life possible on our planet. Each day, Earth receives enough **solar energy**, or energy from the sun, to power human consumption for a quarter of a century. On average, each square meter of Earth's surface receives about 1 kilowatt of solar energy—17 times the energy of a lightbulb. As a result, a typical home has enough roof area to meet all its power needs with rooftop panels that harness solar energy. However, we are still in the process of developing solar technologies and learning the most effective and cost-efficient ways to put the sun's energy to use.

We can collect solar energy using passive or active methods

The simplest way to harness solar energy is through **passive solar energy collection.** In this approach, buildings are designed to maximize absorption of sunlight in winter and to keep the interior cool in the heat of summer. Installing south-facing windows maximizes the capture of winter sunlight. Overhangs shade windows in summer, when the sun is high in the sky and when cooling, not heating, is desired.

Passive solar techniques also use materials that absorb heat, store it, and release it later. Such *thermal mass* (of straw, brick, concrete, or other materials) often makes up floors, roofs, and walls, or can be used in portable blocks. Planting vegetation around a building to buffer the structure from temperature swings is another passive solar approach. Passive solar approaches are an important component of sustainable buildings. By heating buildings in cold weather and cooling them in warm weather, passive solar methods conserve energy and reduce energy costs.

Active solar energy collection makes use of devices to focus, move, or store solar energy. We can use such technologies to heat water and air in our homes and businesses. One common method involves installing *flat plate solar collectors* on rooftops. These panels generally consist of dark-colored, heat-absorbing metal plates mounted in flat glass-covered boxes. Water, air, or antifreeze runs through tubes that pass through the collectors, transferring heat from the collectors to the building or its water tank (**FIGURE 16.7**). Heated water can be stored for later use and passed through pipes designed to release the heat into the building.

Over 200 million households worldwide heat water with solar collectors. Only 1.5 million of these are in the United States, and most of these are used for swimming pools. Active solar heating is used more widely in China and in Europe, where Germans motivated by feed-in tariffs installed 200,000 new systems in 2008 alone. Because solar heating systems do not need to be connected to an electrical grid, they are useful in isolated locations. In Gaviotas, a remote town on the high plains of Colombia in South America, residents use active solar technology for heating, cooling, and water purification. This shows that solar energy need not be confined to wealthy communities or to regions that are always sunny.

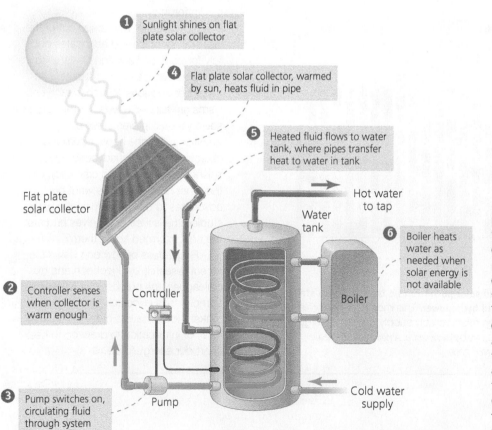

1 Sunlight shines on flat plate solar collector

4 Flat plate solar collector, warmed by sun, heats fluid in pipe

5 Heated fluid flows to water tank, where pipes transfer heat to water in tank

Flat plate solar collector

Hot water to tap

Water tank

6 Boiler heats water as needed when solar energy is not available

Boiler

2 Controller senses when collector is warm enough

Controller

3 Pump switches on, circulating fluid through system

Pump

Cold water supply

FIGURE 16.7 Solar collectors can provide heating. Systems for heating water vary in design, but typically **1** sunlight is gathered on a flat plate solar collector, until a controller **2** switches on a pump **3** to circulate fluid through pipes to the collector. The sunlit collector heats the fluid **4**, which flows through pipes **5** to a water tank. The hot fluid in the pipes transfers heat to the water in the tank, and this heated water is available for the taps of the home or business. Generally an external boiler **6** kicks in to heat water when solar energy is not available.

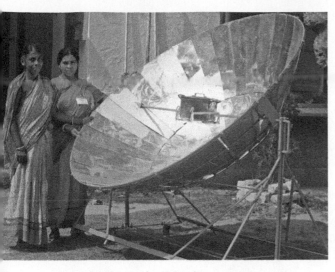

(a) Solar cooker in India

Curved reflectors heat liquid in horizontal tubes

Each curved reflector focuses light on its own small receiver

Curved mirrors reflect light onto absorber tube

Field of heliostats focus light on central power tower

(b) Four methods of concentrating solar power

FIGURE 16.8 **By concentrating solar energy, we can provide heat and electricity.** Solar cookers **(a)** focus solar radiation to cook food. Utilities concentrate solar power with several approaches **(b)** to generate electricity at large scales. At the Solar Two facility in the southern California desert **(c)**, hundreds of mirrors reflect sunlight onto a central receiver atop a power tower, producing electricity for 10,000 households.

(c) The Solar Two power tower facility in California

Concentrating solar rays magnifies energy

As any mischievous young boy who has killed ants with a magnifying glass knows, we can intensify solar energy by gathering sunlight from a wide area and focusing it on a single point. This is the principle behind *solar cookers*, simple portable ovens that use reflectors to focus sunlight onto food and cook it (FIGURE 16.8a). Such cookers are proving extremely useful in the developing world.

At much larger scales, utilities are using the principle behind solar cookers to generate electricity. **Concentrated solar power (CSP)** is being harnessed by several methods (FIGURE 16.8b) in sunny regions in Spain, the U.S. Southwest, and elsewhere. The dominant technology so far is the parabolic trough approach (leftmost diagram in Figure 16.8b), in which curved mirrors focus sunlight onto synthetic oil in pipes. The superheated oil is piped to an adjacent facility where it creates steam that drives turbines to generate electricity. In another approach, numerous mirrors concentrate sunlight onto a receiver atop a tall "power tower" (FIGURE 16.8c). From this central receiver, heat is transported by air or fluids (often molten salts) and piped to a steam-driven generator to

create electricity. CSP facilities can harness light from lenses or mirrors spread across large areas of land, and the lenses or mirrors may move to track the sun's movement.

CSP facilities need to be located in sunny areas, but they have great potential. The International Energy Agency estimates that just 260 km^2 (100 mi^2) of Nevada desert could generate enough electricity to power the entire U.S. economy. Another study estimated that CSP could fulfill one-quarter of global electricity demand by 2050 if we step up investment. German industrialists and investors have spearheaded an ambitious effort to create an immense CSP facility in Africa's Sahara Desert. In this planned $775-billion project, called Desertec, thousands of mirrors spread across vast areas of desert in Morocco would harness the Sahara's sunlight and transmit electricity to Europe, the Middle East, and North Africa. Critics of the project—including Hermann Scheer—say it would be vulnerable to sandstorms and political disputes and would be less reliable and more expensive than the decentralized production from rooftop panels that feed-in tariffs are promoting in Europe. Moreover, many people are growing wary of the environmental impacts that such large-scale developments may pose (see THE SCIENCE BEHIND THE STORY, pp. 472–473).

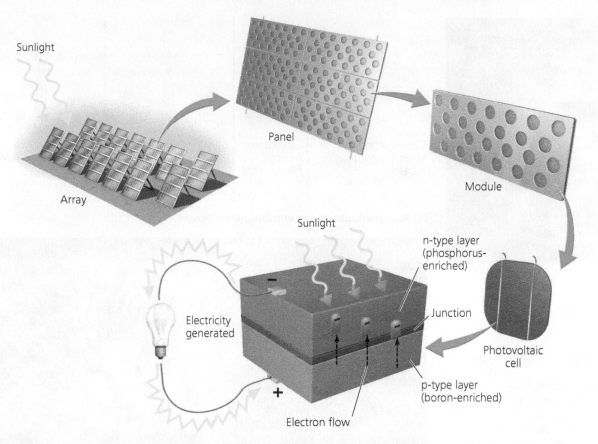

FIGURE 16.9 A photovoltaic (PV) cell converts sunlight to electrical energy. When sunlight hits the silicon layers of the cell, electrons are knocked loose from some of the silicon atoms and tend to move from the boron-enriched "p-type" layer toward the phosphorus-enriched "n-type" layer. Connecting the two layers with wiring remedies this imbalance as electrical current flows from the n-type layer back to the p-type layer. This direct current (DC) is converted to alternating current (AC) to produce usable electricity. PV cells are grouped in modules, comprising panels, which can be erected in arrays.

Photovoltaic cells generate electricity directly

The most direct way to produce electricity from sunlight involves photovoltaic (PV) systems. **Photovoltaic (PV) cells** convert sunlight to electrical energy by making use of the *photovoltaic effect*, or *photoelectric effect*. This effect occurs when light reaches the PV cell and strikes one of a pair of plates made primarily of silicon, a semiconductor that conducts electricity. The light causes one plate to release electrons, which are attracted by electrostatic forces to the opposing plate. Connecting the two plates with wires enables the electrons to flow back to the original plate, creating an electrical current (direct current, DC), which can be converted into alternating current (AC) and used for residential and commercial electrical power (**FIGURE 16.9**). Small PV cells may already power your watch or your calculator. Atop the roofs of homes and other buildings, PV cells are arranged in modules, which comprise panels, which can be gathered together in arrays. Arrays of PV panels can be seen on the roofs of the German houses in the photo that opens this chapter (p. 460).

Researchers are experimenting with variations on PV technology, and manufacturers today are developing **thin-film solar cells,** photovoltaic materials compressed into ultra-thin sheets. Thin-film solar cells are lightweight and far less bulky than the standard crystalline silicon cells shown in Figure 16.9.

Although less efficient at converting sunlight to electricity, they are cheaper to produce. Thin-film technologies can be incorporated into roofing shingles and potentially many other types of surfaces, even highways! For these reasons, many people view thin-film solar technologies as a promising direction for the future.

Photovoltaic cells of all types can be connected to batteries that store the accumulated charge until it is needed. Alternatively, producers of PV electricity can sell their power to their local utility if they are connected to the regional electric grid. In parts of 46 U.S. states, homeowners can sell power to their utility in a process called **net metering,** in which the value of the power the consumer provides is subtracted from the consumer's monthly utility bill. Feed-in tariff systems like Germany's go a step further by paying producers more than the market price of the power. Feed-in tariffs thereby generally offer power producers the hope of turning a profit.

Solar energy is expanding

Although active solar technology dates from the 18th century, it was pushed to the sidelines as fossil fuels came to dominate our energy economy. Funding for research and development of solar technology has been erratic. After the 1973 oil embargo (p. 452), the U.S. Department of Energy funded the installation and testing of over 3000 PV systems, providing a boost to fledgling companies in the solar industry. But later, as oil prices declined, so did government support for solar power.

Largely because of the lack of investment, solar energy contributes just 0.22%—22 parts in 10,000—of the U.S. energy supply, and just 0.1% of U.S. electricity generation. Even in Germany, which gets more of its energy from solar than any other nation, the percentage is only 5%. However, solar energy use has grown by 30% each year worldwide in the past four decades, a growth rate second only to that of wind power. Solar energy is proving especially attractive in developing countries, many of which are rich in sun but poor in infrastructure, and where hundreds of millions of people still live without electricity.

PV technology is the fastest-growing power generation technology today, having recently doubled every two years (FIGURE 16.10). China leads the world in yearly production of PV cells, followed by Germany and Japan. Germany leads the world in installation of PV technology, and German rooftops host over one-third of all PV cells in the world. Germany's investment began in 1998 when Hermann Scheer spearheaded a "100,000 Rooftops" program to install PV panels atop 100,000 German roofs. The popular program ended up easily surpassing this goal, and today over *1.2 million* German rooftops have PV systems.

The United States ranks fifth in production of PV cells, and U.S. firms account for only 4% of the industry. Recent federal tax credits and state-level initiatives may help the United States recover the leadership it lost to other nations in this technology, but China is moving faster and is dominating the market. In fact, the Chinese government's support of its solar industry has led to so much production that supply has outstripped global demand in recent years. Highly subsidized Chinese firms are selling solar products abroad at low prices (often at a loss), driving American and European solar manufacturers out of business. In response, the United States and European nations have slapped tariffs on Chinese imports, while both sides have filed complaints with the World Trade Organization in an escalating global trade dispute.

Despite volatility in the industry as firms try to deal with swings in national policies, global production of PV cells continues to rise sharply, while prices fall (see Figure 16.10). At the same time, efficiencies are increasing, making each unit more powerful. Use of solar technology should continue to expand as prices fall, technologies improve, and governments enact economic incentives to spur investment.

Solar energy offers many benefits

The fact that the sun will continue burning for another 4–5 billion years makes it practically inexhaustible as an energy source for human civilization. Moreover, the amount of solar energy reaching Earth should be enough to power our civilization once we develop technology adequate to harness it. These advantages of solar energy are clear, but the technologies themselves also provide benefits. PV cells and other solar technologies use no fuel, are quiet and safe, contain no moving parts, require little maintenance, and do not require a turbine or generator to create electricity. An average unit can produce energy for 20–30 years.

Solar systems also allow for local, decentralized control over power. Homes, businesses, and isolated communities can use solar power to produce electricity without being near a power plant or connected to a grid. This is especially helpful in developing nations, where solar cookers (see Figure 16.8a) enable families to cook food without gathering fuelwood. This lessens people's daily workload and helps reduce deforestation. In refugee camps, solar cookers are helping to relieve social and environmental stress. The low cost of solar cookers—many can be built locally for $2–10 each—has made them accessible in many impoverished areas. In developed nations, most PV systems are connected to the regional electric grid. As a result, homeowners with PV systems can sell their excess solar energy to their local utility through feed-in tariffs or net metering.

The development and deployment of solar systems are producing many new green-collar jobs. Currently, among major energy sources, PV technology employs the most people per unit energy output, resulting in over 800,000 jobs worldwide (see Figure 16.4).

A major advantage of solar power over fossil fuels is its reduction of greenhouse gas emissions and other air pollutants (see Figure 16.3). The manufacture of photovoltaic cells *does* currently require fossil fuel use, but once up and running, a PV system produces no emissions. Consumers can access online calculators offered by the U.S. Department of Energy and the U.S. Environmental Protection Agency to estimate the economic and environmental effects of installing a PV system. At the time of this writing, these calculators estimated that installing a 5-kilowatt PV system in a home in Fort Worth, Texas, to provide over half of its annual power needs would save the homeowners $681 per year on energy bills and would prevent over 5 tons of carbon dioxide emissions per year—as much CO_2 as results from burning 570 gallons of gasoline. Even in overcast Seattle, Washington, a 5-kilowatt system producing half a home's energy needs can save $310 per year and prevent over 3.5 tons of CO_2 emissions (equal to 390 gallons of gas).

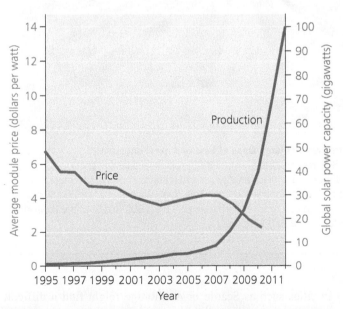

FIGURE 16.10 Global production of PV cells has been growing exponentially, and prices have fallen rapidly. *Data from REN21, 2013. Renewables 2013: Global status report. REN21, UNEP, Paris; and U.S. Department of Energy, EERE, 2011. 2010 Solar technologies market report.*

What Are the Impacts of Solar and Wind Development?

Renewable energy sources and technologies alleviate many of the negative impacts of fossil fuel combustion, and may one day sustainably fulfill our energy needs. However, this does not mean that renewable energy is a panacea free of costs. As our society decides how to pursue energy sources such as solar and wind power, we will need to consider their impacts as well as their benefits.

This has become clear in recent years as the Cape Wind project in Massachusetts and a number of large solar projects in California have brought to the fore a host of issues that some clean-energy proponents had not considered. Scientific study of these impacts is just getting underway, and will be important as energy development proceeds.

The several dozen solar power installations currently under review for the Mojave Desert and other arid regions of California would, if constructed, cover many thousands of acres of land (FIGURE 1).

Desert environments are particularly sensitive, so researchers say we should expect substantial impacts. Besides altering the pristine appearance of an undeveloped landscape, arrays of thousands of mirrors or panels affect communities of plants and animals by casting shade and altering microclimate. Altered conditions tend to hurt native desert-adapted species while helping invasive weeds. At existing solar facilities, the sites are graded and sprayed with herbicide, eliminating plants and damaging fragile soils. Human presence increases as workers maintain

Local residents demonstrate for and against the proposed Cape Wind farm.

the facilities. Solar power plants also require water for cooling and cleaning, and water is scarce in the arid regions hosting most of these facilities. All these impacts will have consequences for plants, animals, and ecosystems.

Large-scale projects need government approval and are subject to the environmental impact statement process. As a result, teams of researchers study conditions at each site to determine what impacts energy

development may have. If impacts are judged to be severe enough, then government agencies can insist that plans be amended.

For instance, the California Energy Commission asked for limits on the proposed Calico Solar Project in southern California in 2010, after biologists concluded that the project would damage habitat of the desert tortoise and bighorn sheep. The company agreed to reduce the size of its footprint by nearly half, reducing estimated impacts to wildlife by 80%, and the Commission approved the project.

In central California, a solar project underwent 18 months of environmental analysis and was approved after the Solargen company agreed to purchase and set aside 23,000 acres of preserved land as "mitigation" for the 3200 acres it was developing. A third California solar project, the Topaz Solar Farm, was scaled back in size after researchers found that scaling back was needed

FIGURE 1 **Solar power farms require large areas of land and exert substantial environmental impacts.** Still, researchers estimate that impacts are less than those demanded by fossil fuels; burning coal for energy uses at least as much land, once one includes the strip mining needed to obtain the coal. This solar plant in Kramer Junction, California, is one of nine that spread across more than 650 ha (1600 acres) of the Mojave Desert, providing power for over 230,000 homes.

Location, timing, and cost can be drawbacks

Solar energy currently has three major disadvantages. One is that not all regions are equally sunny (FIGURE 16.11). People in cities such as Seattle or Anchorage might find it difficult to harness enough sunlight most of the year to rely on solar power. (However, observe in Figure 16.11 that Germany receives even less sun than Alaska, and yet it is the world leader in solar power!)

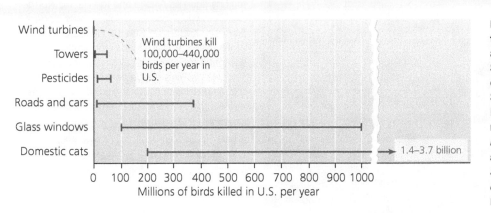

FIGURE 2 **Wind turbines kill birds that fly into them.** Yet far more birds are killed by other human causes. Shown are ranges of recent estimates of yearly bird mortality in the United States from several main causes. Habitat alteration is responsible for still more than any of the causes shown. *Data from American Bird Conservancy, from sources dating through 2010; and Loss, S.R. et al., 2012. The impact of free-ranging domestic cats on wildlife of the United States. Nature Communications 4: Article 1396.*

to protect farmland; minimize aesthetic impacts; and lessen disturbance to tule elk, kit foxes, pronghorn antelope, burrowing owls, and seasonal freshwater pools.

On the U.S. Great Plains, researchers from the National Renewable Energy Laboratory are currently studying impacts of solar installations on prairie ecosystems by comparing a developed site and an undeveloped control site.

Given the impacts of large-scale solar facilities, researchers have determined that installing photovoltaic panels on rooftops of buildings is a low-impact alternative. Simply adding PV panels or roofing tiles to a rooftop has no effect on the landscape. One study, led by five Dutch, German, and American researchers, compared impacts of various ground-based and rooftop PV systems in Germany and in Arizona. The researchers assessed impacts over the systems' entire life cycles (from production to installation to operation). They found that besides avoiding land use impacts, the rooftop systems also emitted significantly fewer greenhouse gases.

A different study in 2008 measured the amount of energy required by PV cells throughout their life cycles and found that replacing fossil fuel energy

with PV solar power would prevent 89–98% of greenhouse gas emissions.

Scientists have also studied health impacts of PV panels. PV cells can pose risks to workers manufacturing them, because they contain toxic chemicals such as cadmium and arsenic and release fine silicon dust that can damage lung tissue. Researchers have concluded that proper attention to worker safety can greatly reduce these risks and that the exposure risks are not much different from other exposure risks we all face in our modern industrialized society.

The overall messages from studies so far are that (1) solar power, even with its impacts, is still cleaner and more sustainable than fossil fuel power; and that (2) we can minimize the impacts of solar power by using rooftop panels and developing better technologies.

Similar messages are emerging from the science on wind power. One major concern is that birds and bats are killed when they fly into the spinning blades of turbines. At California's Altamont Pass wind farm, turbines killed dozens of golden eagles and other raptors in the 1990s. Studies since then at other sites suggest that bird deaths may be a less severe problem than was

initially feared, but uncertainty remains. For instance, one European study indicated that migrating seabirds fly past offshore turbines without problem, but other data show that resident seabird densities have declined near turbines.

On land, the wind industry estimates that about two birds are killed per 1-megawatt-turbine per year. This is far fewer than the hundreds of millions of birds being killed each year by television, radio, and cell phone towers; pesticides; automobiles; glass windows; and domestic cats (**FIGURE 2**). If you own a cat and let it outside, you may be killing more wildlife than most wind farms.

At this point, bat mortality appears to be a more severe problem at wind turbines, but further research is needed. We can reduce wildlife impacts by avoiding development at sites on known migratory flyways or amid prime habitat for bat and bird species that are likely to fly into the blades.

Continued studies on the impacts of wind and solar development should help us find ways to harness renewable energy and attain a sustainable energy future while minimizing the environmental and social impacts of this development. ●

A second drawback is that solar energy is an intermittent resource. Daily or seasonal variation in sunlight can limit stand-alone solar systems if storage capacity in batteries or fuel cells is not adequate or if backup power is not available from a municipal electric grid. Pumped-storage hydropower can sometimes help by compensating for periods of low solar power production.

The third disadvantage of current solar technology is the up-front cost of the equipment. Because of the investment cost, solar power remains the most expensive way to produce

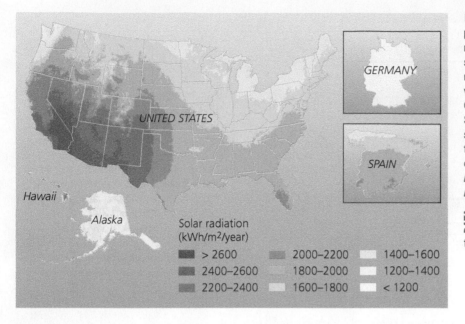

FIGURE 16.11 Solar radiation varies from place to place. Harnessing solar energy is more profitable in sunny regions such as the southwestern United States than in cloudier regions such as Alaska and the Pacific Northwest. However, compare solar power leaders Germany and Spain with the United States. Spain is similar to Kansas in the amount of sunlight it receives, and Germany is cloudier than Alaska! This suggests that solar power can be used with success just about anywhere. *Data from National Renewable Energy Laboratory, U.S. Department of Energy.*

DATA Q Roughly how much more solar radiation does southern Arizona receive than Germany?

Solar radiation (kWh/m²/year)

- > 2600
- 2400–2600
- 2200–2400
- 2000–2200
- 1800–2000
- 1600–1800
- 1400–1600
- 1200–1400
- < 1200

electricity (see Figure 16.5). It may take 20 years or more for most homeowners to break even on an investment in PV arrays or solar collectors. The high costs are due to the fact that the technologies are young and developing. Moreover, they are competing against energy sources (fossil fuels and nuclear power) that have remained relatively cheap as a result of decades of taxpayer support and whose external costs are not included in market prices. As a result, market prices have given governments, businesses, and consumers little economic incentive to switch to solar energy thus far.

However, declines in price and improvements in efficiency of solar technologies so far are encouraging, even in the absence of significant funding from government and industry. At their advent in the 1950s, solar technologies had efficiencies of around 6% while costing $600 per watt. Today, PV cells are showing up to 20% efficiency commercially and 40% efficiency in lab research, suggesting that future solar cells could be more efficient than any energy technologies we have today. Solar systems are becoming less expensive and now can sometimes pay for themselves in less than 10–20 years. After that time, they provide energy virtually for free as long as the equipment lasts.

Wind Power

As the sun heats air in the atmosphere, the movement of differentially heated air masses produces wind. We can harness **wind power** from air's movement by using **wind turbines**, mechanical assemblies that convert wind's kinetic energy, or energy of motion, into electrical energy.

Wind turbines convert kinetic energy to electrical energy

Today's wind turbines have their roots in Europe, where wooden windmills were used for 800 years to grind grain and pump water. The first wind turbine built to generate electricity was constructed in the late 1800s in Cleveland, Ohio. However, it was not until after the 1973 oil embargo that governments and industry in North America and Europe began funding research and development for wind power.

In a modern wind turbine, wind turns the blades of the rotor, which rotate machinery inside a compartment called a *nacelle*, which sits atop a tower (**FIGURE 16.12**). Inside the nacelle

Gearbox (increases rotational speed of blades)

Generator (produces electricity)

Blades

Tower

Nacelle

FIGURE 16.12 A wind turbine converts wind's energy of motion into electrical energy. Wind causes a turbine's blades to spin, turning a shaft that extends into the nacelle. Inside the nacelle, a gearbox converts the rotational speed of the blades, which can be up to 20 revolutions per minute (rpm) or more, into much higher speeds (over 1500 rpm). This provides adequate motion for the generator to produce electricity.

are a gearbox, a generator, and equipment to monitor and control the turbine's activity. Today's towers average 80 m (260 ft) in height, and the largest are taller than a football field is long. Higher is generally better, to minimize turbulence (and potential damage) while maximizing wind speed. Turbines are often erected in groups; such a development is called a **wind farm.** The world's largest wind farms contain hundreds of turbines spread across the landscape.

Engineers design turbines to yaw, or rotate back and forth in response to changes in wind direction, ensuring that the motor faces into the wind at all times. Some turbines are designed to generate low levels of electricity by turning in light breezes. Others are programmed to rotate only in strong winds, generating large amounts of electricity in short time periods. Slight differences in wind speed yield substantial differences in power output, for two reasons. First, the energy content of wind increases as the square of its velocity; thus if wind velocity doubles, energy quadruples. Second, an increase in wind speed causes more air molecules to pass through the wind turbine per unit time, making power output equal to wind velocity cubed. Thus a doubled wind velocity results in an eightfold increase in power output.

Wind power is growing fast

Like solar energy, wind provides just a small proportion of the world's power needs, but wind power is growing fast—doubling every three years (**FIGURE 16.13**). Five nations account for three-quarters of the world's wind power output (**FIGURE 16.14a**), but dozens of nations now produce wind power. Germany had long produced the most, but the United States overtook it in 2008, and China surpassed the United States two years later.

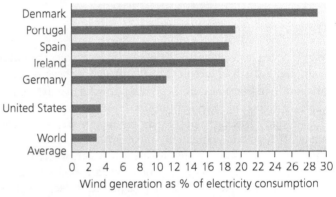

(a) Percentage of global wind power in each nation

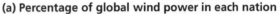

(b) Leading nations in proportion of electricity from wind power

FIGURE 16.14 Several nations are leaders in wind power. Most of the world's wind power capacity **(a)** is concentrated in a handful of nations led by China, the United States, and Germany. Yet tiny Denmark **(b)** obtains the highest percentage of its electricity needs from wind. *Data from (a) Global Wind Energy Council, 2013.* Global wind report: Annual market update 2012. GWEC, Brussels, Belgium; and (b) U.S. Department of Energy, EERE, 2012. 2011 Wind technologies market report.

Denmark leads the world in obtaining the greatest percentage of its energy from wind power. In this small European nation, wind farms supply nearly 30% of Danish electricity needs (**FIGURE 16.14b**). Germany is fifth in this respect, and the United States is 13th. Texas generates the most wind power of all U.S. states, while Iowa and South Dakota each obtain nearly 25% of their electricity from wind.

Wind power's growth in the United States has been haphazard because Congress has not committed to a long-term federal tax credit for wind development, but instead has passed a series of short-term renewals, leaving the industry uncertain about how much to invest. However, experts agree that wind power's growth will continue, because only a small portion of this resource is currently being tapped and because wind power at favorable locations already generates electricity at prices nearly as low as fossil fuels (see Figure 16.5). A 2008 report by a consortium of experts outlined how the United States could meet fully one-fifth of its electrical demands with wind power by 2030.

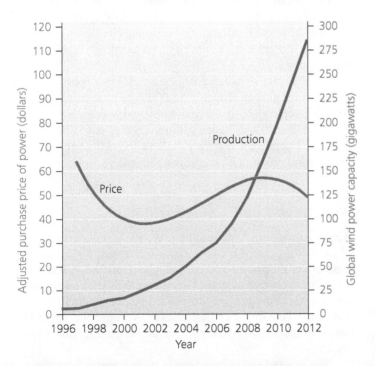

FIGURE 16.13 Global production of wind power has been doubling every three years in recent years, and prices have fallen slightly. *Data from Global Wind Energy Council; and U.S. Department of Energy, EERE, 2012.* 2011 Wind technologies market report.

FIGURE 16.15 **More and more wind farms are being developed offshore.** Offshore winds tend to be stronger yet less turbulent.

Offshore sites hold promise

Wind speeds on average are 20% greater over water than over land, and air is less turbulent over water. For these reasons, offshore wind turbines are becoming popular (FIGURE 16.15). Costs to erect and maintain turbines in water are higher, but the stronger, less turbulent winds produce more power and make offshore wind potentially more profitable. Today's offshore wind farms are limited to shallow water, where towers are sunk into sediments singly or using a tripod configuration. In the future, towers may also be placed in deep water on floating pads anchored to the seafloor.

Denmark erected the first offshore wind farm in 1991, and soon more came into operation across northern Europe, where the North Sea and Baltic Sea offer strong winds. Once Germany raised its feed-in tariff rate for offshore wind from 9 cents to 15 cents per kilowatt-hour in 2009, many projects began construction and today several are operating. By 2013, over 1800 wind turbines were operating in 65 wind farms in the waters of 10 European nations.

In the United States, no offshore wind farms have yet been constructed, but development of the first was approved in 2010 after nine years of debate. The Cape Wind offshore wind farm, if constructed, will feature 130 turbines rising from Nantucket Sound 8 km (5 mi) off the coast of Cape Cod in Massachusetts. In announcing the government's approval, U.S. Interior Secretary Ken Salazar predicted that it would be "the first of many projects up and down the Atlantic coast." Indeed, as of 2013, eight offshore wind developments were in the planning stages off the Northeast coast, one off the Texas coast, and one in Lake Erie.

Wind power has many benefits

Like solar power, wind power produces no emissions once the equipment is manufactured and installed. As a replacement for fossil fuel combustion in the average U.S. power plant, running a 1-megawatt wind turbine for 1 year prevents the release of more than 1500 tons of carbon dioxide, 6.5 tons of sulfur dioxide, 3.2 tons of nitrogen oxides, and 60 lb of mercury,

according to the U.S. Environmental Protection Agency. The amount of carbon pollution that all U.S. wind turbines together prevent from entering the atmosphere is equal to the emissions from nearly 10 million cars, or from combusting the cargo of a 750-car freight train of coal each and every day.

Under optimal conditions, wind power appears efficient in its energy returned on investment (EROI; pp. 431–432. Most studies find that wind turbines produce roughly 20 times more energy than they consume. This EROI value is better than that from most other energy sources. Wind farms also use less water than do conventional power plants.

Wind turbine technology can be used on many scales, from a single tower for local use to farms of hundreds that supply large regions. Small-scale turbine development can help make local areas more self-sufficient, just as solar energy can. For instance, the Rosebud Sioux Tribe of Native Americans set up a single turbine on its reservation in South Dakota. The turbine has been producing electricity for 200 homes and brings the tribe $15,000 per year in revenue. The tribe has now developed a 30-megawatt wind farm nearby, and 20 more turbines are slated to be added soon.

Another benefit of wind power is that farmers and ranchers can lease their land for wind development. A single large turbine can bring in $2000 to $4500 in annual royalties while occupying just a quarter-acre of land. Most of the land can still be used for agriculture. Royalties from the wind power company provide the farmer or rancher revenue while also increasing property tax income for their rural community.

Wind power involves up-front expenses to erect turbines and to expand infrastructure to allow electricity distribution, but over the lifetime of a project it requires only maintenance costs. Unlike fossil-fuel power plants, wind turbines incur no ongoing fuel costs. Startup costs of wind farms generally are higher than those of fossil-fuel plants, but wind farms incur fewer expenses once they are up and running. Moreover, advancing technology is driving down the costs, per unit of electricity produced, of wind farm construction.

Finally, just as solar energy creates job opportunities, so does wind power. Roughly 85,000 Americans and nearly 700,000 people globally are now employed in the wind industry. More than 100 colleges and universities now offer programs and degrees that train people in the skills needed for jobs in wind power and other renewable energy fields.

Wind power has some downsides

Wind is an intermittent resource; we have no control over when it will occur. This is a major limitation in relying on wind as an electricity source, but it is lessened if wind is one of several sources contributing to a utility's power generation. Pumped-storage hydropower can help to compensate during windless times, and batteries or hydrogen fuel (p. 483) can store energy generated by wind and release it later when needed.

Just as wind varies from time to time, it varies from place to place; some areas are windier than others. Global wind patterns combine with local topography—mountains, hills, water bodies, forests, cities—to create local wind patterns.

Resource planners and wind power companies study these patterns closely before planning a wind farm. Meteorological research has given us data with which to judge prime areas for locating wind farms. A map of average wind speeds across the United States (FIGURE 16.16a) reveals that mountainous regions are best, along with areas of the Great Plains. Based on such information, the wind power industry has located much of its generating capacity in states with high wind speeds (FIGURE 16.16b). Provided that wind farms are strategically erected in optimal locations, an estimated 15% of U.S. energy demand could be met using only 43,000 km² (16,600 mi²) of land (with less than 5% of this land area actually occupied by turbines, equipment, and access roads).

However, most of North America's people live near the coasts, far from the Great Plains and mountain regions that have the best wind resources. Thus, continent-wide transmission networks would need to be enhanced to send wind power's electricity to these population centers.

When wind farms *are* proposed near population centers, local residents often oppose them. Turbines are generally located in exposed, conspicuous sites, and some people object to wind farms for aesthetic reasons, feeling that the structures clutter the landscape. Although polls show wide public approval of existing wind projects and of the concept of wind power, newly proposed wind projects often elicit the **not-in-my-backyard (NIMBY)** syndrome among people living

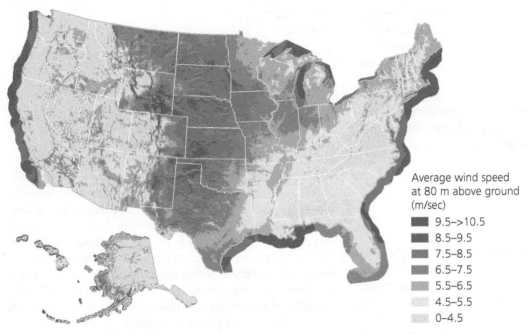

Average wind speed at 80 m above ground (m/sec)

- 9.5–>10.5
- 8.5–9.5
- 7.5–8.5
- 6.5–7.5
- 5.5–6.5
- 4.5–5.5
- 0–4.5

(a) Annual average wind power

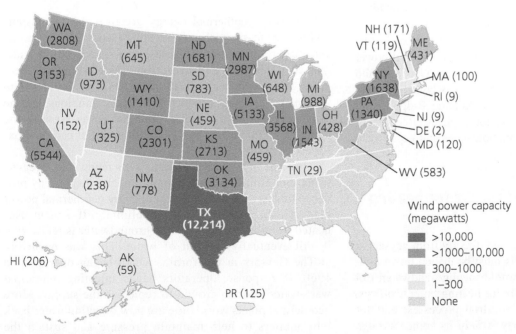

Wind power capacity (megawatts)

- >10,000
- >1000–10,000
- 300–1000
- 1–300
- None

(b) Wind generating capacity, 2013

FIGURE 16.16 Wind speed varies from place to place. Maps of average wind speeds **(a)** help guide the placement of wind farms. Another map **(b)** shows megawatts of wind-power-generating capacity developed in each U.S. state through early 2013. *Sources: (a) U.S. National Renewable Energy Laboratory; (b) American Wind Energy Association, 2013.* 1st Quarter 2013 Market Report.

DATA Q Compare parts (a) and (b). Which states or regions have high wind speeds but are not yet heavily developed with commercial wind power?

nearby. For instance, the Cape Wind project has faced years of opposition from wealthy residents of Cape Cod, Nantucket, and Martha's Vineyard, even though many of these residents consider themselves progressive environmentalists.

Wind turbines also pose a threat to birds and bats, which are killed when they fly into the rotating blades. More research on wildlife impacts is urgently needed (see **The Science behind the Story**, pp. 474–475). One strategy for protecting birds and bats may be selecting sites that are not on migratory flyways or in the midst of prime habitat for species that are likely to fly into the blades.

WEIGHING THE ISSUES

WIND AND NIMBY If you could choose to get your electricity from a wind farm or a coal-fired power plant, which would you choose? How would you react if the electric utility proposed to build the wind farm that would generate your electricity atop a ridge running in back of your neighborhood, such that the turbines would be clearly visible from your living room window? Would you support or oppose the development? Why? If you would oppose it, where would you suggest the farm be located? Do you think anyone might oppose it in that location?

Geothermal Energy

Geothermal energy is thermal energy that arises from beneath Earth's surface. The radioactive decay of elements amid the extremely high pressures deep in the interior of our planet generates heat that rises to the surface through magma and through cracks and fissures. Where this energy heats groundwater, natural spurts of heated water and steam are sent up from below and may erupt through the surface as terrestrial geysers or submarine hydrothermal vents.

Geothermal energy manifests itself at the surface in these ways only in certain areas, and regions vary in their geothermal resources (FIGURE 16.17). One geothermally rich area is in California near Napa Valley's wine country. There, engineers have for years operated the world's largest geothermal power plants, The Geysers. The nation of Iceland also has a wealth of geothermal energy resources because it is built from lava that extruded and cooled at the Mid-Atlantic Ridge, along the spreading boundary of two tectonic plates. Because of the geothermal heat in this region, volcanoes and geysers are numerous in Iceland.

We harness geothermal energy for heating and electricity

Geothermal energy can be harnessed directly from geysers at the surface, but most often wells must be drilled down hundreds or thousands of meters toward heated groundwater. Hot groundwater can be used directly for heating homes, offices, and greenhouses; for driving industrial processes; and for drying crops. Iceland heats nearly 90% of its homes through direct heating with piped hot water. Direct use of naturally

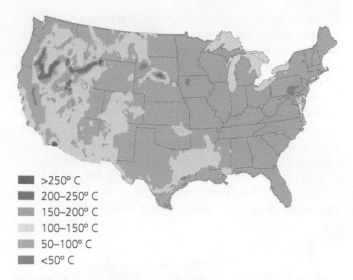

>250° C
200–250° C
150–200° C
100–150° C
50–100° C
<50° C

FIGURE 16.17 Geothermal resources in the United States are greatest in the western states. This map shows water temperatures 3 km (1.9 mi) belowground. *Data from Idaho National Laboratory.*

heated water is efficient and inexpensive, but it is feasible only where geothermal energy is readily available and does not need to be transported far.

Geothermal power plants harness the energy of naturally heated underground water and steam to generate electricity (FIGURE 16.18). Generally, a power plant brings water at temperatures of 150–370°C (300–700°F) or more to the surface and converts it to steam by lowering the pressure in specialized compartments. The steam turns turbines to generate electricity. The world's largest geothermal plants, The Geysers in California, provide electricity for 725,000 homes. Globally, one-third of the geothermal energy we use is for electricity, and two-thirds is used for direct heating.

Geothermal power has benefits and limitations

All forms of geothermal energy greatly reduce emissions relative to fossil fuel combustion. Geothermally heated water can release dissolved gases, including carbon dioxide, methane, ammonia, and hydrogen sulfide. However, these gases generally occur in small quantities, and facilities with filtering technologies produce even fewer emissions. By one estimate, each megawatt of geothermal power prevents the emission of 7.0 million kg (15.5 million lb) of carbon dioxide each year.

In principle, geothermal energy is renewable, because using it does not affect the amount of thermal energy produced underground. However, not every geothermal power plant will be able to operate indefinitely. If a plant uses heated water more quickly than groundwater is recharged, it will eventually run out of water. This was occurring at The Geysers in California, which began operation in 1960. In response, operators began injecting municipal wastewater into the ground to replenish the supply. More geothermal plants worldwide are now injecting water back into aquifers to help maintain pressure and sustain the resource.

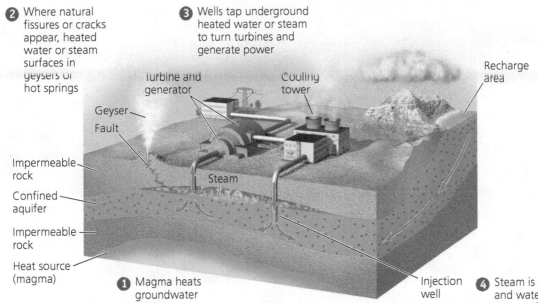

② Where natural fissures or cracks appear, heated water or steam surfaces in geysers or hot springs

③ Wells tap underground heated water or steam to turn turbines and generate power

Recharge area

Turbine and generator

Cooling tower

Geyser

Fault

Impermeable rock

Confined aquifer

Impermeable rock

Heat source (magma)

Steam

① Magma heats groundwater

Injection well

④ Steam is cooled and condensed, and water is injected back into the aquifer to maintain pressure

(a) Geothermal energy

(b) Nesjavellir geothermal power station, Iceland

FIGURE 16.18 Geothermal power plants generate electricity using naturally heated water from underground. With geothermal energy **(a)**, magma heats groundwater ①, some of which escapes through surface vents such as geysers ②. A power plant may tap into heated water and channel steam through turbines to generate electricity ③. Once used, steam may be condensed into water and pumped back into the aquifer to maintain pressure ④. At Iceland's Nesjavellir power station **(b)**, steam piped in from wells heats water from a lake. The heated water is sent through an insulated pipeline to the capital city, where residents use it for washing and space heating.

A second reason geothermal energy is not always renewable is that patterns of geothermal activity in Earth's crust shift naturally over time. As a result, an area that produces hot groundwater now may not always do so. In addition, the water of many hot springs is laced with salts and minerals that corrode equipment and pollute the air. These factors may shorten the lifetime of plants, increase maintenance costs, and add to pollution.

The greatest limitation of geothermal power is its restriction to regions where we can tap energy from naturally heated groundwater. Places like Iceland, northern California, and Yellowstone National Park are rich in naturally heated groundwater, but most areas of the world are not.

Enhanced geothermal systems might widen our reach

To overcome the limitation of geothermal energy to areas where naturally heated groundwater occurs, engineers are currently developing **enhanced geothermal systems (EGS).** In the EGS approach, engineers drill deeply into dry rock, fracture the rock, and pump in cold water. The water becomes heated deep underground and is then drawn back up and used to generate power. EGS thereby uses natural thermal energy underground but supplies the water, which can be reused repeatedly. In theory we could use EGS widely in many locations. Germany, for instance, has little heated groundwater, but feed-in-tariffs have enabled an EGS facility to operate profitably there.

EGS technology shows significant promise, and a 2006 report estimated that heat resources below the United States alone are enough to power the world's energy demands for several millennia. However, EGS also appears to trigger minor earthquakes. Unless we can develop ways to use EGS safely and reliably, our use of geothermal power will remain more localized than our use of solar, wind, bioenergy, or hydropower.

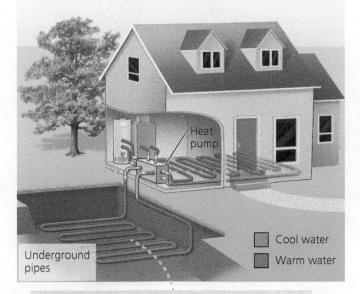

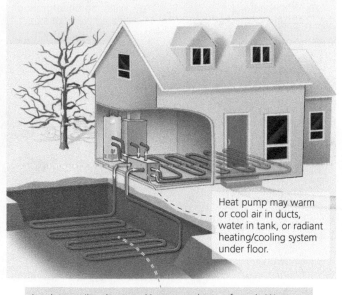

In summer, soil underground is cooler than surface air. Water flowing through the pipes transfers heat from the house to the ground, cooling the house.

In winter, soil underground is warmer than surface air. Water flowing through the pipes transfers heat from the ground to the house, warming the house.

Heat pump

Underground pipes

Cool water
Warm water

Heat pump may warm or cool air in ducts, water in tank, or radiant heating/cooling system under floor.

FIGURE 16.19 Ground-source heat pumps provide an efficient way to heat and cool air and water in one's home. A network of pipes filled with water and antifreeze extend underground. Soil is cooler than air in the summer (**left**), and warmer than air in the winter (**right**), so by running fluid between the house and the ground, these systems adjust temperatures inside.

Heat pumps make use of temperature differences above and below ground

Although heated groundwater is available only in certain areas, we can take advantage of the temperature differences that exist naturally between the soil and the air just about anywhere. Soil varies in temperature from season to season less than air does, because it absorbs and releases heat more slowly and because warmth and cold do not penetrate deeply belowground. Just several inches below the surface, temperatures are nearly constant year-round. Geothermal heat pumps, or **ground-source heat pumps (GSHPs),** make use of this phenomenon.

Ground-source heat pumps provide heating in the winter by transferring heat from the ground into buildings, and they provide cooling in the summer by transferring heat from buildings into the ground. This heat transfer is accomplished with a network of underground plastic pipes that circulate water and antifreeze (FIGURE 16.19). Because heat is simply moved from place to place rather than being produced using outside energy inputs, heat pumps can be highly energy-efficient.

More than 600,000 U.S. homes use GSHPs. Compared to conventional electric heating and cooling systems, GSHPs heat spaces 50–70% more efficiently, cool them 20–40% more efficiently, can reduce electricity use by 25–60%, and can reduce emissions by up to 70%.

Ocean Energy Sources

The oceans are home to several underexploited energy sources resulting from continuous natural processes. Of the four

approaches being developed, three involve motion, and one involves temperature.

We can harness energy from tides, waves, and currents

Just as dams on rivers use flowing fresh water to generate hydroelectric power, we can use kinetic energy from the natural motion of ocean water to generate electrical power.

Scientists and engineers are working to harness the motion of ocean waves and convert this mechanical energy into electricity. Many designs for machinery to harness **wave energy** have been invented, but few have been adequately tested. Some designs for offshore facilities involve floating devices that move up and down with the waves. A prime example is the snake-like wave energy converter shown on the front cover of this book. Built by the Scottish company Pelamis (a Latin word denoting a genus of sea snake), variations on this jointed, columnar design have been deployed in several parts of the world. Machinery and hydraulic fluids inside the floating columns use wave motion to generate electricity, which is transmitted to shore via undersea cables.

Wave energy is greatest at deep-ocean sites, but transmitting electricity to shore is expensive. Some designs for coastal onshore facilities funnel waves from large areas into narrow channels and elevated reservoirs, from which water then flows out, generating electricity as hydroelectric dams do. Other coastal designs use rising and falling waves to push air into and out of chambers, turning turbines (FIGURE 16.20). The first commercially operating wave energy facility began operating in 2011 in Spain, using technology tested for a decade in

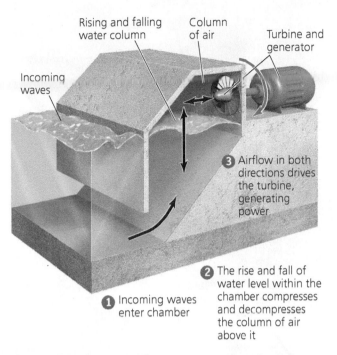

FIGURE 16.20 **Coastal facilities harness energy from ocean waves.** In one design, as waves enter and exit a chamber **1**, the air inside is alternately compressed and decompressed **2**, creating airflow that rotates turbines **3** to generate electricity.

Key callouts (clockwise):
- Rising and falling water column
- Column of air
- Turbine and generator
- Incoming waves
- **3** Airflow in both directions drives the turbine, generating power
- **2** The rise and fall of water level within the chamber compresses and decompresses the column of air above it
- **1** Incoming waves enter chamber

The ocean stores thermal energy

Each day the tropical oceans absorb solar radiation with the heat content of 250 billion barrels of oil—enough to provide 20,000 times the electricity used daily in the United States. The ocean's sun-warmed surface is warmer than its deep water, and **ocean thermal energy conversion (OTEC)** is based on this gradient in temperature.

In the *closed cycle* approach, warm surface water is piped into a facility to evaporate chemicals, such as ammonia, that boil at low temperatures. These evaporated gases spin turbines to generate electricity. Cold water piped up from ocean depths then condenses the gases so they can be reused. In the *open cycle* approach, warm surface water is evaporated in a

FIGURE 16.21 **Ocean tides change roughly every six hours.** Tides are extreme at Canada's Bay of Fundy, where boats docked at high tide **(a)** become stranded on the mud at low tide **(b)** as the water recedes.

(a) High tide

(b) Low tide

Scotland. Demonstration projects exist in Europe, Japan, and Oregon.

We are also developing ways of harnessing energy from tides. The rise and fall of ocean tides twice each day moves large amounts of water past any given point on the world's coastlines. Differences in height between low and high tides are especially great in long, narrow bays such as Alaska's Cook Inlet or the Bay of Fundy between New Brunswick and Nova Scotia (FIGURE 16.21). Such locations are best for harnessing **tidal energy,** which is accomplished by erecting dams across the outlets of tidal basins. The incoming tide flows through sluice gates and is trapped behind them. Then, as the outgoing tide passes through the gates, it turns turbines to generate electricity (FIGURE 16.22). Some designs generate electricity from water moving in both directions.

The world's largest tidal generating station is South Korea's Sihwa Lake facility (see Figure 16.22, inset photo). This power station opened in 2011 and is just larger than the La Rance tidal facility in France, which has operated for nearly 50 years. Smaller facilities operate in Canada, China, Russia, and the United Kingdom. The first U.S. tidal station began operating in 2012 in Maine, and one is scheduled to be built in New York City's East River starting in 2013. Tidal stations release few or no pollutant emissions, but they can affect the ecology of estuaries and tidal basins. Five more tidal stations are planned in South Korea, but some have been delayed in the wake of concerns over environmental impacts.

A third way to harness marine kinetic energy is to use the motion of ocean currents, such as the Gulf Stream. Devices like underwater wind turbines have been erected in European waters to test this approach.

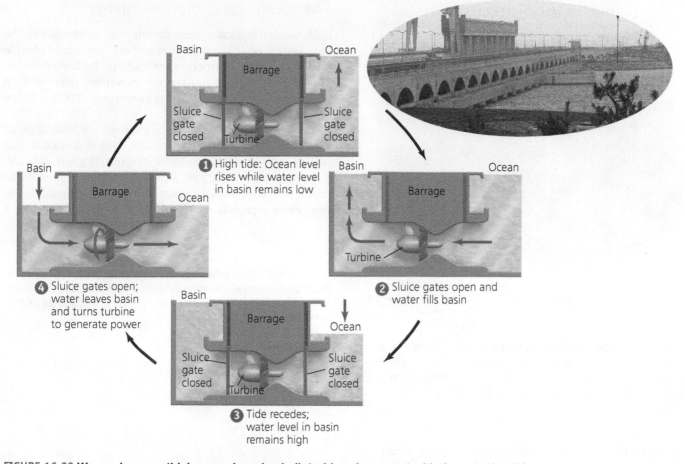

FIGURE 16.22 We can harness tidal energy by using bulb turbines in concert with the outgoing tide. At high tide ❶, ocean water is let through the sluice gates, filling an interior basin ❷. At low tide ❸, the basin water is let out into the ocean, spinning turbines to generate electricity ❹. This technology is used at the new Sihwa Lake tidal generating station (**photo**) in South Korea.

vacuum, and its steam turns turbines and then is condensed by cold water. Because ocean water loses salts as it evaporates, the water can be recovered, condensed, and sold as desalinized fresh water for drinking or agriculture. OTEC research has been conducted in Hawaii and elsewhere, but costs remain high, and so far no facility operates commercially.

WEIGHING **THE ISSUES**

YOUR NATION'S ENERGY? You are the president of a nation the size of Germany, and your nation's congress is calling on you to propose a national energy policy. Your country is located along a tropical coastline. Your geologists do not yet know whether there are fossil fuel deposits or geothermal resources under your land, but your country gets a lot of sunlight and a fair amount of wind, and broad, shallow shelf regions line its coasts. Your nation's population is moderately wealthy but is growing fast, and importing fossil fuels from other nations is becoming expensive.

What approaches would you propose in your energy policy? Name some specific steps you would urge your congress to fund. Are there trade relationships you would seek to establish with other countries? What questions would you fund your nation's scientists to research?

Hydrogen

Each of the renewable energy sources we have discussed can be used to generate electricity more cleanly than can fossil fuels. However, electricity cannot be stored easily in large quantities for use when and where it is needed. This is why most vehicles rely on gasoline from oil for power. The development of fuel cells and of fuel consisting of hydrogen—the universe's simplest and most abundant element—shows promise as a way to store considerable quantities of energy conveniently, cleanly, and efficiently. Like electricity and like batteries, hydrogen is an energy carrier, not a primary energy source. It carries energy that can be converted for use at later times and in different places.

Some yearn for a "hydrogen economy"

Some energy experts envision that hydrogen fuel, together with electricity, could serve as the basis for a clean, safe, and efficient energy system. In such a system, electricity generated from intermittent renewable sources, such as wind or solar energy, could be used to produce hydrogen. Fuel cells—essentially, hydrogen batteries (**FIGURE 16.23**)—could then use hydrogen to produce electrical energy to power vehicles,

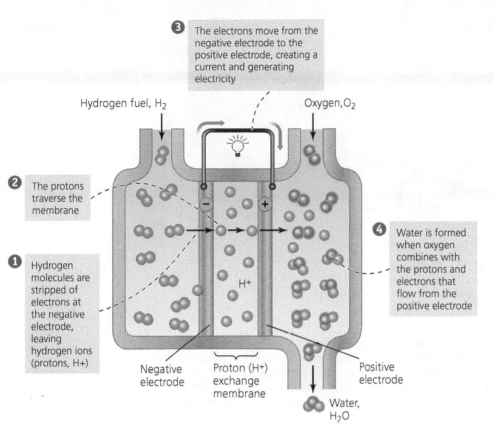

③ The electrons move from the negative electrode to the positive electrode, creating a current and generating electricity

Hydrogen fuel, H$_2$

Oxygen, O$_2$

② The protons traverse the membrane

① Hydrogen molecules are stripped of electrons at the negative electrode, leaving hydrogen ions (protons, H+)

H+

Negative electrode

Proton (H+) exchange membrane

Positive electrode

④ Water is formed when oxygen combines with the protons and electrons that flow from the positive electrode

Water, H$_2$O

FIGURE 16.23 Hydrogen fuel drives electricity generation in a fuel cell, creating water as a waste product. Atoms of hydrogen are split **①** into protons and electrons. The protons, or hydrogen ions **②**, pass through a proton exchange membrane. The electrons, meanwhile, move from a negative electrode to a positive one via an external circuit **③**, creating a current and generating electricity. The protons and electrons then combine with oxygen **④** to form water molecules.

computers, cell phones, home heating, and other applications. NASA's space programs have used fuel-cell technology since the 1960s.

Basing an energy system on hydrogen could alleviate dependence on foreign fuels and help fight climate change. For these reasons, governments are funding research into hydrogen and fuel-cell technology, and automobile companies are investing in research and development to produce vehicles that run on hydrogen. A decade ago the island nation of Iceland decided to move toward a "hydrogen economy" and to set an example for the rest of the world to follow. Iceland achieved several early steps in its 30- to 50-year plan to phase out fossil fuels, such as converting buses in the capital city of Reykjavik to run on hydrogen fuel. But the global economic downturn in 2008–2009 and delays in manufacturing hydrogen cars have delayed its progress. Meanwhile, Germany is one of several other nations with hydrogen-fueled city buses (FIGURE 16.24), and it plans by 2015 to launch a network of hydrogen filling stations for hydrogen cars that are being designed.

Hydrogen fuel may be produced from water or from other matter

Hydrogen gas (H$_2$) does not tend to exist freely on Earth. Instead, hydrogen atoms bind to other molecules, becoming incorporated in everything from water to organic molecules. To obtain hydrogen gas for fuel, we must force these substances to release their hydrogen atoms, and this requires an input of energy. Scientists are studying several potential ways of producing hydrogen. In the process of **electrolysis**, electricity is input to split hydrogen atoms from the oxygen atoms of water molecules:

$$2H_2O \rightarrow 2H_2 + O_2$$

Electrolysis produces pure hydrogen, and it does so without emitting the carbon- or nitrogen-based pollutants of fossil fuel combustion. However, whether this strategy for producing hydrogen will cause pollution over its entire life cycle depends on the source of the electricity used for the electrolysis. If coal is burned to generate the electricity, then the process will not reduce emissions compared with reliance on fossil fuels. However, if the electricity is produced by some less-polluting renewable source, then hydrogen production by electrolysis would create much less pollution and greenhouse warming than reliance on fossil fuels. The "cleanliness" of a future hydrogen economy would, therefore, depend largely on the source of electricity used in electrolysis.

The environmental impact of hydrogen production will also depend on the source material for the hydrogen. Besides water, hydrogen can be obtained from biomass and from fossil fuels. Obtaining hydrogen from these sources generally requires less energy input but results in emissions of carbon-based pollutants. For instance, extracting hydrogen from the methane (CH$_4$) in natural gas entails producing one molecule of the greenhouse gas carbon dioxide for every four molecules of hydrogen gas:

$$CH_4 + 2H_2O \rightarrow 4H_2 + CO_2$$

Thus, whether a hydrogen-based energy system is cleaner than a fossil fuel system will depend on how the hydrogen is extracted.

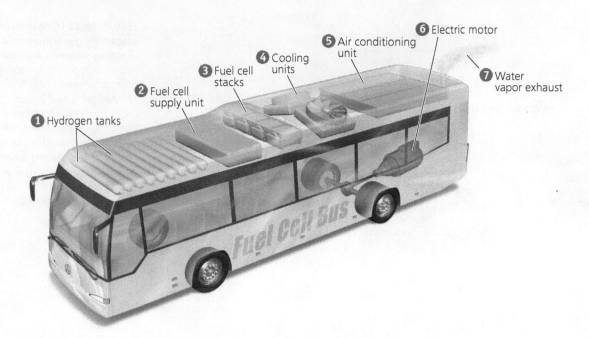

FIGURE 16.24 In one type of hydrogen-fueled bus operating in some German cities, hydrogen is stored in nine fuel tanks ❶. The fuel cell supply unit ❷ controls the flow of hydrogen, air, and cooling water into the fuel cell stacks ❸. Cooling units ❹ and the air conditioning unit ❺ dissipate waste heat produced by the fuel cells. Electricity generated by the fuel cells is changed from direct current (DC) to alternating current (AC) by an inverter, and it is transmitted to the electric motor ❻, which powers the operation of the bus. The vehicle's exhaust ❼ consists simply of water vapor.

Fuel cells produce electricity by joining hydrogen and oxygen

Once isolated, hydrogen gas can be used as a fuel to produce electricity within fuel cells. The chemical reaction involved in a fuel cell is simply the reverse of that for electrolysis. An oxygen molecule and two hydrogen molecules each split, and their atoms bind to form two water molecules:

$$2H_2 + O_2 \rightarrow 2H_2O$$

Figure 16.23 shows how this occurs within one common type of fuel cell. As shown in the diagram, hydrogen gas (usually compressed and stored in an attached fuel tank) is allowed into one side of the cell, and the movement of the hydrogen's electrons from one electrode to the other creates the output of electricity.

Hydrogen and fuel cells have costs and benefits

One major drawback of hydrogen at this point is a lack of infrastructure. To convert a nation such as Germany or the United States to hydrogen would require massive and costly development of facilities to transport, store, and provide the fuel.

Another concern is that some research suggests that leakage of hydrogen from its production, transport, and use could potentially deplete stratospheric ozone and lengthen the atmospheric lifetime of the greenhouse gas methane. Research into these questions is ongoing, because scientists do not want society to switch from fossil fuels to hydrogen without first knowing the risks.

Hydrogen's benefits include the fact that we will never run out of it, because it is the most abundant element in the universe. Hydrogen can be clean and nontoxic to use, and—depending on its source and the source of electricity for its extraction—it may produce few greenhouse gases and other pollutants. Water and heat are the only waste products from a hydrogen fuel cell, along with negligible traces of other compounds. In terms of safety for transport and storage, hydrogen can catch fire and explode, but if kept under pressure, it may be no less safe than gasoline in tanks.

Hydrogen fuel cells are energy-efficient. Depending on the type of fuel cell, 35–70% of the energy released in the reaction can be used. If the system is designed to capture heat as well as electricity, then the energy efficiency of fuel cells can rise to 90%. These rates are comparable or superior to most nonrenewable alternatives.

Fuel cells are also silent and nonpolluting. Unlike batteries (which also produce electricity through chemical reactions), fuel cells will generate electricity whenever hydrogen fuel is supplied, without ever needing recharging. For all these reasons, hydrogen fuel cells may soon be used to power cars, much as they are already powering buses operating on the streets of some German cities.

Conclusion

Rising concern over air pollution, global climate change, health impacts, and security risks resulting from our dependence on fossil fuels—as well as concerns over supplies of oil and natural gas—have convinced many people that we need to shift to renewable energy sources that pollute far less and that will not run out. Renewable sources with promise for sustaining our civilization far into the future without greatly degrading our environment include solar energy, wind power, geothermal energy, and ocean energy sources. Moreover, by using electricity from renewable sources to produce hydrogen fuel, we may be able to use fuel cells to produce electricity when and where it is needed, helping to create a nonpolluting and renewable transportation sector.

Renewable energy sources have been held back by limited funding for research and development and by competition with established nonrenewable fuels whose market prices do not cover external costs. Despite these obstacles, renewable technologies have progressed far enough to offer hope that we can shift from fossil fuels to renewable energy. To what degree we can also limit environmental impact will depend on how soon, how quickly, and how carefully we make the transition—and to what extent we put efficiency and conservation measures into place.

Reviewing Objectives

You should now be able to:

Outline the major sources of renewable energy, summarize their benefits, and assess their potential for growth

- The "new renewable" energy sources include solar, wind, geothermal, and ocean energy sources. They are not truly "new," but rather are in a stage of rapid development. (p. 462)

- The new renewables currently provide far less energy and electricity than we obtain from fossil fuels or other conventional energy sources. (pp. 462–463)

- Use of new renewables is growing quickly, and this growth is expected to continue as people seek to move away from fossil fuels. (pp. 462–463)

- Relative to fossil fuels, the new renewables alleviate air pollution, reduce greenhouse gas emissions, and can self-renew. They can diversify a society's energy mix and bring income and jobs to communities. (pp. 463–464)

- Government subsidies have long favored nonrenewable energy, but investment and public policies such as feed-in tariffs can speed our transition to renewable sources. (pp. 464–465)

Describe solar energy and the ways it is harnessed, and evaluate its advantages and disadvantages

- Energy from the sun's radiation can be harnessed using passive methods or by active methods involving powered technology. (p. 468)

- Solar technologies include flat plate collectors for heating water and air, mirrors to concentrate solar rays, and photovoltaic (PV) cells to generate electricity. (pp. 468–470)

- PV solar is today's fastest-growing energy source. (p. 471)

- Solar energy is perpetually renewable, creates no emissions, and enables decentralized power. (p. 471)

- Solar radiation varies in intensity from place to place and time to time, and harnessing solar energy remains expensive. (pp. 472–474)

Describe wind power and how we harness it, and evaluate its benefits and drawbacks

- Energy from wind is harnessed using wind turbines mounted on towers. (pp. 474–475)

- Turbines are often erected in arrays at wind farms located on land or offshore, in locations with optimal wind conditions. (pp. 475–477)

- Wind power is one of today's fastest-growing energy sources. (p. 475)

- Wind energy is renewable, turbine operation creates no emissions, wind farms can generate economic benefits, and the cost of wind power is competitive with that of electricity from fossil fuels. (p. 476)

- Wind is an intermittent resource and is adequate only in some locations. Turbines kill some birds and bats, and wind farms often face opposition from local residents. (pp. 473, 476–478)

Describe geothermal energy and the ways we make use of it, and assess its advantages and disadvantages

- Thermal energy from radioactive decay in Earth's core rises toward the surface and heats groundwater. This energy may be harnessed by geothermal power plants and used to directly heat water and air and to generate electricity. (pp. 478–479)

- Geothermal energy can be efficient, clean, and renewable. However, naturally heated water occurs near the surface only in certain areas, and this water may be exhausted if it is overpumped. (pp. 478–479)

- Enhanced geothermal systems allow us to gain geothermal energy from more regions, but the approach can trigger earthquakes. (p. 479)

- Ground-source heat pumps heat and cool homes and businesses by circulating water whose temperature is moderated underground. (p. 480)

● **Describe ocean energy sources and how we can harness them**

- Ocean energy sources include the motion of tides, waves, and currents, and the thermal heat of ocean water. (pp. 480–482)

- Ocean energy is perpetually renewable and holds much promise, but technologies have seen limited development thus far. (pp. 480–482)

● **Explain hydrogen fuel cells and weigh options for energy storage and transportation**

- Hydrogen can serve as a fuel to store and transport energy, so that electricity generated by renewable sources can be made portable and used to power vehicles. (pp. 482–483)

- Hydrogen can be produced cleanly through electrolysis, but also by use of fossil fuels—in which case its environmental benefits are reduced. (p. 483)

- Fuel cells create electricity by controlling an interaction between hydrogen and oxygen, and they produce only water as a waste product. (pp. 482–484)

- Hydrogen infrastructure requires much more development, but hydrogen can be clean, safe, and efficient. Fuel cells are silent and nonpolluting, and they do not need recharging. (p. 484)

Testing Your Comprehension

1. What proportion of our energy now comes from renewable sources? What is the most prevalent form of renewable energy we use? What form of renewable energy is most used to generate electricity?

2. What factors and concerns are causing renewable energy use to expand? Which two renewable sources are experiencing the most rapid growth?

3. Contrast passive and active solar heating. Describe how each works, and give examples of each.

4. Define *photoelectric effect*. Explain how photovoltaic (PV) cells function and are used.

5. Describe several environmental and economic advantages of solar power. What are some disadvantages?

6. How do modern wind turbines generate electricity? How does wind speed affect the process? What factors affect where we place wind turbines?

7. Describe several environmental and economic benefits of wind power. What are some drawbacks?

8. Define *geothermal energy*, and explain three main ways in which it is obtained and used. Describe one sense in which it is renewable and one sense in which it is not renewable.

9. List and describe four approaches for obtaining energy from ocean water.

10. How is hydrogen fuel produced? Is this a clean process? What factors determine the amount of pollutants hydrogen production will emit?

Seeking Solutions

1. Explain how Germany accelerated its development of renewable energy by establishing a system of feed-in tariffs. Do you think the United States should adopt a similar system? Why or why not?

2. For each source of renewable energy discussed in this chapter, what factors stand in the way of an expedient transition from fossil fuel use? What could be done in each case to ease a shift to these renewable sources?

3. Do you think we can develop renewable energy resources to replace fossil fuels without significant social, economic, and environmental disruption? What steps would we need to take? Will market forces alone suffice to bring about this transition, or will we also need government?

Do you think such a shift will be good for our economy? Why or why not?

4. Explain the circumstances under which using hydrogen fuel could be helpful in moving toward a low-emission future. If you could advise policymakers of Iceland, Germany, or the United States on hydrogen, what would you tell them?

5. **THINK IT THROUGH** You have just graduated from college, gotten married, landed a good job, and purchased your first home. You and your spouse plan to stay in this home for the foreseeable future and are considering installing flat plate solar collectors and/or PV panels on your roof. What factors will you consider, and what

questions will you ask before deciding whether to make the investment in solar energy?

6. **THINK IT THROUGH** You are the CEO of a company that develops wind farms. Your staff has presented you with three options, listed below, for sites for your next development. Describe at least one likely advantage and at least one likely disadvantage you would expect to encounter with each option. What further information would you like to know before deciding which to pursue?

- Option A: A remote rural site in North Dakota
- Option B: A ridge-top site in the suburbs of Philadelphia
- Option C: An offshore site off the Florida coast

Calculating Ecological Footprints

Assume that average per capita residential consumption of electricity is 12 kilowatt-hours per day, that photovoltaic cells have an electrical output of 15% incident solar radiation, and that PV panels cost $1000 per square meter. Now refer to Figure 16.11 on p. 474 and estimate the area and cost of the PV panels needed to provide all of the residential electricity used by each group in the table.

	Area of photovoltaic cells	Cost of photovoltaic cells
You		
A resident of Arizona		
A resident of Alaska		
Total for all U.S. residents		

1. What additional information would you need to increase the accuracy of your estimates for the areas in the table above?

2. Considering the distribution of solar radiation in the United States, where do you think it will be most feasible to greatly increase the percentage of electricity generated from photovoltaic solar cells?

3. The purchase price of a photovoltaic system is considerable. What other costs and benefits should you consider, in addition to the purchase price, when contemplating "going solar"?

Mastering**ENVIRONMENTALSCIENCE**™

STUDENTS
Go to **MasteringEnvironmentalScience** for assignments, the etext, and the Study Area with practice tests, videos, current events, and activities.

INSTRUCTORS
Go to **MasteringEnvironmentalScience** for automatically graded activities, current events, videos, and reading questions that you can assign to your students, plus Instructor Resources.

Index

Note: Page numbers followed by n indicate footnotes, *f* refer to figures and *t* refer to tables. Page numbers in **bold** refer to definitions of key terms.